Motion and Time Study

fourth edition

Motion and Time Study

Principles and Practices

MARVIN E. MUNDEL, Ph. D.

Principal, M. E. Mundel & Associates
Management Consultants
Silver Spring, Maryland

PRENTICE-HALL, INC., Englewood Cliffs, New Jersey

Printed in the United States of America

13-603035-1

Library of Congress Catalog Card No.: 77-95751

Current printing (last digit):
10 9 8 7 6 5 4 3 2 1

PRENTICE-HALL INTERNATIONAL, INC., London
PRENTICE-HALL OF AUSTRALIA, PTY. LTD., Sydney
PRENTICE-HALL OF CANADA, LTD., Toronto
PRENTICE-HALL OF INDIA PRIVATE LTD., New Delhi
PRENTICE-HALL OF JAPAN, INC., Tokyo

Preface

This book is intended to provide a systematic, practical, and yet scientifically correct treatment of present-day motion and time study. My aim has been to present in organized form the basic principles pervading successful work rather than a description of everything that has been done, regardless of relative merit or value. The development of these principles is examined so that they may be understood and applied naturally rather than as clerical procedures. Many of the examples are given in considerable detail so that the highly important reasoning processes involved in the application of the procedures are discernible. The relationship of motion and time study to the newer industrial engineering techniques involving mathematical models has been indicated where appropriate.

Many recently-developed concepts and techniques have been included in this book. For instance, a generalized theory of managerial control has been introduced to provide a framework for relating the material of this book to the whole of management activity. A concept of a *hierarchy of work-units* has been introduced and used to relate the chapters dealing with work measurement to the entire range of human effort and managerial control. These materials have been carefully evaluated in actual working situations to determine the desirability of including them.

Although the largest part of the text is devoted to the *how* of motion and time study, as seems appropriate, great care has been taken to keep the *why, when, and where* carefully in focus. The material is oriented to the serving of objectives; techniques are treated solely as a means of achieving these objectives.

The scope of application of the examples chosen includes not only direct and indirect work, agricultural work, and office activities, but also the broad variety of activities that characterize all government organizations, and other service occupations. The illustrations have been kept in the form in which they would appear in practice, so that they may provide working guides. Care has been taken to provide broad coverage without creating a book of excessive size.

The sections on work measurement have been designed to reflect the greatly increased variety and scope of applicability of modern techniques. Many of the newer techniques have already been applied so widely that I have been able to cite extended and varied illustrations to assist in guiding the practitioner.

As a final major feature, this book has also been designed to facilitate the use of the same material by a large variety of people whose individual interest in motion and time study may be highly diverse. In this manner, within the limits of their interest, they will all have a common ground for communication and understanding. To this end, the chapters that discuss general aspects of the field have carefully been kept separated from those presenting a discussion of techniques and the specifics of application. Those chapters that present the details of techniques and applications have been divided into two parts; a main body and *supplemental material*. The supplemental material for each chapter is paged directly behind the body of the chapter to which it applies. The presentation in the body of the chapter has been made as short and concise as appeared consonant with an adequate explanation, and contains, with a few exceptions, only a single illustration of relative simplicity. More complex illustrations, ramifications of the techniques and modifications, are presented in the supplemental material. Topics with a heavy mathematical content, which are not necessary for an understanding of the basic material in the body of the chapter, are also included in the supplemental material. Further, an illustration of a complete hierarchy of work-units for a government agency, to which frequent reference may be desired, is given as a separate appendix, rather than being included in the supplemental material of the chapter in which the topic is introduced. Two other appendices deal with the two basic alternatives of time study rating and their supporting material. Hence, these topics are readily accessible for reading in connection with any of the chapters to which they are applicable. A bibliography and a problem section are also given. The problems are of a wide variety in order to provide an instructor with a maximum number of models for problems he may wish to generate to replace those given, after the book has been in use for an extended time. The index has been carefully compiled to facilitate the use of the book as a handbook-type reference.

Hence, the generalist who wishes only a brief presentation, the person who wishes a general familiarity with all of the techniques, and the person who wishes to pursue some or all of the techniques to a more exhaustive level of detail may all work from the same material. For instance, the generalist may confine his reading to the general subject chapters, Chapters 1, 2, 3, 17, and 25. The person who wishes to acquire a general familiarity with the totality of the subject may confine his reading to the main body of all of the chapters, delving into the supplemental material of only those chapters in which he has a special interest. The person who wishes to fully utilize the resources of this book should read all of the materials and appendices. The person who is seeking some specific information will be aided by the variety of ways provided in the index for locating the appropriate sections.

During the past twenty-five years the traditional approaches as well as the new approaches described in this book have been thoroughly tested by applications to the direct and indirect work of light and heavy industry and to a wide variety of government activities ranging from the Secret Service of the U.S. Department of the Treasury to the Animal Health Division of the U.S. Department of Agriculture. They have also been used with thousands of college students and industrial seminar participants in many countries.

In particular, during the ten years that I taught at Purdue University, I also served under the Fulbright Program as visiting lecturer at the University of Birmingham, England. There, through the good offices of the late Professor T. U. Matthew, I met numerous British industrial engineers and toured many British plants. The opportunities for study and discussion that the visit made possible are reflected in this book.

Also, I undertook to organize and operate on a national basis a management engineering training program for the United States Army Ordnance Corps, which employs over 160,000 civilians. The techniques of motion and time study played an important part in this program, and the opportunity to work with these techniques on such a wide scale has influenced the thinking throughout this book.

During the next ten years when I worked as a consultant engineer, I had the opportunity to serve as seminar team leader of groups assigned to introduce industrial engineering into Japan, followed by a period during which I served as a Visiting Professor at Keio University in Tokyo and as a consultant to a broad variety of industries. These experiences occasioned a careful scrutiny of many of the basic assumptions previously associated with much motion and time study technology.

Subsequently, as Principal Staff Officer for Industrial Engineering in the Executive Office of the President, U.S. Bureau of the Budget, I had a unique opportunity to work with a broad variety of government service activities.

Most recently, again working as a consultant engineer with industrial concerns in America and abroad, as well as with a wide variety of government agencies, I have been faced with an enormous range of problems.

In this book I have included those approaches that were basic to successful work throughout the above broad areas of activity.

In writing this book I have also drawn freely on the background provided by the pioneer work of Frank B. and Lillian M. Gilbreth and on the teaching of the man who started me in this field, Professor David B. Porter of New York University. The influence of Lillian M. Gilbreth, a colleague during my ten years at Purdue, has also been profound. Many other individuals and groups have helped make this book possible.

I owe much to the cooperation given my activities over the years by L. P. Persing of the General Electric Co.; Dean Parsons of the Perfect Circle Co.; J. F. Rittenhouse, Jr. and F. Savage of C. G. Conn, Ltd.; L. J. Fletcher of the Caterpillar Tractor Co.; John Harder of R. G. LeTourneau, Inc.; Claude Campbell and Guy Avery of Acme Steel Co.; Guy Bates of General Motors Corp.; and Charles Winkleman of Belden Manufacturing Co. I am also indebted to American Steel Foundries, L. S. Ayres & Co., City Ice and Fuel Co., Sayco Valve Corp., and the Hotel Sherman. I owe much to Mr. C. J. Allen of Patrick Cudahy, Inc., who has so magnificently cooperated in maintaining for six years a thorough statistical analysis of the results of an industrial application of the objective time study technique. I am also indebted to Mr. L. Piel of Johnson Service Co.; Mr. C. DeWitt and Mr. G. Kaplan of Western Printing and Lithographing Co.; Mr. R. Amstutz, Mr. R. Solger, Mr. A. Mandele, and Mr. M. Ottow of the S & C Electric Company; the industrial engineering staff of S. C. Johnson Co.; Mr. F. Pleva of Herbst Shoe Co.; Mr. E. Schendel of Trostel Leather Co.; Mr. A. Erickson of Barber-Colman Co.; Mr. J. Ruedebusch and Mr. G. Ploger of Mirro Aluminum Co.; Mr. A. T. Tseng and Mr. J. Carpenter of the Diamond-Gardner Corp.; Mr. R. Klockzim of Inland Steel Co.; Mr. Lacey Randolph of the American Steel Foundries; Mr. R. Belt of Hamilton Manufacturing Co.; and Mr. Evan Scheele of Evco, Inc., for their cooperation on applications that are reflected either in examples or in the approach to various problems treated in this book.

Mr. W. Spooner and Commander Ginn of the Navy Bureau of Ships, Mr. John Blake of the Long Beach Naval Shipyard, Mr. M. Peal of Benecia Arsenal, and Colonel J. MacGruder of the Air Force Advanced Logistics School have all influenced the making of the book.

To Mr. B. Carlberg, Mr. L. Fahlin, Mr. L. Rask, Professor R. Kristensson, and Mr. Yngve Svensson of Sweden, I am deeply indebted for their assistance, cooperation, and advice on much presented in this book. Likewise to Anne Shaw (Mrs. J. Pirie), Mr. R. M. Currie, Mr. P.B.R. Gibson, Mr. R. Connelly, and Mr. W. Rodgers of Great Britain; Mr. A. Takanaka, Mr. N. Isogai, Mr. T. Harada, Mr. K. Yoneda, and Mr. S. Sakai of Japan; and Professor H. H. Hilf of West Germany.

Further, particularly with respect to the sections dealing with time standards for indirect work, I am deeply indebted to Mr. Louis Mayne and Dr. Donald Houston of the Consumer Protection Program of the U.S. Department of Agriculture. When Mr. Mayne was with that activity he set the stage for the wide-scale testing and use of the new techniques; Dr. Houston provided the veterinarian knowledge, the arduous leg work, and the devoted attention required for seeing the techniques fully developed and put to their proper use. In connection with the continuation of this effort, special thanks are due to Dr. R. Sommers, Dr. W. Caplinger, Dr. J. Stein, Dr. H. Steinmetz, Dr. V. Berry, and Dr. A. Geisman, all of the Consumer Protection Program of the Consumer and Marketing Service, for their substantial and continuous support. Their help has been invaluable in this effort, which was one of the pilot projects of extending motion and time study on a broad scale into a varied service-type activity.

I also want to thank Mr. Cy Smith, the former Administrator of the Consumer and Marketing Service, U.S. Department of Agriculture, and Mr. Rodney Leonard, his successor, for the opportunity they have provided for developing some of the new techniques presented in this book. I am also thankful to Mr. Ernest Jenkinson, the Director of the Operations Analysis Branch of the Service, for the support given my activities. Special thanks are due to Mr. Stanley Loomis, who has provided inspired liaison with all of the groups who have been involved. Numerous other individuals in the Service have provided much assistance.

Also, I want to thank Mr. Kojiro Yamaoka, the Executive Director of the Yanmar Diesel Engine Company of Osaka, Japan, and the numerous engineers of that company who have worked with me in making so many industrial applications of the newer techniques included in this book. The products of the Yanmar Diesel Engine Company range from small, ultra-high precision, fuel injection pumps, to custom built 3000 horsepower diesel-engine generator and pump sets. The activities range from light and heavy foundry through light, heavy, and ultra-high precision machining and include continuous and custom assembly. The support and overhead activities extend over the typical wide range of a modern diversified and multiplant industrial organization. An ideal test ground was provided for the development, test, and application of the enormous range of motion and time study technology needed to support managerial control over such a broad range of activities. My debt really extends to the whole of the Yanmar organization.

I should also give special thanks to Mr. Tsuneo Ono, formerly of the Japan Management Association, and to Professor Ziro Yamauti of Keio University in Tokyo, both of whom made feasible the large-scale testing of the techniques in this book in a wide variety of Japanese industries; also to Mr. Takeshi Kawase, who worked with me on so many projects. Further, with respect to my work in Japan. I should like to thank the management of the Nippon Electric Company, the Mitsubishi Heavy Industries, Inc., the Kawasaki Dockyard Company, the Japan Steel Tube Company, the Toyo Rayon Company, the Kanebo Spinning Company, the Matsushita Electric

x **Preface**

Company, and the engineers at those companies for the assistance I have received.

I have a large and continuing debt to the personnel of the Army Management Engineering Training Agency, particularly Mr. Lynn Bryant, the Director; Mr. James Jensen, the Deputy Director; Mr. William Shallman, the Chief of Industrial Engineering; and Mr. Vincent Poulin for the steady aid they have given to my work.

Acknowledgment should also be made of the assistance received from Mr. Gerald Sparer of the Department of Health, Education, and Welfare, and to Mr. Art Jebbins, Mr. A. Weinberg, Mr. Donald Clark, Miss Edith Mahon, and Mr. Andrew Latvala of the U.S. Department of the Interior.

Work on the new approaches has also been greatly aided by Dr. E. Saulman, Dr. G. Wise, Dr. R. Omohundro, Dr. J. Atwell, Dr. R. Brown, and Dr. W. McCallon of the Animal Health Division of the Agricultural Research Service, U.S. Department of Agriculture. Mention should also be made of the superb support work in making applications provided by Mr. Horace Robinson and Mr. Charles Hendrix of the Administrative Services unit of that organization.

Thanks are also due to my former colleagues in the Executive Office of the President, Bureau of the Budget, for the many thought-provoking discussions in which we engaged. Also, acknowledgment should be made of the suggestions and advice received from Mr. R. Thelwell and Mr. B. Usilaner of that organization.

The list, if extended to include all those whose effect is discernible anywhere in the book, would become much longer. I have attempted to single out those whose contribution is large, but the others were also important. I hope no one feels slighted by being left out; no slight is intended.

Finally, I would like to thank my patient book typist, Mrs. Helen Townsend, who so graciously provided the enormous effort that took this work from initial draft to finished copy.

Marvin E. Mundel

Contents

xi

CHAPTER 1

Motion and Time Study and its Place in Managerial Activity

The term *motion and time study* refers to a broad branch of knowledge dealing with the scientific determination of preferable work methods, with the appraisal, in terms of time, of the value of work involving human activity, and with the development of material required to make practical use of these data.

The motion study aspect[1] consists of a wide variety of procedures for the description and scientific analysis of work methods, considering (1) the raw materials, (2) the design of the outputs (products or services), (3) the process or order of work, (4) the tools, workplace, and equipment for each individual step in the process, and (5) the human activity used to perform each step, in order to determine (or design) a preferable work method. The criterion of preference is usually economy of money, but effectiveness of the activity, ease or economy of human effort, economy of time, or economy of material— as well as other criteria, discussed in later chapters—frequently may take precedence.

The time study aspect[2] consists of a wide variety of procedures for determining the amount of time required, under certain standard conditions of measurement, for tasks involving some human activity. However, it is difficult to separate completely these two aspects inasmuch as a specified method, frequently in the form of a written standard practice employing

---

[1] The terms *methods study* and *work design* are also commonly used.
[2] The term *work measurement* is also commonly used.

1

one of the techniques of motion study, is one of the conditions of time measurement and, also, time measurements are often a part of the basis on which alternative methods are compared. In addition, method determination and time appraisal complement each other's utility in application. The combined term—motion and time study—is used to denote all three phases of activity: method determination, time appraisal, and the development of material for the application of these data.

In any activity or occupation, motion and time study can be usefully employed to help find a preferred way of doing the work and assist in effectively managing or controlling the activity. The approach of motion and time study fits equally well when applied to heavy or light factory, office, production, maintenance, staff or supervisory work, farm work, housework, surgery, cafeteria work, department store or hotel work, the whole range of government activities, battle activities, and any other human activity. What is accomplished may vary from job to job. The nature of the raw material will vary widely. In one case it may be information; in another it may be some simple or complex substantive material. The outputs may be services, responses to another group's actions, or any one of the almost infinite variety of products found in a modern society. The varieties of process are almost limitless. The varieties of tools, equipment, and workplaces (using these terms in the broadest sense to refer to things worked with and places worked at) is enormous. However, the requisite human efforts will in all cases be composed of the same basic acts and the information relating to the economical use of human effort will be universally applicable. The problem of determining a feasible and preferable method of accomplishing the work will be always present. The problem of determining the required amount of human worktime will be a normal concomitant. Regardless of the variation in accomplishment or field of knowledge some procedure must be employed to design the work and to determine the amount of time required to perform it. Procedures have to be selected from among the broad variety of available motion and time procedures to effectively assist in applying available knowledge to the solution of the design and measurement problems.

Motion and time study may well be used to provide a means for cooperative activity between the various divisions of an organization in selecting, planning or designing, and controlling the proper integration of materials, design of product or work achieved, process, tools, workplaces and equipment, and human activity. Motion and time study techniques are aids for systematically performing certain managerial tasks. This is not the same as saying that motion and time study includes all management, any more than one would say that accounting embraces all phases of business operation because it is used in most of them. Both motion and time study and accounting are tools that may be used in the majority of organizations to assist in solving certain problems.

Management, whether it is supervisory management, middle management, or top management, in either industry, service, or government endeavors, may be described as a task which can be represented by the following steps. These steps are continually repeated, essentially in a cyclic fashion, with a feedback (a flow of information) taking place between and among the various steps as well as between the first and final step.[3]

1. Determine quantitative objectives for a given span of time in conformance with guiding principles or assigned criteria, considering known limitations and freedoms of action.
2. Plan a series of programs (outputs to be produced in accord with a time-phased plan) for achieving the desired objectives.
3. Determine the workload (necessary activities which must be performed to accomplish the programs).
4. Determine the resources required to perform the workload, such as man-job time use, equipment time use, and material.
5. Acquire authority to employ these resources to perform the workload.
6. Use the resources to accomplish the workload, constantly constraining and improving the manner of use.
7. Determine the workload accomplished and the resources consumed, compare with the workload planned and the resources estimated as required, and take corrective action, as necessary, to cause performance to conform to plan.
8. Determine the amount of program accomplished, compare with the program planned, and take corrective action, as necessary, to cause conformance.
9. Determine the degree of accomplishment of objectives, compare with original objectives, and take corrective action, as necessary.

The cycle of managerial control described above is shown graphically in Figure 1.1, with only the major feedbacks indicated.

The defining of the task of management in such mechanistic terms is neither to deny the importance of such problems as motivating or leading people nor to deny the need to give weight to human values. The mechanistic description is merely the definition of the matrix in which these problems occur. Much more will be said about human problems in a subsequent chapter.

It is in facilitating or assisting in the decision making process in the performance of various of these steps in the cycle of managerial control that motion and time study procedures have their application. For instance, in performing step 2 of managerial control, *plan programs*, the problems of

---

[3] The definition of management and the cyclic diagram are a slight modification of material extracted from M. E. Mundel, *A Conceptual Framework for the Management Sciences*. New York, N.Y.: McGraw-Hill Book Co., 1967, pp. 159–172.

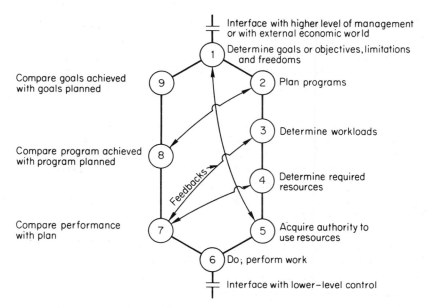

Fig. 1.1 — Cycle of managerial control.

designing the outputs, selecting the materials, designing or selecting the tools, equipment, workplaces, and methods must be solved. Various motion study techniques may be usefully employed to assist in systematically solving the problems associated with performing this second step of managerial control. Of course, which particular techniques are of value will be affected by the nature of the outputs in question, the level of managerial control, and the degree of detail being handled at that level.

Similarly, in proceeding from step 2, *plan programs*, to step 3, *determine workload* (the setting forth of a list of the quantities of activities to be performed), the techniques of motion study will be of assistance. Again, which specific techniques are of value will be affected by the same factors mentioned with respect to step 2.

In proceeding from step 3, *determine workload*, to step 4, *determine required resources*, the techniques of time study are employed in determining the amount of man-time (and the use-time of any adjuncts to the work) which will be required to perform the workload. These time study (or work measurement) data will again be used to assist in the performance of step 6, *do*, to constrain the actual performance of the work.

Subsequently, steps 7, 8, and 9, the steps of managerial control wherein the plans are compared to performance, will be assisted by information flow systems. The techniques of motion and time study will not only be useful in designing the manner of providing these information flow systems, but the time study data used to convert the data of step 3 to that needed for step 4 will be used to evaluate the new data carried by these information flow systems.

In short, motion and time study techniques are neither the managerial process nor a substitute for it, but are a series of techniques which may be usefully employed to assist in the performance of many of the steps in the managerial process. Naturally, in assisting the higher levels of managerial control the techniques which are suitable will usually differ from those which are suitable for lower levels of managerial control wherein the attention is focused on smaller details. Also, the nature of the outputs will have an effect upon the suitability of any particular technique.

It seems appropriate at this point to introduce a few brief examples of the results of the application of motion and time study to give further substance to the subject of this discussion.

Enveloping a Plant Magazine

Original method. Preparing the plant magazine shown in Figure 1.2 for mailing involved stuffing the magazine into a preaddressed envelope and turning in the flap of the envelope. The face of the envelope bore the sender's name in the upper left-hand corner, the second-class postmark in the upper right-hand corner, the address in the center, and postmaster's instructions in the lower left-hand corner. Thirty-one thousand of these magazines were stuffed into envelopes each week.

Improved method. The magazine was redesigned, doubled in size, and folded an additional time. One-half of the back page was used for all of the information that had previously appeared upon the envelope. The improved magazine is shown in Figure 1.3. This enabled the company to put out a

Fig. 1.2—Original plant magazine and envelope.

Fig. 1.3—Improved magazine format.

magazine of twice the size for less money than was involved in the original method.

Assembling the Bearing and Oil Seals to a Heavy Steel Roller Wheel

Original method. This roller wheel was used on the tailgate of heavy earth-grading equipment. In the original method, one of the oil seals was inserted first. Because there was nothing under this oil seal, it had to be hammered in edgewise and then turned into position with the thumb. This procedure caused the oil seal to enter farther into the bore than was required. After the operator inserted the first oil seal, he turned this heavy steel roller wheel over and dropped the bearing into the bore. Since the first oil seal was farther in the bore than was necessary, he then had to take a ram and lead mallet and hammer the first oil seal back to its desired location, as shown in Figure 1.4. For clarity, only a few parts are shown on the bench. The ram was used to distribute the pressure over the entire surface of the bearing and prevent damaging it. After the oil seal was hammered back, it was possible to put in the second oil seal. Inasmuch as the bearing provided a support for this oil seal, it was easier to assemble than the first, even though it was identical.

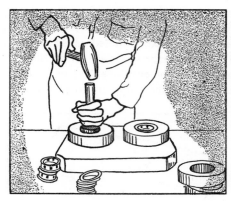 

Fig. 1.4—*Original workplace for assembling roller wheels.*   Fig. 1.5—*Improved workplace for assembling roller wheels.*

Improved method. Two steel spacers were welded to the bench, as shown in Figure 1.5. For clarity, only a few parts are shown on the bench. These spacers were the exact thickness of an oil seal. The operator first positioned the roller wheel over these spacers and then dropped the roller bearing into place. The spacer on the workplace held the bearing up in its proper position, permitting the insertion of the first oil seal in the same easy manner as was used on the second in the original method. After the first oil seal was in place, the roller wheel was turned over and the second oil seal was added as easily as was the first. This method was not only faster, in that an operator could achieve two and a quarter times as much production with the same effort, but easier, since the heavy work of using the lead mallet and ram was eliminated.

Sorting Day-old Chicks

Original method. As soon as the operator finished inspecting a box of chicks, he placed the lid on the box of inspected chicks, which was on the left side of the table, and then carried this box back to the rack of chicks that had been brought from the incubator. He then came back to the table, obtained the cover and the box in which the chicks had come (in the last inspection), and moved them across the table, placing the box on the left side of the table and the cover alongside the left of the table. He then again walked over to the chick rack and obtained a fresh box of chicks for inspection. He lifted the cover off this box and placed it alongside the table on the right. He lifted the chicks out of the box, four or five at a time, as shown in Figure 1.6, placed them on the table, and inspected them. He then placed the first-grade chicks in the box to his left and, when necessary, stepped back a foot and turned around to deposit the second-grade chicks in the box behind him. Rejects were thrown in a can under the table. He continued this until the hundred-odd chicks in the box were inspected, and then repeated the cycle.

Improved method. The operator was seated on a stool. The rack of chicks had been brought up close to him. It was now possible without getting up

Fig. 1.6—Original method of inspecting chicks.

Fig. 1.7—Improved method of inspecting chicks.

to turn around in the chair and pick out a fresh box of chicks or replace a box of inspected chicks in the rack. He placed the box of chicks for inspection on the table directly in front of him and inverted the cover over the box at an angle, as shown in Figure 1.7 He placed a piece of paper over the holes in the cover of the box and, with two scoops of his hands, lifted the entire twenty-five chicks (there are usually more than the nominal twenty-five) out of one of the four compartments in the box and put them on the inverted cover. As he inspected them, he moved the first-grade chicks back into the compartment from which he had withdrawn them and placed the second-grade chicks in the box to his right. If the number in the box was too low, he added chicks to the box from the box to his left. Both hands were engaged in sorting the chicks. After the twenty-five were placed on the lid in front of the inspector, he picked out the obviously good chicks and placed them in the box in front of him; the obviously second-grade chicks he put into the box to his right. Those which were doubtful he left for further scrutiny before placing them in the proper container. By performing the operation in this new manner, the operator was able to inspect 95 per cent more chicks than with the original method, and the inspection was better.

Handling Work to Sandblast Room

Original method. As shown in Figure 1.8, the materials handler worked at a chipping bench until the sandblaster signaled that he needed more work. The handler then went to the unloading spot, where the painters had left an empty skid, dragged the skid to the loading spot, where the process conveyor ended, and loaded the skid with parts that were ready for sandblasting. Next,

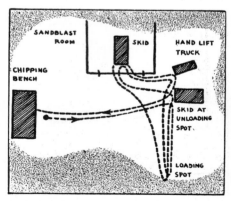 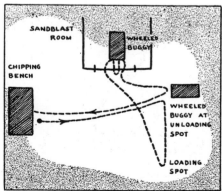

Fig. 1.8—*Plan view of factory floor show-*
   ing path of materials handler
   with original method.

Fig. 1.9—*Plan view of factory floor show-*
   ing path of worker with wheeled
   buggies.

he went to get the hand-lift truck, pulled it to the sandblast room, opened the door, placed the lift truck under the skid, and lifted the skid of blasted parts. He moved this skid to the unloading spot and lowered it. He then took the lift truck to the freshly loaded skid, lifted it, moved it into the sandblast room, lowered it, took out the lift truck (which would be damaged if sand-blasted), lowered the door of the sandblast room, stored the truck and returned to chipping, traveling 244 feet to do the total task.

Improved method. As shown in Figure 1.9, the skids and lift truck were replaced with wheeled buggies. On the signal from the sandblaster, the materials handler went from the chipping bench to the unloading spot and rolled the empty buggy to the loading spot and loaded it. When it was loaded, he rolled it to the sandblasting room, opened the door, rolled out the buggy of blasted parts, rolled in the new buggy, stepped out, closed the door, rolled the buggy of blasted parts to the unloading spot, and returned to chipping. The new method saved 47 per cent of the material handler's time and required him to move only 128 feet.

Manufacturing a Radar Coil

Original method. Flat rings were punched from soft iron stock. These rings were sprayed on both sides and bound into the coil shown in Figure 1.10. In the illustration, a few rings are turned up to show the construction. This process involved several handlings, punch presses, assembly, and considerable scrap in the form of punchpress skeleton.

Improved method. The coil was constructed by winding a long narrow strip of slightly different metal into the coil, with the laminations parallel to the axis rather than perpendicular as in the original design. This new coil is shown in Figure 1.11. The end is loose to show the construction. This new material

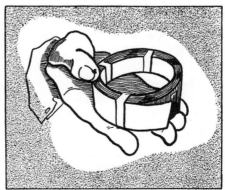

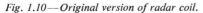

Fig. 1.10—Original version of radar coil.   *Fig. 1.11—New design of radar coil.*

could be sprayed in continuous strip form. By eliminating several handlings, punch-press work, and scrap, this new method saved $131,000 a year.

Citrus Picking[4]

Citus fruit was chosen[5] because it is Israel's leading export. The investigation was carried out at the request of the grove owners, the agricultural workers' union, the Citrus Board, and the Ministry of Agriculture.

Scores of workers in selected and varied groves were studied for some weeks by men who recorded the methods used and kept a close tally of the output and, with the aid of stop-watches, of the time spent on picking, resting, and delays caused by shortage of equipment (boxes, ladders, etc.). Experiments were made with various methods of picking, and one method was finally selected as superior. Production norms based on time studies were set for various types of groves. The data were so extensive, so well collated and analyzed that at one sitting the results were accepted by both the association of grove owners and the agricultural workers' union.

In cooperation with the adult vocational training division of the Ministry of Labor courses were held for over 250 grove foremen, out of a total of 600, showing them the selected method and training them to instruct workers. Colourful instructional posters were displayed at all groves. A simple, profusely illustrated brochure describing the selected method and containing other work aids was printed in three languages (Hebrew, Yiddish and Arabic) and distributed to all the workers, most of whom were new immigrants with little or no literacy.

Although all groves did not make all the necessary changes, the industry as a whole employed during the 1952–53 season 7,000 pickers instead of the 9,000 employed the season before, and 40 per cent more exportable fruit was picked.[6] Thus there was not only a substantial increase in productivity but also a decrease of spoiled fruit. Where payment by results was introduced, workers' earnings were increased by 20 to 40 per cent.

Motion and Time Study Applied to the Manufacture of a Whole Product

The preceding illustrations have been primarily confined to three types: (1) improvements on a single operation on a product, (2) improvements on some of the steps on a product, and (3) improvement of a component of a larger product. Despite the magnitude of the typical results, the reader may

[4] Hy Fish, "Raising Productivity in Israel," *The International Labor Review* (Geneva, Switzerland), Vol. LXVIII, Nos. 4–5, Oct.-Nov. 1953.

[5] By the Israel Productivity Office.

[6] There were no dismissals, since picking is a seasonal occupation and the normal turnover of labor from season to season exceeds 75 per cent. (Fish's footnote.)

be wondering what the net result might be if the techniques were brought to bear upon the whole of the manufacturing of a more complex product or a larger product, or the whole of a manufacturing activity or a governmental operation. The next five examples, therefore, instead of illustrating the details of the changes, consist primarily of a presentation of the net results obtained when various motion and time study techniques were applied on a larger scale than in the preceding examples.

1. A Diesel-engine Fuel-pump Manufacturing Plant

Various motion and time study techniques were applied to assist in improving the product design, process, equipment, labor utilization, and product flow. The production of the plant was raised from 20,000 units per month to 60,000 units per month without changing the number of employees and without extensive automation.

2. A Shipyard

Various motion and time study techniques were used to develop time standards and controls so that the number of man-hours could be determined in advance of the work and labor effectively dispatched. The labor required to erect a ship was reduced by 45 per cent.

3. Office of the Solicitor, U.S. Department of the Interior

Various motion and time study techniques were applied to assist in forecasting the amount of the workload which could be anticipated and in converting this into a statement of the required number of lawyers. Subsequently, procedures were designed for using these data for monitoring the output and backlog of the approximately 200 lawyers working in 29 offices in the United States thereby assisting in the shifting of lawyers among the locations in order to keep abreast of workload.[7]

4. Livestock Market News Service, U.S. Department of Agriculture

Time study technology was applied to provide a basis for determining the manning needed for each of the 42 cities in which the Livestock Market News Service maintained an office. These data permit the manning to be rationally

[7] *Workload Analysis Reporting System.* Office of the Solicitor, U.S. Department of the Interior, November 1967.

adjusted when the workload in any city shows significant changes. These data also assist in the determination of the additional cost of extending the Service to an additional market area or the determination of which services must be curtailed when funds are short. They also permit the identification of offices whose workload is such that they are convenient places for training new employees.

5. *A Large Manufacturer of Automotive Electrical Components*

Since 1945, Joseph Lucas, Ltd., the largest producer of automotive electrical equipment in the United Kingdom, has been applying motion and time study techniques as a fundamental tool in an effort to increase productivity and reduce costs. Goals are set and progress measured in terms of indices. Three of the indices used are as follows:

1. Technical index $= \dfrac{\text{rationalized time}}{\text{current standard time to produce product}} \times 100$

   The rationalized time is the estimated standard time considering possible improvements in design and production methods. This index reflects motion study effects.

2. Labor index $= \dfrac{\text{current standard time}}{\text{current performance time}} \times 100$

   The current performance time reflects shortcomings such as waiting for materials, machine breakdown, or failure on the part of the operators. This index reflects time study measures and their uses.

3. Productivity index $=$ labor index $\times$ technical index

   This index combines the effects of motion study and time study.

It is to be noted that all of these indices are designed so that the value of the index when the goal is achieved is 100 per cent. The progress of Joseph Lucas, Ltd. on one product, as measured with these indices, with an intensive motion and time study program, is shown in Figure 1.12.

Numerous other illustrations could be cited. Motion and time study has been applied to improving or designing the pattern for activities ranging from the loading of naval guns to the cleaning of cow barns. However, the foregoing detailed examples indicate a fair variety of applications.

For the purpose of showing the effect of using the methodology of motion and time study, in all cases jobs that were improved were shown. However, it should be understood that the techniques of motion and time study are most useful, even if less dramatic, when they are employed to design an effective method from the outset of the activity. As the various techniques of motion study are later discussed, the procedures used to develop many of these improved methods will be given in detail to demonstrate how almost

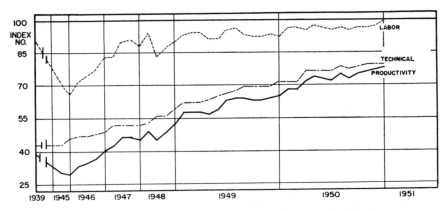

Fig. 1.12—Labor, technical, and productivity indices, Joseph Lucas,
Ltd., from 1939 to 1951.

anyone familiar with these techniques could have arrived at similar results. These procedures are equally effective for the initial design of efficient methods. In the sections on time study, the methods used to evaluate the magnitude of the change will be given. In the section on application, the means of seeing the new methods adopted as practice will be discussed.

CHAPTER 2

The Human Factor

The following chapters are devoted mainly to a systematic discussion of techniques and procedures for the development of improved work methods and for the setting of standards for human performance. As was indicated in Chapter 1, these techniques play a vital role in the managerial process so necessary for the effective control of human undertakings. These techniques have had a vital role in increasing the productivity of undertakings in the industrial, service, and government sectors of the modern world. The continued growth of these undertakings, growth in size, complexity and variety, increases rather than decreases the need to apply these techniques. The growth of enterprises also creates a need for new motion and time study techniques.

In the following chapters, in keeping with the subject of this book, the emphasis will be on the techniques of motion and time study rather than on what is called the "human factor," although there is no intention of minimizing its importance. In that people are a basic element of any enterprise, any discussion of either the old or new techniques must include an examination of the interaction between these techniques and people. However, rather than scattering the material relating to the human factor throughout the book or repeating it in each chapter, it has been gathered together in this chapter which should be considered as a prologue to each of the chapters which follow.

In any activity the application of the techniques of motion and time study has profound effects upon the conditions and wages of employment. These effects may be classified as long- or short-run effects; the actual impact may be economic, emotional (psychological or sociological), or mechanical (physiological), or more likely a combination of these. However, it should be noted that people do not react to this sort of impact as purely economic, emotional, or mechanical men, but to the combination of these aspects as perceived by them; their reactions are influenced by past experience, mental outlooks, social relations, general economic conditions, and so forth.

In many cases, the very introduction of an innovation or change in the way of doing work, whether the change is in the work method or in the managerial control procedure, substitutes the unknown for the known. The unknown creates a generalized fear often difficult to isolate. In other cases, ego problems created by the obsolescence of a skill or by a change in managerial control procedures which reduces or appears to reduce the freedom of action of the employee, or the real or imagined economic effects of such a change, may enter into the main problem. Externally imposed change also implies criticism of past practice, and people resist the change to avoid the acceptance of the implications. All of these aspects may be confused in a problem of innovation; motion and time study techniques are essentially systematic ways of finding innovations. Conflict may ensue unless proper measures are taken.

The complexity of the interaction of all of the factors affecting the reaction of a person to his job (and innovations) was superbly illustrated by a classic experiment performed at the Hawthorne Works of the Western Electric Co. in the late 1920's.[1]

This experiment was performed in order to obtain answers to the following questions:

1. Do employees actually get tired out?
2. Are rest pauses desirable?
3. Is a shorter working day desirable?
4. What is the attitude of employees toward their work and toward the Company?
5. What is the effect of changing the type of working equipment?
6. Why does production fall off in the afternoon?[2]

In this experiment, six girls (five assemblers and one material handler) were selected from a group of one hundred assembling telephone relays. Previous to the selection, it had not been customary to keep individual production records and the entire group of one hundred was paid on the basis of the output of the group. For a period of two weeks a record was kept of the individual production of the six selected girls to provide a base record. This record was kept without their knowledge.

The six girls were then told of the purposes of the experiment and, after agreeing to participate, were moved into a test room physically separated from the large group. They worked in this test room for five weeks, without any other changes in the conditions of work, with no change in the basis

---

[1] G. A. Pennock, "Investigation of Rest Periods, Working Conditions and Other Influences," *Personnel Journal*, Vol. VIII, No. 5, Feb. 1930.

[2] *Ibid.*, p. 297.

of computing pay, in order to establish a base record for the new conditions.

For the next eight weeks they were paid on a new basis, a group rate based on the production of the five assemblers in the test room, rather than on the basis of the whole group of one hundred as previously. Production increased by about 4 per cent.

For the next four weeks, the group was given ten-minute rest pauses twice a day, and again daily and weekly output rose.

For the next four weeks, the group was given six five-minute rest pauses, further reducing the working time. The girls expressed some dislike of this constant interruption of the flow of work and the output curves showed a small decrease.

For the next eleven weeks, the group was given a fifteen-minute rest pause in the morning with refreshments supplied by the Company, and a ten-minute break in the afternoon. Despite the loss of production time, output returned to the highest level previously obtained in the experiment.

For the next seven weeks, the group stopped a half-hour earlier each day. This was accompanied by a spectacular rise in both daily and weekly output. (At this point in the experiment unforeseen circumstances necessitated replacing two of the operators.)

For the next four weeks, the working day was shortened by an additional half-hour. The hourly output rose so that the daily and weekly output diminished only slightly.

For the next twelve weeks the group returned to working the full day but retained the fifteen-minute mid-morning refreshment break and the ten-minute afternoon break. Daily and weekly output reached a new high.

For the next twelve weeks, the half-day of work on Saturday was eliminated. Daily output increased. Weekly output fell somewhat, but remained above all but two of the previous highs.

For the next twelve weeks, the workers returned to all but one of the original conditions of work; no rest pauses, no refreshments, no shortened hours, but they were paid as a group of six. The daily and weekly outputs rose to record highs and continued to rise throughout the entire twelve weeks.

For the next thirty-one weeks, the group returned to rest pauses with the company supplying the morning-break beverage and the girls supplying their own food. The output rose again, establishing a new high.

It became obvious that more was happening than was attributable directly and mechanically to the experimental changes. Mr. Pennock, in charge of the investigation, explained, "The results are mainly due to changes in the mental attitude."[3]

Elton Mayo further explained the increases in productivity as follows:

The supervisor took a personal interest in each girl and her achievement;

[3] Elton Mayo, *The Human Problems of an Industrial Civilization*. New York, N.Y.: The Macmillan Co., 1933, p. 70.

he showed pride in the record of the group. He helped the group to feel that its duty was to set its own conditions of work (oriented with the organization's objectives); he helped the workers find the "freedom" of which they so frequently spoke in the course of the experiment.[4]

The interpolation inserted in the preceding quotation has great importance. Implicit in Dr. Mayo's remarks is the assumption that the supervisor (representing the organization) and the workers understood each other and *communicated successfully.*

> Successful communication between individuals depends upon something more than a common language, a common set of words. People and groups with different experiences and social places, although having in common many of the same words, may vary widely in mental attitudes. These differences in modes of thought and ways of viewing things may make communication in some instances almost impossible. The trained expert with his precise and logical vocabulary has difficulty in communicating with the layman. The customary ways of thinking of the skilled toolmaker, for example, are quite different from those of the non-machine minded unskilled worker. They differ also from those of the engineer, the accountant, the marketing expert, the executive, or the administrator. As it is commonly expressed, people with different ways of thinking do not "get" each other.[5]

In brief, the Hawthorne experiment resulted in increases in productivity because of mutual understanding and acceptance of the changes as compatible with the objectives of both parties.

Indeed, it may be taken as axiomatic that the members of a group will not cooperate willingly in an activity they do not understand.[6] It should be obvious that the application of motion and time study has not only problems of communication, but that the communication must result in motivation, viz., an active acceptance of the change.

Those applying the techniques of motion and time study may have one objective in mind; those to whom it is applied may "understand" this somewhat differently. Even if the understanding is correct, the evaluation of the suitability of the objective may differ and motivation to a state of active participation may become a difficult problem.

In substance, whether the changes resulting from motion and time study will really assist the worker or be an advantage to him is not the only problem. Of importance also is what the worker thinks the changes will do to him. The problem is further complicated because in the past, in all too many cases, motion and time study activities have been used in an unscientific fashion

---

[4] *Ibid.*, p. 71.

[5] F. J. Roethlisberger, *Management and Morale.* Cambridge, Mass.: Harvard University Press, 1941, p. 62.

[6] Mayo, *op. cit.*, pp. 119–120; see also, A. Zander, "Resistance to Change—Its Analysis and Prevention," *Advanced Management*, Vol. 15, No. 1, Jan. 1950, pp. 9–11.

as cover for programs requiring excessive effort from employees. (Even the determination of whether effort is excessive or not is not a simple problem, as will be seen in subsequent chapters.) Also, in some cases motion and time study activities have been allowed to cause some unemployment; this fear is frequently uppermost in the worker's mind. In the particular area of work within the comprehension of the worker he may know that there is much excess manpower long before management begins to apply motion and time study techniques in order to determine the amount of manpower really required. The fear of potential unemployment may have a real basis. Even if management has established a reputation for moving excess workers to other work rather than discharging or laying them off, there is still the fear of change unless active steps are undertaken to minimize it. When motion and time study techniques are applied to work other than direct work one often encounters a deep-rooted skepticism with respect to the useful potential for change. In government activities one hears the remark, "But we don't make shoes!" With other indirect groups the common retorts are, "Our work can't be planned!"; "You can't measure us with a stop-watch!" Some of these remarks may be true although they may not have any bearing on the suitability of applying motion and time study techniques. They all reflect a variety of fears; fears that undue regimentation will ensue, fears that undue effort will be required. These fears may not be related to a fear of unemployment or to a preference for any easy way of working. Indeed, the more the true attitude of the group is to dedicated effort the more they may fear the consequences of motion and time study. They fear the unknown.

Many will agree that any activity that does not benefit society deserves to fall by the wayside. Where the general effects are desirable, but the local effects entail hardship (whether it is real or imaginary makes no difference) for some individuals, then the activity should continue, but means of lessening or removing the undesirable results must be found. Only the most socially blind persons will point to the long-run effects of motion and time study and disregard the few individuals who may suffer, or expect these few individuals to submit willingly to hardship "for the good of the group." Calling unemployment "temporary technological unemployment" neither makes it more pleasant nor assists in communicating in a manner which will gain mutual cooperation in effecting changes. In many plants, trades, and organizations that are backward in method and procedure, this fear of unemployment often forces retention of needlessly uneconomical ways of doing work.

It must, however, be borne in mind that unless working methods continually improve, unless each working hour continually becomes more productive, a society will become economically static, and the standard of living will no longer rise. Indeed, such a condition includes factors that will inevitably depress the standard of living.

The employment of the techniques of motion and time study must not be considered a mere mechanical problem but must be so carried on and applied that it relates properly to the people who are affected.

A crisis was occasioned in one plant with 1,300 employees by the introduction of a new method that made it possible for 15 employees easily to perform the work previously requiring 50 persons. The plant management averted a crisis by guaranteeing employment for the displaced workers, including carrying them on the payrolls until the normal turnover and expansion of production made vacancies for them. This was accompanied by an extensive education program concerning the need for the change and the consequences of not making the change. It was not sheer altruism, of course, that prompted this action. A trained worker, adjusted to the plant organization, represents considerable value. This action, which postponed only temporarily the obtaining of the benefits of the new method, set the stage for willing cooperation in plant-wide methods improvement.

In another plant a crisis arose during contract negotiations. Although the plant did not have a piece-work system, they did have time standards and expected the direct production workers to perform at some reasonable per cent of these. The union, during the contract negotiations charged that the standards were capricious; that some were relatively easy to attain; that others were impossible. For this reason the union requested that all time standards be abolished and that all time study work cease. The company felt that time standards were so vital to their continuing in business that they could not yield on this point. They had the standards evaluated and found that the charge of excess variation was valid. They offered to restudy all tasks and set more consistent standards. The argument was protracted. A federal mediator failed to bring the two sides into some sort of an agreement. A strike ensued. After six weeks the union agreed to go back to work with the understanding that the company and union representatives would later work out a mutually agreeable clause with respect to time standards and time study. These negotiations were protracted. The union would not budge from its position that time standards and time study must be abolished. The company was adamant in its need for such standards. During the negotiations the company exerted a large effort to review and correct all time standards. At the same time they examined all cases of failures to attain a reasonable performance with a cause-seeking rather than a fault-finding attitude. No disciplinary actions were taken. The plant remained sullen; time study men were reviled; negotiations continued without progress. This state of affairs continued for six months. Finally the company tried a new approach. They set up a group of meetings with the employees. The 1,100 employees were taken in groups of 50 during paid-for working time. The works manager, personnel manager, the chief industrial engineer, the area time study man and the appropriate foremen attended each meeting. Each meeting lasted one hour. During the first thirty minutes the employees were shown a short series of 20 slides accompanied by a tape-recorded talk explaining the time study methods used and the reasons why time standards were considered so vital to the company. During the second thirty minutes the management representatives answered all questions. If unanswered questions remained at the end of the assigned hour the employees were promised an opportunity to attend another meeting and this meeting was held at the end of the series of meetings.[7] The results were immediate and profound. The whole attitude of the plant brightened; time study men were greeted and given cooperation; the union withdrew its request for further negotiations; the efforts of the company to make the standards more consistent were accepted as the correct approach.

The Consumer and Marketing Service of the United States Department of Agriculture has had an extremely successful motion and time study program. In this case the success may be traced directly to the involvement of line managers and operating people in the studies rather than having them done by technicians.

In all cases, some solution is possible, although it may differ from the ones just given. It surely seems foolish to continue to burden ourselves with the hard way of doing work when more economical methods are feasible, but are not adopted because we have not learned to install them cooperatively. Toil is certainly not that sweet. Also, pride in work must be expanded to include not only pride in what is done but also pride in doing it as economically as possible.

It should be noted that the results at Hawthorne, referred to earlier, were greatly influenced by the group's feeling that it was setting its own conditions of doing work. This, unfortunately, does not point the way towards an easy means of effectively employing motion and time study techniques in all applications. As will be seen in the next chapter, the most effective methods may require changes in factors, many of which are far beyond the scope or knowledge of the worker. Hence, it is not always possible to give the worker direct participation in developing the innovations.

At this point the advantage of designing effective methods prior to the outset of an activity should be obvious. Problems of resistance to change, worker displacement, and retraining may largely be avoided. Only through the use of the techniques of motion and time study, as a design tool, may such a goal be approached. However, there is no limit to the perfection of methods. Therefore, designing effective methods prior to beginning work only minimizes the problem of introducing change; it does not eliminate it.

While the preceding discussion has emphasized worker problems, this is not the whole picture. Management resistance to change is often as great.

[7] The slides and tape, of course, had been shown to all managers (including foremen) before the start of the meetings with the employees.

For motion and time study to achieve its fullest and most fruitful use, it must be thought of as a series of techniques applicable to problems affected by all the functions of all the individuals of an organization: from workers to sales and design engineers in a plant; from buyers to delivery men in a department store, and so forth. For all of these functions to be properly integrated into an economical operating pattern, supervisors at all levels must be educationally equipped to cooperate intelligently in the motion and time study approach, even to the extent of actually applying motion and time study as a normal part of their activity. They must also be emotionally susceptible to change and innovation and have adequate executive direction, the latter greatly conditioning the former. For any executive adequately to direct or participate in an activity, he usually must be well acquainted with the procedures used, their capacities and limitations. To aid subordinates in performing their work properly, he should have a good grasp of how their work should be performed. Consequently, we may say that the top executive attitude toward change and the procedures used to bring about change is one of the important human factors affecting the success of the motion and time study work. This holds true with respect to both the aspect of improving methods and that of designing methods.

Furthermore, a motion and time study department must actually justify its existence in an organization by reporting on its achievements. Because a well-operated motion and time study group usually cooperates in achieving a desired result with other staff or line groups, these reports pose a real problem in that they must not confuse the true role played by each group or individual concerned. Also, an effective motion and time study group will have its effect "before the fact"; they will participate in developing effective methods prior to the start of work. Their achievements will be "cost avoidance" or "excess manpower avoidance" rather than cost or manpower reductions; the improvement may merely make it possible to accomplish more without increased cost. A reasonable evaluation of the group's efforts in such circumstances poses an even more complicated problem.

In summary, it is suggested that, because of the "human factor," a motion and time study group or an individual engaged in performing such functions must not only execute the necessary technical activities in a sound, accurate fashion, but also actively take part in furthering the integration of motion and time study into the organization by:

1. Disseminating motion and time study information throughout the whole organization, not only to overcome the normal resistance of people affected by it, but also to aid everyone in the organization to cooperate in finding better ways of doing work. Communication must be maintained with each working group, to permit their objectives and problems to be understood and integrated into the design of effective

applications. Formal training courses, supervisor conferences, information via the house organ, and person-to-person discussions of each issue are desirable. The ideal situation occurs when innovations are originated, or at least participated in, by persons as close to the point of application as possible.

2. Submitting adequate financial and narrative reports of its activities to management, properly crediting cooperating, participating, or originating individuals or groups.

3. Actively seeking equitable solutions for possible hardships connected with technological changes.

Also, because of the "human factor," all members of the organization should actively undertake to understand the procedures and techniques of motion and time study. In the typical manufacturing organization practically all members of the "production" group are able to understand the drawings used to describe the product. For motion and time study to be of greatest value, all members of any organization must similarly be able to read the job designs, process designs, and control system designs described with the procedures and techniques of motion and time study. Thus they may equip themselves to take part in cooperative action for finding equitable ways of raising the standard of living through more effective production, without increased effort, and without hardship.

CHAPTER 3

The Scope of Motion and Time Study

The improved methods described in Chapter 1 were the results of the use of motion study techniques, as defined there; the evaluation of the magnitude of the changes was the result of the use of time study techniques; and the actual application of these data involved the phase of developing some type of instructional material or standard practice with which, or from which, the people were trained to do the job in the desired manner as well as some. procedure for guiding their efforts. As was noted earlier, this book makes use of the term *motion and time study* to describe the entire field of activity. The terms *work simplification, work study, work standardization, work measurement, time study, standards work, motion study, methods research,* as well as many others, are in common use either for parts of this field or to describe the entire field. While this is not an important issue, this book, for clarity, will use only those terms suggested in the first chapter, in the sense in which they were suggested.

This book is divided into four sections, as follows:

1. General overview and background material of motion and time study: Chapters 1 through 3.
2. The motion study aspect: Chapters 4 through 16.
3. The time study (or work measurement) aspect: Chapters 17 through 24.
4. The application of motion and time study data: Chapter 25.

This is only a general breakdown because, as was noted in the first chapter, all of these aspects are interrelated.

The fundamental philosophy of motion and time study involves three assumptions:

1. There are usually numerous ways to perform any task, but with the knowledge obtainable at any one time, one method is usually superior to the others.
2. The scientific method of solving problems is more productive of better work methods than is undisciplined ingenuity.
3. A standard of performance, or a time value for work, may be determined so as to permit dimensioning the required manpower inputs into any organization, thus permitting the creation of a true managerial design.

In other words, motion and time study procedures may be said to be based on the assumptions that for every job there is always, in the light of present knowledge, a "one best way,"[1] that a scientific method is the surest way of determining this "one best way," and that the time value of work may be measured in consistent units. It should be noted that the concept of the "one best way" does not rule out the determination of a still better method when our basis of preference, our knowledge, or our ability is altered.

The scientific method of solving problems involving the determination of a preferred way of doing a job, a preferred method of production, or a preferred method of doing new work requires the application of a logical procedure consisting of the following steps:[2]

1. *Aim*—Determination of objective in terms of area of job to be changed, and establishment of criteria for evaluating the preferability or success of solutions.
2. *Analysis*—Analysis of the work method into subdivisions or steps, pertinent to the job, appropriate to its scope, possessing known characteristics, or concerning whose performance information is already available.
3. *Criticism*—The application to the analysis of basic data, or check lists of desirable arrangements of the steps into a preferable work pattern and of information concerning desirable ways of performing each of the steps.

[1] A phrase coined by Frank B. and Lillian M. Gilbreth, the originators of much of our motion study. Some psychologists have objected to this attitude because, as they have well established, individual differences in people point to the desirability of individualized motion patterns. However, the differences between various alternative methods are usually so gross and the requirements of individuals so minute in contrast, that the "one best way" as selected is usually preferable for all the workers involved. Indeed, the question of individual differences is not even pertinent in cases concerning the flow of material through a plant, or the design of an output.

[2] These steps, which merely represent a pattern of thinking, could be divided into a greater or lesser number. The breakdown chosen seemed convenient.

4. *Innovation*—The formulation (or synthesis) of a new suggested procedure for performing the work.
5. *Test*—The testing, by means of the data previously used in step 3, of the desirability of the method formulated in step 4, with respect to the objectives set up in step 1.
6. *Trial*—The sample application of the method tested in step 5 to ascertain the completeness with which all variables have been taken into account.
7. *Application*—The final standardization, installation, evaluation, and maintenance of the improved work method.

This general procedure is usually the same whether the work is in an office, in a light or heavy industry, on the farm, in a hospital, laundry, service station, library, or home, or in any government activity. It is merely the details of performing the various steps that change with the requirements of the problem.

The main body of knowledge in motion and time study consists of procedures for each of the seven steps of the scientific method and may be grouped as follows:

1. Systematic means of selecting a feasible-appearing objective.
2. Procedures for analyzing work into appropriate units possessing known characteristics.
3. Check lists of desirable and undesirable features applicable to these analyses.
4. Means of describing the new method prior to performance.
5. Means of checking, prior to performance, the desirability of the new method.
6. Means of observing the initial application of a method and evaluating such observations.
7. Procedures for setting down work methods in such a manner as to aid in training people to follow the desired procedures; means of determining the time that should be required for the job and means of controlling standards (both method and time).

Before a systematic means of selecting a feasible-appearing objective can be discussed, we must first examine and divide the total area of application of motion and time study into reasonable sections. Such a division will provide additional terms for clearly describing our objectives.

To improve[3] a work method it may be necessary to begin by introducing innovations or changes in any one of the five areas that affect its performance. These areas are:

---

[3] The use of the word "improve" does not necessarily imply an existing working situation. The method under study may well be in the planning stage, but it is still subject to "improvement."

1. *Human activity*

   The hand and body motions or the perceptive or cognitive activity or their sequence may be changed to ease or improve the task.

2. *Work station (tools, workplace layout, or equipment)*

   The design of any single work station or the equipment used for any part of the task may be modified.

3. *Process or work sequence*

   The order or condition in which the various work stations receive the in-process output may require change or the number of work stations may be modified.

4. *Output design*

   The product design or the form of goods sold or the material sent out (in the case of a substantive product) or the nature of the completed service (in the case of a service type output) may require either a slight or drastic change in order to facilitate the attainment of the objectives of improvement.

5. *Inputs*

   The incoming supplies or raw materials (for substantive products) or the incoming information (for service outputs) brought into the organization may require a change with respect to the form, condition, specification, or timing of the arrival in order to allow the desired improvements to be made.

A change in any one of these areas, other than area 1, usually involves changes in other areas with lower numbers. Indeed, the reason for introducing a change in output design may be to effect economies in one of the preceding areas; a change in inputs may be advantageous despite the increased cost of what is obtained if this increased cost is more than offset by better equipment usage, labor savings, or an improved service.

The situation, with substantive outputs, may be represented by a diagram, as in Figure 3.1. Essentially the same situation exists with service outputs, although minor changes in the words selected to describe the situation help clarify the concept. With service outputs, the "supplier" supplies information or a request. The "customer" is the one who receives the service; with government activities this person may not be a customer in the usual sense of the word. Further, with government services the supplier and customer may be the same person. However, the same five separable parts of the situation will exist and must be recognized as potential areas for change.

To facilitate, in actual cases, the discussion of potential changes let us designate innovations involving a change in the manner of performing the work at any single location such as *A, B, C, D,* or *E* in Figure 3.1, provided

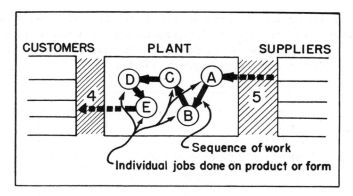

Fig. 3.1 — Diagram of areas affected by motion and time study.

the change of equipment would not cost more than $100,[4] as *Class 1 changes* to correspond to the list of areas of change. *Class 2 changes* are those introduced by a change costing more than $100 in the equipment used at any single location, such as *A* or *B*, of Figure 3.1. Area 1 changes usually accompany changes of this type for maximum gain.

Class 3 changes are those introduced by a change of the sequence of jobs *A, B, C,* etc., brought about by adding, eliminating, combining, or changing the order of jobs. This frequently involves area 2 or area 1 changes as well, for maximum improvement.

Class 4 changes are those introduced by a change in the form or nature of the output (product design) moving across area 4 of Figure 3.1. Such changes will usually involve all lower areas of change as well.

Class 5 changes are those introduced by a change in some characteristic of the inputs flowing across area 5 of Figure 3.1. Such changes will usually also involve all lower areas of change.

The class of change sought on a particular job is a function of how far the analyst thinks it desirable, or feels able, to carry the improvement. In the examples given in Chapter 1, the amount of change varied greatly. In the case of the radar coil, even the specification of the raw material and the design of the final product were changed; in the case of the chick sorting, nothing was changed except the layout of the workplace and the pattern of hand and body movements. These are the two extreme cases. Altogether, as has been shown, five classes of possible changes exist, with the characteristics sum-

---

[4] The $100 limit is arbitrary and represents a common level at which a supervisor's or foreman's authority for authorizing a purchase or requisition on a service department ends. If the limit in any particular organization is different, then the line of demarcation between Class 1 and Class 2 changes should also be shifted.

marized in Figure 3.2. It should be noted that the higher the number of change, the more items usually changed, although there will be many exceptions to this general rule. Also, the higher the class of change, the more authority required, and the more people affected.

Class of Change	Hand and Body Motions	Tools, Workplace, and Equipment	Process	Product	Raw Material
1	New	Minor changes	Same	Same	Same
2	New	New (Radical)	Same	Same	Same
3	New	New	New	Same	Same
4	New	New	New	Modified	Same
5	New	New	New	Modified	New

Note: The word *modified* appears in the "Product" column to emphasize that this is only a modification rather than a different product for a different purpose. Also, in any row, the item farthest to the right undergoing change, indicates where the change must usually be initiated.

Fig. 3.2—Outline of the five classes of change possible with motion and time study.

For instance, a Class 1 change may be initiated by almost anyone in an organization. A Class 2 change may involve the superior of a first line supervisor for authority to purchase, or the tool superintendent[5] for design of the jigs or tools. Indeed, a Class 2 change may be initiated by the tool division. A Class 3 change may involve all groups mentioned in the preceding classes, plus the process division; a Class 4 change may require the additional cooperation of the engineering (or design) and sales division; and a Class 5 change may include all the previously mentioned groups, plus the purchasing department. In service organizations equivalent groups will be involved but the titles will vary over such a wide range that a single example would not appear to be of particular value.

These five classes of change may be considered as a guide to areas in which changes are possible or as a guide to "organized brainstorming" as opposed to random hunting.

The next chapter will describe the systematic means of selecting a feasible-appearing objective, which is the first step in the scientific method. It will

[5] The occupational titles given here are samples and may vary from plant to plant. They certainly will be different in service organizations.

also outline a procedure for selecting a suitable analysis technique for performing the four subsequent steps. Which analysis technique is to be used will be a function of the class of change sought and the physical characteristics of the subject of the methods scrutiny, together with some economic considerations. Each technique will be treated in a separate chapter.

Time study, or the appraisal of work in terms of time, will be treated in detail later in this book. This type of measurement is vital in the modern managerial process. Unless one can determine, in advance, how long work should take, the managerial functions are essentially based on "rule of thumb" rather than on fact. The newer and more sophisticated mathematical techniques of scheduling, or the planning of output-mix, by means of linear or dynamic programming, frequently depend upon time study to give accurate coefficients for the variables in the required systems of equations. Time study in this manner influences many managerial decisions.

Figure 1.12 showed the effects of an extensive motion and time study program on one product at Joseph Lucas, Ltd. During this program raw material specifications were changed, designs altered, process sequence and factory layout changed, tooling redesigned and operators trained to perform new jobs with new methods. Time standards were used as guides for supervisors, for manpower planning, and for payment by means of an incentive pay plan. The entire fabric of the industrial plant was subjected to change as a result of the motion and time study program.

It should be obvious at this point that a motion and time study analysis may affect many different levels in an organization. If the techniques that follow are understood by all concerned, cooperative action for selecting economical operating procedures may take place much more easily than if all the initiative and action originate in a single staff department. The staff department may still be necessary to coordinate the work and to carry the burden on extensive projects, but motion and time study affects, and should be thought of as being part of, everybody's job.

CHAPTER 4

How to Start the Analysis

The first step in applying the scientific method to the solution of motion and time study problem is:

Aim——*Determination of objective in terms of area of work to be changed, and establishment of criteria for evaluating the preferability or success of solutions.*

The performance of this step has three parts:

1. Selection of the criteria of success of solution.
2. Rough determination of the degree of change which is warranted or needed.
3. Contemplation of the apparently feasible areas of change and the selection of the most feasible area of change.

1. Selection of the Criteria of Success of Solution

To determine our degree of success, we must know what it is we are seeking to achieve. Therefore, the person seeking a better method must determine his criterion first, using his knowledge of the activity to guide him.

Some possible criteria of success of solution are given in the list which follows. The list has been oriented toward manufacturing situations. For industries or activities other than manufacturing these criteria would either need to be restated or special priorities be given to selected items. For instance, in department store work as with other profit-oriented service activities, customer service is of extreme importance. In medical work, patient safety may have an overwhelming priority. In government activities, conformance with externally imposed limitations concerning money or manpower may be a primary objective.

1. *Maximum financial advantage through*
   a. Less direct labor time
   b. Less direct labor effort
   c. Less indirect labor
   d. Better balance of direct and indirect labor
   e. Fewer or more steps (depending on product and volume)
   f. Less skill (lower-priced labor)
   g. More skill (more productive labor)
   h. Less equipment usage
   i. Cheaper equipment
   j. Less space
   k. Less scrap
   l. Higher yield of high value product[1]
   m. Less expensive material

2. *Maximum conformance with externally imposed restrictions[2]*
   a. Fewer people
   b. Less time for critical skills
   c. Less time on critical equipment
   d. Less time in production
   e. Less space
   f. Less critical material
   g. Less working capital

3. *Better product in respect to function, salability, or acceptability.*
   This may be a long-range aspect of number 1, although it may involve greater cost of operation on a particular job. However, in many situations it may be accomplished with less cost and is then doubly desirable.

4. *Better material control*
   This is also an economic objective, as it relates to inventory cost, scheduling and control functions, and customer service.

2. *Rough determination of the degree of change that is warranted.*

The type of decision that must be reached in this part of the step can perhaps be best understood by considering a few illustrations. Let us assume that we are contemplating changing the method of doing one operation on a product. The operation requires sixty man-hours per week and the product will probably be made for ten weeks. With a labor rate of $2.85 per hour

---

[1] Particularly applicable to process industries.
[2] That is, availability, customer requirements, government restrictions, etc.

this means a labor expenditure of $1,710 on this operation. A 25 per cent cost reduction will return a gross of $427.50 against which we will have to charge all cost of analysis, physical changes, and possible training. In this case, our decision would be that changes would have to be quickly arrived at and be low in installation cost. This decision would temper our method of performing the next step. However, in contrast with the data cited, activities are encountered where more than 100 people are performing the same operation, day after day, and it is anticipated that the activity will continue indefinitely. Obviously, if in such a case there is a reasonable chance of obtaining an improvement, the amount of effort and money that may be expended is quite different and the techniques chosen will reflect these different facts.

For a second case, let us assume that a government agency is contemplating some change in an existing manner of distributing food to needy or hungry people. A sizeable segment of the population and a large amount of money are involved. One of the existing complaints may be that the people, in general, are not satisfied (or feel denigrated) by the types of food distributed and by the method of distribution. Some radical changes seem in order so that social acceptability may obtained. Of course, in this situation some techniques other than motion and time study will also be involved, but this was also true in the first case. The economic analysis was not motion and time study; economic analysis and motion and time study both were used, even if the economic analysis used in the first problem was simple. In the case of the food distribution problem the economic analysis aspect and the social analysis aspect will assume more importance and be more complex than in the first example cited but the motion and time study aspect still exists. As mentioned in Chapter 1, the motion and time study techniques are merely an aid to managers; they are not a substitute for management or managers or for other disciplines or fields of knowledge.

For a third case, let us assume we are attempting to increase the control of stock in order to cut down pilferage in a mail-order house or warehouse. In this case we may have only an estimate of present probable pilferage, an estimate of potential pilferage, and a realization that the less chance of pilferage taking place, the less chance of unpleasant consequences if and when a culprit is detected. This last consideration is hardly an economic one, yet all these data may assist us in arriving at a rough decision that an improved control of stock is desirable, provided it is not more expensive than the present system (although there may be leeway even on this). Hence, our rough decision would be that if pilferage is a real danger, even extensive change is warranted, although we may merely break even on costs and savings.

For a fourth case, let us assume we are studying the work done during a submarine torpedo attack. Cutting a ten-second operation by two seconds may be of negligible economic value by itself (after all, the crew is available), but it may make all the difference in a war. If we were the analysts in such a case, we would probably decide that even extensive change is warranted and give minimum consideration to limiting the time and cost of creating the change.

To sum up this part: the analyst roughly considers the importance of the job on a monetary basis or otherwise, depending on which is suitable, and sets himself rough limits concerning the nature of the change and the expenditure of time and money.

3. *Contemplation of the apparently feasible areas of change and the selection of the most feasible area of change.*

As an aid in contemplating his possible objectives, the method analyst may use a *possibility guide*. Even when he does not use one, his thinking should follow its pattern.

The possibility guide is a device for systematically listing all possible changes that are suggested by the person familiar with the activity or output under scrutiny. The possiblity guide also allows the showing of the consequences of each suggestion for the purpose of assisting in the selection of the most feasible type of change and thus helps the analyst to select the appropriate analysis procedure for performing the next step of the motion and time study.

It is worth noting that a listing of possible changes often can be made by a person possessing only a slight familiarity with the work under scrutiny. In many cases, such a person can suggest more possibilities than a person so familiar with the job that he cannot see beyond it, although this relative blindness of the latter is only a state of mind and not an irremediable condition. The largest number of possibilities can usually be suggested by a person familiar with the work but still open-minded about it.

The making of a possibility guide is most easily accomplished in two steps:

1. Listing the suggestions on a preliminary possibility guide form, sometimes called a possiblity list.
2. Detailing the consequences of each suggestion on a detailed possibility guide form.

Typical forms for use during the two-step preparation of a possibility guide will be shown in illustrations later in this chapter.

The subject of a motion and time study scrutiny may be classified under one of the following five classes which, as was previously shown, are all interrelated:

1. A job
2. The equipment on a job
3. The process

4. The product design
5. The raw materials

If the subject of the study is "a job," then the Class 1 and 2 suggestions will relate to this task. The Class 3, 4, and 5 possibilities relate to the job only as it is a part of the sequence in which it lies. However, these aspects should always be considered, since frequently one way to improve a job is to change the sequence so that the job is eliminated, combined with another job, placed more advantageously in the sequence, or, at least, made simpler.

If the subject of the scrutiny is "the equipment on a job," then the remarks in the preceding paragraph again apply.

If the subject of the scrutiny is "the process," then the Class 4 and 5 possibilities concern the product design and the raw materials as they affect the process. With "the process" under scrutiny the Class 1 and 2 possibilities may be exceedingly numerous, as they can be listed for each job in the process. One usual procedure is to find the most time-consuming job in the process and develop a better method for it, provided it is found necessary to do this job at all. Although this is often most productive, still one should bear in mind that some of the less time-consuming steps, if not eliminated by a process change, may yield a greater percentage of savings than can be gained from an improvement of a more important operation.

Possibility guides in respect to "the design" or "the raw materials" are similar in nature to those constructed in respect to "the process."

The procedure for using a possibility guide can perhaps best be illustrated by an actual example. The general procedure will be the same no matter in which of the previously listed five groups the subject of the scrutiny belongs.

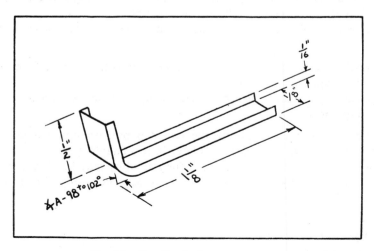

Fig. 4.1 — Details of relay armature arm.

Let us examine an example in detail so as to fully describe the procedure for "thinking through" a possibility guide. The example concerns a relay armature arm used in an automobile turn signal flasher system. Our objective or criterion of success is *to lower costs*.

We would naturally have to have some familiarity with the process, a famil-

Type of Chart _Preliminary Possibility Guide_____

Method _Present process_____	Machine No. ═══════
Operation _Mfg._____	Operation No. ═══════
Criterion _Lower cost_____	Part No. _124 R_____
Part name _Armature Arm_____	Chart by _L. Edmond_
Operator_ ═══════	Date charted _2/16/_

Suggestion Number	Class of Change	Description	Other classes affected
1	5	Use sheet stock	4, 3, 2, 1
2	5	Purchase formed to size and shape	3, 2, 1
3	4	Redesign relay to allow more tolerance in arm eliminating inspection	3, 2, 1
4	3	Inspect at punch press as part of operation	2, 1
5	2	Dual inspection fixture, electric response	1
6	1	Tip fixture to make easier, weigh to count at inspection	
7	1	Distribute work to both hands at inspection	

If more space is needed paste additional sheet on here.

Fig. 4.2—Preliminary possibility guide for manufacture of relay armature arm.

iarity that could best be acquired by viewing the actual process, but the following description will have to suffice. The armature arm was used in a thermal relay designed to flash a light on and off. The raw material was in the form of U-shaped steel stock, five feet long, and had the dimensions of the U shown in Figure 4.1. The stock was issued as production orders required and was cut to length and formed in a punch press. The pieces were banked at the press, moved by tubs to an inspection station, and sorted by the angle *A*. Pieces outside of the limits were rejected. If any sizeable number of pieces were rejected, they were rebent to shape. The pieces were then sent in small tubs to the relay assembly-line station where they were welded into the relay.

The first thing we should do is to go completely through the Check List for Possibility Guide, jotting down all possible suggestions on a preliminary form, as is done in Figure 4.2. The body of the typical form is divided into four columns as shown. The first column is for a consecutive numbering of the suggestions, so that others commenting on the list may easily identify what they are referring to, or to facilitate discussion. The second column identifies the class of change contained in the possibility or suggestion. The description column is the possibility itself, and the last column lists the other areas that would probably be affected. This last column is a guide for future expansion of the possibilities for fuller examination.

A partial check list begins below. The analyst may find it desirable to expand this list as he acquires more experience with this approach. In any case, the analyst will add to the list in an informal manner as he acquires experience in a particular field of work. To the experienced analyst each problem is no longer totally new; some previously acquired information may be applied to the new situation to assist in producing a solution. However, each field of activity has its own uniqueness. The check list given here is primarily oriented around manufacturing. In any service activity, such as an area of government activity, a suitable check list would be quite different; the questions in it would reflect a codification suitable for retrieving the specialized knowledge pertinent to the particular activity under scrutiny.

The questions in the check list given here are numbered to correspond to the class of change they refer to, but are listed in the order used, the higher classes being taken first, as we usually start with the highest class of change and work down to Class 1.

CHECK LIST FOR POSSIBILITY GUIDE

    5. Can a slightly different raw material be ordered or can the same material be ordered in a form that would be more advantageous? Can we change:
       a. Shape
       b. Size
       c. Packaging

    d. Quantity packed together
    e. Material
    f. Amount of processing done by supplier
    g. Color
    h. Finish
    i. Any other specification
    j. The product so as to make any material or auxiliary material unnecessary

4. Can the product be made, sold, or sent out in a more advantageous form? Can we:
    a. Modify design
    b. Pack differently
    c. Change finish
    d. Change weight
    e. Change tolerances

3. a. Can we do the different jobs along the route between receiving and shipping in a different order?
    b. Is any step unnecessary?
       1. What does it accomplish?
       2. Why is it done?
       3. What would happen if it were not done?
    c. Can we combine any steps?
    d. Can we advantageously break any job into two or more separate operations?

2. a. Can any new tools or equipment or a change in the workplace make any job in the sequence easier? (This is almost always possible.)
    b. Can any tool or equipment be eliminated advantageously?
    c. Can any two tools be combined?

1. Can a new motion pattern make any job in the sequence easier? This is almost invariably true. Specific suggestions are usually more easily made after the method analyst is more familiar with the man-analysis techniques; hence, at this point, a mere list of the possible jobs that may be looked into or some rough suggestions will probably be all the student is capable of. (The analyst also tries to eliminate motions. In actual practice, as will be evident later, this part of the analysis may be done in more detailed fashion.)

With the aid of the questions on the check list, the preliminary possibility guide of Figure 4.2 would be made up as follows: (It is suggested that the reader check these to follow the procedure.)

Suggestion on Preliminary Possibility Guide	*Check List Question That Suggested Possibility*
1	5a
2	5f
3	4e
4	3c
5	2a
6	1
7	1

Following this, the analyst would expand the possibilities into the form shown in Figure 4.3.

POSSIBILITY GUIDE

Name of ~~Operation~~ Mfg. Process, Armature Arm - 124R

Operation Number ___—___

File Number ___124R___

Analysis by ___L. Edmond___

Date ___2/16/___

Class of Change	Hand and Body Motions	Tools, Workplace and Equipment	Process	Product Design	Raw Material
1	Distribute work to both hands on inspection	Tip fixture. Scale to weigh count (on inspection)			
2	Balanced hand pattern	Dual inspection fixture, electric response (See above also)			
3	Fit into pattern of press operation	Fixture convenient for press operator	Inspect at punch press as part of operation		
4	Check assembly motions for affect of redesign	Check assembly fixtures for affect of tolerance	Eliminate inspection From press send to assembly	Redesign relay to allow more tolerance in arm	
5	Eliminated No inspection See box above, tho.	No equipment Simple die to blank, no forming	No process Eliminate inspection	No change L shape, no channel	Purchase formed Sheet stock instead of channel

Fig. 4.3 — Detailed possibility guide for manufacture of relay arma-ture arm.

The possibility guides were made, as is usual, prior to any other formal analysis, by a person somewhat familiar with the manufacture of the arma-ture arm.

On the basis of the possibility guide, his experience, and an analysis of the economic and psychological factors concerned, the analyst must also deter-mine which one of the five areas of possible change is the most promising one to start with as a tentative objective. This is particularly important because the specific analysis technique chosen for the second step of the logical procedure will be a function of the area in which change is sought.

Changes starting with a Class 1 (hand and body motions) or Class 2 (work station) change will affect only the way an individual does his job and the equipment he uses; the work of the persons who work with the product (or paperwork) before and after him is not affected. Hence, in such cases, the second main step of the logical procedure will involve *man analysis*, or a technique to determine how the man performs his job, or, in the case of a job that is not yet being performed, how it is proposed that the man perform it.

Changes starting with a Class 3 (process or work sequence), Class 4 (output design), or Class 5 (inputs) change will involve a study of the flow of the output, or a *product analysis* technique as the main second step.

If the decision is to seek a Class 1 or 2 change, the second main step of the scientific approach to better methods will involve the use of a *man analysis* technique, whereas if the decision is to seek a Class 3, 4, or 5 change, the next step will involve a *product analysis* technique.

The basic analysis techniques, which will be detailed in later chapters, are:

For use in performing *Man Analysis*:

1. Process chart-man analysis (usually accompanied by a flow diagram)
2. Work activity analysis and work sampling
3. Operation chart
4. Multiple activity charts
   a. Man and machine chart
   b. Multiman chart
5. Micromotion charts
   a. Simo chart
   b. Memomotion chart and memomotion reconnaissance
6. Chronocyclographic analysis
7. Visual analysis
8. A wide variety of time study techniques, including work sampling (used mainly as a means of determining expected performance although of considerable use in methods improvement)

For use in performing *Output or Product Analysis*:

1. Process chart-product analysis (usually accompanied by a flow diagram)
2. Horizontal time bar charts
3. Network diagrams
4. Functional forms analysis
5. Process chart-combined analysis

The particular class of change chosen as an objective in any case is a function of many factors.

The higher classes of change often take longer to install, affect more people, and usually require higher authority. Hence, in addition to the relative desirability or apparent feasibility of the individual suggestions, the following factors must be taken into consideration in detail when making a final decision.

Economic and psychological factors affecting change include:

1. How great is the actual or expected volume, and how often does the job occur?
2. How long will the job exist?
3. How much time, per unit, is spent on the job?

4. How much time is available for working up the change?
5. How much equipment is already invested in the job?
6. How much analysis time will be required?
7. How much loss of production, sales, or service will occur during a change?
8. How much retraining will be required?
9. What is the possible saving by means of the improvement?
10. What is the position of the analyst in the organization?
11. What are the personalities involved?
12. What are the policies that affect the problem?
13. Is the product for internal use or for customers?
14. What do the other groups in the organization who will be affected think of the feasibility of the suggestion?

The importance of each factor will vary from case to case. Their particular order, as given here, does not necessarily indicate their relative importance. The analyst must weigh and evaluate them for each situation.

In all cases the class of change selected, together with the physical characteristics of the job or process in question, would determine which of the analysis techniques previously listed would next be used. This relationship will come into sharper focus when the analyst acquires greater familiarity with all of the techniques listed.

The possibility guide serves the purposes of:

1. Aiding in systematically listing possible changes and collecting material from which to determine an objective
2. Aiding in determining a suitable analysis technique
3. Indicating which divisions in the organization will be affected

It should be noted that these are the prime functions of the possibility guide.

In addition to the above list, the supervisor should find the possibility guide of considerable assistance in:

1. Reviewing an analyst's initial thinking and approving of a clear-cut objective
2. Delineating the scope of a project assigned to an analyst

In any case the analyst should never lose sight of the desirability of eliminating a job. This is the ultimate improvement for any single job. Consequently, even when the objective is a Class 1 or 2 change, it is usually good practice to make a rough product analysis after the possibility guide and before using any man analysis technique. This will allow the analyst to be reasonably certain that he is not analyzing an unnecessary job or an unnecessary phase of the job.

SUMMARY — POSSIBILITY GUIDES

1. Uses:
   a. *Aiding in systematically listing possible changes and collecting material from which to determine an objective.*
   b. *Aiding in determining a suitable analysis technique.*
   c. *Indicating which divisions in the organization will be affected.*
2. How made:
   a. *A form such as shown in Figure 4.2 may be used or a blank sheet of paper may be substituted.*
   b. *The analyst states his criterion of success.*
   c. *The analyst makes a rough determination of the degree of change that is warranted.*
   d. *The analyst, with the aid of a check list, lists the possibilities that occur to him, tempering his imagination with the decision reached in the previous step, identifies each possiblity as to class of change and other areas affected, and gives each an identifying number.*
   e. *The analyst expands each possibility on a detailed possibility guide form, such as Figure 4.3, or on a blank sheet of paper, so that he may examine the consequences of each item.*
3. How used:
   a. *With the aid of business and manufacturing knowledge and with consideration of the economic and psychological factors involved, the analyst selects which class of change or which possibility appears most feasible. Several persons may well participate in this step.*
   b. *With the above decision and the nature of the job in mind, he selects an appropriate analysis technique.*
4. What then:
   The analyst is now ready for step 2 (analysis) of the logical approach. Note: The trained analyst may not make a formal possibility guide, yet his thinking should follow its pattern. Experience suggests, however, that the actual following of the above steps is usually much more productive than the informal approach.

Supplemental Material [3]

The two illustrations that follow were deliberately chosen from areas other than manufacturing and were selected to suggest how the possibility-guide approach may be used no matter what the output or field of activity.

Figures 4.4 and 4.5 are the preliminary and detailed possibility guides made prior to an improvement of the peeling operation in a tomato canning factory during World War II. A study of these, together with the list of economic and psychological factors, aided in selecting the objective, as may be seen from the following discussion.

The Class 5 change was rejected as requiring too many years to develop; hence, it was not of immediate value. The Class 4 changes were rejected by

---

[3] As described in the preface, whenever feasible each chapter which treats a technique is divided into two parts: (1) a basic presentation for those whose time is limited and desire only a basic familiarity with the subject, and (2) supplemental material for those who wish to pursue the subject to greater depth.

Type of Chart PRELIMINARY POSSIBILITY GUIDE

Method CONVERSE, IND. PLANT   Machine No. ︶

Operation PEELING WHOLE   Operation No. 4

CRITERION LESS LABOR   Part No. ︶

Part name TOMATO   Chart by Roundel

Operator LUCY WOOD   Date charted 2/4/

SUGG No.	CLASS OF CHANGE	DESCRIPTION	OTHER CL. AFFECTED
1	5	VERY FREE PEELING TOMATO	4,3,2,1
2	4	PACK JUICE	3,2,1
3	4	PACK WITH PEELS	3,2,1
4	3	PEEL INTO CANS	2,1
5	2	CHANGE TOMATO CONVEYOR HEIGHT;	
		ELIMINATE BUCKETS, CONVEYOR FOR	
		PEELED TOMATOES	1
6	2	NEW DESIGN PEELING KNIVES FOR ALL	
		PEELERS	1
7	2	AUTOMATIC PEELER	1
8	1	EASIER PEELING MOTION PATTERN	
.			

If more space is needed paste additional sheet on here

Fig. 4.4—Preliminary possibility guide for peeling of whole tomatoes in canning factory.

	**POSSIBILITY GUIDE** File Number T-4

Name of Operation _PEEL WHOLE TOMATOES_   Analysis by MUNDEL
Operation Number _4_   Date 2/4/

Class of Change	Hand and Body Motions	Tools, Workplace and Equipment	Process	Product Design	Raw Material
I	EASIER PEELING MOTION PATTERN				
2	ELIMINATE PEELING EASIER MOTIONS LESS ARM AND BACK MOTIONS	AUTO. PEELER NEW KNIFE DESIGN NEW CONVEYOR HGT. AND PEELED TOM. CONVEYOR			
3	PLACE IN CAN SAVE LATER REHANDLING	CAN CONVEYOR TO PEELERS	PEEL DIRECTLY INTO CANS		
4	ELIMINATE PEELING " BUT ADD CORING	JUICERS BUT PEELING LINE ELIMINATE CORE LINE ONLY	JUICE PROCESS ELIMINATE PEELING CORING ONLY	PACK JUICE PACK WITH PEELS	
5	PEEL WITH ONE MOTION OR SHAKE VERY MUCH FASTER	COULD USE #2 SUGGESTIONS	COULD CHANGE AS WITH #3 OR LEAVE ALONE	WOULD HAVE TO FLAVOR TEST	VERY FREE PEEL- ING TOMATOES

Fig. 4.5 — Detailed possibility guide for peeling of whole tomatoes in canning factory.

the sales department as contrary to market demand or as requiring too long to test. The Class 3 changes were found inadvisable owing to the difficulty of wartime development and procurement. Therefore, all effort was first expended on a Class 1 improvement of peeling, the most labor-consuming operation, with considerable success.

Figures 4.6 and 4.7 are the preliminary and detailed possibility guides for the sale of a pair of women's nylon hose in a large Midwest department store. The Class 5 suggestion was selected as most feasible. Subsequent detailed product and man analysis proved that it was most desirable and it was installed with considerable labor and cost savings.

Type of Chart _Preliminary possibility guide_

Method _Present_   Machine No. _~_

Operation _Sale of pair of Nylons_   Operation No. _~_

Criterion _Less time for customer and clerk_   Part No. _~_

Part name _Nylon hose_   Chart by _Ann Ayerite_

Operator— _~_   Date charted _12/4/_

Sugg No.	Class of change	Description	Other classes affected
1	5	Purchase stockings, prepacked, a pair to a container.	4, 3, 2, 1
2	4	Prepack in receiving, a pair to a container	3, 2, 1
3	3	Sell from samples on counter, pack hose without showing actual pair to customer	1
4	2	New packing desk for silk and Nylon hose counter instead of department desk for packing	1
5	2	New cash register, one for each counter	1
6	1	Teach girls easy way to fold and wrap hose.	

If more space is needed paste additional sheet on here.

Fig. 4.6—Preliminary possibility guide for sale of pair of nylons in department store.

44

POSSIBILITY GUIDE

Name of Operation _Selling pair of women Nylon hose_

Operation Number _____

File Number _WW-H-1_

Analysis by _Ann Agate_

Date _12/41_

Class of Change	Hand and Body Motions	Tools, Workplace and Equipment	Process	Product Design	Raw Material
1	Teach girls easy way to pick and wrap hose				
2	Less walking / Less walking	Cash register for each counter / Packing bench for hose counter			
3	Much less walking	Sample display unit / See above and also	Sell from samples on counter without showing actual pairs to customer		
4	See above / Less handling also	See above / Packing at hose at receiving	See above / Also, prepack in warehouse	Prepack in receiving, one pair to a package	
5	See above	See above on line #3	See above on line #3	Give customers prepack without opening	Buy prepacked Nylon stockings

Fig. 4.7—Detailed possibility guide for sale of pair of nylons in department store.

CHAPTER 5

Process Chart—
Product Analysis

The second step of the scientific procedure for determining better method is:

Analysis—Analysis of the work method into subdivisions or steps, pertinent to the job, appropriate to its scope, possessing known characteristics, or concerning whose performance information is already available.

The specific procedure selected for performing this step will be a function of the class of change finally sought and the characteristics of the subject of the scrutiny. The procedure selected will usually provide the framework for most of the succeeding steps as well. This chapter deals with only one device for performing these steps: the process chart-product analysis.

A process chart-product analysis is a graphic means of portraying (or a schematic model of) the separable steps of the procedure involved in performing the work required to modify an output from one stage of completion to another. This technique is primarily applicable when:

1. The timing of various batches moving through various steps, or the time relationships among the steps are not primary aspects under consideration.
2. The relationship between successive steps is relatively simple.
3. The output is essentially substantive.

In most cases, if the problem does not meet the restrictions enumerated, other techniques which will be discussed in subsequent chapters will be more helpful in making an analysis.

A process chart-product analysis would be used under the following circumstances:

1. As a last check prior to the application of a man analysis technique.

This would occur when the decision reached after step 1 of the scientific approach was to seek a Class 1 or 2 change. The process chart-product analysis would be used to verify the necessity of doing a particular job before attempting to improve it.

2. When the decision was to seek a Class 3, 4, or 5 change.

When the volume is great and the job of long duration, and where the time for extended analysis and the authority for complex change are available, it is usually desirable to exhaust all possible means of achieving a Class 3, 4, or 5 change before modifying any single job.

3. When planning for a product or a layout.

Process charts-product analysis should be made whenever possible for all materials, prior to the inception of production, to aid in designing the best possible process and layout before the beginning of work. This anticipatory planning is much cheaper, although less spectacular, than changes made subsequently. In all cases of plant layout and process planning, the process charts for the contemplated components or products should be made in connection with the plans for layout and used to obtain the best possible process and layout; that is, least handling, least number or cost of operations, least scrap, best control, smallest workable in-process inventory, or whatever are the appropriate criteria of preference. When a variety of products are contemplated, the various products may have conflicting requirements. In such cases, a weighted evaluation of the various products' requirements must be made.[1] Adequate use of process charts-product analysis for such uses is facilitated by an intimate knowledge of product and process requirements and peculiarities. In competent hands, or with proper cooperative assistance from the various plant groups, such charts are valuable as a tool for the attainment of efficient plant layout and effective process planning, and as a source of suggestions for new equipment and tool design. Process charts-product analysis are also a guide to the over-all analysis of plant operation.

The steps commonly used, and the symbols used to represent them, are given in Table 1. The process involved in manufacturing, processing, or handling the parts, components, or product is usually portrayed graphically,

[1] This may lead to a problem in linear programming or some mathematical model of the situation as contrasted with the process chart which is only a schematic model. If a mathematical model may be created, the best solution may be determined in a much more mechanistic fashion but the process chart is frequently a vital aid in fashioning the mathematical model.

TABLE 1

Symbols for Process Chart-Product Analysis

Symbol	A.S.M.E. Symbol	Name	Used to Represent
◯	◯	Operation	Something done to the product at essentially one location.
▢	▢	Quantity Inspection	A special form of operation involving the verification of the quantity of a product present against some record of the quantity that is supposed to be there.
◇		Quality Inspection	A special form of operation involving the verification of some attribute or quality of a product against a standard.
◯	⇨	Movement	A change in the location of a product which does not change it in any other way.
▽	◗	Temporary Storage	The storage of a product under conditions such that it may be moved or withdrawn from storage without a requisition.
▽	▽	Controlled Storage	Storage of a product under controls such that a requisition or receipting is needed to withdraw it.

in terms of these steps, by means of these symbols, to aid in ease of understanding and to break the sequence into relatively homogeneous steps. The use of these or some standardized set of symbols[2] is desirable because the classification of the steps into categories possessing known characteristics

[2] The A.S.M.E. proposed a standard set of symbols; see *Operation and Flow Process Charts*. New York, N.Y.: A.S.M.E., 1947. These differ from those used for the charts in this book. The symbols which appear in these illustrations most closely resemble those used in the past and better separate distinct activities. The symbols are to serve the function of *analysis* as defined and not vice versa. In many cases, additional symbols may be of great help inasmuch as these charts are schematic rather than exact models of situations, and changes in schematic presentation are desirable if they contribute to clarification. However, a new variety of symbol should only be introduced if it offers distinct advantages. For a useful and novel set of symbols see W. W. Phillips and S. W. Earle, "Cycle Charting—With 'Handligs,'" *Factory Management and Maintenance*, Vol. III, No. 8; Aug. 1953, pp. 105–107.

is of prime importance in this work, and the breakdown should be visually apparent. The symbols act as flags identifying the various types of steps. Also, the use of standardized steps and symbols permits the charts to be easily understood by others, and this is especially important with a technique leading to Class 3, 4, or 5 changes, inasmuch as such changes frequently require a large number of cooperating individuals and groups. However, standardization should not be considered a rigid requirement if additional or different symbols will clarify the schematic model. The problem being charted, rather than the chart, should be the focus of attention.

A standard analysis must be used if we hope to develop standard procedures for improving processes, rather than remain content to approach each problem as something entirely new. However, the standard analysis should be thought of as the procedure of breaking the sequence into steps, rather than the rigid and blind use of a given set of steps. The standardization should be of the general form rather than of the details of charting; these may change as dictated by the requirements of the problem.

The steps given in Table 1 have been chosen as appropriate to the scope of most industrial activity while separating different types of activity and different areas of responsibility, as follows:[3]

Operation—A step that usually requires labor and/or equipment, is the only type that may add value to the product, and is usually a responsibility of the production group aided by the tooling or "processing" staff.[4]

Quantity Inspection—A step that usually requires labor, may require equipment, provides control, and is usually a responsibility of the production control group.

Quality Inspection—A step that usually requires labor and equipment, provides control, and is usually a responsibility of the inspection or quality control group.

Movement—A step that usually requires labor and equipment, and is usually a responsibility of the materials handling group.

Temporary Storage—A step that requires space, adds to inventory, and is usually caused by the process design or plant layout, hence is a responsibility of the group or groups having jurisdiction over these designs.

Controlled Storage—A step that requires space and labor, represents inventory, and is usually a responsibility of the inventory, material, or stock control group.

---

[3] At times, it may be desirable to use more or fewer steps. A scrutiny of those listed here and the areas of responsibility thus separated would suggest that this set approaches a minimum number. It should also be apparent that the selection of the steps is of much more importance than the selection of the particular symbols used to represent them. However, a given set of symbols should be used consistently, to avoid confusion.

[4] It may assist analysis to separate *do* operations (those that add value to the product, from *get ready*, *put away*, or facilitative operations.

Our *criticism* of a process portrayed in process chart form will generally follow a very simple pattern. For instance, the first four symbols given in Table 1 sort out and identify places where work is done with or on the product.

We should learn not only to question the desirability of any occurrence of the first symbol, but also to seek its optimum location in the sequence, which is often a function of the peculiarities of the material being worked with. The next two symbols refer to special forms of the same type of step shown in the first symbol except that the purpose is control. We may well also question these symbols and seek their best place in the sequence, which again is often a function of the material worked with or the process. These first three types of steps usually consume labor; the fourth category, movement, is likewise, usually, a labor consumer. A standard way of reducing an excessive labor (consumption) in any move represented by this fourth symbol is to change the method to some more economical means of transportation, depending on the exact nature of the case. [5]

The last two symbols classify steps that are primarily nothing other than space occupancy and represent inventory. One is also a control point. We may well question the desirability of such inventory occurring at the point where it does, its size, and the desirability of controlling it.

Further, the assignment of any step to one of the six categories suggested indicates the staff group from which cooperation and assistance must be sought.

The application of process charts-product analysis may be best understood by an examination of some actual cases. Those which follow have been so arranged that they tend to increase in complexity as well as illustrate the various uses and different classes of change that may result from the application of this technique. [6]

Only Case I appears in the main body of the chapter; the remaining cases are in the Supplemental Material appended after the chapter summary.

Case I illustrates a use of a simple process chart-product analysis for a last check prior to the application of a man analysis technique.

Case II illustrates a use of a simple process chart-product analysis leading to a Class 3 change involving reduced handling.

Case III illustrates a use of a much longer process chart-product analysis for a Class 3 change affecting not only handling but the location of operations. The illustration is drawn from a service industry to show the range of application of this technique.

Case IV illustrates a use of a reduced-detail process chart-product analysis

---

[5] See any reference on Materials Handling or Transportation.

[6] The use of the *before and after* presentation in these cases should not cause the reader to lose sight of the use of the process chart-product analysis as a design tool. It is of great value for describing a contemplated process and may assist in the improvement of this design before it becomes practice.

for a complex problem of replanning a whole process with the intent of a drastic Class 3 change, but which eventually led to a Class 4 change.

Case V illustrates a use of a process chart-product analysis that led to the creation of a mathematical model (linear programming) of the problem.

CASE I   A USE OF A SIMPLE PROCESS CHART-PRODUCT ANALYSIS AS A LAST CHECK PRIOR TO THE APPLICATION OF A MAN ANALYSIS TECHNIQUE

Let us assume that we have been assigned the task of reducing the cost of manufacture of the radio tube filament (cathode heater) shown in Figure 5.1. The filament proper, a coil of double coiled tungsten wire, was slipped

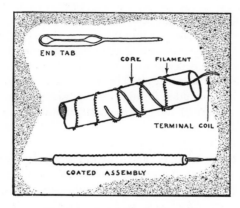

Fig. 5.1 — Original tube filament.

over a thin ceramic core and molybdenum end coils were slipped over the ends. The end coil held the filament firmly to the rod and provided several points of electrical contact. The subassembly was then sprayed with a ceramic coating and baked until the coating vitrified. During vitrification some of the ceramic would usually run down the end coils. Before the nickel end tabs could be welded to the end coils this excess ceramic had to be chipped away. The nickel end tabs were used to weld the filament onto the supporting members in the tube. Much production was lost during the chipping operation inasmuch as frequently too much ceramic would chip off, leaving one of the end coils bare. A heater with a bare end coil could not be used because it might cause a short circuit between the heater and the cathode. Also, many of the heaters were broken in half during the chipping operation. The total loss of production during the chipping operating was approximately 33 per cent.

Let us say we wished to improve the original method of chipping the excess ceramic from the end coil. Since as much as 33 per cent of all filaments were lost on this operation, this was obviously a job that should be improved. Let us further assume that a possibility guide had been constructed as explained in Chapter 4 and that a Class 1 or 2 change was the maximum that appeared economically feasible. A man analysis technique was thus indicated, but a process chart-product analysis of a part of the work of manufacturing the filament would have been constructed first to make sure the chipping operation was necessary, before an attempt was made to improve it.

Figure 5.2 is a process chart-product analysis of part of the manufacturing procedure for the radio-tube filament described above. A form such as shown in Figure 5.2 or a blank sheet of paper may be used.

There should be at least four columns: the first, for the quantity usually worked on or typical of that step (with storages this column usually shows the number that may accumulate at that point); the second, a distance column to be used with each movement symbol to show the distance covered by the move; the third, a symbol column to identify the general characteristics of each step;[7] the fourth, a description column to summarize the work done or the nature of the step or its location. The unit time or cost for each step may sometimes be usefully included in additional columns.

The length of the part of the process analyzed in circumstances like this example will be a function of:

1. The scope of activity of the analyst.
If he is a department foreman, he is usually not in a position to carry the work outside of his department. The same is true of the worker who may use motion and time study to develop better methods for his own job.

2. The certainty that Class 3, 4, and 5 changes are out of the question.
Some analysts advise a complete process chart-product analysis prior to any man analysis, but this is often not expedient when immediate improvement is possible with Class 1 and 2 changes.

A process chart-product analysis, such as given in Figure 5.2, is best constructed from an actual observation of the production process.

Unfortunately, discrepancies between what is supposed to be happening, what the analyst may think happens, and what is actually happening are not at all uncommon.

Step by step, the analyst should trace the product and make suitable entries for each step. An adequate description for each step may be found by answering questions like those which follow. The analyst need not follow

---

[7] The symbols may be preprinted in this column so that, instead of drawing the symbols, the analyst need only connect the appropriate ones. Compare Figures 5.5 and 5.7 with Figures 5.2 and 5.3. However, too common dependence on a preprinted form of this type may tend to deter or preclude the portrayal of processes of wider scope as shown in Figure 5.11.

Type of Chart	_Process Chart – Product Analysis_	
Method	_Original_	Machine No. ⌒
Operation	_Assembly_	Operation No. ⌒
		Part No. _117Z4GT_
Part name	_Filament_	Chart by _P.Schame_
Operator–	⌒	Date charted _6-4-_

Quantity	Distance	Symbol	Explanation
1		○	Filament to core
50		▽	At core bench in trays
	5'	○	To next bench
50		▽	At coil bench in trays
2		○	Add terminal coils
25		▽	At coil bench in trays
	20'	○	To spray booth
25		▽	At spray booth in trays
25		○	Spray ceramic coat & place in boats
50		▽	At spray booth in boats
	10'	○	To oven
50		▽	At oven in boats
50		○	Bake & place in trays
50		▽	At oven in trays
	22'	○	To bench
50		▽	At chip bench in trays
1		○	Chip excess ceramic (.33% loss)
50		▽	At chip bench in trays
	3'	○	Along bench
50		▽	At tab bench in trays
1		○	Weld on nickel tabs
50		▽	At tab bench in trays
	106'	○	To assembly department
		▽	Assembly parts stockroom in trays
Summary	○ – 6	○ – 6 ▽ – 1 ▽ – 11	Dist. 166 ft.

If more space is needed paste additional sheet on here.

Fig. 5.2—*Process chart-product analysis for original method of manufacturing filament.*

the outline rigorously but should approach the general pattern. With a small amount of practice, this becomes almost second nature.

Name of Step	Answer These Questions in the "Description"
Operation	Who does what where?
Quantity inspection	What units against what record by whom?
Quality inspection	What attribute of the product by what device to what limits?
Movement	From where to where by what means?
Temporary storage	Where?
Controlled storage	Where, under what control?

It is usually desirable to place a summary of the chart at the bottom, as has been done in Figure 5.2.

In most cases it is desirable to make a sketch of the part of the plant concerned and trace the path of the product on this sketch, which is then called a *flow diagram*. In the case being discussed this was not necessary.

After the chart has been constructed, the next step is the third step of our logical procedure:

> **Criticism**—*The application to the analysis of basic data or check lists of desirable arrangements of the steps into a preferable work pattern, and of information concerning desirable ways of performing each of the steps.*

The performance of this step adequately usually presupposes, as with the possibility guide, some familiarity with the type of process or the nature of the goods, or some general knowledge concerning the type of business.

The usual method of performing this third step consists of studying the chart with a check list of questions, such as the list which follows, and with reference to a floor plan if necessary. Assistance may be sought from other staff groups concerned, as indicated by the steps shown on the chart.

If the analyst was familiar with the product and applied each of these check-list questions with an open mind, rather than trying to find why each suggestion could be rejected, he would find, with the aid of question 1d, that if the tabs were applied prior to the ceramic, the chipping would be unnecessary. This was suggested in this plant but was not successful because the nickel tabs melted at the temperatures used to vitrify the ceramic.

The subsequent application of question 1f suggested a tab with a higher melting point, made of molybdenum, in this case. Although the molybdenum tabs worked, they proved more expensive than the scrap they eliminated, and hence were not economically feasible.

Applications of questions 1f and 1e finally led to the suggestion of leaving the tabs off and mounting the filament in the tube by means of the end coils. This proved successful. The new procedure is shown in Figure 5.3. It is quite

CHECK LIST FOR PROCESS CHART–PRODUCT ANALYSIS

Basic Principles
A. Reduce number of steps
B. Arrange steps in best order
C. Make steps as economical as possible
D. Reduce handlings
E. Combine steps if economical
F. Shorten moves
G. Provide most economical means for moving
H. Cut in-process inventory to workable minimum
I. Use minimum number of control points at most advantageous places

1. Can any step be eliminated?
   a. As unnecessary (Ask: *Why is it done?*)
   b. By new equipment (Ask: *Why is present equipment used?*)
   c. By changing the place where it is done or kept (Ask: *Why is it done there?*)
   d. By changing the order of work (Ask: *Why is it done in its present order?*)
   e. By changing the product design (Ask: *Why is it done as it is?*)
   f. By changing the specifications of the incoming supply (Ask: *Why is it ordered in its present form or used at all?*)

2. Can any step be combined with another?
   Are there any possible changes that would make this feasible in
   a. Workplace
   b. Equipment
   c. Order of steps
   d. Product design
   e. Specification of supply or any raw material

3. Can the steps be rearranged so as to make any shorter or easier?

4. Can any step be made easier?
   (If this looks like a possibility, make further detailed analysis of this step. Analyses for this purpose will be discussed in later chapters.)

obvious that the procedure finally adopted is highly preferable to a better method of chipping. This conclusion is also demonstated in the recapitulation at the end of this chart of the proposed method.

The analyst will facilitate his future activity if he will accumulate information on ways, peculiar to his industry or type of work, of improving the various types of step—that is, specific ways of achieving the general suggestions implied by the check-list questions.

The analyst might well make a file sheet for each check-list question and subquestion and, as he changes processes, note the principles on appropriate sheets. For instance, in the case discussed, on the sheet for check-list question 1d he might have written:

If a coating flows over a part, thus interfering with subsequent spot welding, spot-weld the part prior to applying the coating.

On the sheet for question 1f:

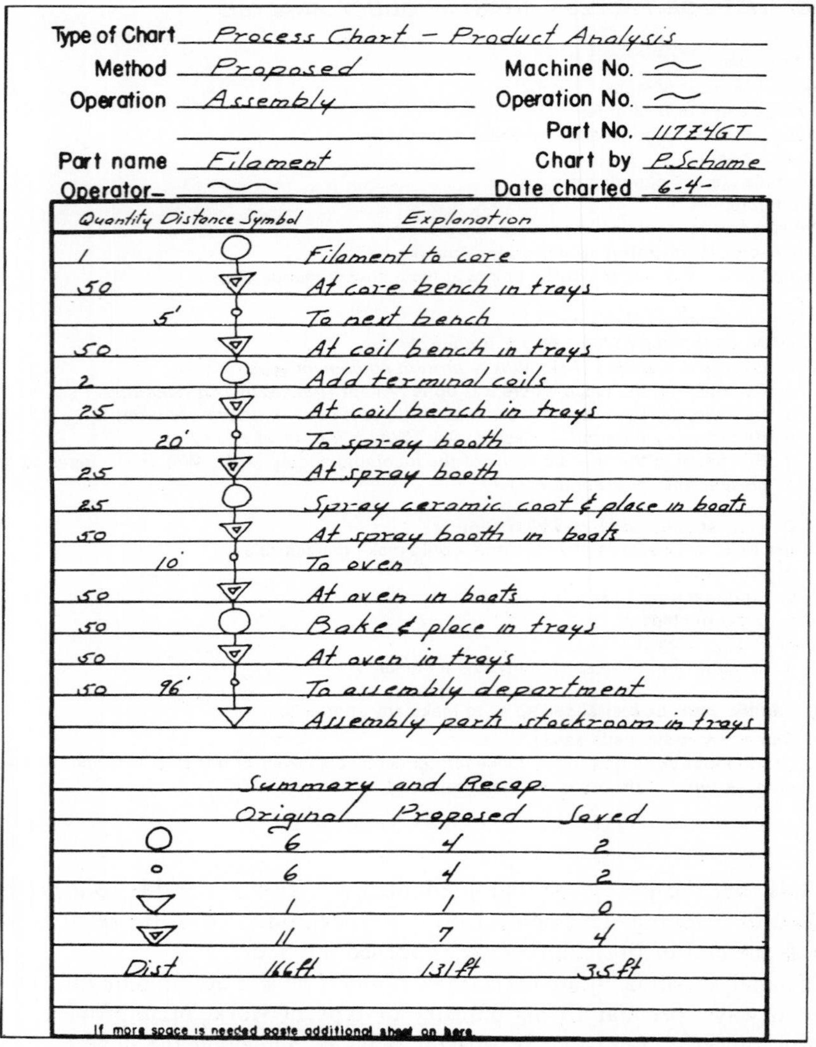

Type of Chart _Process Chart – Product Analysis_

Method _Proposed_   Machine No. ⌒

Operation _Assembly_   Operation No. ⌒

                              Part No. _1173467_

Part name _Filament_   Chart by _P.Schame_

Operator _⌒_   Date charted _6-4-_

Quantity	Distance	Symbol	Explanation
1		○	Filament to core
50		▽	At core bench in trays
	5'	○	To next bench
50		▽	At coil bench in trays
2		○	Add terminal coils
25		▽	At coil bench in trays
	20'	○	To spray booth
25		▽	At spray booth
25		○	Spray ceramic coat & place in boots
50		▽	At spray booth in boots
	10'	○	To oven
50		▽	At oven in boots
50		○	Bake & place in trays
50		▽	At oven in trays
50	96'	○	To assembly department
		▽	Assembly parts stockroom in trays

Summary and Recap.

	Original	Proposed	Saved
○	6	4	2
○	6	4	2
▽	1	1	0
▽	11	7	4
Dist	166 ft.	131 ft	35 ft

If more space is needed paste additional sheet on here.

Fig. 5.3—Process chart-product analysis for proposed method of manufacturing filament.

If a part may be more conveniently assembled prior to a heat-treating operation but is not, because the heat will damage it, try a material that will not be affected by the heat-treatment.

On the sheet for question 1e:

Question the real function of a part, particularly tabs on heavy heater filaments.

Such files become extremely valuable when built up.

Step 4 of the logical method is:

> **Innovation**—*The formulation of a new suggested procedure for performing the work.*

This step was performed when the process chart-product analysis shown in Figure 5.3 was constructed.

Step 5 of the logical method is:

> **Test**—*The testing, by means of the data previously used in step 3 (the check list), of the desirability of the method formulated in step 4, with respect to the objectives set up in step 1.*

In the case discussed here, the final suggested solution quickly meets this test. In actual practice, it is also desirable to discuss each step, especially this one, with all those who will be affected by the change. The process chart-product analysis greatly facilitates these discussions.

Step 6 of the logical method is:

> **Trial**—*The sample application of the method tested in step 5 to ascertain the completeness with which all the variables have been taken into account.*

In the case being discussed, some sample tubes with the new filaments were made up and completely tested to make sure that the quality of the tube had not been adversely affected.

The seventh and last step of the logical method is:

> **Application**—*The final standardization, installation, evaluation, and maintenance of the improved work method.*

In the case of the filament change, the drawings of the parts were reissued, the purchase specifications and requirements changed, and a new route sheet issued for the process. New costs were computed, and the change thus became the new standard practice.

In the preceding case, a Class 5 change, the elimination of a raw material, proved much more desirable than the improvement of a specific operation. Such an elimination is not an uncommon event, even when the analyst thinks a Class 1 or 2 change is all that is feasible. The better the analyst, however, the less likely he will overlook such a possibility of eliminating a raw material, yet the making of a process chart-product analysis before the man analysis is an excellent safeguard and a good means of checking the suitability of the tentative objective chosen from the possibility guide.

The general procedure involving the seven steps of the scientific method is the same no matter what the class of change sought and no matter what the product is. Naturally, the details change from case to case.

It is interesting to note that in the case just examined, the particular change which was suggested by a careful study of the process chart-product analysis might have been arrived at by another approach. If the filament design had been subjected to what is called *value analysis* the same recommendation might have resulted. *Value analysis* is the subjecting of each part of a product to a careful searching scrutiny to determine what the particular part contributes to the functioning of the whole, and what alternatives of materials, configuration, and so forth, exist that might be advantageous from the viewpoint of the criterion of success. Of course, a study of the process by which a product and its components are produced is often a useful part of such a study. Thus, value analysis and process charts are both adjuncts to the total procedure for finding improvements. Value analysis is concerned with an intensive consideration of Class 4 and 5 changes; process charts-product analysis present a broader picture. Of course, not all process chart-product analyses lead to Class 4 or 5 changes; in some cases the change does not rise above a Class 3. This is outside of the normal scope of value analysis. Hence, it would appear that the two approaches, rather than being competitive, complement each other.

SUMMARY — PROCESS CHART–PRODUCT ANALYSIS

1. Uses:
   a. *For a last check prior to a Class 1 or 2 change.*
   b. *For information leading to a Class 3, 4, or 5 change.*
   c. *When planning for a product or layout.*
2. How made:
   a. *A form may be used, as in Figure 5.2, or a blank sheet of paper may be substituted. For simple processes a form with preprinted symbols, as in Figure 5.5, may be convenient.*
   b. *The analyst should actually observe the process if possible. If the item is not in production, or if direct observation is inconvenient, a scale floor plan should be used. Actual observation is frequently more desirable, inasmuch as discrepancies between what is supposed to be the process and what actually is the process are not uncommon.*
   c. *Pick a convenient starting place for the analysis.*
   d. *Classify the first step into the proper category by means of Table 1.*
   e. *On the first line of the chart, place the proper symbol and description. If the step is a movement, pace off the distance or measure it by some means. In all cases, in the quantity column show the amount handled as a unit on that step, or if the step is a storage, the usual maximum quantity. If the time used for the step is desired, time the step with an ordinary watch or a stop-watch, or consult the file of standard times if it is available.*
   f. *On the second line place the proper symbol for the second step, and so forth.*
   g. *Every time the item moves from one workplace to another, waits, is inspected, or is worked on, a separate entry should be made. However, movements on a workplace in the course of which the item is worked on should not usually be separately noted.*
   h. *The various conventions for charting are shown in Figure 5.4.*
3. How used:
   Each step of the process is questioned with the check list given.
4. What then:
   A process chart-product analysis is drawn for a resulting suggested improved method in order to permit a final check and to provide a means of describing the proposed new method.

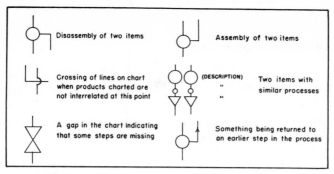

Fig. 5.4—*Conventions for process chart-product analysis.*

PROCESS CHART—PRODUCT ANALYSIS

ORIGINAL
136, 54, 45 — Method / Department(s)
TRUCKING — Job name
REFRIGERATOR SHELVES — Part name
700-216 — Part number
CREECH — Chart by
2-4- — Date charted

SUMMARY

		Original	Improved	Difference
○		1		
◇		0		
□		0		
•		3		
▽		5		
▽		0		
Total		9		
Dist.		215'		

Quantity	Distance	Symbol	Explanation
X crates		○ ◇ □ ∘ ▽ ▽	Bulk storage- Foundry
4 crates	100'	○ ◇ □ ∘ ▽ ▽	By Buda truck - Dept. 136 Trucker
80 crates		○ ◇ □ ∘ ▽ ▽	Daily bank, Dept. 45
1 crate	100'	○ ◇ □ ∘ ▽ ▽	By hand truck, Dept. 54 Trucker
10 crates		○ ◇ □ ∘ ▽ ▽	Hourly bank, Dept. 54
1 crate		○ ◇ □ ∘ ▽ ▽	Open crate, Dept. 54 Trucker
100 Shelves		○ ◇ □ ∘ ▽ ▽	In crate
100 Shelves		○ ◇ □ ∘ ▽ ▽	By hand truck- Dept. 54 Trucker
100 Shelves		○ ◇ □ ∘ ▽ ▽	Automatic plater loading area
		○ ◇ □ ∘ ▽ ▽	
		○ ◇ □ ∘ ▽ ▽	
		○ ◇ □ ∘ ▽ ▽	
		○ ◇ □ ∘ ▽ ▽	
		○ ◇ □ ∘ ▽ ▽	
		○ ◇ □ ∘ ▽ ▽	
		○ ◇ □ ∘ ▽ ▽	
		○ ◇ □ ∘ ▽ ▽	
		○ ◇ □ ∘ ▽ ▽	
		○ ◇ □ ∘ ▽ ▽	
		○ ◇ □ ∘ ▽ ▽	
		○ ◇ □ ∘ ▽ ▽	
		○ ◇ □ ∘ ▽ ▽	
		○ ◇ □ ∘ ▽ ▽	

Fig. 5.5—*Process chart-product analysis for original method of handling refrigerator food shelves from bulk storage to plating
department.*

Supplemental Material

CASE II   A Use of a Simple Process Chart-Product
Analysis Leading to a Class 3 Change Involving
Reduced Handling

Figure 5.5 is a process chart-product analysis of the handling of food
shelves for a refrigerator, from bulk storage in the plant to the plating

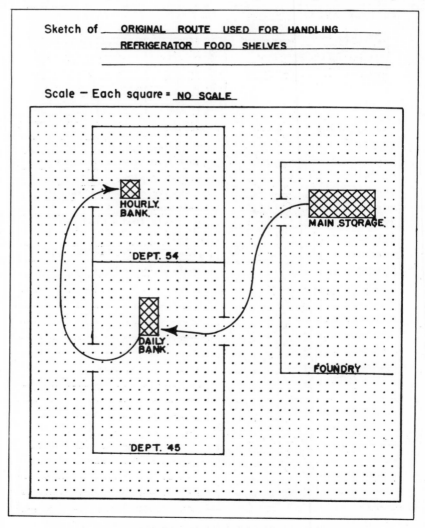

*Fig. 5.6 — Flow diagram for original method of handling refrigerator
food shelves from bulk storage to plating department.*

department; Figure 5.6 is a flow diagram of the work shown on the chart. In this case, the process chart-product analysis was made after the possibility guide indicated a Class 3 change was desirable.

A somewhat different form was used to draw the process chart-product analysis shown in Figure 5.5. Attention is called to the footnote on page 52.

When the process chart was questioned with the check list, the proposed process chart-product analysis and the new flow diagram shown in Figures

PROCESS CHART – PRODUCT ANALYSIS

PROPOSED
136, 54 _____ Method
TRUCKING _____ Department(s)
REFRIGERATOR SHELVES _ Job name
700-216 _____ Part name
CREECH _____ Part number
2-4- _____ Chart by
_____ Date charted

SUMMARY

	Original	Improved	Difference
○	1	1	0
◇	0	0	0
□	0	0	0
•	3	2	−1
▽	5	3	−2
▼	0	0	0
Total	9	6	−3
Dist.	215'	75'	−140'

Quantity	Distance	Symbol	Explanation
X crates		○◇□∘▽▽	Bulk storage - Foundry
1 crate	15'	○◇□∘▽▽	By hand truck - Dept. 54 trucker
1 crate		○◇□∘▽▽	Open crate - Dept. 54 trucker
100 Shelves		○◇□∘▽▽	In crate
100 Shelves	60'	○◇□∘▽▽	By hand truck - Dept. 54 trucker
100 Shelves		○◇□∘▽▽	Automatic plater loading area

Fig. 5.7—Process chart-product analysis for proposed method of handling refrigerator food shelves from bulk storage to plating department.

5.7 and 5.8 resulted; they outline a new method that was installed with the following advantages:

1. In Dept. 45, 900 square feet of floor space, sorely needed for other use, were made available.
2. Reduced the trucking distance for the Dept. 54 trucker by 80 feet per

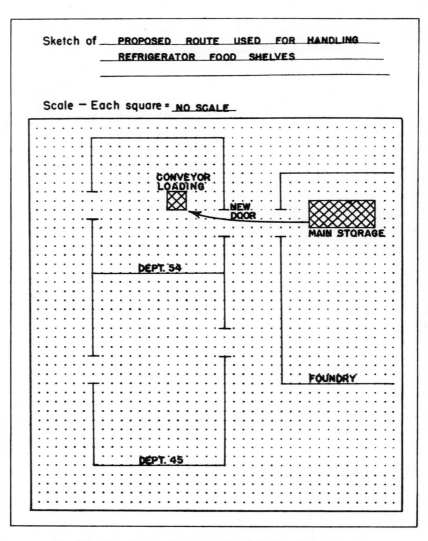

Fig. 5.8 — Flow diagram for proposed method of handling refrigerator food shelves from bulk storage to plating department.

trip, 80 trips per day, with the consequent saving of labor, time, and cost and damage due to rehandling.

3. Eliminated the use of the Buda truck on 20 trips per day, a round-trip distance of 200 feet from the foundry to the daily bank, saving $1,740 per year.

4. Eliminated the uncrating area in Dept. 54, relieving the congestion.

These advantages were made possible by the installation of the new door shown in Figure 5.8, which, together with the movement of some equipment blocking access to it, cost $580; an amount recovered in four months from the savings from the reduced use of the Buda truck alone.

CASE III   A Use of a Process Chart to Rearrange and Relocate the Steps in a Process

This case is drawn from a service industry to illustrate further the use of the process chart-product analysis for activities even more dissimilar to those covered in the first three illustrations. Figure 5.9 is a process chart-product analysis from a large Midwest department store of the sequence of work on a wrongly addressed package, of which delivery could not be made. The possibility guide in this case suggested a Class 4 change, that is to say, making wrongly addressed packages correctly addressed packages at the first addressing. A campaign was undertaken with the sales force to cut down the incidence of wrong addresses on sales slips. It is worth noting that during the year checked there were 4,796 wrongly addressed customer packages in this store, a number that was not considered excessive for a store of its size.

In addition to the campaign to cut down wrongly addressed packages, which was aided by the demonstration available on the process chart showing all of the work caused by a wrong address, the process chart was subjected to the same treatment detailed in Case I for the radio-tube filament. This resulted in the proposed chart, shown in Figure 5.10, which was the method eventually adopted.

In summing up the advantages indicated in the summary at the end of Figure 5.10, the analysts, who were employees of the store, stated:

1. There will be considerable improvement in customer service resulting from the saving of time and handling between the Service Center and the Main Store.

2. There will be a great saving in distance traveled, movement, and delays of packages, which will result in less possibility of breakage and loss. To put it briefly, we will save roughly 9,600 *package-miles* of transportation per year with an accompanying reduction of work and loss hazard.

3. There will be a reduction in traffic for the shuttle truck and freight elevators. There will also be some reduction in handling time by personnel at the Service Center and the Main Store.

Type of Chart	PROCESS CHART – PRODUCT ANALYSIS				

Method ORIGINAL   **Machine No.** ——

Operation REDELIVERY   **Operation No.** ——

                                        Part No. ——

Part name PACKAGE   **Chart by** BAKER

Operator ————————————   **Date charted** 1/4/

QUANTITY	SYMBOL	DISTANCE	EXPLANATION
1 PKG.	○	80'	WRONGLY ADDRESSED PACKAGE CARRIED FROM DELIVERY TRUCK TO DELIVERY OFFICE SERVICE CENTER
	◇		CHECKED WITH TELEPHONE BOOK AND CITY DIRECTORY FOR OBVIOUS W.A. ERROR.
15 PKGS.	▽		AWAIT SHUTTLE TRUCK TO STORE WITH OTHER W.A. PACKAGES FOR DAY
	○		LOADED ON HAND TRUCK
	▽		ON HAND TRUCK
	○	40'	TO SHUTTLE TRUCK
	▽		NEAR SHUTTLE TRUCK
	○		LOADED ON SHUTTLE TRUCK
	▽		ON SHUTTLE TRUCK
	○	5000'	TO MAIN STORE DOCK
	▽		AT STORE DOCK
	○		UNLOADED FROM SHUTTLE TRUCK ON DELIVERY DOCK
	▽		ON DELIVERY DOCK
	○	85'	TO SOUTH FREIGHT ELEVATORS
	▽		AWAIT ELEVATOR PICK-UP
	○	10'	MOVED ON TO ELEVATOR
	○	100'	TO 7TH FLOOR
	○	10'	MOVED OFF ELEVATOR
	▽		AWAIT MOVE TO WRONG ADDRESS ROOM
	○	80'	TO WRONG ADDRESS ROOM
	▽		AWAIT WRONG ADDRESS CHECK
1 PKG.	○		REMOVE FROM HAND TRUCK
	◇		CHECK WITH TELEPHONE BOOK, CITY DIRECTORY AND CHARGE AUTHORIZATION (BY PHONE)
	▽		CORRECT ADDRESS FOUND, DUPLICATE DELIVERY VOUCHER FILLED OUT

If more space is needed paste additional sheet on here.

Fig. 5.9a—Process chart-product analysis for original method of handling wrongly addressed packages in a department store (continued).

Type of Chart	PROCESS CHART — PRODUCT ANALYSIS

Method	ORIGINAL	Machine No.
Operation	REDELIVERY	Operation No.
		Part No.
Part name	PACKAGE	Chart by
Operator		Date charted

Quantity	Symbol	Distance	Explanation
	◯		DUPLICATE DELIVERY VOUCHER PINNED TO PACKAGE
	◯		ADDRESS CORRECTED ON DELIVERY DOCKET ON PACKAGE
	○		PACKAGE PLACED ON HAND TRUCK FOR CORRECTLY ADDRESSED PACKAGES
20 PKGS.	▽		AWAIT PICK-UP TO ELEVATORS
	○	80'	TO SOUTH FREIGHT ELEVATORS
	▽		AWAIT ELEVATOR
	○	10'	MOVED ON TO ELEVATOR
	○	100'	TO STREET FLOOR
	○	10'	MOVED OFF ELEVATOR
	○	70'	TO DELIVERY DEPARTMENT—WEST BUILDING
	▽		AWAIT DELIVERY ROUTE CHECK
	◯		MARKED FOR ROUTE IDENTIFICATION DUPLICATE DELIVERY VOUCHER PULLED
	○	20'	TO SHUTTLE TRUCK
	○		LOADED ON SHUTTLE TRUCK
	▽		ON SHUTTLE TRUCK
	○	5000'	TO SERVICE CENTER
	▽		AT SHUTTLE DOCK
	○		UNLOADED ON SHUTTLE DOCK
1 PKG.	○	90'	MOVED TO PROPER DELIVERY BIN AND STACKED IN BIN
	▽		AWAITS NEXT REGULAR DELIVERY WHEN IT WILL BE LISTED ON LOG
	○	12'	MOVED TO TRUCK
	○		LOADED ON TRUCK
	▽		ON TRUCK

SUMMARY				
O–3	○–25	▽–17	◇–2	DIST.–10,797'

If more space is needed paste additional sheet on here.

Fig. 5.9b—(Concluded) Process chart-product analysis for original method of handling wrongly addressed packages in a department store.

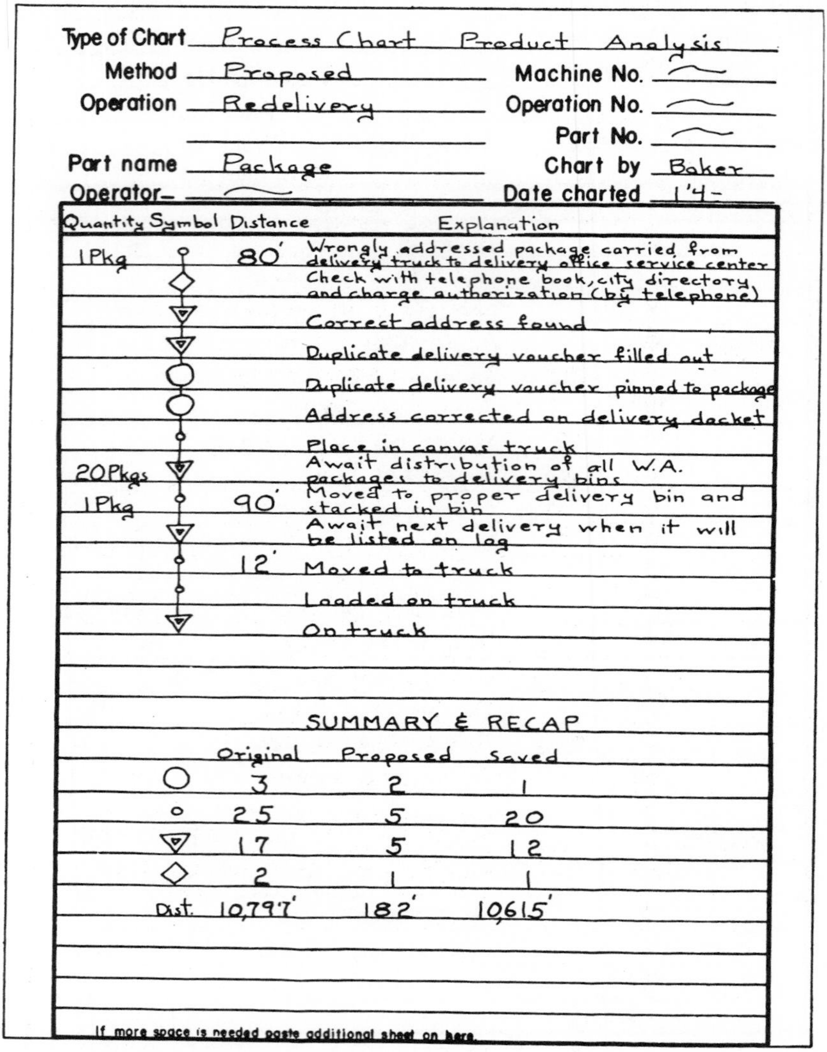

Type of Chart	_Process Chart___Product___Analysis_
Method	_Proposed_
Operation	_Redelivery_
Part name	_Package_
Operator—	

Machine No.	⌒
Operation No.	⌒
Part No.	⌒
Chart by	_Baker_
Date charted	_1'4-_

Quantity	Symbol	Distance	Explanation
1 Pkg	○	80'	Wrongly addressed package carried from delivery truck to delivery office service center
	◇		Check with telephone book, city directory, and charge authorization (by telephone)
	▽		Correct address found
	▽		Duplicate delivery voucher filled out
	○		Duplicate delivery voucher pinned to package
	○		Address corrected on delivery docket
	○		Place in canvas truck
20 Pkgs	▽		Await distribution of all W.A. packages to delivery bins
1 Pkg	○	90'	Moved to proper delivery bin and stacked in bin
	▽		Await next delivery when it will be listed on log
	○	12'	Moved to truck
	○		Loaded on truck
	▽		On truck

SUMMARY & RECAP

	Original	Proposed	Saved
○	3	2	1
○	25	5	20
▽	17	5	12
◇	2	1	1
Dist.	10,797'	182'	10,615'

If more space is needed paste additional sheet on here.

Fig. 5.10—*Process chart-product analysis for proposed method of handling wrongly addressed packages in a department store.*

CASE IV   A Reduced Detail Process Chart-Product
Analysis for a Complex Problem of Replanning a Whole
Process with the Intent of a Drastic Class 3 Change,
but Which Eventually Led to a Class 4 Change

Figure 5.11 is an abbreviated version of a process chart-product analysis
for the manufacture of a cork shell-plug used in semifixed large-calibre

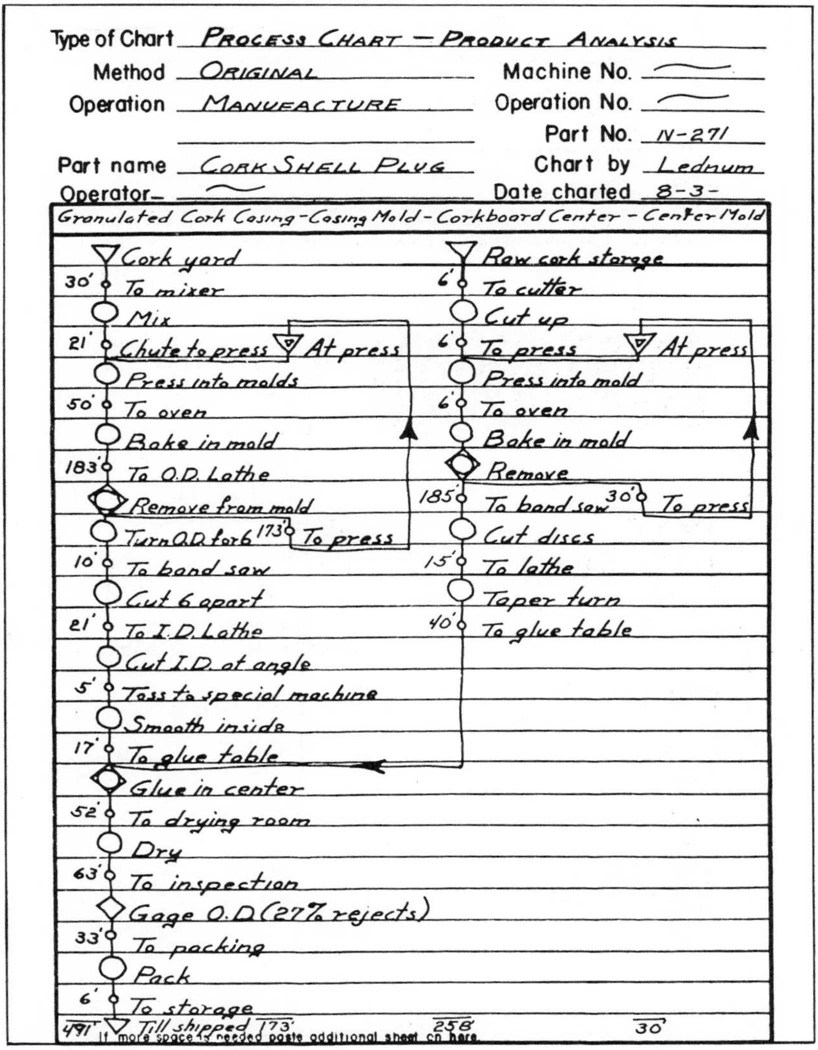

Fig. 5.11—Abbreviated version of process chart-product analysis for
original method for manufacture of cork shell-plugs.

ammunition. The parts of the shell-plug at various stages are shown in Figure 5.12. Since the possibility guide indicated that a radical Class 3 change was apparently feasible and a considerable amount of detail was involved, the analyst, who had considerable experience, decided to construct his process chart so as to include all components, but left out the temporary storages and the quantity handled at each step. This is occasionally desirable. In fact, when planning a new process before a tentative layout is available,

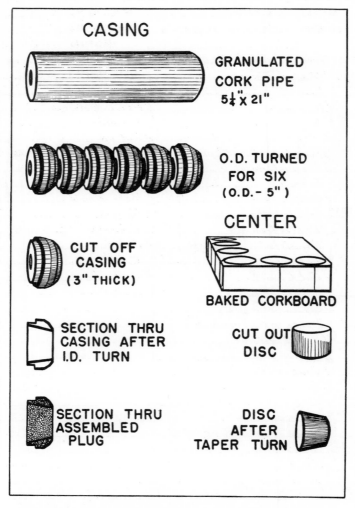

*Fig. 5.12—Parts of cork shell-plug at various stages of manufacture
using methods charted in Figures 5.11 and 5.14.*

even the movement symbols may be left out. The original layout, however, of the part of the plant making these plugs is shown in Figures 5.13a and 5.13b, but only those machines engaged in plug manufacture have been labeled. Because the product lines are shown, this is a flow diagram.

The note on the original chart, at the final inspection, illustrates one of the difficulties this plant was having. This difficulty, a sizeable loss of production, was traced to warpage created by the gluing operation.

The application of the scientific method to this process by the analyst, who was familiar with cork products, resulted in the improved process chart-product analysis shown in Figure 5.14. The improved layout that made this revision possible is shown in Figures 5.15a and 5.15b. Note the reduction of

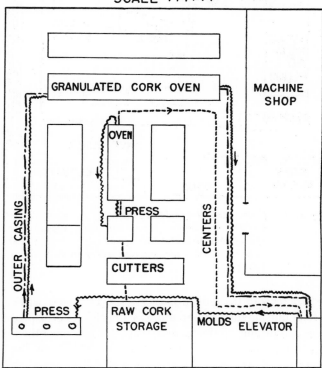

SKETCH OF LAYOUT OF BASEMENT FOR ORIGINAL METHOD
SCALE

Fig. 5.13a—Original flow diagram of basement of plant for manufacture of cork shell-plugs. (See process chart in Figure 5.11.) The broken and wavy lines indicate the flow of material (continued).

SKETCH OF LAYOUT OF FIRST FLOOR FOR
ORIGINAL METHOD

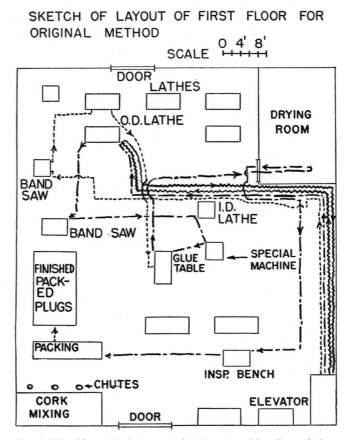

Fig. 5.13b—(Concluded) *Original flow diagram of first floor of plant
for the manufacture of cork shell-plugs.* (See process
chart in Figure 5.11.) *The broken and wavy lines continue the paths of the materials shown on the basement
floor plan.*

steps in the process and the reduction of rejects. The latter was achieved by
placing the final outside turning operation in a position in the process following the gluing and drying, so that any warpage did not affect the final dimensions. Truing up the inside could thus be eliminated, raising the change to
Class 4. There is also considerable reduction in the travel of the cast-iron
baking molds used for the granulated cork parts.

On the basis of this experience and with additional use of the check list,
the process was later again redesigned with another Class 4 change, as shown

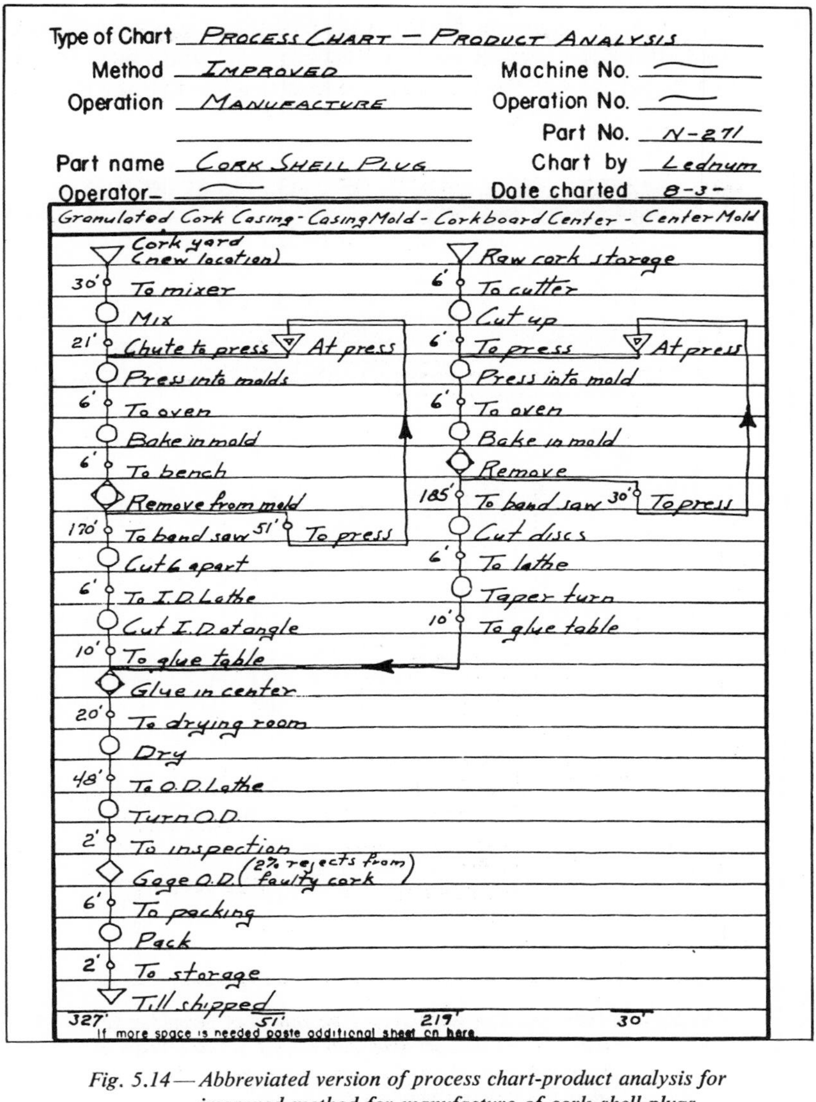

Type of Chart __PROCESS CHART — PRODUCT ANALYSIS__

Method __IMPROVED__   Machine No. ___

Operation __MANUFACTURE__   Operation No. ___

Part No. __N-271__

Part name __CORK SHELL PLUG__   Chart by __Lednum__

Operator- ___   Date charted __8-3-__

Granulated Cork Casing - Casing Mold - Corkboard Center - Center Mold

Cork yard (new location) — To mixer 30' — Mix — Chute to press 21' — At press — Press into molds — To oven 6' — Bake in mold — To bench 6' — Remove from mold — To band saw 170' — To press 51' — Cut 6 apart — To I.D. Lathe 6' — Cut I.D. at angle — To glue table 10' — Glue in center — To drying room 20' — Dry — To O.D. Lathe 48' — Turn O.D. — To inspection 2' — Gage O.D. (2% rejects from faulty cork) — To packing 6' — Pack — To storage 2' — Till shipped

Raw cork storage — To cutter 6' — Cut up — To press 6' — At press — Press into mold — To oven 6' — Bake in mold — Remove — To band saw 185' — To press 30' — Cut discs — To lathe 6' — Taper turn — To glue table 10'

327'   51'   219'   30'

If more space is needed paste additional sheet on here.

Fig. 5.14 — Abbreviated version of process chart-product analysis for improved method for manufacture of cork shell-plugs.

71

in the process chart-product analysis in Figure 5.16. Distances do not appear on this chart, inasmuch as the chart was drawn before the plant was laid out. The parts of the plug at various stages of manufacture with this second improved process are shown in Figure 5.17. The plant was actually set up later on the basis of this second proposed process, and plugs were produced for less than 25 per cent of the cost with the first original method.

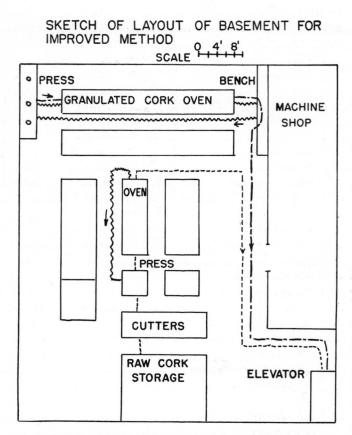

SKETCH OF LAYOUT OF BASEMENT FOR IMPROVED METHOD

SCALE 0 4' 8'

Fig. 5.15a—Improved flow diagram for basement of plant for the manufacture of cork shell-plugs. (See process chart in Figure 5.14.) *The broken and wavy lines indicate the flow of material* (continued).

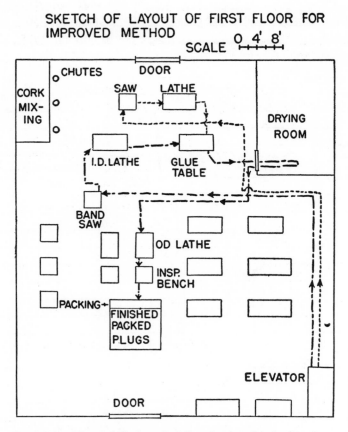

SKETCH OF LAYOUT OF FIRST FLOOR FOR
IMPROVED METHOD

Fig. 5.15b—(Concluded) *Improved flow diagram for the first floor
of plant for the manufacture of cork shell-plugs.* (See
process chart in Figure 5.14.) *The broken lines continue
the paths of materials shown on the basement floor plan.*

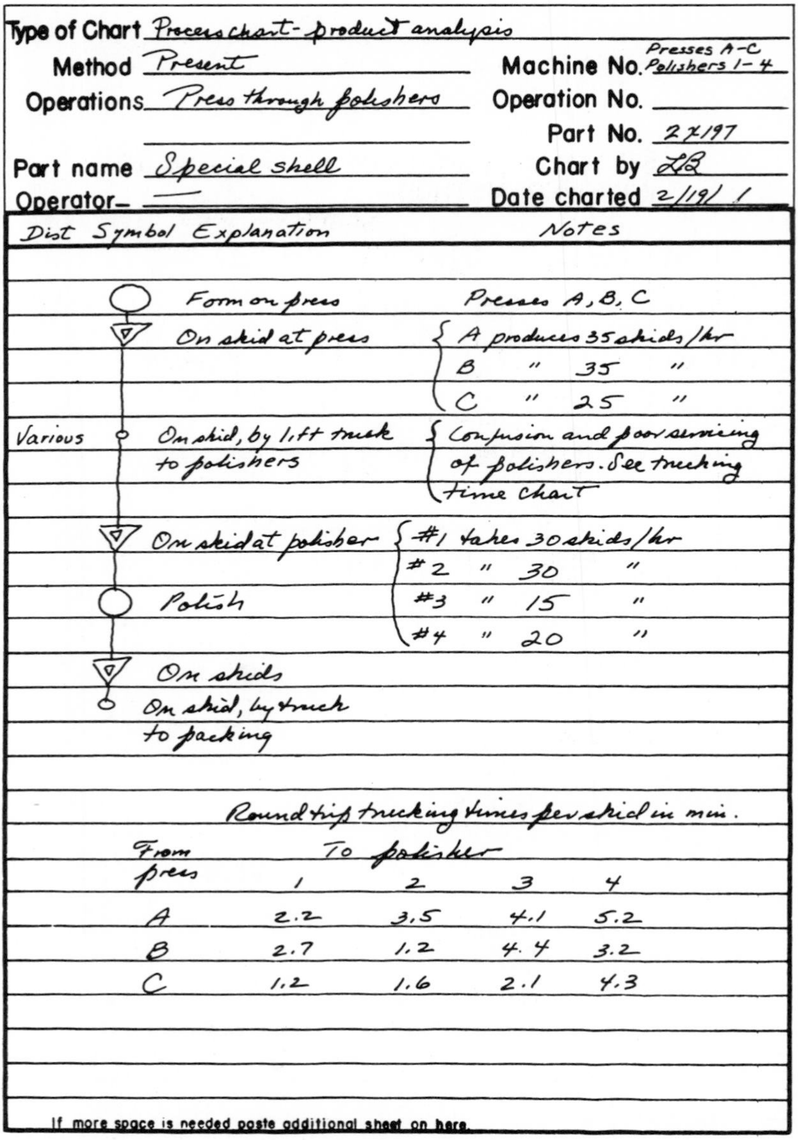

Type of Chart *Process chart - product analysis*

Method *Present*

Machine No. *Presses A-C / Polishers 1-4*

Operations *Press through polishers*

Operation No. _____

Part No. *2 X 197*

Part name *Special shell*

Chart by *LB*

Operator _____

Date charted *2/19/ /*

Dist	Symbol	Explanation	Notes
	◯	Form on press	Presses A, B, C
	▽	On skid at press	{ A produces 35 skids/hr
			B " 35 "
			C " 25 "
Various	◯	On skid, by lift truck to polishers	{ Confusion and poor servicing of polishers. See trucking time chart
	▽	On skid at polisher	{ #1 takes 30 skids/hr
			#2 " 30 "
	◯	Polish	#3 " 15 "
			#4 " 20 "
	▽	On skids	
	◯	On skid, by truck to packing	

Round trip trucking times per skid in min.

From press	To polisher			
	1	2	3	4
A	2.2	3.5	4.1	5.2
B	2.7	1.2	4.4	3.2
C	1.2	1.6	2.1	4.3

If more space is needed paste additional sheet on here.

Fig. 5.16—*Abbreviated version of process chart-product analysis for second improved method for manufacture of cork shell-plugs. Since this chart was made prior to the layout, the distance for each movement was not available.*

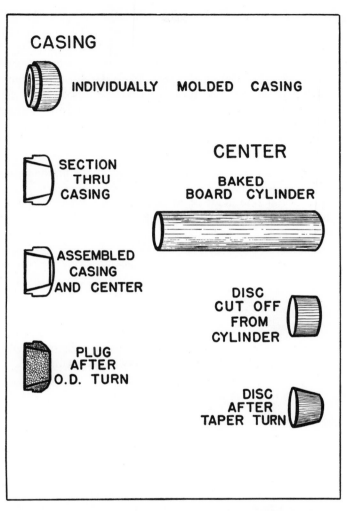

CASING

INDIVIDUALLY MOLDED CASING

SECTION
THRU
CASING

CENTER

BAKED
BOARD CYLINDER

ASSEMBLED
CASING
AND CENTER

DISC
CUT OFF
FROM
CYLINDER

PLUG
AFTER
O.D. TURN

DISC
AFTER
TAPER TURN

*Fig. 5.17—Parts of cork shell-plug at various stages of manufacture
using proposed new process indicated in Figure 5.16.*

CASE V   A USE OF A PROCESS CHART-PRODUCT ANALYSIS THAT
LED TO THE CREATION OF A MATHEMATICAL MODEL[8]

Figure 5.18 is the process chart-product analysis for part of the manufacture of a pressed aluminum article. This particular product was made during only a small part of the year on presses and polishers that were parts of machine lines set up to manufacture other products, which were made in great volume during the rest of the year. Note the various quantities produced by each machine and the various trucking times given at the bottom of the chart. (These trucking times were determined by means of time studies.)

This analysis was made because of confusion in trucking from the presses to the polishers. The analyst wished to determine the most efficient hourly trucking pattern.

A problem of this type may be solved with the aid of a mathematical model of the situation, as follows:

Let the quantity of skid loads of parts going from Press A to polisher #1 be represented by the letter D, from A to polisher #2 by E, and so forth, as follows:

From Press	To Polisher			
	#1	#2	#3	#4
A	D	E	F	G
B	H	I	J	K
C	L	M	N	O

Let the trucking time be represented by T. Taking the information from the process chart, we may now write the following equations:

$$D + E + F + G = 35$$
$$H + I + J + K = 35$$
$$L + M + N + O = 25$$
$$D + H + L = 30$$
$$E + I + M = 30$$
$$F + J + N = 15$$
$$G + K + O = 20$$

$$2.2D + 3.5E + 4.1F + 5.2G + 2.7H + 1.2I + 4.4J + 3.2K + 1.2L + 1.6M + 2.1N + 4.3O = T$$

This system of equations, a mathematical model of the situation, may be solved by linear programming methods[9] to produce $T = 211.5$ minutes, its lowest possible value, when:

$$D = 30, E = 0, F = 0, G = 5, H = 0, I = 20, J = 0,$$
$$K = 15, L = 0, M = 10, N = 15, O = 0.$$

[8] The numbers involved have been altered to facilitate presentation.
[9] For methods of solution see N. Reinfeld and W. Vogel, *Mathematical Programming*. Englewood Cliffs, N.J.: Prentice-Hall, Inc., 1958.

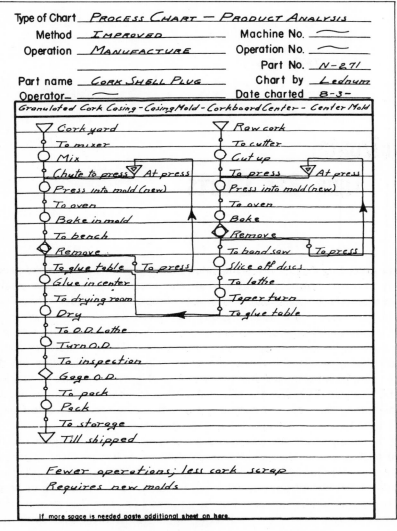

Type of Chart _PROCESS CHART — PRODUCT ANALYSIS_

Method _IMPROVED_   Machine No. _____

Operation _MANUFACTURE_   Operation No. _____

                            Part No. _N-271_

Part name _CORK SHELL PLUG_   Chart by _Lednum_

Operator_ _____   Date charted _8-3-_

Granulated Cork Casing - Casing Mold - Corkboard Center - - Center Mold

Casing	Center
▽ Cork yard	▽ Raw cork
To mixer	To cutter
◯ Mix	◯ Cut up
Chute to press ▽ At press	To press ▽ At press
◯ Press into mold (new)	◯ Press into mold (new)
To oven	To oven
◯ Bake in mold	◯ Bake
To bench	◇ Remove
◇ Remove	To band saw To press
To glue table To press	◯ Slice off discs
◯ Glue in center	To lathe
To drying room	◯ Taper turn
◯ Dry	To glue table
To O.D. Lathe	
◯ Turn O.D.	
To inspection	
◇ Gage O.D.	
To pack	
◯ Pack	
To storage	
▽ Till shipped	

Fewer operations; less cork scrap

Requires new molds

Fig. 5.18—Process chart-product analysis of part of manufacturing
    sequence.

CHAPTER 6

Horizontal
Time Bar Charts

In the preceding chapter it was indicated that with certain problems of process study, various techniques other than the process chart-product analysis possessed certain advantages. One set of conditions under which other techniques were more advantageous was given as: *the timing of various batches moving through the various steps, or the time relationship among the steps are the primary aspects under consideration.* Under conditions such as listed above, provided that the interrelationships among the steps are relatively simple, a horizontal bar time chart is of great assistance in making a useful analysis. This chapter will deal with such charts. When the relationships among the steps are complex, a network diagram, treated in Chapter 7, is usually a more advantageous analysis tool.

A horizontal time bar chart is a graphic means of portraying the time relationships among the separable steps of the procedure involved in performing the work required to modify an output from one stage of completion to another.[1] The definition, one will note, is similar to the definition of process chart-product analysis, except for the emphasis on *time*. The process chart-product analysis, with the usual variety of conventions for portraying steps,

---

[1] In many ways the horizontal time bar chart resembles the preliminary phase of a Gantt chart. I have avoided calling the horizontal bar time chart a Gantt chart in that it is not used in all of the ways that a Gantt chart is used; merely a few of the Gantt chart conventions are used; this chapter deals only with this one type of chart and is not at all a definitive treatment of Gantt charts. For a complete treatment of Gantt charts one should consult any edition of the following two books: W. Grant Ireson and Eugene L. Grant

emphasizes the sequence and nature of steps; the horizontal time bar chart is primarily an aid in examining the time relationships among a given set of steps and for considering alternatives wherein the primary change is with respect to timing.

A horizontal time bar chart is of assistance with studies of the sequence of the steps of production with both substantive and service outputs. With substantive outputs it is usually used to assist in determining Class 3 type changes; with service outputs it usually assists in achieving Class 4 or 5 type changes.

A horizontal time bar chart is most easily drawn on an ordinary sheet of graph or cross-section paper as shown in Figure 6.1.

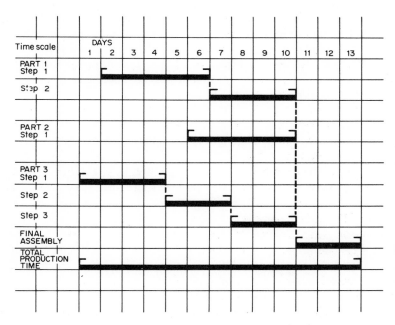

Fig. 6.1 — Horizontal time bar chart showing the time relationships among the various production steps of a component of a larger product.

Figure 6.1 is the horizontal time bar chart showing the time relationships among the various production steps of a component of a larger product.

(Eds.), *Handbook of Industrial Engineering and Management.* Englewood Cliffs, N.J.: Prentice Hall, Inc.; Harold B. Maynard (Ed.), *Industrial Engineering Handbook.* New York, N.Y.: The McGraw-Hill Book Co. The classic book on the subject is: Wallace Clark, *The Gantt Chart.* New York, N.Y.: The Ronald Press Co., 1922. [This last book has also been printed in Britain (1934) and translated and published in 13 other countries.]

The component itself consisted of three parts. The component was produced on a batch-lot basis. In Figure 6.1 a separate line and a separate bar is used to indicate the processing of each part. The length of each bar is proportional to the time required to process the batch through the particular step. In the preparation of such a chart the analyst must select a scale appropriate to the time values encountered in the problem. The scale chosen for the problem illustrated in Figure 6.1 was one day per vertical line. The distance from the start of the first bar to the completion of the last bar is proportional to the amount of time required to produce the entire batch of the component.

The study was undertaken because of a problem whose basic nature concerned the use of time. The larger product, of which this component was a part, was manufactured to order. The lead time between the receipt of the typical order and the required delivery date did not leave enough time to permit orderly procurement of the raw material and the production of the components, even with overtime and night-shift work when materials were finally procured. Hence, a more rapid procurement procedure, a longer delivery time, or a shortened production time appeared as a necessary improvement. However, industry practices precluded a lengthening of the delivery time; procurement had been reduced to the apparent limit; changes were needed in the actual production cycle.

The problem, as portrayed in Figure 6.1, reveals some characteristics which frequently are found in problems of this kind. First, some change in the total time to produce the component could be achieved by changing only the time needed for the steps used to produce part 3. Parts 1 and 2, which are produced independently of the production of part 3, could readily be started earlier if part 3 took less time to produce. Under such conditions part 3 is referred to as the *critical* part. However, if the time for the steps on part 3 is reduced beyond a certain point, part 1 (whose production time exceeds that of part 2) will become the critical part. With most problems of this type the location of *critical* moves in a similar fashion as various improvements are made.

The improved method shown in Figure 6.2 was finally devised and later successfully adopted. It should be noted that the improved procedure meets the criterion of success, shorter production time, but that it differs from the original method in two important ways. First, the entire batch of a part is not processed completely through a step before the subsequent work on the batch begins. Second, the total time of machine usage is increased. The solution may be described as a trade-off; one advantage was gained at the cost of one or more disadvantages. In this particular case, the advantage of being able to meet customer delivery dates as well as avoid the use of overtime and night work (which previously only reduced rather than eliminated the lateness) more than offset the additional cost of both the more frequent handling of material from step to step (because of the overlapped steps) and the additional cost of increased total machine time. (The increased total machine

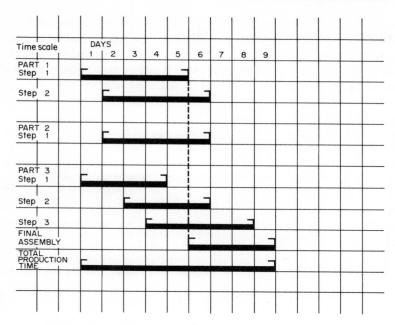

*Fig. 6.2—Horizontal time bar chart of improved method for product
shown in Figure 6.1.*

time was caused by production stoppages affecting several steps simultaneously rather than merely the step on which the broken tool, and so forth, occurred.)

In the development of the improved method the analyst considered various
basic ways of evolving alternative time relationships, such as are given in the
check list which follows:

CHECK LIST FOR HORIZONTAL TIME BAR CHARTS[2]

1. Can the time be shortened by reducing the time for a critical step or steps?
   a. By devising a new procedure for a step or steps
   b. By assigning more resources to work simultaneously on a step or steps
2. Can the time be shortened by overlapping steps?
3. Can troublesome steps be undertaken earlier in the procedure in order to allow defects to
   be detected sooner so that an increased amount of time is available for corrective action?
4. Can better service be given if some of the service outputs, or partial service outputs, are
   generated earlier in the process?
5. Can some of the required outputs be avoided if some of the outputs are generated earlier
   in the process?

[2] Each check-list question has implicit in it a given criterion of success. With different
criteria of success the reverse of the suggestion may be appropriate.

In cases other than the one given as an example it may be desirable to differentiate different types of steps with different types of shading or different colors. It seems undesirable to lay down hard and fast rules in that the purpose of the chart is to aid the analyst; the chart is not an end in itself; the analyst should introduce changes as he needs them.

SUMMARY — HORIZONTAL TIME BAR CHARTS

1. Uses:
   For aiding in the development of a Class 3, 4, or 5 change when:
   a. *The timing of the various batches moving through the various steps of a process is the primary aspect under consideration and the interrelationships among the steps are relatively simple.*
   b. *The time relationship among the steps of a process is the primary aspect under consideration and the interrelationships among the steps are relatively simple.*
2. How made:
   a. *An ordinary sheet of graph or cross-section paper is usually adequate.*
   b. *A separate line is used for each separable part of the output and separable step on each part.*
   c. *A bar, whose length is proportional to the time required for the step, is drawn on each line in such a way that it shows the place of that time interval on the total time continuum.*
3. How used:
   The time relationship is examined with respect to both the criterion of success and questions such as given in the check list.
4. What then:
   A horizontal time bar chart is drawn for the resulting suggested improved method in order to permit a final check of the feasibility and to assist in evaluating the improvement with respect to its effect upon the time aspects of the problem. The new chart also provides a means of describing the proposed new method.

Supplemental Material

One additional example should be sufficient to suggest a large variety of problems involving timing and strategy, different from the example given in the main body of the chapter, for which the horizontal time bar chart is a useful aid in examining alternative procedures. For the most part, problems of this type concern service rather than substantive outputs and may have widely varying criteria of success.

Figure 6.3 is a general presentation of two alternative procedures for adjusting an automobile accident insurance claim relating to a personal injury. Method *A* was the method originally in use. For Method *A* the procedure could be charted using historical data. For accidents of different severity the average amount of negotiator and legal time and the cost of such time could be determined as well as the average amount of benefits payed. Thus, total direct costs could be determined. However, with a service output, direct

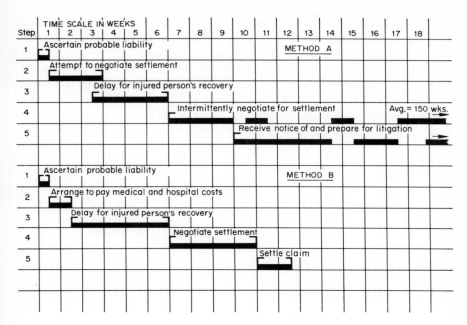

Fig. 6.3—General presentation of two alternative procedures for adjusting an automobile accident insurance claim relating to a personal injury.

costs do not tell the whole story. The quality of the service has many indirect effects.

Method B of Figure 6.3 represents an alternative procedure reflecting the philosophy of check-list questions 4 and 5. The change in strategy is based on the assumption that if the initial determination of liability indicates that it is probable that the company will be obliged to remunerate the injured person, that a prompt and unquestioning initial payment of the hospital bills will produce the following benefits:

1. No time will be spent in negotiating during the period of the person's recovery during which negotiations may be slow and difficult.
2. A more amenable attitude toward final settlement on the part of the complainant much earlier in the total sequence. This will produce savings in negotiating time and in final payments in that final payments might otherwise include the litigant's cost of litigating.
3. An improved insurance company "image" leading, perhaps, to more clients.

In the above case so many intangible factors are involved that the problem of which alternative is the best could only be determined by testing Method

B. However, a test of Method *B* yielded data which permitted the conversion of the theoretical diagram (or model) of Method *B* to a statement of the real world. The value of Method *B* could be determined.

In the above illustration it was not meant to imply that the motion study technique of the horizontal time bar chart solved the problem. The technique was merely a vehicle to assist in examining alternatives; a method of using symbols to facilitate thinking and discussion. This is the basic function of most of the charting methods described in this book.

CHAPTER 7

Network Diagrams

In Chapters 5 and 6 various ways of analyzing processes were discussed with a process defined as *all of the steps required to modify an output from one stage of completion to another.* However, there are process design problems which are far too complex to handle with either of the two techniques discussed to this point. Such problems are encountered in designing the total process for projects such as: the construction of a new ship, a new metropolitan subway, or similar complex object; the design and construction of dams or new aircraft; in the planning of a new government service such as an anti-poverty program; or the planning for and holding of a national convention for a scientific society, and so forth.

Each of these problems differs from the type of problem previously discussed in that the process has within it a complex system of *dependencies.* The term *dependencies* refers to the requirement of completing some activities before being able to start other activities, regardless of the amount of resources (men or equipment) employed. In process charts-product analysis and in horizontal time bar charts the dependencies were essentially simple and the sequence of steps flowed, merged, or separated in a simple fashion. When the dependencies are tangled and do not progress in a uniform fashion, some other system of charting is required to assist in analysis. Such process design problems are also frequently characterized by one or more of the following additional differentiating characteristics (as compared with the type of problem for which the process chart-product analysis or the horizontal time bar chart is of assistance):

1. The output under scrutiny has a large number of components.
2. Many of the component outputs are service type outputs, such as

designs completed,[1] arrangements with other groups completed, information gathered, and so forth, and these service outputs are vital to the
process.

3. The relationships among the steps of the process with respect to time are
   of vital importance to the design of a satisfactory process.
4. The complexity of the process and the scope of the work are such that
   an initial analysis of the whole precludes the feasibility of examining
   the work to the degree of detail typical of the usual process chart-
   product analysis.

With complex projects, of the type which have been described, an analysis
technique employing a *network diagram* has been shown to be of great value
in developing an effective process design. A *network diagram*[2] is a graphic
method of displaying the relationships between and among the steps in a
process.

A simple network diagram[3] is shown in Figure 7.1. Each circle (or square)

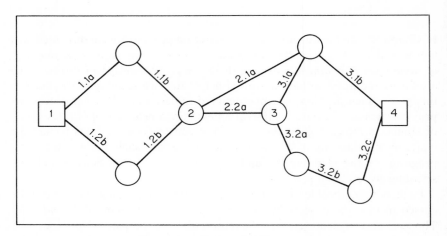

Fig. 7.1 — A simple network diagram.

[1] In order to differentiate a service output from the activity of producing it, the description of the output will always include a past tense verb.

[2] Diagrams of this type have been given great publicity in connection with their use in
the development of the U.S. Navy missile, Polaris. Such diagrams were employed in the
design of the process and in the operation of a control system called Performance Evaluation and Review Technique. This later was commonly referred to by its acronym PERT.
Hence, in the literature such diagrams are commonly called PERT charts. They are also
called *link diagrams, critical path planning*, and so forth. *Network diagrams* has been
selected as the more generally descriptive term, not to be identified with a particular
technique but to refer generically to all versions of the general approach which will be
described.

[3] A typical network diagram of a complex process may describe a process which will

of Figure 7.1 represents a *status* achieved by the performance of activities. A *status* is a partial or complete service or substantive output completed. A square may be used in place of a circle to represent an important status so as to make the chart easier to read; otherwise the meaning of the square is similar to that of the circle. The chart also may be drawn without squares or a variety of symbols may be employed, although differentiation of the status steps will be based on different criteria than used for the separation of the steps of a process chart-product analysis. The common criteria for differentiation will be the importance of reaching the status, or some aspect of the consequence of achieving the status, as contrasted with the process chart-product analysis where the basis of separation was the nature of the activities.

The performance of activities required to achieve a status is represented by the lines. In contrast with the varieties of status on network diagrams, the activities on a network diagram are usually differentiated with respect to only one criterion: their importance with respect to affecting the minimum time in which one can expect to complete the project. For instance, the network diagram of Figure 7.1 has been redrawn in Figure 7.2 with the expected time[4] for performing each activity added under the activity identifica-

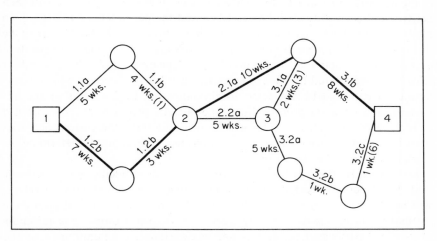

Fig. 7.2—Network diagram of Figure 7.1 redrawn with the expected time for performing each activity added under the activity identification.

range from a hundred to several thousand steps. Obviously, such examples are beyond the scope of this book. However, as the discussion progresses it should become increasingly obvious that the more complex the problem of process design, the more useful the network diagram becomes.

[4] The development of these time values, representing the time study aspect of this type of problem, will be discussed later in this book in Chapter 22.

tion. From these values the *critical path*, indicated by the heavy lines used in Figure 7.2 for some of the activities, has been determined. The *critical path* is the system of dependencies which determines the minimum time in which the project can be expected to be completed. It can also, of course, be described as the maximum time pathway through the network. In the preparation of Figure 7.2 the *slack times* were also computed and are indicated by the numbers in parentheses under some of the activity lines. The *slack time* is the additional time which could be taken in performing the activities represented by a non-critical pathway through the network without causing any delay on the total project. Naturally, the slack times may not be totaled through the network but may be totaled only to the point where the non-critical path joins a status which is either dependent upon an activity associated with the critical path or is a dependency of an activity which is in the critical path. Hence, the slack times of Figure 7.2 do not appear under each non-critical activity. They are only under the final activity of the non-critical paths.

In actual practice, the preparation of a network diagram is usually a team project; a group of individuals knowledgeable in the various disciplines involved in the project will participate. The first step will be the setting forth of the network in general form such as shown in Figure 7.1. The nature of each activity and each status will be described and the dependencies indicated. In contrast with the horizontal time bar chart the network diagram may be drawn before the time values for each activity are known. The configuration (the sequence of activities, status points, and dependencies) can be checked for feasibility and altered to achieve apparent feasibility (if necessary). The configuration can also be subjected to simplification to reduce it to the apparently most simple process. Subsequently, the group is usually enlarged to include representatives of those who will undertake the various activities in order to add the time values for each of the activities and to determine the critical path and the slack times.

Subsequently, the work of improving the method begins. Let us assume that the objective is to reduce the project time. The critical path, therefore, will be closely examined. For instance, in Figure 7.2, the critical path from status 1 to status 2 is the pathway 1.2a, 1.2b. The slack time of the adjoining non-critical pathway 1.1a, 1.1b is one week. Hence, the minimum required time to proceed from status 1 to status 2 may be reduced by not more than one week if the changes are confined to pathway 1.2a, 1.2b. There is no apparent advantage to expending more effort and money on this pathway to reduce the time by more than one week unless additional reductions can be achieved in pathway 1.1a, 1.1b. Of course, the reduction of the critical pathway 1.2a, 1.2b may not be worth the cost. It remains then in the critical path.

Let us examine an example which resembles the preceding general illustration. A city may be planning a subway. They are at status 1; the route and general design have been agreed upon. The first section of the critical path[5] may consist of the following two activities:

1. Determine who are the owners of the property under which the subway must pass or upon which the stations must emerge.
2. Acquire either an easement or title to the property, as may be appropriate.

The non-critical pathway joining the above pathway may consist of the following two activities:

1. Locate which utilities will be interfered with by the subway.
2. Relocate the various utilities.

The critical path time, perhaps, could be reduced by a change in the strategy of acquiring easements or titles, such as increasing the amount of money offered, and so forth. However, any expenditure of effort or money beyond that required to cause the time for the critical path to be equal to the non-critical path would not decrease the total project time. If additional resources were available they would have to be expended thereafter on both pathways to have any useful effect. If, in the above illustration, a way to shorten the critical path could not be found, it could be that the steps have not been divided into small enough activities. If the planning time is sufficient, an analysis may be made with smaller activity steps.

It is still possible that even with smaller activity steps, no way to shorten the critical path can be found. The network diagram is still of great value. First, a complete and feasible plan exists. Second, during the actual activity managerial attention can be directed with greatest attention at the activities associated with the critical path so that delays beyond this controlling value are minimized. The non-critical paths permit some delays without delaying the whole project. There are, however, certain dangers if the above thinking is carried too far. For instance, in the illustration used, the utility crews who have the responsibility of moving the interfering lines have, without doubt, other work. If utilized properly by their management, they are fully employed. Hence, from their point of view they have no slack time; if they are late on the non-critical path associated with the subway route they will be late on other work. Their management must think of the slack time only as a limit on their freedom of corrective action in rescheduling work if delays occur within their sphere of activity; the slack time is not really an indication of a totally permissive delay. The slack is only slack with respect to the subway schedule.

Obviously, in most cases the object of improvement is to achieve one of the following criteria of success:

1. Reduce the over-all time for the project.

[5] Obviously these steps in actual practice would be broken up into much smaller steps. I have avoided going into details in order to keep the illustration simple.

2. Reduce the over-all cost of the project.
3. Usefully employ the slack time to improve the project.
4. Control the impact of the project on the organization, society, or the economy with respect to employment, rate of expenditure, utilization of scarce resources, and so forth.

With complex projects, such as are usually subjected to network diagram analysis, means of achieving such improvement cannot be generalized; they will be specific to the various fields of work. However, certain routine techniques can be and have been generalized. Procedures have been devised for transcribing networks into a data form suitable for entering into computers. Programs (computer routines) have been devised for examining networks and determining the critical paths and the slack times; for examining potential reductions in activity times for the effect upon the critical path and the network. Routines have also been devised for examining the effect of changes in variables such as suggested by the fourth criterion of success given above. This computer aid, however, is routine. People must still be employed to generate either the change or the limitation (to conform to some specific statement of a criterion of success) to give to the computer to recalculate the network.

The above discussion is not meant to suggest that a computer is an inevitable concomitant of a network diagram. Simple network diagrams are handled much more economically by manual means. Even complex projects supported by a network diagram without a computer have a far better chance of having an effective process design than those planned by informal methods. However, when computers are available there is a definite point at which they are more economical than manual methods.

The final network diagram forms a basis for managerial control. The time values for each activity are used to develop a schedule in real time. These data are the inputs to a production control system. Such systems, however, are beyond the scope of discussion of this book.

SUMMARY — NETWORK DIAGRAMS

1. Uses:
   As an aid in designing a complex process when the process has within it a complex system of dependencies. The output of the process may be a service or substantive output, or a combination of both.

2. How made:
   A group of individuals, knowledgeable in the disciplines involved in the process, set forth the configuration of activities, status points, and dependencies which represent an apparently most simple feasible process.

3. How used:
   Time values are determined for each activity and the critical paths and slack times are

determined. Ways are examined to alter the network and its characteristics in order to con-form to one or more criteria of success.

4. What then:
   The final network diagram forms a basis for the subsequent managerial control of the process.

Supplemental Material

CASE I   THE USE OF A NETWORK DIAGRAM TO PLAN SHIP ERECTION ACTIVITY IN A SHIPYARD

Modern ship erection work employs a block system. Large sections of a ship, referred to as blocks, are assembled apart from the shipway (or graving dock) proper. Subsequently, the large blocks are lifted to the shipway by large cranes, aligned with the blocks already in place, tack-welded and guyed, and then welded to the other blocks to become an integral part of the ship. A simplified view of a ship showing how the hull is divided into blocks is shown in Figure 7.3. The broken lines show the division into blocks.

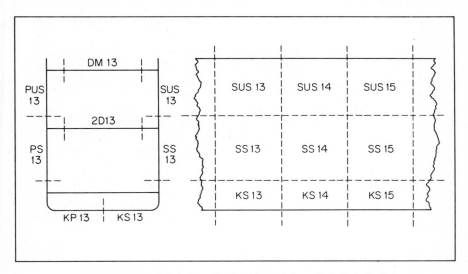

Fig. 7.3—A simplified view of a ship showing how the hull is divided into blocks.

In identifying the blocks in Figure 7.3 the following system of notation was employed:

KS13 = keel block, starboard, ship section 13
KP13 = keel block, port, ship section 13
SS13 = side block, starboard, ship section 13

PS13 = side block, port, ship section 13
SUS13 = upper side block, starboard, ship section 13
PUS13 = upper side block, port, ship section 13
2D13 = second deck block, ship section 13
DM13 = main deck block, ship section 13

Other ship section blocks are similarly identified but have different numbers; to simplify the illustration, the engine room blocks, deckhouse blocks, stern blocks, bow blocks, and so forth, have been left out of this example. As one might anticipate, there are a large number of dependencies in the ship erection process. A network diagram, such as appears in Figure 7.4 is com-

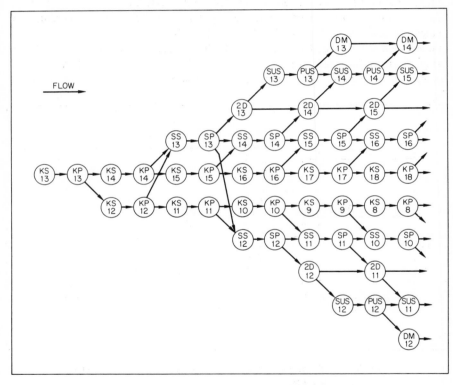

Fig. 7.4—A network diagram commonly employed to set forth the basically feasible ship erection process.

monly employed to set forth the basically feasible erection schedule. The network diagram of Figure 7.4 differs from the network diagrams of Figures 7.1 and 7.2 with respect to the conventions employed. The lines are used to indicate only the dependencies; the circles indicate both the activities and the status which results from the activities. As will be seen later, this modification increases the utility of this network diagram for the manner in which it is used. Further, it greatly simplifies the actual charting and reading.

In most cases, particularly with ships larger than the yard was originally planned for (and this is a common event), the network diagram of Figure 7.4 must be modified or converted to a production schedule so as to meet the criterion; *control the impact of the project on the organization.* The reader will note that the right side or later phase of the network diagram indicates periods when the freedom exists, within the dependencies, to work on eight blocks simultaneously. To have eight blocks to work on within one day requires the yard to have sufficient assembly areas so that eight blocks may be assembled and readied for lifting when needed, as well as a plate shop that will prepare sufficient plates for such assemblies. Further, the yard must have sufficient crane capacity for lifting and holding the blocks in place for a sufficient time for the fitting, guying, and tack welding to be performed until the time when the crane may safely disengage. With the increasing size of ships, a shipyard seldom has sufficient facilities to utilize the freedoms shown on the network diagram. The network diagram of Figure 7.3 must be converted to a schedule within the limitations of the shipyard organization. Hence, each circle on a network diagram as shown in Figure 7.3 is dimensioned in terms of such items as the following:

1. Plate shop support hours for preparation of parts
2. Assembly area needed
3. Assembly time needed and number of men
4. Crane lift time until safe disengagement is possible
5. Shipfitters time after lift of block and number of men
6. Tackwelders time after lift of block and number of men
7. Welders time and number of welders after crane disengage, before dependent block may be lifted and fitted, and so forth.

Using the above dimensions and a knowledge of the yard capability, the network diagram is redrawn with all work to be performed on successive days aligned into successive vertical columns, with the totals of each dimensional aspect shown under each column. The chart is further modified to equalize the workload per day as much as possible. The resultant network diagram becomes a tentative production schedule. Taking into account the anticipated delays from inclement weather, the schedule is checked against the delivery requirements. Further modifications may be required. The final network diagram becomes the basis for the actual scheduling and control activity.

CASE II   The Use of a Network Diagram to Plan
a National Project

The U.S. National System of Interstate and Defense Highways is a Federal-State cooperative program designed to provide a coast-to-coast, border-to-border, 41,000-mile system of ultra-modern controlled access highways. The Interstate Highway System is designed to effectively handle the 1975 volume of traffic. Naturally, all of the construction work could not be undertaken simultaneously. The impact on employment, the amount of equipment, reinforcing rod, concrete, and so forth, required, would dislocate other activities in the society. Further, the impact of such large simultaneous expenditures would dislocate the economy. Therefore, a network diagram, such as employed in the shipyard in Case I above, must be constructed (with each section of highway treated as a block), and a master plan evolved to fit the total Interstate Highway project into the nation's society and economy. The procedure is similar to that used in the shipyard. The variables, of course, are more numerous and somewhat more difficult, in some cases, to dimension accurately. Subsequently, each section of the highway must be planned in detail. In this subsequent planning, a network diagram such as shown in Figures 7.1 and 7.2 might be more appropriate. The technique needs to be adapted to fit the problem, rather than vice versa. This basic fact is too often ignored. Many varieties of network diagrams may be employed, depending on the circumstances.

CHAPTER 8

Process Chart—
Man Analysis

After the possibility guide or other preliminary analysis is made, it may be decided to seek a Class 1 or 2 change. This decision implies that the change will affect but a single job or work station and calls for the use of a man analysis technique for the main second step of the scientific method—*analysis*. A man analysis technique is also required if a single job or operation is to be designed.

The technique chosen to perform this step will usually and primarily be a function of the physical characteristics of the job. However, in some cases the choice will also be influenced by factors similar to those given in the list of the psychological and economic factors affecting class of change, such as the position of the analyst in the organization (and the techniques at his command). All this, of course, may be preceded by a preliminary study with a process chart-product analysis to make sure the job is necessary.

Some jobs or work stations are of such a nature that a considerable area is covered by the work of an individual, like many of the jobs of maintenance and service employees, machine tenders, materials handlers, warehouse employees such as stockpickers, mail clerks, roving inspectors, and certain clerical employees. In addition, many tasks in fields of activity other than manufacturing are similar in nature, such as much of the work of hotel maids and bellmen, restaurant bus boys, department store salesclerks, hospital nurses and orderlies, librarians, farmers, and many members of the armed forces. The process chart-man analysis is frequently the proper technique for the main second step in such cases.

The process chart-man analysis is a graphic means of portraying the separable steps a person performs when doing a task that requires him to move from place to place in the course of his work.

It is an analysis of what the *person does* and not of the steps performed in sequence on the product or material. The chart is an aid to a clear understanding of the activities of persons performing work that requires them to move from place to place. Care must be exercised not to confuse this analysis with a process chart-product analysis. The end result of a process chart-man analysis is usually a Class 1 or 2 improvement, although useful changes of greater complexity often become apparent.

The process chart-man analysis is also used to design a job to be performed by a man; the process chart-product analysis, the sequence on a product.

No matter where they occur, the jobs are usually broken down into the same type of steps. The steps given here appear appropriate for most active as opposed to cognative activities. Experience has shown that with the breakdown into steps like those given in Table 2, a considerable number of possibilities of elimination, rearrangement, combination, and facilitation are

TABLE 2

Symbols for Process Chart–Man Analysis

Symbol	A.S.M.E. Symbol	Name	Used to Represent
○	○	Operation	The doing of something at one place.
□	□	Quantity Determination	A special form of operation involving the person determining the quantity of an item present.
◇		Inspection	A special form of operation involving the person comparing an attribute of a product with a standard, or verifying the quantity present.
○	⇨	Movement	A change in location; moving from one place to another.
▽	D	Delay	Idleness. Waiting or moving, provided the movement was not part of the job and the time could have been spent waiting.

usually discernible; hence, a breakdown of this type is often highly productive.

Because a limited number of easily drawn and differentiated symbols are available, the symbols for process chart-man analysis are the same as those used with process chart-product analysis, although they are fewer in number and are used to denote different steps to adapt them better to the problems peculiar to man activity.

The first three types of steps, it should be noted, refer to work done at one place but indicate different degrees or types of responsibility. Further, only the first type may indicate a step that adds value to the output.[1]

The fourth type of step is affected primarily by the layout of the work area but is also influenced by the sequence.

The fifth type of step is usually undesirable unless it provides needed rest, in which case its position in the sequence of work is important. The graphic presentation achieved with a chart of this type is an aid to understanding and it should be remembered that this is the main purpose of these analysis procedures; hence, the standard steps and symbols should not be followed slavishly. If circumstances arise wherein the use of other steps or other symbols appears to be of more assistance in performing analysis, the analyst should not hesitate to use them.

Four general types of jobs may be encountered when applying process charts-man analysis.

1. The work has a single repeated cyclic.

In such cases a single cycle will be charted with a cycle defined as all the steps necessary to bring a unit of output to the state of completion typical of the operation, or all of the steps typical of a single performance of the task.

2. The work is cyclic but there are several subcycles performed with different frequency.

For instance, the worker may perform subcycle *A* on each part and then subcycle *B* for ten parts together, subcycle *B* occurring one-tenth as often as *A*. In such a case, a chart will be drawn not only showing one performance of each subcycle but also indicating their frequency.

3. The work varies from cycle to cycle.

    a. In some cases (as in some maintenance work) the variation may be primarily due to operator habit and not inherent in the work; consequently, the analyst may plot several cycles to give him more material from which to develop a preferable work pattern.

    b. The variation may be inherent in the job and each subsequent performance may differ in detail but not in general pattern. In such a case, sample cycles are drawn up for study with the general pattern

---

[1] It may assist analysis to separate *do* operations (those which add value to the product) from *get ready*, *put away*, or facilitative operations.

indicated and the details that may change so noted. Attention is paid on a weighted basis to the factors controlling the variation.

In either a or b, a more complex type of study, *memomotion study*, described in Chapter 15, may be particularly useful in some cases.

4. The task may be such that there is no cycle or pattern.

This is usually true of supervisory and similar activities. In such cases the study of a process chart-man analysis may lead only to general suggestions, on the basis of which the individual who must constantly plan his task can in the future do a better job of planning. In such cases another technique, called *work activity analysis* and described in Chapter 9, may be much more productive of useful changes.

The application of process chart-man analysis, as with product analysis, may be best understood by a study of selected examples. The examples given have been chosen as follows.

Cases I, II, and *III* are examples of the use of a process chart-man analysis to the first listed type of job, those with a single repeated cycle, and illustrate the application of the analysis technique to inspection, machine setup, and farmwork. The wide range of applicability of the technique is thus shown. In addition, the examples demonstrate how various classes of change may result.

Case IV, an examination of cocktail-ice sacking in an ice plant, illustrates the use of a process chart-man analysis for the second listed type of task containing subcycles with different frequencies.

Case V is an example of the application of a process chart-man analysis to a job possessing greater variation, type 3b of the list of types of tasks, and is a study of a department store salesclerk. Showing the application of the analysis technique to activity with the specified inherent variation this case further demonstrates the wide range of work to which this technique may be applied.

The complete application of the scientific approach will be detailed fully only with the first case; the others will show steps 2, 3, and 4 primarily to illustrate the use of the process chart-man analysis for analysis, criticism, and innovation. Also, only Case I appears in the main body of the chapter; the remainder appear as supplementary material.

The use of the *before and after* presentation in these cases should not cause the reader to lose sight of the use of the process chart-man analysis as a design tool.

CASE I   Wire Inspector (Simple Cyclic Work)

A possibility guide had suggested a Class 1 or 2 change as the most feasible and a process chart-product analysis of the production of wire had indicated that the job was necessary at its present place in the sequence. Because the task required the inspector, who checked the quality of wire from six machines drawing copper wire, to move from machine to machine as he worked, and because the work essentially consisted of a single cycle continually repeated, a simple process chart-man analysis was constructed as the main second step, *analysis*, of the scientific approach.

As is preferred, the analyst actually observed the job being performed (if

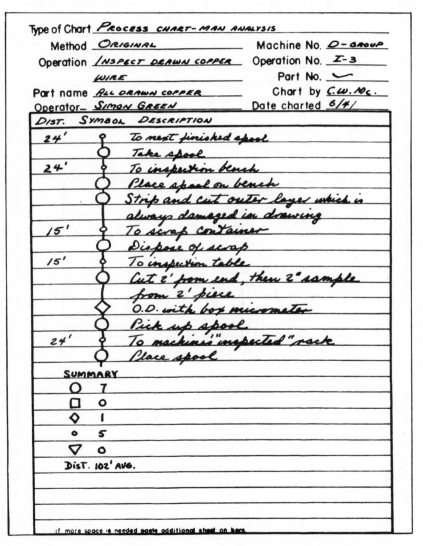

Fig. 8.1—*Process chart-man analysis for original method of inspecting production of copper wire.*

the job had been in the planning stage only, he would have had to work from the tentatively suggested procedure) and picked a suitable starting place for a cycle. Any place in the task would be satisfactory, but the first step attributable to some definite product or accomplishment is usually better, since it makes the chart easier to understand. He classified the first step of the cycle into the proper category from Table 2 and made a suitable entry on the first line of Figure 8.1, which is the original process chart-man analysis for

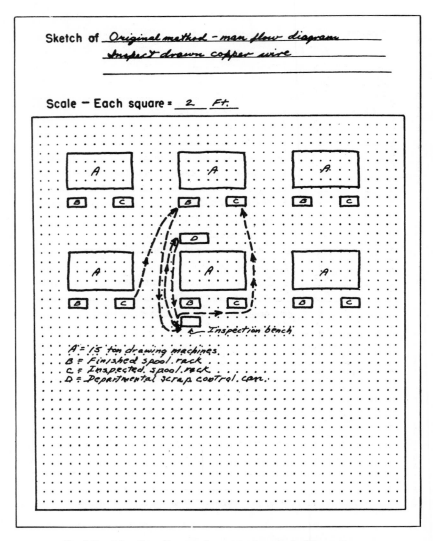

Fig. 8.2—*Man flow diagram for original method of inspecting production of copper wire.*

the wire inspector. (A form with preprinted symbols may also be used; see Figure 5.5.) In contrast to a process chart-product analysis, this chart has only three basic columns: distance, symbol, and explanation or description. The time for each step may often be usefully included, as will be shown with later examples. The analyst proceeded to record each subsequent step on a new line of the chart until a whole cycle was charted. Note that the analyst chose in places to break the work done between moves into several steps, apparently feeling that some of them might later be eliminated, combined, or rearranged. This is quite satisfactory, but the analyst should be careful to use the same degree of detail when drawing proposed or revised charts, so that the charts will be comparable rather than falsely indicating a saving by a mere change in amount of detail on the chart. A flow diagram for the man, as shown in Figure 8.2, is usually a useful adjunct.

CHECK LIST FOR PROCESS CHART—MAN ANALYSIS

Basic Principles
A. Eliminate all possible steps
B. Combine steps
C. Shorten steps
D. Place in best sequence
E. Make each step as economical as possible
  1. Can any operation be eliminated, combined, shortened, or made easier?
    a. As unnecessary
    b. By changing the order of work
    c. By new or different equipment
    d. By changes in the layout; by grouping equipment better
    e. By changing the form of the product sent out
    f. By more knowledge on part of the worker
  2. Can any movement be eliminated, combined, shortened, or made easier?
    a. By leaving out operations
    b. By changing the places where things are kept
    c. By shifting some operations to another job into which they fit more conveniently
    d. By changing the layout
    e. By changing equipment
    f. By changing the order of work
    g. By conveyors (make sure they are economical)
  3. Can delays be eliminated, combined, or shortened?
    a. By changing the order of work
    b. By changing the layout
    c. By new or different equipment
  4. Can countings or inspections be eliminated, combined, shortened, or made easier?
    a. Are they really necessary; what happens after they are done and the information obtained?
    b. Do they provide unnecessary duplication?
    c. Can they be performed more conveniently by another person?
    d. Are they done at the best point in the sequence?
    e. Can sample inspection or statistical control be used?
  5. Can any step be made safer?
    a. By changing the order of work
    b. By new or different equipment
    c. By changing the layout

The third step of the scientific method, *criticism*, is performed with the aid of the Check List for Process Chart-Man Analysis Given. Each step in the original process chart-man analysis should be checked with the applicable principles and questions.

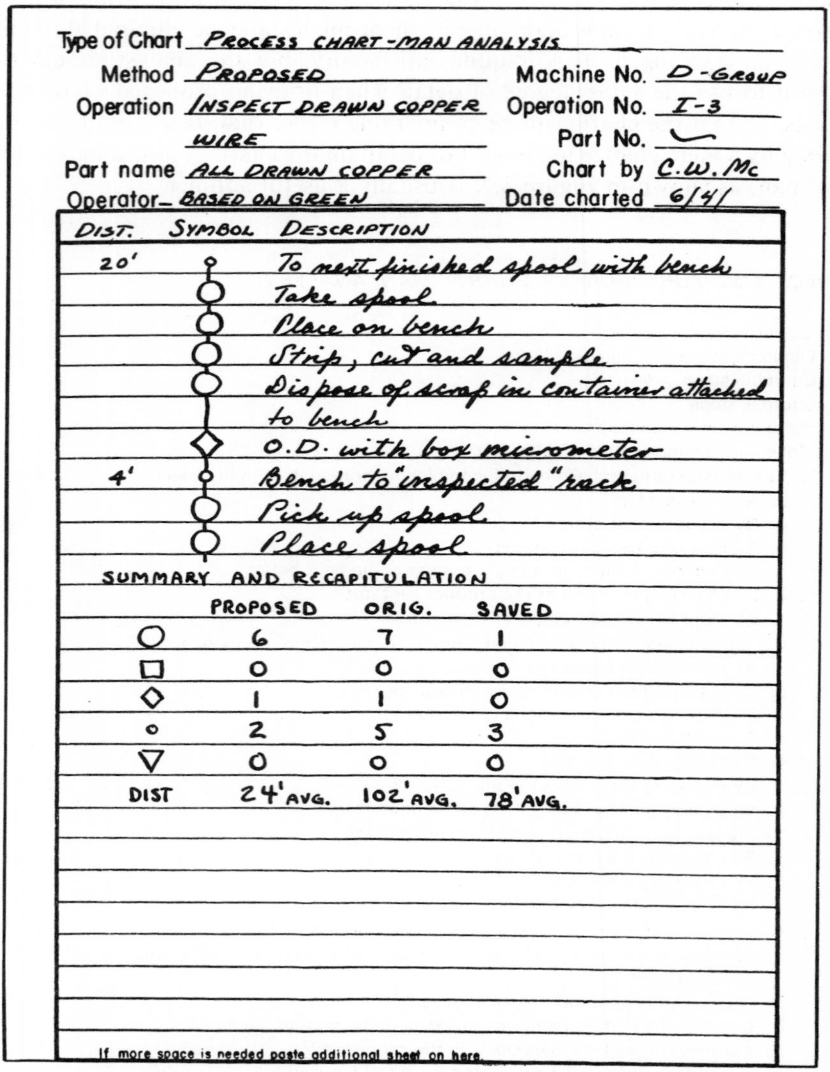

Type of Chart *PROCESS CHART-MAN ANALYSIS*
Method *PROPOSED*   Machine No. *D-GROUP*
Operation *INSPECT DRAWN COPPER*   Operation No. *I-3*
WIRE   Part No. ⌣
Part name *ALL DRAWN COPPER*   Chart by *C.W.Mc*
Operator *BASED ON GREEN*   Date charted *6/4/*

DIST.	SYMBOL	DESCRIPTION
20'	○	*To next finished spool with bench.*
	○	*Take spool.*
	○	*Place on bench*
	○	*Strip, cut and sample.*
	○	*Dispose of scrap in container attached to bench*
	◇	*O.D. with box micrometer*
4'	○	*Bench to "inspected" rack*
	○	*Pick up spool.*
	○	*Place spool*

SUMMARY AND RECAPITULATION

	PROPOSED	ORIG.	SAVED
○	6	7	1
□	0	0	0
◇	1	1	0
○	2	5	3
▽	0	0	0
DIST	24' AVG.	102' AVG.	78' AVG.

If more space is needed paste additional sheet on here.

Fig. 8.3 — Process chart-man analysis for proposed method of inspecting production of copper wire.

In the case of the wire inspector, the analyst found questions 1a, 2b, and 2e of value.

The fourth step, *innovation*, is performed by preparing a proposed method, based on the suggestions obtained in step 3. A proposed method with only a Class 1 change for the procedure used by the wire inspector is shown in Figures 8.3 and 8.4, which are the proposed process chart-man analysis and new man flow diagram. As the summary at the end of the chart indicates, the

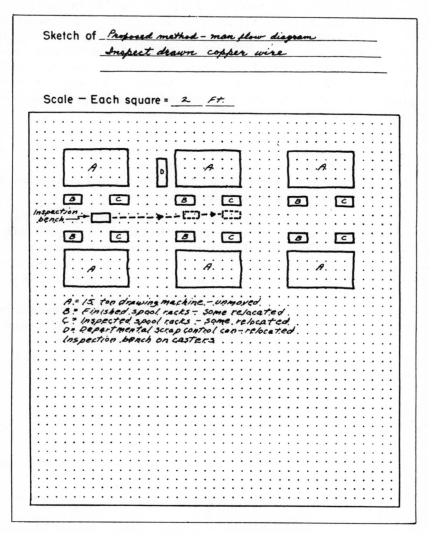

Fig. 8.4—*Man flow diagram for proposed method of inspecting production of copper wire.*

inspector's duty was considerably reduced. The savings could be used to give him more machines to check without increased effort, or to enable him to make more checks per machine, or to do a more thorough inspection job, or to inspect the product sooner after production, any one of which would be a worthwhile improvement.

The fifth step, *test*, is performed by rechecking this proposed method with the check list to make sure the best obtainable method is being proposed. It is worth noting that with this technique, as with process chart-product analysis, the analyst may well build himself a file of inestimable value by preparing a file sheet for each question and subquestion, and recording, after each job studied with this technique, the specific way the inherent suggestion was applied, to facilitate future work with this technique. No complete list of such suggestions is given here, as they are usually peculiar to an industry or type of product. However, in the case being discussed, the analyst might well have made notations under questions 1a, 2b, and 2e, as follows:

1a. *Avoid unnecessary cutting of wire which does not aid task.*

2b. *Place scrap can close to inspector, even making it integral with inspection table to avoid extra travel with each piece of waste.*

2e. *Make inspection fixtures portable so inspector can take them to job. If workbench is needed, provide casters on workbench.*

The sixth step, *trial*, would be aided by using the proposed process chart-man analysis or a suitably modified version, depending on the personality of the inspector, as a basis for training him to try this method. After a suitable acquaintance period with this new method, a time study was made to evaluate the new method, which was found to take only 52 per cent of the time of the original method.[2]

The seventh step, *application*, would consist of recording the method in such a form that the practice proposed in Figures 8.3 and 8.4 can be maintained until the next improvement. This type of recording will be shown in later chapters. The good analyst, it should be realized, recognizes subsequent improvement as almost inevitable.

SUMMARY — PROCESS CHART—MAN ANALYSIS

1. Uses:
   a. *For information leading to a Class 1 or 2 change when the person moves from place to place while performing his job.* Note: *Higher classes of change are occasionally suggested from an analysis of this type and should not be overlooked.*
   b. *For designing a job which requires the worker to move from place to place while performing it.*

---

[2] The writer is indebted for this illustration to Mr. C. W. McFarland, formerly instructor in Industrial Engineering at Purdue University.

2. How made:
   a. *A form like that in Figure 8.1 or a blank sheet of paper may be used.*
   b. *The chart may begin at any point in a cycle of work, considering a cycle as the complete set of steps necessary to bring a unit of the output to the degree of completion typical of the work. However, it is usually most convenient to begin with the first step connected with a particular unit and end on the last step before the next similar unit is worked on or a new routine is started.*
   c. *The first work step should be carefully classified according to the categories of Table 2, and the symbol, explanation (and, if the step is a movement, the distance), entered on the first line of the chart. The distance may be paced, estimated, measured on the actual floor plan, or scaled from a drawing. The explanation should be as succinct as possible.*
   d. *If the time for the step is desired, time it with an ordinary watch or stop-watch.*
   e. *Subsequent steps should be entered on subsequent lines, with the information placed in such a way that the symbols, explanations, and so forth, form separate columns for easy reading.*
   f. *Care should be exercised to make one entry for every separable phase of the work. Each time the worker moves from one place to another, an entry should be made. Each time the worker works at a workplace, an entry should be made. In some cases, two distinctly separate activities may follow each other at a workplace without an intervening movement, and two operation symbols, one after the other, may be convenient.*
   g. *The steps should represent the activities of the worker, what he does to the product, and where he goes, rather than what happens to the product.*
   h. *If the job has several subcycles with different frequencies, each subcycle should be charted, separated from the others, and its frequency of occurrence noted.*
   i. *If the job has a variable cycle, classify as below and handle as indicated.*
      1. *Due to operator habit:*
         Chart several versions, to have more to work from.
      2. *Inherent and each different:*
         Plot general pattern, marking parts that are constant and parts that vary from cycle to cycle.
      3. *No pattern or cycle:*
         Plot a selected period of work as it occurs.
         (*In many cases, a* work activity analysis *described in Chapter 9, is more useful.*)
   j. *In any case, a man flow diagram, which is a plan view of the area covered by the worker, with his path indicated thereon, is often a useful adjunct to the process chart-man analysis.*
3. How used:
   a. *Each step of the process is questioned with the check list given.*
4. What then:
   a. *A process chart-man analysis is drawn for a resulting suggested improved method in order to permit a final check and to provide a means of describing the proposed new method.*

Supplemental Material

CASE II   MACHINE SETUP (SIMPLE CYCLIC WORK)

This application of the process chart-man analysis was made in a large steel-casting plant by cooperative action on the part of the general foreman of the core room, the shop superintendent, the general foreman of the pattern shop, the master mechanic, and the industrial engineer who supplied these men with the time values shown on the charts at their request. It would not be

an overstatement to say that the ability of all of these individuals to understand and work with suitable motion and time study techniques was a fundamental prerequisite in the development of the improved method.

The core blowing machine shown in Figure 8.5 was one of several in use.
Many different cores had to be blown on each machine and a possibility
guide indicated that Class 1 and 2 changes were desirable. The operation of

Fig. 8.5 — Core blower.

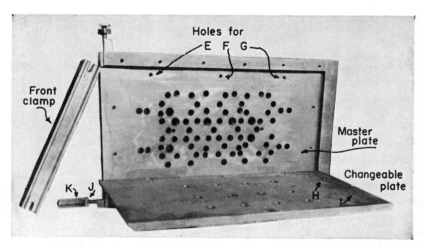

*Fig. 8.6 — Master blow plate and a core box blow plate, both dis-
assembled from core blower of Figure 8.5.*

the core blower naturally divides into two phases, "setup" and "do," with each core box. While a considerbale number of changes were made in the method of "do," this discussion is confined to the development of Class 1 and 2 changes in the "setup." The setup consists of switching core boxes, which is done by the materials handler, and changing blow plates, which is done by the blower operator. Each core box usually requires a different blow plate, which covers different holes in the master blow plate attached to the machine. The master blow plate and a specific core box blow plate are both shown in Figure 8.6. They have been removed from the machine for purposes of illustration. To show the parts involved in this job, the clamps, screw holes, and bolts are similarly identified on this photograph and in Figure 8.5. Figure 8.7 shows the worker in the act of changing blow plates.

Fig. 8.7 — Worker changing blow plates on core blower.

The process chart-man analysis for the original method is shown in Figures 8.8a and 8.8b. A time column was found to be a useful addition in this case, and the industrial engineer supplied existing time study values on request. Application of the check list aided in replacing this original method with the improved method shown in Figures 8.9a and 8.9b. The method of holding the blow plate in place was changed to that indicated in Figure 8.10.

The savings from this change are given below in the excerpt from the report made to the works manager of the plant by the men who developed this change.

Type of Chart	Process Chart–Man Analysis			

Method	Original		Machine No.	24C6

Operation Changing Blow Plates   Operation No. Set Up

Part No. ——

Part name Blow Plates   Chart by W.L. Mosbey

Operator Joe Small   Date charted 12/4/

Distance	Symbol	Description	Time
20'	○	To dolly	.10 min.
	○	Get dolly	.05
20'	○	Carry dolly to table	.10
	○	Place dolly on blower table	.05
3'	○	To blower bench	.02
	○	Get Wrench	.05
3'	○	Wrench to blower	.02
	○	Place wrench on top of blower head	.02
	○	Wind up blower table	.40
	○	Take off 3 bolts (ABC) and 1 side clamp (D)	.73
6'	○	To other side of blower	.05
	○	Take off 3 bolts (EFG) and 1 side clamp (H)	.73
3'	○	To bench	.02
	○	Aside wrench and get screw driver	.06
6'	○	To rear of blower	.05
	○	Remove 2 rear screws (HI) from blow plate	.35
6'	○	To bench with clamps, bolts and screws	.15
	○	Place parts, get wrench	.19
3'	○	To blower	.02
	○	Loosen nuts (JKLM) and take off front clamp	.88
	○	Place wrench on blower	.02
	○	Wind down table	.13
15'	○	Pull bench to front of blower	.40
	○	Pull dolly out with plate	.13
15'	○	Plate to storage	.20

If more space is needed paste additional sheet on here.

Fig. 8.8a—*Process chart-man analysis for original method of changing blow plates* (continued).

Type of Chart PROCESS CHART-MAN ANALYSIS

Method ORIGINAL (CONTINUED) Machine No. ______

Operation CHANGING BLOW PLATES Operation No. ______

Part No. ______

Part name ______ Chart by ______

Operator ______ Date charted ______

DISTANCE	SYMBOL	DESCRIPTION	TIME
	O	STORE PLATE AND GET NEXT ONE	.16
15'	o	NEW PLATE TO BLOWER	.20
	O	PLACE PLATE ON DOLLY	.15
	O	AIR CLEAN BLOWER AND PLATE	1.15
	O	PUSH DOLLY AND PLATE INTO PLACE	.79
	O	WIND UP TABLE	.15
	O	PUSH BENCH AWAY FROM BLOWER	.20
	O	AIR CLEAN CLAMPS AND 6 BOLT HOLES	1.08
	O	PICK UP WRENCH AND FRONT CLAMP & TIGHTEN 4 NUTS	.18
6'	o	TO REAR OF BLOWER WITH DRIVER AND SCREWS	.10
	O	PLACE SCREWS	1.09
6'	o	TO BENCH	.10
	O	GET CLAMPS, BOLTS, ASIDE DRIVER	.11
3'	o	TO SIDE OF BLOWER	.05
	O	ATTACH CLAMP ON ONE SIDE-3 BOLTS	1.59
6'	o	TO OTHER SIDE	.05
	O	ATTACH CLAMP-3 BOLTS	1.59
3'	o	TO FRONT OF BLOWER	.02
	O	PLACE WRENCH	.03
	O	WIND DOWN TABLE	.22
	O	PULL OUT DOLLY	.05
20'	o	TO DOLLY STORAGE	.10
	O	STORE DOLLY	.05
20'	o	RETURN TO BLOWER	.10
164		SUMMARY O 31	14.83
		o 18	

If more space is needed paste additional sheet on here.

Fig. 8.8b—(Concluded) *Process chart-man analysis for original method of changing blow plates.*

Type of Chart	PROCESS CHART – MAN ANALYSIS		
Method IMPROVED		Machine No. 24C6	
Operation CHANGING BLOW PLATES		Operation No. SET UP	
		Part No. ———	
Part name BLOW PLATES		Chart by W.L. MOSBEY	
Operator– SYNTHESIZED		Date charted 12/4/	

DISTANCE	SYMBOL	DESCRIPTION	TIME
	○	GET DOLLY FROM SIDE OF BLOWER	.10 MIN
	○	PLACE ON BLOWER TABLE	.05
	○	WIND UP TABLE	.40
3'	○	TO BENCH FOR WEDGE LOOSENING TOOL	.02
	○	GET TOOL	.02
6'	○	TO REAR OF BLOWER	.04
	○	STRIKE WEDGE	.10
3'	○	TO FRONT OF BLOWER	.04
	○	PLACE MALLET, GET WRENCH	.05
3'	○	TO BLOWER	.02
	○	OFF 4 NUTS AND FRONT CLAMP, SET ON HEAD	.60
	○	PULL OUT WEDGE, PLACE ON HEAD	.16
	○	WIND DOWN TABLE	.13
	○	PULL BENCH IN FRONT OF BLOWER	.40
	○	PULL OUT DOLLY	.13
15'	○	PLATE TO STORAGE	.20
	○	STORE AND GET NEW PLATE	.16
15'	○	PLATE TO DOLLY	.20
	○	PLACE PLATE ON DOLLY	.15
	○	AIR CLEAN BLOWER AND PLATE	1.15
	○	POSITION PLATE AND DOLLY	.79
	○	WIND UP TABLE	.15
	○	PUSH BENCH AWAY	.20
	○	OIL WEDGE	.20
	○	PLACE AND DRIVE WEDGE	.23

If more space is needed paste additional sheet on here.

Fig. 8.9a — *Process chart-man analysis for improved method of changing blow plates* (continued).

Type of Chart	PROCESS CHART – MAN ANALYSIS		

Method __IMPROVED (CONTINUED)__   Machine No. _____

Operation __CHANGING BLOW PARTS__   Operation No. _____

_____   Part No. _____

Part name _____   Chart by _____

Operator– _____   Date charted _____

DISTANCE	SYMBOL	DESCRIPTION	TIME
	◯	AIR CLEAN CLAMP	.26
	◯	PLACE CLAMP AND TIGHTEN	.60
	◯	WIND DOWN TABLE	.22
	◯	PULL OUT DOLLY	.05
	◯	HANG DOLLY ON SIDE OF BLOWER	.10

SUMMARY AND RECAPITULATION

	IMPROVED	ORIGINAL	SAVED
◯	24	31	7
○	6	18	12
DIST.	45	164	119
TIME	6.92 MIN.	14.83 MIN.	7.91 MIN.

If more space is needed paste additional sheet on here.

Fig. 8.9b—(Concluded) *Process chart-man analysis for improved method of changing blow plates.*

111

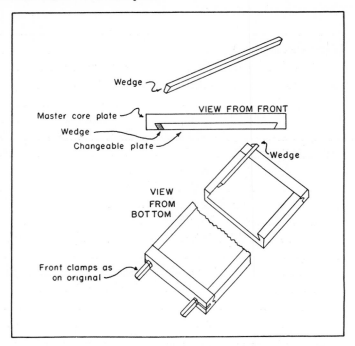

Wedge

Master core plate

VIEW FROM FRONT

Wedge

Changeable plate

Wedge

VIEW
FROM
BOTTOM

Front clamps as
on original

Fig. 8.10—Details of new method of holding blow plates in place.

Analysis of the steps required by the proposed method indicates that the time required for changing a blow plate will be approximately 7.00 minutes. The present type of plate requires 15.00 minutes to change. A saving of 8.00 minutes per plate change is indicated.

An average of 15 plate changes per day are made. A saving of two blower hours per day would result from the change. Two blower hours cost $3.50 in direct wages. Since the hours saved can be used for needed production, we may include overhead in the saving, which increases it to $13.70 per day, or $3,400 per year.

In addition to measurable savings in blower time, it appears that a saving should be made as a result of decreasing the incidence of blow plates sagging in the center, which has become a problem with the present method. The reverse tapers and support on all sides of the blow plate should help.

The cost of changing over to the new method would be $280 per blower and $12 for each plate. New plates would cost $8 more than present plates but may repay this in an extended life. An expenditure of $1,080 is anticipated to obtain the $3,400 increase in production, which should return the investment in less than four months from increased production alone.

CASE III   PLANTING CORN (SIMPLE CYCLIC WORK)

The corn belt of the United States raises a great deal of what is called hybrid corn. The seed for this is raised in special fields and results from the controlled

Type of Chart: PROCESS CHART — MAN ANALYSIS		
Method ORIGINAL	Machine No. DEERE	
Operation PLANTING CORN FOR HYBRID SEED	Operation No. ——	
	Part No. ——	
Part name HYBRID SEED	Chart by D.B.	
Operator J. JENKINS	Date charted 6/4/	

DISTANCE	SYMBOL	EXPLANATION
	O	DRIVE ACROSS FIELD PLANTING
	O	TURN AROUND AT END
3'	o	CLIMB DOWN FROM TRACTOR
6'	o	TO BACK OF PLANTER
	O	REMOVE POLLENATOR SEED BOX
	O	CLEAN FOOT AND PLANTER PLATE
6'	o	TO OTHER SIDE OF PLANTER WITH POLLENATOR BOX
	O	REMOVE END SEED PARENT BOX
	O	CLEAN FOOT AND PLANTER PLATE
	O	ATTACH POLLENATOR SEED BOX
6'	o	TO OTHER END
	O	ATTACH SEED PARENT BOX
6'	o	TO TRACTOR
3'	o	CLIMB UP
	SUMMARY	
	O	8
	o	6
DIST. WALKED	30'	

If more space is needed paste additional sheet on here.

Fig. 8.11 — Process chart-man analysis for original method of plant-ing corn for hybrid seed.

113

cross-pollination of two corns—a seed parent, from which the ears are used but which is detasseled as it grows, and a pollinator, which is allowed to keep its tassels and supplies the male element for fertile kernels. The planted rows must not have any stray seeds of the wrong variety.

The original process chart-man analysis shown in Figure 8.11 was made from a study of a farmer planting corn for seed as described, using a four-row corn planter to produce a field as sketched in Figure 8.12.

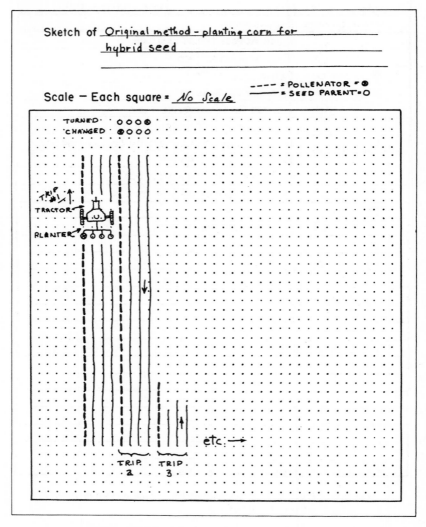

Fig. 8.12—Sketch of movement of farmer and planter and layout of field with original method of planting corn for hybrid seed.

A study of these charts with a check list in a search for an easier and quicker method, which would be highly useful since more advantage could be taken of a break in the weather, resulted in the suggested method shown in the process chart-man analysis of Figure 8.13 and in the sketch in Figure 8.14.

Examination of these will show, however, that the analyst's intention of producing a Class 1 or 2 change was overreached, and a Class 4 change is

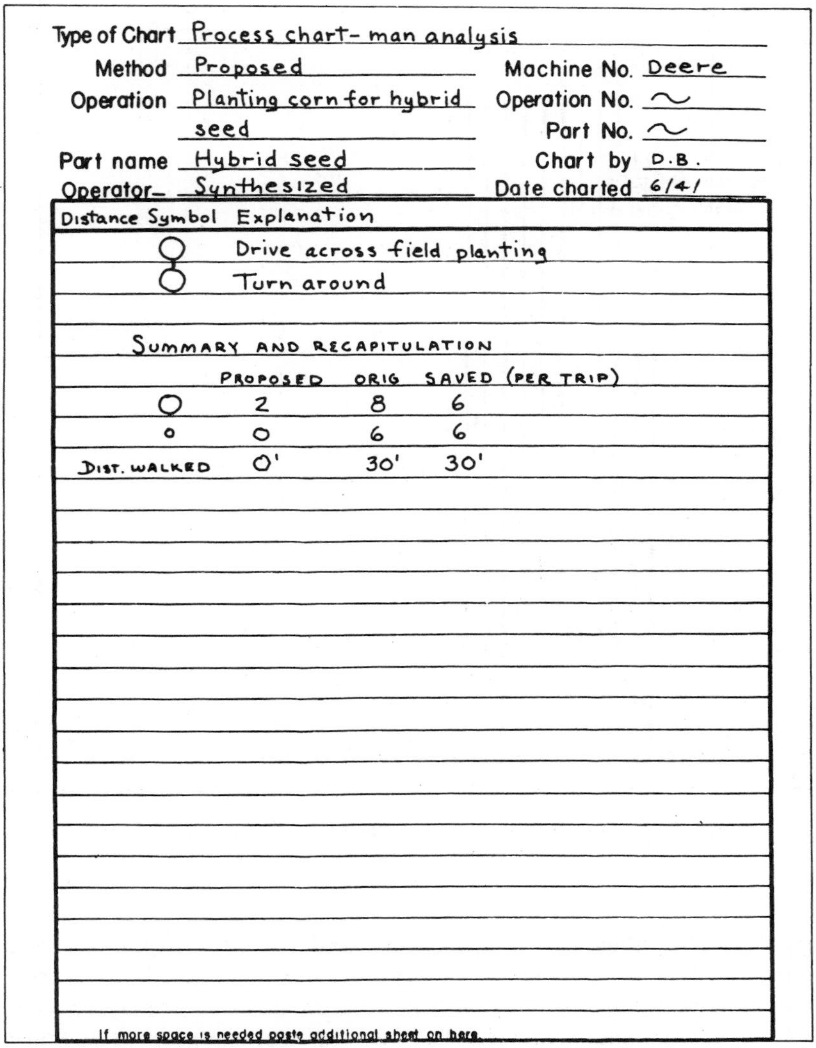

Type of Chart _Process chart- man analysis_

Method _Proposed_   Machine No. _Deere_

Operation _Planting corn for hybrid_   Operation No. _～_

seed   Part No. _～_

Part name _Hybrid seed_   Chart by _D.B._

Operator _Synthesized_   Date charted _6/4/_

Distance	Symbol	Explanation
	⊖	Drive across field planting
	⊖	Turn around

SUMMARY AND RECAPITULATION

	PROPOSED	ORIG	SAVED (PER TRIP)
◯	2	8	6
○	0	6	6
DIST. WALKED	0'	30'	30'

If more space is needed paste additional sheet on here.

Fig. 8.13—Process chart-man analysis of proposed method for planting corn for hybrid seed.

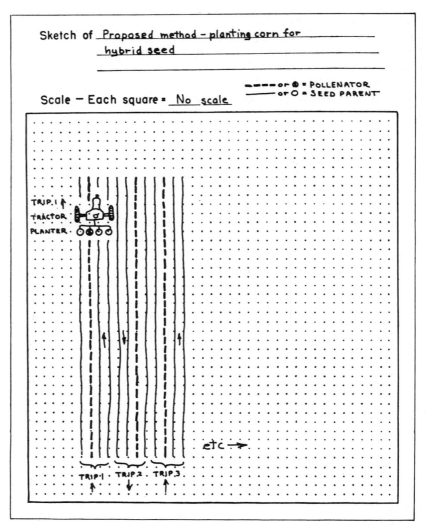

Fig. 8.14—Sketch of movement of farmer and planter and layout
of field with proposed method for planting corn for hybrid
seed.

suggested. The different arrangement of seed parent and pollinator rows
could possibly affect pollination. When cases like this occur in industry, the
suggestions must be discussed with more individuals than may have been
originally contemplated, namely, the design or sales engineers in addition to
the original list of tool designer, foreman, and worker. In the case of the corn,
the equivalent additional consultant is the farm manager, hybrid corn seed

specialist, or horticultural extension worker, who could check on the suitability of the proposed method. The reduction in work in the proposed method is obvious, and the writer, who is no agriculturalist, has been given to understand that it is used.

CASE IV   SACKING COCKTAIL-ICE (WORK WITH SUBCYCLES)

This application of the process chart-man analysis was made in a large ice plant. Cocktail-ice is crushed ice. It is prepared in a room cold enough to prevent clumping of the small pieces. It is sacked from a hopper into 50-pound sacks which are wire-tied at the top. The ice is then held in a storage room below melting temperature. The original method is shown in Figure 8.15 and has four subcycles, A, B, C, and D. A, the filling of the sack, is performed on each of ten bags before the worker performs B, which occurs only once for ten bags. The worker then performs C ten times, once for each bag, and then D once for all ten bags. An additional column has been added to the chart to provide a place for identifying the subcycles and to give their frequency of occurrence. Two distance and time columns are used, one to give the time for each step and one to give the prorated distance or time per bag. The times are in seconds and could be estimated from the sweep-second hand of a wrist watch.

The proposed method, shown in Figure 8.16, took 26 per cent less time, or, in other words, increased production 35 per cent. This proposed method required the following changes: the workplace had to be rebuilt with a supply bin for bags on the right of the hopper mouth, a support in the center for the bag being filled, and a place on the left for tying bags, with a holder for tie wires and a shelf for the tier; the hopper opening had to be adjusted to fill the bag more slowly and cut off when full; and the worker's mittens had to be replaced with gloves, to permit him to work with them on.

It is worth noting that although the improved method in this case reduced the job to a simple cyclic task, this is by no means necessary to the improvement of all work with subcycles.

CASE V   SALESCLERK (WORK VARIES FROM CYCLE TO CYCLE)

This study was made with a process chart-man analysis, despite extreme variation from cycle to cycle. Because the exact order and amount of action of the women's hosiery salesclerk were subject to customer wish or whim, the process chart-man analysis, shown in Figure 8.17, of a salesclerk selling two pairs of nylon hose was merely representative of one type of performance. Application of the check list suggested several changes. A display wheel for use at the counter was constructed to show continuously all seasonal shades (see question 2b). Despite the soiling of the display merchandise, there was

Type of Chart _Process chart-man analysis_

Method _Original_   Machine No. _B.I._

Operation _Sacking cocktail-ice_   Operation No. _~_

     Part No. _~_

Part name _50 lb. bags_   Chart by _L.K._

Operator _J. Johnson_   Date charted _7-4-_

Dist. per bag	Dist	Ident and frequency	Symbol	Explanation	Time Sec.	Time per bag
11	11'	A	P	To empty bags	3	3
		1/bag	O	Pick up bag	1	1
3	3'	do 10		To hopper mouth	1	1
			O	Place and fill bag	14	14
11	11'			To storage with bag	4	4
			O	Place bag	1	1
1.3	13'	B		To far side bin and remove gloves	4	
		1/10 bags				
		do 1	O	Aside gloves, pick up tier and wires	6	1.8
1.3	13'			To storage area	4	
			O	Place tool and wires on bag	4	
		1/bag C	O	Fold top of bag	5	5
		do 10	O	Tie bag	10	10
1.3	13'	D 1/10 bags		To far side of bin	4	
		do 1	O	Aside tool, wires, don gloves	6	1
28.9'						

SUMMARY PER BAG

O	5.3	
o	3.3	
DIST	28.9'	
TIME	41.8 SEC	

If more space is needed paste additional sheet on here.

Fig. 8.15—Process chart-man analysis for original method of sacking cocktail-ice.

118

Type of Chart _Process chart - man analysis_

Method _Proposed_   Machine No. _B.I_

Operation _Sacking cocktail ice_   Operation No. _~_

                 Part No. _~_

Part name _50# sacks_   Chart by _L.K._

Operator _Synthesized_   Date charted _7-4-_

Distance	Symbol	Explanation	Time - Sec.
11'	○	To hopper mouth	3
	○	Aside full bag	2
	○	Place empty bag	4
	○	Fold top of bag	5
	○	Tie bag	12
11'	○	To storage area with bag	4
	○	Place bag	1
			31

Summary and recapitulation

	Proposed	Original	Saved
○	5	5.3	.3
○	2	3.3	1.3
Dist	22'	28.9	6.9
Time (sec)	31	41.8	10.8

If more space is needed paste additional sheet on here.

Fig. 8.16 — Process chart-man analysis for proposed method of sacking cocktail-ice.

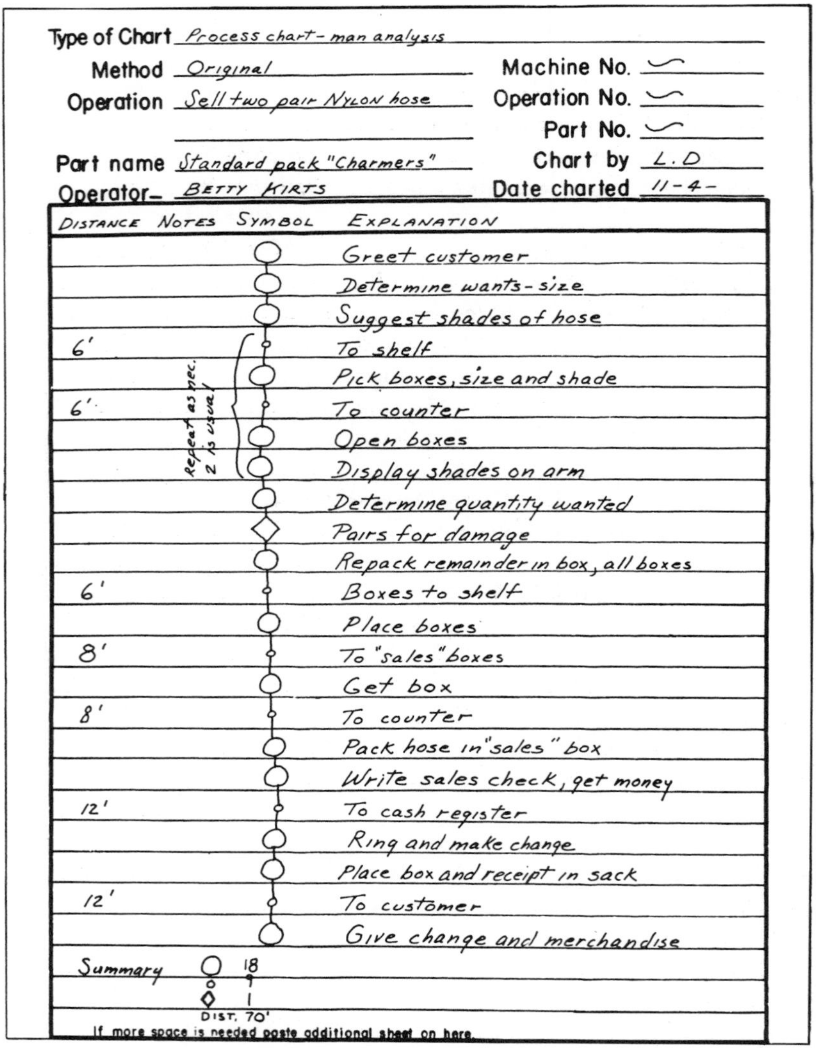

Type of Chart _Process chart- man analysis_

Method _Original_   Machine No. ⌣

Operation _Sell two pair Nylon hose_   Operation No. ⌣

Part No. ⌣

Part name _Standard pack "Charmers"_   Chart by _L.D_

Operator— _BETTY KIRTS_   Date charted _11-4-_

DISTANCE	NOTES	SYMBOL	EXPLANATION
		◯	Greet customer
		◯	Determine wants-size
		◯	Suggest shades of hose
6'			To shelf
		◯	Pick boxes, size and shade
6'	Repeat as nec. 2 is usual.		To counter
		◯	Open boxes
		◯	Display shades on arm
		◯	Determine quantity wanted
		◇	Pairs for damage
		◯	Repack remainder in box, all boxes
6'			Boxes to shelf
		◯	Place boxes
8'			To "sales" boxes
		◯	Get box
8'			To counter
		◯	Pack hose in "sales" box
		◯	Write sales check, get money
12'			To cash register
		◯	Ring and make change
		◯	Place box and receipt in sack
12'			To customer
		◯	Give change and merchandise

Summary   ◯ 18
            ○ 9
            ◇ 1
            DIST. 70'

If more space is needed paste additional sheet on here.

Fig. 8.17—Process chart-man analysis for typical original method of selling nylon hose.

less loss than with the original method. With the original method, stockings were occasionally snagged while checking them for the customer. Individually-packed (see question 1e) pairs of hose in sealed cellophane bags or cellophane covered semiboxes eliminated the need (present in the original method) for examining the merchandise for store damage before sale. Increase in sales per unit time, more rapid customer service, and better display were all advantages connected with the improved process chart-man analysis of the hosiery clerk shown in Figure 8.18. Note, however, that the change indicated is Class 5, and a considerable number of executives in the store, including the buyer and, through him, the vendor, had to be consulted before the change could be accomplished. This is not a usual result of a process chart-man analysis, but it can happen.

Type of Chart *Process chart - man analysis*		
Method *Improved*	Machine No. ⌣	
Operation *Sell two pair Nylon hose*	Operation No. ⌣	
	Part No. ⌣	
Part name *Pre-pack "Charmers"*	Chart by *L.D*	
Operator *Betty Kirts*	Date charted *1-4-*	

DISTANCE	SYMBOL	EXPLANATION
	◯	Greet customer
	◯	Determine wants – size
	◯	Show shades on counter display wheel,
		inserting arm as customer requests
6'		To shelf
	◯	Pick individual packs of shade, size and quantity
6'		To customer
	◯	Write sales check, get money
12'		To cash register
	◯	Ring and make change
	◯	Place hose and receipt in sack
12'		To customer
	◯	Give change and merchandise

Summary and comparison

	Improved	Original	Saved
◯	8	18	10
∘	4	9	5
◇	0	1	1
Dist	36'	70'	34'

If more space is needed paste additional sheet on here.

Fig. 8.18—*Process chart-man analysis for typical improved method of selling nylon hose.*

CHAPTER 9

Work Activity Analysis and Work Sampling

In the usual office or plant there are some jobs that appear to possess no cycle or repetitive pattern. Supervisory tasks often fall into this category, as indicated in Chapter 8. Many clerical, service, and maintenance jobs fit into a similar classification, depending on the nature of the organization in which they occur.

There are numerous reasons why one might wish to improve or facilitate such tasks: the backlog of work may be growing; the time lag between assignment and completion of work may be excessive; important but postponable aspects of the work may be neglected; the amount of manpower expended may be thought excessive; the effort required to perform the necessary work may be unreasonable. Indeed, the pressure for improvement may be intense because of the possible widespread influence on other tasks of a job of this general nature.

It should be obvious that a possibility guide for a task of this type is difficult to construct without some means of obtaining additional insight into the task. There is no clear-cut "present method" as with a repetitive or cyclic job. Likewise, a process chart-man analysis of the entire task, made for a period of time, might yield helpful information but would probably include much extraneous detail that would tend to mask the significant problem. Also, it might be very difficult to prepare.

A process chart-product analysis of "products" that passed through such a job might provide too great a bulk of data to deal with economically. Further, part of the solution to more effective activity may be in possible changes in the functions assigned such a worker: in the organization or sequence of the numerous tasks performed in discharging these functions; in changes in the physical method of performing and the facilities used for each separate task. Only the effect of the last two aspects, the physical method and the facilities, would be revealed in the more common motion study analysis approach. However, such information might be deeply buried in the data and hard to discern.

In cases like these, three techniques are of use for performing the second step, *analysis*, of the scientific method: (1) work activity analysis, (2) work sampling, and (3) memomotion study. The first two are discussed in this chapter. Memomotion study is presented in Chapter 15.

A work activity analysis is a chronological record, usually accompanied by a summary tabulation, of the nature of the activities performed, work-units produced, and the time spent at each activity by an individual performing a variety of tasks.

"A work sampling study consists of a large number of observations taken at random intervals; in taking the observations, the state or condition of the object of study is noted, and this state is classified into predefined categories of activity pertinent to the particular work situation. From the proportions of observations in each category, inferences are drawn concerning the total work activity under study."[1]

Work activity analysis observations preserve the sequence of work in the records, but they may require a considerable expenditure of time, and are therefore seldom extended over a long period. Work sampling observations, on the other hand, do not record the sequence but can be made in an intermittent fashion and do not constitute a heavy workload. Hence, work sampling studies are often used to cover an extended period. The techniques are often used to complement each other.

On jobs where the daily pattern is very different from day to day, work sampling yields, for a given amount of study effort, a more complete picture. On jobs where the daily pattern is similar from day to day, work activity analysis gives a more complete picture more rapidly. Both techniques are samples, in that only a portion of the total work is studied. Work activity analysis can be described as intensive sampling, while work sampling is usually extensive sampling.

Either technique may reveal the following:

1. The need for a change in functions assigned an individual.
2. Which parts of the job occupy enough of the total time to merit being studied in detail with other techniques such as process chart-man analysis, process chart-product analysis, operation chart, and so forth.

[1] R. E. Heiland and W. J. Richardson, *Work Sampling*. New York, N.Y.: McGraw-Hill Book Company, 1957, p. 1. Copyright © 1957 by McGraw-Hill Book Company.

In addition, the work activity analysis may more readily reveal the need for changing the timing or sequence of the numerous tasks performed.

Because of the varied nature of the work to which such analyses are commonly applied, and because insight into the nature of the specific work is the first objective of such analyses, the basis for separating the work into pertinent steps is usually different from job to job.

Work Activity Analysis

With work activity analysis, which will be discussed first, the separation is frequently on the basis of what might be called outputs; that is, the results of each separate situation calling for a pattern of action or response. For example, a clerk might separate her work into these categories: (1) letters typed, (2) phone call answered, (3) person located, (4) filed material located and delivered, and so forth. Of course, if the study is also going to delve into the work-generating mechanism in an attempt to reduce the amount of outputs needed, then these categories for activity must be compounded so that (*1*) *letters typed* is divided into subcategories. Each of the subcategories will represent letters generated from a different cause system. The same division must be made of the other categories (*2*), (*3*), (*4*), and so forth.

This is in contrast to the steps used for a process chart-product analysis, which separate different types of activity and areas of responsibility on a product, or the steps for a process chart-man analysis, which separate different types of physical actions.

In addition, a work activity analysis is frequently made by the person doing the work rather than by a separate observer, although this is not a necessary aspect. A form like that shown in Figure 9.1 is commonly used, although an ordinary ruled sheet of paper may be easily columnated for this purpose. The essential features of work activity analysis are:

1. The chronological listing of work as performed
2. The indication of the time spent at each task, as it occurs
3. The noting of the work-count for each occurrence of each task

The work-count is the quantity of action performed or work-units produced of the type described, or the physical count of the product, such as pages typed, entries made, items filed, workers talked to, and so forth, as appropriate to the task being recorded. It is helpful if the work-unit selected for each separable activity is as closely related to the amount of work called for as possible, i.e., "pages typed" rather than "documents copied," by a copy typist, and so forth. As will be more obvious later, the work activity analysis shows the time for each separate action in the work count; the work sampling study does not.

WORK ACTIVITY ANALYSIS				531216-01

Name, working title, grade, rank or classification. (Please print)
JOSEPHINE GALLAPAGOS , OFFICE MANAGER , R4
Organizational segment or unit, supervisor, date
CONF. CENTER , RLM, 16 DEC

TIME SPENT		HOW SPENT	UNITS	REMARKS
Began	Blank	Describe forms handled, work data assembled, errands run, idle periods, etc.	Quantity of actions completed	
8:45	5	Talked on phone to publicity section	1	
8:50	2	Answered phone call	1	
8:52	4	Entered part time help hours in ledger	4 entries	
8:56	4	Distributed checks to part time help	4	
9:00	4	Prepared material for publicity section	1 page	
9:04	1	Phone call for Mr. Jones	1 call	
9:05	1	Phone call for me from Mr Alt wishing copy of letter he could not find	1	
9:06	6	Work conference with Clerk Typ. on what has transpired; what's to do	1	
9:12	5	Search for Mr. alt's letter	1	
9:17	3	Organized work for day	1	
9:20	2	Phone call, Mr. Jones	1	
9:22	3	Called Mr Smeet for Mr Jones	1	
9:25	4	Called Mr Toner for Mr Jones	1	
9:29	1	Found Mr Alt's letter and sent out	1	
9:30	2	Helped Mr Gordo find scissors	1	
9:32	13	Conference with Mr Gordo on layout for bulletin	1	
9:45	2	Began ditto's; material for Mr Elm	0	
9:47	10	Located material in file for Mr Jones	3	
9:57	4	Continued Elm's ditto's	0	
10:01	5	Work conference with Mr. Jones	1	
10:06	2	Explained and gave ditto work to part-time help (kept some)	1	
10:08	9	Ditto work, continued	1	
10:17	8	Mail opening and distribution	14 pcs.	
10:25	15	Ditto work, continued	2	
10:40	10	Helped locate file material for Jones	4	
10:50	11	Ran off dittos	2, 50 each	
11:01	2	Turned over ditto stapling and finishing to part time help	1	
11.03	9	Called M.G.S. Co. with information requested in morning mail; sent out bulletins	1	.
11:12	2	Phone call for Mr Jones	1	
11:14	3	Greeted visitors and sent to Jones	2	
11:17	2	Phone call requesting information	1	
				continued

Fig. 9.1—Work activity analysis form for manager of small office.

When the person doing the work is asked to maintain his own record, considerable care should be exercised to be certain the supervisor and the worker both understand the purpose of the analysis. Their sincere cooperation must be obtained, or the final record may contain an excessive bias in any of several directions.

A common procedure is:

1. Enlist the cooperation of the supervisor.
2. Explain to the worker the purpose of the record and how to keep it.
3. Help the worker until sure that he fully understands.
4. Ask the worker to keep the record for a period adequate to sample that activity. His advice and his supervisor's may be sought on this aspect.

When a coordinated group is being studied, it is usually preferable to have the entire group maintain records simultaneously. The explanation may be made simultaneously to all members of the group and all questions answered. Then each member of the group may be worked with to insure that each individual starts and maintains an adequate record.

As with preceding techniques, the details of this approach are explained here by selected examples. *Case I* concerns a study of activity of the manager of a small office; *Case III* a study of an electrical maintenance department in a hotel. Only Case I appears in the main body of the Chapter. Case III apears in the appended supplemental material. (The intervening Case II will deal with work sampling.)

CASE I   OFFICE-MANAGER OF A SMALL OFFICE

A section of a work activity analysis kept by the manager of a small office is shown in Figure 9.1. Here is a summary of this section. (To be meaningful, the summary used in practice would have to cover a longer period. This short summary is given here so that the reader can check against Figure 9.1 and understand the procedure of summarizing.)

Type of Activity	Minutes	Number of Occurrences
Type, run ditto, staple, etc.	41	5
Phone calls	31	10
Search for files or materials	28	5
Receive instructions	18	2
Instruct or plan	13	4
Handle incoming mail	8	1
Clerical duties related to part-time help	8	2
Originate material	4	1
Greet and direct visitors	3	1
TOTAL	154	31

The analysis was made because of an excessive time lag on high priority work, difficulty in determining the status of various items of work in-process, and a need to increase the capacity of the office to handle an anticipated increase in work without an increase in office staff.

A study of the summaries of several days' records, together with the detailed records, indicated the predominant activities were, in order of time spent:
For the office-manager—

1. Phone activity
2. Typing and miscellaneous routine clerical activities
3. Searching for filed material, supplies or equipment
4. Planning, supervision, and receiving instructions
5. Mail sorting

For the clerk-typist—

1. Various clerical activities
2. Package-handling errands
3. Receiving work assignments

For the part-time help—

1. Mailing activities
2. Errands for supplies
3. Delays for work assignments
4. Duplicator operation
5. Stapling materials

Considering these data together with the check list, the following were discerned as defects in the office operation, as then staffed:

1. Inadequate time was given to planning or planning was inadequate. Errands were not combined for part-time help. Clerk-typist was not excluded from this activity. Work to be done was not reorganized periodically and not "farmed out" effectively.
2. Inadequate gathering of similar material made it difficult to obtain extended activity of a given type by clerk-typist and part-time help, i.e., duplicator operation, copy typing, and so forth.
3. The office-manager was not segregating suitable work for herself that could be performed between phone calls and supervisory activities. Probably doing an excessive amount of clerical work; neglecting planning.
4. Inadequate organization of supply area and poor filing required excessive time for locating items; discouraged people served from getting own materials.
5. Desk of office-manager was not arranged for basic work of phone activity, note taking, and planning. Space for fill-in work was not available without usurping space from major functions.

A discussion of these items with the office-manager and subsequent action was responsible for a considerable increase in office effectiveness.

In many similar cases concerning jobs with no pattern or cycle, a self-analysis of this type, together with advice from staff and supervisor, may lead to considerable increases in effectiveness.

1. Are tasks appropriate to one job?
2. Are tasks occurring in too erratic a fashion?
3. Can planning make continuous activity at each task possible for a longer period of time?
4. Are the workplace or workplaces appropriate for the distribution of tasks?
5. Can any work be eliminated by a physical rearrangement or by use of different equipment?
6. Would a redistribution of work among the group increase over-all effectiveness?
7. Would a different order of doing tasks eliminate or facilitate the work?
8. Is any recurring type of task of sufficient magnitude to justify more detailed study with other motion study techniques?

Work Sampling

Work sampling, like work activity analysis, may be made by the worker or supervisor rather than by a staff analyst. In this respect, both of these techniques have certain inherent advantages, as one might deduce from the discussion in Chapter 2.

A work sampling study differs from a work activity analysis in that the observations are made at intervals rather than continuously. This procedure is also described in the early literature as Ratio-Delay Study; it was first described by L. H. C. Tippett.[2] This feature requires some additional pre-planning as compared to work activity analysis although the subsequent carrying out of the study may follow a pattern very similar to that of a work activity analysis.

The first step is to define and prepare a list of the states or conditions in terms of which the object of the study can be classified. If we are studying the activities of a person, these conditions may be such as to separate each "*where, doing what, with what.*" The particular listing selected should be related to the object of the study. As a general principle, however, one should bear in mind that excess details obtained, as with work activity analysis, may be subsequently combined, but actions not separately identified when making the study cannot subsequently be separated. Therefore, too much detail is less likely to cause difficulty in interpreting the results than too little.

[2] See: L. H. C. Tippett, "Ratio-Delay Study," *Journal of Textile Institute Transactions*, Vol. XXXVI, No. 2, Feb. 1935; R. L. Morrow, *Time Study and Motion Economy*. New York, N.Y.: The Ronald Press Company, 1946, pp. 176–199; C. L. Brisley, "How You Can Put Work Sampling to Work," *Factory*, Vol. 110, No. 7, July 1952, pp. 84–89; J. S. Petro, "Using Ratio-Delay Studies To Set Allowance," *Factory*, Vol. 106, No. 10, Oct. 1948, p. 94.

The second step in planning a work sampling study is to determine a suitable number of randomized observation times. The timing of the observations must be totally unrelated to the natural periods of the events being studied; randomization or stratified randomization is a means of obtaining this unrelatedness.

The total number of observations made must be sufficient to obtain a reliable sample of recordings, and the recordings should be spread out over a sufficient number of days in order to include an adequate sample of days. The number of observations required may be computed after one has determined the objective of the study. If we are merely seeking insight into the task, far looser limits of accuracy may be satisfactory, as compared to studies where we may be seekings percentages to apply in work measurements affecting wages or task goals. The formulas which follow state the mathematical characteristics of the sample and may be used to compute the sample size for any desired limits of accuracy.[3]

$$\sigma_p = \sqrt{\frac{p(1-p)}{N}}$$

where

σ_p = a measure of the variability of the value of p obtained from N observations, possessing the following properties: 68 per cent of samples of N size would give a value for p within $p \pm \sigma_p$, 95 per cent of the samples of N size would give a value for p within $p \pm 2\sigma_p$.

p = per cent of events of one type contained in N observations of the situation, expressed as a decimal.

N = total number of observations.

Hence, if we wish to evaluate p so that our sampling error is reduced to the point where we may say the chances are 95 out of 100 that p is correct within ± 1 per cent, then:

$$2\sigma_p = .01 = 2\sqrt{\frac{p(1-p)}{N}}$$

and

$$N = 40,000 \, [p(1-p)]$$

If we wish to evaluate p such that our sampling error is reduced to the point where we may say the chances are 95 out of 100 that p is correct to within ± 1 per cent of p, then:

$$2\sigma_p = .01p = 2\sqrt{\frac{p(1-p)}{N}}$$

and

[3] For a complete treatment of this type of problem see any text on Statistical Quality Control.

$$N = \frac{40,000}{p^2} [p(1-p)]$$

If we wish to evaluate p so that our sampling error is reduced to the point where we may say the chances are 95 out of 100 that p is correct to within ± 5 per cent of p, then:

$$2\sigma_p = .05p = 2\sqrt{\frac{p(1-p)}{N}}$$

and

$$N = \frac{1600}{p^2} [p(1-p)]$$

Table 3 gives the number of observations for $\frac{95}{100}$ probability of p being within ± 5 per cent of the correct percentage, p being within ± 1 per cent of the correct percentage, for p being within an error range equal to ± 1 per cent of p, and for p being within an error range equal to ± 5 per cent of p, for values of p from 1 to 99.

Most of the values of N given in Table 3 are larger than those required for qualitative studies. However, Table 3 will be referred to later in respect to work measurement and it seemed desirable to give it but once, and in complete form. For the most part, in qualitative studies, the column headed 5 Per Cent of Total will be a reasonable guide.

When we have decided upon the total number of observations to be made, we may divide this by either the number of observations it is convenient to make per day, or we may divide by the number of days we wish to study. Dividing by the number of observations it is convenient to make per day gives us the number of days we must study. Dividing by the number of days we wish to study gives us the required number of observations per day. In either case, since the computation is only a guide, modifications may be made, provided they are compatible with the objective of the study.

Next, the actual observation times must be arranged in a random pattern. There are four general methods of doing this.

1. The first hour of the working day may be identified by the figure 1, the second hour by the figure 2 and so on. A table of random numbers is used to obtain a series of three-digit figures, the first digit representing the hour of the working day and the next two digits, the minutes. Numbers representing hours not in the working day or impossible minute values are discarded. A sufficient number is obtained to give the required observation times for each day of the study. Each day should have a separate list. For example, let us say our working day runs from 8 A.M. to 5 P.M. Let 8 A.M. be designated by the figure 1, 9 A.M. by 2, and so forth, down to 4 P.M. by 9.

A short section of a random number table and its interpretation are illustrated here.[4]

---

[4] Table from Heiland and Richardson, *Work Sampling*, pp. 226–227.

Random Numbers	*Interpretation*
907	4: 07 P.M.
882	Impossible minute value; discard
544	12: 44 P.M.
720	2: 20 P.M.
838	3: 38 P.M.
010	Impossible hour value; discard
413	11: 13 A.M.

The list of observation times would be arranged in chronological order for actual use.

2. A second method is to stratify the observations by hours. To do this, we divide the number of observations to be made per day by the number of working hours. Following this, we again use the random number table to give us two-digit figures to represent the minutes for each hour. Using the same working day as before, and the same values from the random number table, the following would result, for one observation per hour:

90	Impossible minute, discard
78	Impossible minute, discard
82	Impossible minute, discard
54	8: 54 A.M.
47	9: 47 A.M.
20	10: 20 A.M.
83	Impossible minute, discard
80	Impossible minute, discard
10	11: 10 A.M.
41	12: 41 P.M.

The list is in chronological order. If more than one observation per hour was required, the values for each hour would need rearrangement for actual use. Each day would have its own list of time values.

3. If a great number of observations is required, an observer may go continuously through the area where the observations are to be made, randomizing his route but making constant observations.

4. A series of cards (i.e., 3 × 5 file cards) may be used, the number of cards corresponding to the total number of observations desired. We may number these cards in order, one for each minute of the working day, say, 8: 01, 8: 02, 8: 03, and so on, doing this a sufficient number of times to use all the cards. The cards may then be shuffled and dealt into piles, one pile for each day of the study. Each pile should then be arranged in chronological sequence. Duplicate cards should be exchanged for other cards, selected at random from other piles. These cards may later be used to record the actual observations.

In practice, the work of preparing categories, observation times, and lists

TABLE 3

Values of N (Number of Observations) at $\frac{95}{100}$ Probability of Not Exceeding Error Indicated, for Values of p (Per Cent of Activity)

	Values of N					Values of N			
p in Per Cent	Error				p in Per Cent	Error			
	5 Per Cent of Total	1 Per Cent of Total	1 Per Cent of p	5 Per Cent of p		5 Per Cent of Total	1 Per Cent of Total	1 Per Cent of p	5 Per Cent of p
1	16	396	3,960,000	158,400	51	400	9,996	38,431	1,537
2	32	784	1,960,000	78,400	52	400	9,984	36,923	1,477
3	47	1,164	1,293,000	51,720	53	399	9,964	35,472	1,419
4	62	1,536	960,000	38,400	54	398	9,936	34,074	1,363
5	76	1,900	760,000	30,400	55	397	9,900	32,727	1,309
6	92	2,256	626,667	25,067	56	395	9,856	31,429	1,257
7	102	2,604	531,429	21,257	57	392	9,804	30,175	1,207
8	118	2,944	460,000	18,400	58	390	9,744	28,966	1,159
9	131	3,276	404,444	16,178	59	387	9,676	27,797	1,112
10	144	3,600	360,000	14,400	60	384	9,600	26,667	1,067
11	157	3,916	323,636	12,945	61	381	9,516	25,574	1,023
12	169	4,224	293,333	11,733	62	377	9,424	24,516	981
13	181	4,524	267,692	10,708	63	373	9,324	23,492	940
14	193	4,816	245,714	9,829	64	369	9,216	22,500	900
15	205	5,100	226,667	9,067	65	365	9,100	21,538	862
16	216	5,376	210,000	8,400	66	360	8,976	20,606	824
17	226	5,644	195,294	7,812	67	354	8,844	19,701	788
18	236	5,904	182,222	7,289	68	349	8,704	18,824	753
19	246	6,156	170,526	6,821	69	343	8,556	17,971	719
20	256	6,400	160,000	6,400	70	337	8,400	17,143	686
21	266	6,636	150,476	6,019	71	330	8,236	16,338	654
22	275	6,864	141,818	5,673	72	323	8,064	15,556	622
23	284	7,084	133,913	5,357	73	316	7,884	14,795	592
24	292	7,296	126,667	5,067	74	308	7,696	14,054	562
25	300	7,500	120,000	4,800	75	300	7,500	13,333	533
26	308	7,696	113,846	4,554	76	292	7,296	12,632	505
27	316	7,884	108,148	4,326	77	284	7,084	11,948	478
28	323	8,064	102,857	4,114	78	275	6,864	11,282	451
29	330	8,236	97,931	3,917	79	266	6,636	10,633	425
30	337	8,400	93,333	3,733	80	256	6,400	10,000	400
31	343	8,556	89,032	3,561	81	246	6,156	9,383	375
32	349	8,704	85,000	3,400	82	236	5,904	8,780	351
33	354	8,844	81,212	3,249	83	226	5,644	8,193	328
34	360	8,976	77,647	3,106	84	216	5,376	7,619	305
35	365	9,100	74,286	2,971	85	208	5,100	7,059	282
36	369	9,216	71,111	2,844	86	193	4,816	6,512	261
37	373	9,324	68,108	2,724	87	181	4,524	5,977	239
38	377	9,424	65,263	2,611	88	169	4,224	5,455	218
38	381	9,516	62,564	2,503	89	157	3,916	4,944	198
40	384	9,600	60,000	2,400	90	144	3,600	4,444	178
41	387	9,676	57,561	2,302	91	131	3,276	3,956	158
42	390	9,744	55,238	2,210	92	118	2,944	3,478	139
43	392	9,804	53,023	2,121	93	102	2,604	3,011	120
44	395	9,856	50,909	2,036	94	92	2,256	2,553	102
45	397	9,900	48,889	1,956	95	76	1,900	2,105	84
46	398	9,936	46,957	1,878	96	62	1,536	1,667	67
47	399	9,964	45,106	1,804	97	47	1,164	1,237	50
48	400	9,984	43,333	1,733	98	32	784	816	33
49	400	9,996	41,633	1,665	99	16	396	404	16
50	400	10,000	40,000	1,600					

may be done by an analyst, or by or with the supervisors of the working group. In the case of professional activities, the person on whom the observations are to be made may do this preparatory work himself.[5]

The actual observations may be taken by an analyst, by the supervisor, or by the worker. It is common practice when performing work sampling for methods study to have the supervisors make the observations. This not only reduces the workload of making such studies, but permits the helpful participation which was described in Chapter 2.

The common procedure is similar to that given for a work activity analysis:

1. Enlist the cooperation of the supervisor and explain the purpose, nature, and method of making the study.
2. Explain to the workers the purpose of the study.
3. Help the supervisor prepare the necessary lists of categories and times.
4. Help the supervisor for a sufficient time to assure that he fully understands.
5. Have the supervisor obtain observations over the required period.

As with work activity analysis, the details of work sampling as a method analysis technique are explained by means of selected examples. *Case II* concerns a study of the activities of a warehouse crew; *Case IV* concerns a study of dentists. (*Case IV* is in the Supplemental Material.)

CASE II   STUDY OF A WAREHOUSE CREW

A large midwestern manufacturer established a large warehouse in order to reduce seasonal manufacturing peaks. During peak activity the warehouse work-force was augmented, when necessary, by workers drawn from the production areas. The management considered the required amount of augmentation to be excessive. The industrial engineering department was requested to examine and improve the methods used by the 94-man warehouse crew.

In order to gain insight into the activities performed, the industrial engineering department decided to make a work sampling study prior to the use of other more intensive motion study analsyses.

A series of meetings was held with the nine foremen of the warehouse. The objectives and methods of work sampling were explained. The foremen compiled a list of activity categories, which was duplicated onto $8\frac{1}{2}'' \times 11''$ forms as shown in Figures 9.2a and 9.2b.

Each foreman was supplied with 10 sets of forms and a table of random numbers. Using the table of random numbers and method 2 previously

[5] M. E. Mundel, "Motion and Time Study in Dentistry," *Journal of the American Dental Association*, Vol. 57, No. 10, Oct. 1958, pp. 520–524.

WORK SAMPLING - MATERIALS HANDLING DATA SHEET _____ DATE____								
	7:30	8:30	9:30	10:30	12:00	1:00	2:00	3:00
PRODUCT								
Carry or lift								
Reach								
Roll drums								
Place or stack by hand								
Sample								
Package (to group)								
PACK (For Shipment)								
Make Wood boxes								
Staple boxes								
Fill								
Tape								
Band								
Stencil								
Mark or stencil								
Tie strings and bind								
Relieve jam on conveyor								
Weigh								
Check and inspect								
TRUCKING								
Loading								
Spotting								
Riding								
Empty								
Loaded								
Leading								
Empty								
Loaded								
Repair								
Inspect								
Walk - no load								
PALLETS								
Inspect								
Aside for repair								
Repair								
Stacking								
Unstacking								
CLERICAL								
Check orders								
Run press								
Write								
Telephone								
Check inventory								

Fig. 9.2a—Work sampling observation sheet for warehouse study
(continued).

described, each foreman inserted a specific reading time for each of the eight hours of each work day. (Inasmuch as the day started at 7: 30 A.M., the interval between 7: 30 A.M. and 8: 30 A.M. was used as the first hour of the day and so forth.) No samples were taken during the lunch period, 11: 30 A.M. to 12: 00 noon. Each foreman had a different series of times; each day was different.[6]

[6] Each foreman started at a different place on the random number table so as to avoid duplication.

WORK SAMPLING - MATERIALS HANDLING DATA SHEET_____DATE____

	7:30	8:30	9:30	10:30	12:00	1:00	2:00	3:00
DUNNAGE								
Prepare								
Place								
Remove								
CAR OR TRUCK								
Open								
Close								
Prepare								
Install load heaters								
Talk with supervisor or expeditor								
IDLE								
For material, truck elevator								
or stock								
For instructions								
For machine breakdown								
Avoidable								
Personal								
Break								
MISCELLANEOUS								

Fig. 9.2b—(Concluded) *Work sampling observation sheet for warehouse study.*

Each day, at each reading-time on the sheet for that day, each foreman made a tour of the areas covered by his workers and inserted a tally mark in the column opposite the appropriate activity, one tally mark for each worker. The foremen avoided using a fixed route through their areas to avoid a possible bias of the tallies. The study covered 10 days or two weeks of operation. (Actually, each foreman had 11 sets of sheets, but the first sheet was used for a practice run and was discarded.)

The summary of all the tallies and the percentage of time indicated for each activity are given in Figure 9.3.

These data were examined with the check list for work sampling previously given. A study of the data indicated that substantial opportunity lay in the *Idle* and *Clerical* categories and in the time for *Carrying or lifting* product.

Delays at the elevator were reduced by equipping the elevator with a truck to serve loading and unloading areas at each floor; avoidable delay was reduced by better supervision; clerical time was greatly reduced by supplying two full-time clerical personnel who were much more efficient at this work than the material handlers whose duties had previously included this activity; the areas where product was lifted or carried were subsequently studied in detail with other methods analysis techniques. It is worth noting that previous to the work sampling, the foremen had felt that pallet repair was a major

Summary—Work Sampling—Materials Handling Data Sheets

	Totals	Per cent
TRUCKING		26.1
Loading	61	.8
Spotting	105	1.4
Riding		
Empty	502	6.8
Loaded	515	6.9
Leading		
Empty	177	2.4
Loaded	171	2.3
Repair	18	.2
Inspect	16	.2
Walk—no load	381	5.1
IDLE		26.1
For material, truck elevator or stock	632	8.5
For instructions	37	.5
For machine breakdown	5	.1
Avoidable	344	4.6
Personal	176	2.4
Break	743	10.0
PRODUCT		17.1
Carry or lift	824	11.1
Reach	182	2.5
Roll drums	22	.3
Place or stack by hand	189	2.6
Sample	16	.2
Package (to group)	26	.4
PACK (for shipment)		8.0
Make wood boxes	8	.1
Staple boxes	23	.3
Fill	47	1.6
Tape	25	.3
Band	—	—
Stencil	11	.1
Mark or stencil	110	1.5
Tie strings and bind	51	.7
Relieve jam on conveyor	1	.0
Weigh	16	.2
Check and inspect	312	4.2
CLERICAL		7.7
Check orders	197	2.7
Run press	30	.4
Write	167	2.3
Telephone	86	1.2
Check inventory	312	4.2
CAR OR TRUCK		3.9
Open	5	.1
Close	22	.3
Prepare	78	1.1
Install load heaters	—	—
Talk with supervisor or expediter	179	2.4

	Totals	Per cent
DUNNAGE		1.7
Prepare	26	.4
Place	55	.7
Remove	44	.6
PALLETS		1.1
Inspect	2	0
Aside for repair	1	0
Repair	5	.1
Stacking	39	.5
Unstacking	37	.5
MISCELLANEOUS		8.1
Clean up area	25	.3
Deliver orders	33	.4
Replace tools	1	0
Making glue	3	0
Receiving instruments	3	0
Farmed out	2	0
Cutting stencil	15	.2
Moving equipment	6	.1
Assemble metal shelves	3	0
Hammer nail	3	0
Fill out time card	4	.1
Carry dunnage	2	0
Unload dunnage	4	.1
Deliver dunnage	2	0
Paint equipment	51	.7
Attend postal clinic	3	0
Vacation	4	.1
Check needs of blocking	2	0
Expediter talks to worker	81	1.1
First Aid	8	.1
Check loading	18	.2
Copy miscellaneous items	2	0
Seal cars	9	.1
Operate elevator	17	.2
Safety meeting	20	.3
Give instructions to truck driver	1	0
Sharpen pencil finished	1	0
Observing trains of goods	120	1.6
Pressing conveyor switch	22	.3
Miscellaneous	111	1.5
Lab delivery	3	0
Inventory meeting	12	.2
Patching bag	1	0
Pick up orders	2	0
Tank car sampling	2	0
Fill drums	1	0
Wiping drums	1	0
Paint and clean printing press	5	.1
Emptying cans	4	.1
Cut and scrape obsolete labels	4	.1
Charging conveyor truck	3	0
Intercommunications	4	.1
GRAND TOTAL	7423	99.7

Fig. 9.3—Summary of data from work sampling study of warehouse crew.

problem. This study indicated this was a small problem and saved the time for a needless major investigation.

SUMMARY — WORK ACTIVITY ANALYSIS

1. Uses:
    a. *For analysis of a job that appears to possess no cycle or repetitive pattern.*
    b. *May lead to:*
        1. *Changes in functions assigned.*
        2. *Changes in organization or sequence of tasks.*
        3. *Determination of sections of total task worth analyzing with other motion study techniques.*
2. How made:
    a. *A form such as Figure 9.1 or a ruled columned sheet of paper may be used.*
    b. *For a selected period, the worker usually keeps a chronological record of tasks performed, time spent on each task, and the work-count for each occurrence of each type of task. This requires that the supervisor's cooperation be obtained and the worker be:*
        1. *Instructed as to purpose of study*
        2. *Taught to keep the record*
        3. *Checked as to method of recording*
3. How used:
    a. *The data gathered are summarized in a fashion appropriate to the specific objectives of the study.*
    b. *The summaries and the details are scrutinized, usually by staff, supervisor, and worker, with respect to the check list given and other appropriate questions.*
4. What then:
    a. *A revised general pattern may be evolved to achieve the objectives sought. A method of grouping activities for more expeditious handling or a method of facilitating time-consuming ones may be evolved.*
    b. *Certain tasks may be designated for study with other motion study techniques.*

SUMMARY — WORK SAMPLING (FOR METHOD ANALYSIS)

1. Uses:
    a. *For analysis of a job that appears to possess no cycle or repetitive pattern, particularly when a considerable period is required for the occurrence of all phases and activities within the job.*
    b. *May lead to:*
        1. *Changes in functions assigned.*
        2. *Changes in organization of task.*
        3. *Determination of sections of total task worth analyzing with other motion study techniques.*
2. How made:
    a. *An objective is stated.*
    b. *A set of categories is defined.*
    c. *Using estimates of the magnitude of each category and a determination of the accuracy required, a sample size (number of total observations to be made) is determined. The number per work period is determined and observation times are selected so as to randomize these times.*
        1. *The supervisors and workers are informed of the purpose and method of the study.*

2. *Their assistance is obtained as needed.*
    3. *If the supervisor is to make the observations, he is so taught.*
    d. *The observations are made.*
3. How used:
    a. *The data gathered are summarized in a fashion appropriate to the specific objectives of the study.*
    b. *The summaries and the details are scrutinized, usually by staff, supervisor, and worker, with respect to the check list given and other appropriate questions.*
4. What then:
    a. *A revised general pattern may be evolved to achieve the objectives sought. A method of grouping activities for more expeditious handling or a method of facilitating time-consuming ones may be evolved.*
    b. *Certain tasks may be designated for study with other motion study techniques.*

Supplemental Material

CASE III   ELECTRICAL MAINTENANCE DEPARTMENT IN HOTEL (WORK ACTIVITY ANALYSIS)

In this instance the material for a work activity analysis was available in the form of job tickets used to assign jobs to the men and to record the use of their time. A job ticket existed for each task assigned.

The job tickets were classified and summarized both by individuals and for the electrical maintenance group as a whole.

One category which appeared in the summary was of particular interest. Replacing burned-out hall light bulbs took an average of 9 hours and 43 minutes of work per day. Further investigation revealed that there were 856 hall lights, the lights burned 24 hours per day, and the average life was 56 days.

Lights were replaced when hall maids reported outages. The task, each time it was performed, required the electrical worker to get a job ticket, obtain a light bulb from the storeroom, take out a ladder, use the freight elevator to reach the floor, locate and replace the burned-out bulb, and so forth.

Questions like question 3 of the check list for work activity analysis led to a complete replanning of this phase of the electrical work. First, the hotel management realized that since 15.35 lights, on the average, were being replaced at irregular intervals during each day, it was most probable that there were always lights out. Secondly, they decided that an outage of one per cent was tolerable.

Reference to a mortality curve for light bulbs, of the type being used, indicated that if a fresh set was installed at one time, one per cent would burn out in 28 days. Calculations showed that if 9 hours and 43 minutes were not used per day in relamping, the total time accumulated in 28 days was approximately 263 man-hours, or approximately 39 hours more than the total work time of one man. The largest portion of this time could be eliminated if once every 28 days an electrician was assigned to the task of changing all hall lamp bulbs whether they were burning or not. The economy of discarding the half-consumed light bulbs was easily determined. The bulbs cost 8 cents each, new, and at the end of 28 days the remaining total lamp bulb value was only $34.52. With a large fraction of 263 man-hours to save, the advantage of cyclic lamping was obvious.

Using a cyclic lamping procedure once every 28 days in place of replacement of outages, and taking advantage of a similar procedure for ballrooms and public rooms, one electrician was released. Additional advantages were obtained in terms of more freight elevator time available for other functions, and better hall lighting.

CASE IV   A Study of Dental Activity (Work Sampling)

In 1954 the Milwaukee Dental Research Group, an informally organized group of dental practitioners, decided to attempt to ease the strain of dentistry by applying motion and time study to their work. In order to determine what types of activity would offer the greatest potential for improvement, a work sampling study was made by several members of the group. The observation times were randomized by means of method 4 previously described, and the observations were made by either the dentist or his assistant. An interval alarm clock was used to indicate the exact reading time and this clock was reset after each reading as indicated by the next card in the day's deck.

A typical summary for a dentist with one chair-assistant was as follows:

Location and Activity	Per Cent of Total time	
IN OPERATORY		77.7
Preparing, placing, finishing, trimming, mixing and polishing fillings	25.6	
Making examinations	8.6	
Scaling and cleaning teeth	7.6	
Adjusting, cementing, and trying dentures	7.1	
Seating and excusing patient	5.5	
Taking and carving wax impressions	3.7	
Talking to patient	2.9	
Taking, checking, and explaining roentgenograms	2.9	
Giving prophylaxis	2.1	
Giving fluoride treatment	2.1	
Placing base	2.1	

Location and Activity	Per Cent of Total time	
Applying silver nitrate	1.8	
Giving local anesthetic	1.8	
Extracting teeth	.8	
Holding celluloid strip	.3	
Adjusting head rest	.3	
Treating perodental pocket	.3	
Placing cavity liner	.3	
Relieving toothache	.3	
Waiting for anesthetic to take effect	.3	
Preparing penicillin	.3	
Mixing alginate	.3	
IN OFFICE		17.7
Personal and idle	8.4	
Writing and going over records	3.7	
Phone	1.8	
Financial work and mail	1.0	
Talking to assistant and patient	.8	
Talking to assistant	.8	
Dictating instructions	.3	
Checking roentgenograms	.3	
Signing cards	.3	
IN LABORATORY		3.7
Working on prosthetics	3.4	
Waxing impression trays	.3	
OUT OF OFFICE		2.7
Attending meetings	2.6	
TOTAL		100.7

All of the samples gave this same general form indicating:

1. The operatory was major time consumer.
2. The flow of work and the work external to the mouth were the critical elements.

Therefore, a technique which preserved a record of the flow of work and gave the movements of the dentist as a whole together with the activities of the assistant, if there was one, seemed most appropriate for making a more detailed study. Memomotion study was therefore selected and further studies using this technique were made and are described in Chapter 15.

However, a different summary of the work sampling data permitted additional conclusions to be drawn. A comparison of four types of practices sampled gave the following tabulation:

Results of Random Sampling During Office Hours

	Dr. A	Dr. B	Dr. C	Dr. D
PRODUCTIVE TIME	No Assistant	1 Assistant	2 Assistants	3 Assistants
1. Restorative	20%	29%	$35\frac{1}{2}$	27%
2. Prosthetics	4	7	7	$19\frac{1}{2}$
3. Oral exam. & diag.	6	11	10	15
4. Oral surgery	$7\frac{1}{2}$	1	$\frac{1}{2}$	$5\frac{1}{2}$
5. Miscellaneous[1]	$3\frac{1}{2}$	2	4	4
Total	41	50	57	71
NON-PRODUCTIVE				
6. Nec. gen. obligations	1	$5\frac{1}{2}$	$8\frac{1}{2}$	$5\frac{1}{2}$
7. Dental service delegatable	14	26	24	$16\frac{1}{2}$
8. General business	13	$5\frac{1}{2}$	4	—
Total	28	37	$36\frac{1}{2}$	22
9. Personal business	5	12	1	—
10. Idle	26	1	$5\frac{1}{2}$	7
Total	31	13	$6\frac{1}{2}$	7

[1] Local anesthetic averages $2-2\frac{1}{2}$%

These data together with data concerning work-count or volume of work performed in each office was of great value to the group in examining the most desirable type of operation for each practice.

CHAPTER 10

Information Flow Analysis

"When one designs some physical object consisting of a number of parts, one provides some mechanical means of keeping the parts together and some physical means for the parts to act upon each other. With a design for an integrated human-group activity, the holding together of the various parts and the acting of the parts upon one another in order to accomplish the desired goals are attained by a phenomenon called *communication*."[1] Communication is the transmission of thoughts, opinions, information, or attitudes by speech, writing, or signs. This chapter is concerned with communication from men to men with or without the intervention of some mechanical means of transmitting, collating, interpreting, manipulating, or arraying the information. This definition of the scope of the chapter eliminates the details of the subjects of instructing machine tools, computational or communication equipment with tape or card programs, and so forth, but still leaves a very large area for scrutiny. No organization exists without a continuous flow of information among men. Continuous methods improvement in the area of communication is a necessity in the tempo of the modern world if an organization is not to be overwhelmed by the problems of reacting in a timely manner to the enormous number of pertinent facts internal and external to its activity.

The simplest type of information flow analysis is the analysis and improve-

[1] M. E. Mundel, *A Conceptual Framework for the Management Sciences*. New York, N.Y.: McGraw-Hill Book Company, 1967, p. 24.

ment of a single step in a communication system, such as the preparation of a data input to a machine-aided system, the manual preparation of a data summary, the preparation of a dispatch schedule, a time ticket, a requisition, or any other formal communication. If the objective is to achieve a Class 1 or 2 change on the particular step in the communication system, then either the process chart-man analysis or one of the other man analysis techniques described in later chapters may be satisfactory for the subsequent analysis and development of an improvement. The special notes on form design that appear later in this chapter may also be of value.

However, as with any output, a larger problem almost always exists. The total procedure, or any sizeable segment of it, for producing an output is either a design problem or an area for change that holds a much larger potential for improvement than any single step in the process. This is as true of an information flow system as it is of the processing of a substantive output, but the study of the flow of information presents a special type of problem as compared to the usual "product" analysis. The communication means (card, tape, form, or voice channel) is of practically no value before information is inserted or entered upon it. Subsequently, the means of conveying the information is still, of itself, of little value but the information it carries may have considerable utility. The card, tape, voice, or form is merely a means of retaining or conveying information as part of a communication system. The means may be important to the system of flow but the item of value is the information conveyed. The value of the information is in its utility to the individuals who either make decisions or take action based on the information. Hence, the timeliness, accuracy, and understandability of the information are vital criteria of the effectiveness of a communication system as well as the cost of operating such a system. Timeliness and accuracy are aspects of a communication describing its relationship with the real world or information source; understandability describes the necessary characteristic of the communication at its point of impact. These are factors somewhat different from the factors which are considered in the analysis and improvement of the processing of a substantive product. It should therefore be obvious that analysis, step 2 of the scientific method, will be somewhat distinctive in a situation involving communication if we are to divide the work into units pertinent to such a job, appropriate to its scope, and possessing known characteristics.

This chapter will describe two techniques for aiding in the performance of the *analysis* step when the problem concerns an information system. Several varieties of the second technique will be discussed. The two techniques are:

1. Function forms analysis chart
2. Process chart-combined analysis

These techniques are used in examining the flow of information in situations such as:

1. The flow of control information in relation to output flow
2. The flow of information where its relationship to man work is important
3. The processing and use of information for decision making and so forth.

The functional forms analysis chart is a tabular presentation of the activities of an organization and the forms the organization uses for communication in performing each activity in order to indicate areas with too many different or overlapping forms, or too few. It is usually used to analyze and improve an existing situation.

The process chart-combined analysis is a graphic means of portraying the step-by-step procedure used with an information flow system, when the work done involves more than one work station. It may also show the interrelationships between any two or more items such as several data collections, information and material, information and workers, and so forth. Such charts are particularly useful for analyzing the effectiveness of most control or information reporting procedures, or for designing a control or information flow procedure.

Four illustrative cases are given. *Case I* illustrates the use of the functional forms analysis chart to obtain information. Space limitations prevent the discussion of the 514 forms involved in the part of the analysis shown. *Case II* illustrates use of a process chart-combined analysis for the study of part of the C.O.D. procedure in a department store, which led to a Class 5 (new form, etc.) change. *Case III* merely introduces a more complex type of chart for situations that are more complex than in *Case II*, and shows three methods of charting a situation. *Case IV* shows the use of one of the more complex charts to study and improve the flow of engine repair information in a military establishment. Only Cases I and II appear in the body of the chapter; the remainder are included in the supplemental material. Computer system flow charts are not included because of the large amount of material available on this subject both in computer company manuals and other books devoted solely to the subject of computational processes.

The potential savings from an analysis of the flow of paperwork or the design of forms should not be underestimated. A study of the processing of a charge-send sale at the F. & R. Lazarus & Co. department store in Columbus, Ohio, showed that the steps needed could be reduced from 234 to 165—a reduction of over 25 per cent in the paperwork. A study made by the Army Ordnance Corps showed that a change in its correspondence formats could save at least $1,028,000 of typing time per year.

A good deal of the work with forms is often facilitated by a redesign of the form itself. The information on redesign given here was used in Case II described in this chapter and may be applied in many other cases. Because the application in these cases is rather involved, discussion of them does not include the details of the redesign of the forms, and other simple illustrations are used in the statements of principles that follow.

Principles of Design for Typewriter Forms

1. *Design the form for the user and his equipment.* Figure 10.1 shows an interoffice letter form in its original format, with the date on the right and the standard items on the left. As the form was used, this involved extra hand

Fig. 10.1 — Original inter-office communication form.

settings of the typewriter carriage. Training the typists, and the new form shown in Figure 10.2, made interoffice memos flow more rapidly. Many companies have adopted variations of this form to fit their customs.

2. *Provide spacing on the form to correspond to the typewriter.* This is quite obvious but often neglected, particularly with the lines on forms that are to be reproduced by a photographic process and with some reduction in size.

3. *Place as many items as possible against the left-hand stop to which the carriage is returned when the line is shifted.* See Figure 10.2. The same principle can be applied to an ordinary business letter and reduces the time by from 15 to 25 per cent.

4. *Eliminate all excess material from typing.* When similar items are typed

```
                        PURDUE  UNIVERSITY
                DIVISION  OF  TECHNICAL  INSTITUTES
                      LAFAYETTE,  INDIANA

                  INTER-OFFICE COMMUNICATION


        TO:    L.D. Miller
        FROM: A.K. Branaham
        RE:    Films for practice in time study rating


              The motion and time study laboratory has produced a new
              series of films for rating catalogued as, "F 18-2B, Edition
              II, Film for Rating."

              The Extension Dept. should have several copies of this series.
              You may obtain the originals from Professor Mundel and place
              his order for duplicates with yours.

              AKB
```

Fig. 10.2—Improved inter-office communication form typed with improved procedure.

on the form each time, use preprinted items with check boxes. Make sure the check boxes are placed in accordance with rule 3.

5. *Provide automatic and consistent sequence of spaces on the forms wherever possible.* Many common forms have boxes for information scattered in such a way that setting typewriter tabulator stops is not feasible. The filling in of such forms by hand is also a laborious operation. In addition, the scatter of information makes the task of the reviewer or user of the information more difficult than it needs to be.

6. *In all cases, evaluate both the change in cost of the typist's time and the change in cost of the user's time.* In most instances, however, both benefit from the same changes.

Functional Forms Analysis

CASE I   THE USE OF THE FUNCTIONAL FORMS ANALYSIS CHART

The functional forms analysis chart shown in Figure 10.3 was developed by a government agency, but is applicable to any activity. While it may be necessary to use different categories of the column headings, the principle will be the same wherever it is used. Figure 10.3 shows a blank functional forms analysis chart. Figure 10.4 shows the definitions used for the column headings as well as part of a filled-in chart, covering 514 forms, for a divisional

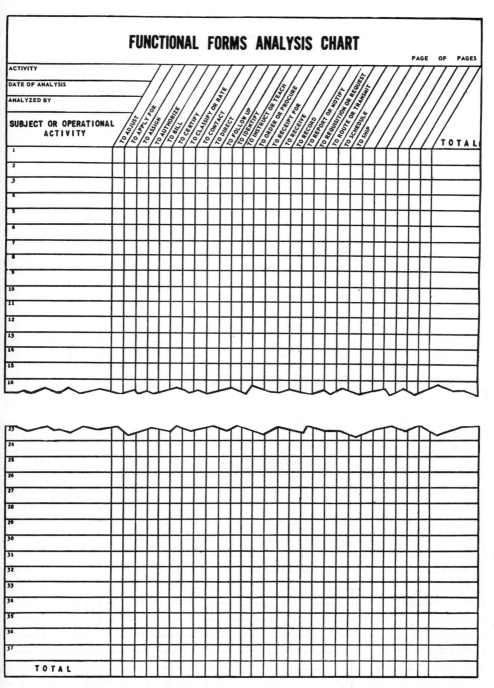

Fig. 10.3 — Blank functional forms analysis chart, Dept. of Army
Form No. 553, Government Printing Office.

DEFINITIONS OF BASIC ACTIONS OR FUNCTIONS AS USED ON DA FORM 553

1.	TO ADJUST	to cause a revision to be made (to correct errors or discrepancies, obtain data or material omitted, increase or decrease quantities or amounts: to alter data, to amend, change, modify, cancel, reject)
2.	TO APPLY FOR	to request something which may or may not be granted
3.	TO ASSIGN	to appoint, allot, designate, apportion, or set apart
4.	TO AUTHORIZE	to empower, permit, sanction or to approve action (also passes and permits)
5.	TO BILL	to invoice or charge for
6.	TO CERTIFY	to attest to the truth of (affidavit, oath)
7.	TO CLASSIFY OR RATE	to relegate according to quantity, condition, grade, rank or class
8.	TO CONTRACT	to offer and accept in writing (an agreement)
9.	TO DIRECT	to give an order to (command) travel, duty, etc.
10.	TO FOLLOW UP	to remind of uncompleted action (tickler files, suspense files and forms, and follow up letters)
11.	TO IDENTIFY	to aid in proof or recognition of, to name (also personnel identification cards)
12.	TO INSTRUCT OR TEACH	to inform, advise, or counsel (*how to do it*, not *you are instructed to, etc.*)
13.	TO ORDER OR PROCURE	to secure or purchase, to give an order for labor, work, material, equipment or supplies
14.	TO RECEIPT FOR	to acknowledge delivery or payments; given by recipient in exchange for material delivered or payment made
15.	TO RECEIVE	to accept or admit as credible
16.	TO RECORD	to set down in permanent form for the sole purpose of registering or recording
17.	TO REPORT OR NOTIFY	to transmit a required notification, or account of status, progress, or action, usually in detail, to transmit an unsolicited statement
18.	TO REQUISITION OR REQUEST	to formally request by authority, to ask for
19.	TO ROUTE OR TRANSMIT	to send an attachment along a circuit of persons or places – (transmit – to send an attachment to another person or place) (messages)
20.	TO SCHEDULE	to outline regularly recurring events, or write a plan of future events; not merely a listing frequently entitled *Schedule of*
21.	TO SHIP	to send through any regular channel of transportation, as by rail

INSTRUCTIONS FOR USE

1. Basic actions or functions are listed across the top.
2. In the left hand column you will list the subjects and operational functions that pertain to your operation.
3. Enter in the proper columns the number of forms that apply to each subject and function.
4. This analysis will reveal the number of forms performing duplicate functions. Subject all such form to the detailed item analysis provided by DD FORM 85.

EXAMPLE

FUNCTIONAL FORMS ANALYSIS CHART

PAGE   OF   PAGES

ACTIVITY O. & J. Div. A.G.O.

DATE OF ANALYSIS 20 April 19

ANALYZED BY John Doe

SUBJECT OR OPERATIONAL ACTIVITY	TO ADJUST	TO APPLY FOR	TO ASSIGN	TO AUTHORIZE	TO BILL	TO CERTIFY	TO CLASSIFY OR RATE	TO CONTRACT	TO DIRECT	TO FOLLOW UP	TO IDENTIFY	TO INSTRUCT OR TEACH	TO ORDER OR PROCURE	TO RECEIPT FOR	TO RECEIVE	TO RECORD	TO REPORT OR NOTIFY	TO REQUISITION OR REQUEST	TO ROUTE OR TRANSMIT	TO SCHEDULE	TO SHIP	TOTAL
1. Transportation	1			2					1			1				3	3			9		20
2. Allotments of Pay	5		23	3												4	9	1				45
3. Recruitment																5						5
4. Civ. Personnel	7			8	10				1							2	9	4				41
5. Telephone						2										2	12					16
6. Equipment	1			2	18							8		8	33	23	22		1			116
7. Communications				1										2	10	33	20		25			91
8. Appropriations	3	1	1	1												5	1					12
9. Printing			3	1	2	6						10	2	1		3	6		2	2		38
10. Enlisted Men	2	1	2	10	4											4	5	2				30
11. Education	4			8								19				13	6					50
12.																						

Fig. 10.4—Sample functional forms analysis chart from reverse of Dept. of Army Form No. 553.

office. In this case, many of the boxes indicate places where a detailed scrutiny of the individual forms might produce savings. The instructions for use of the form are contained in Figure 10.4.

Process Chart-Combined Analysis

In the preparation of a process chart-combined analysis, each item shown on the chart is usually displayed so that a horizontal line drawn across the chart at any point passes through symbols that indicate events occurring at the same time.

The chart used may be one of several varieties, depending on the complexity of the problem involved. The form of the chart should be carefully chosen so as to fit the requirements of the problem.

Inasmuch as a system of communication is being studied, the route of the information is a reflection of the formal and informal organization concerned. Alterations of a procedure may have far reaching implications concerning the structure of an organization. An analyst seeking merely to improve a procedure must take proper cognizance of this possibility, and seek adequate participation in the analysis by all levels of management. On the other hand, it should be understood that a widespread analysis of the procedures in an organization is an excellent approach to a critical study of the organization structure. The process chart-combined analysis may be used as a basis for designing an effective organization. The reader is reminded, in this respect, of a parallel aspect of process charts-product analysis, which may be used to design an effective manufacturing procedure and plant layout, as in Case IV, Chapter 5.

If the flow of information involves the flow or processing of forms, the part of the chart dealing with the flow of the forms is increased in clarity by the separation of the steps given in Table 4 together with the symbols used for charting them. Many of these steps are different from those used to chart a "product" and are designed to separate unique acts, pertinent to paperwork as is the basic function of an *analysis* technique. The last two items given in Table 4 may also be advantageously used on the *material* or *man* columns on the process chart-combined analysis if such items are also charted. It should be understood that in some cases there may be a need to differentiate the steps of the work to a greater degree, and subvarieties of these steps and symbols or additional ones may be used. For instance, it might be desirable to differentiate various types of operations by putting a "?" in the symbol if a decision characterizes the step, a "c" for a computation, and so forth.

If the situation involves an analysis of the processing of information through a computer system, a totally different set of symbols may be neces-

TABLE 4

Process Chart–Combined Analysis Symbols for Use with Forms

Symbol	Name	Used to Represent
	Origin of form	Form first being made out.
	Origin of form	Form first being made out in duplicate.
	Origin of form	Form first being made out in triplicate, etc.
	Operation	Work being done on form; computations or additional information added, etc.
	Inspection	Correctness of information on form checked by comparison with other source of information. (Use ------- broken line drawn to other source if other source appears on chart and line is aid to clarity.)
	Information take-off	Information being taken off form for entry onto another or for use by someone. Point of line indicates symbol on other parallel chart where information is going. (Use --------- broken line to indicate destination if destination appears on chart and line is aid to clarity.)
	Disposal	Form or copy destroyed.
	Movement	A change in location of form, not changing it.
	Delay	Forms waiting to be worked on, such as in desk basket.
	File	Forms in a file, organized in some formal fashion.
	Item change	Change in item charted.
	Gap	Activities not pertinent to study and hence not charted in detail.

sary. For instance, the IBM system flowchart manual (C20-8152) recognizes, separates, and provides symbols for the following items:

Processing	Input or output
Punched card	Perforated tape
Document	Transmittal tape
Magnetic Tape	Disk, drum, random access
Offline storage	Display
Online keyboard	Sorting, collating
Clerical operation	Auxiliary operation
Keying operation	Communication link

If the problem concerns a mixed communication system with voice, mechanical, and visual communication, such as at a missile launch site or in an airplane cockpit, a different set of separable steps, such as the following, will be more suitable than the two mentioned to this point.

Read	Change posture
Cognize	Transmit mechanically
Speak	Compute
Listen	Compare
Manipulate	Wait for data output
Change position	Feed data

CASE II   C.O.D. PROCEDURE IN DEPARTMENT STORE

This application of the process chart-combined analysis was made in a large midwest department store. The section of the chart shown in Figure 10.5 deals with the procedure used to check in the C.O.D. receipts and undelivered C.O.D. packages of the delivery truck drivers. With the original method, the truck drivers in the evening often had to wait their turn for the C.O.D. cashier, thus causing a considerable overtime expense for both drivers and C.O.D. cashiers at the "delivery center." It was this overtime that the analyst particularly sought to eliminate without unduly slackening the controls over the considerable amounts of money and goods that were handled.

The analyst, who had decided that a Class 3, 4, or 5 change was desirable, had also decided that a process chart-combined analysis was the only feasible way of setting down the interrelationships between the various persons and forms involved in the task. To do this, he first made separate notes, in the form of process chart-product or man analysis as necessary, using the special symbols from Table 4 for the notes dealing with any form or written material. These notes were then used to construct the process chart-combined analysis of the original method shown in Figure 10.5.

To perform step 3, the *criticism step*, the original process chart-combined

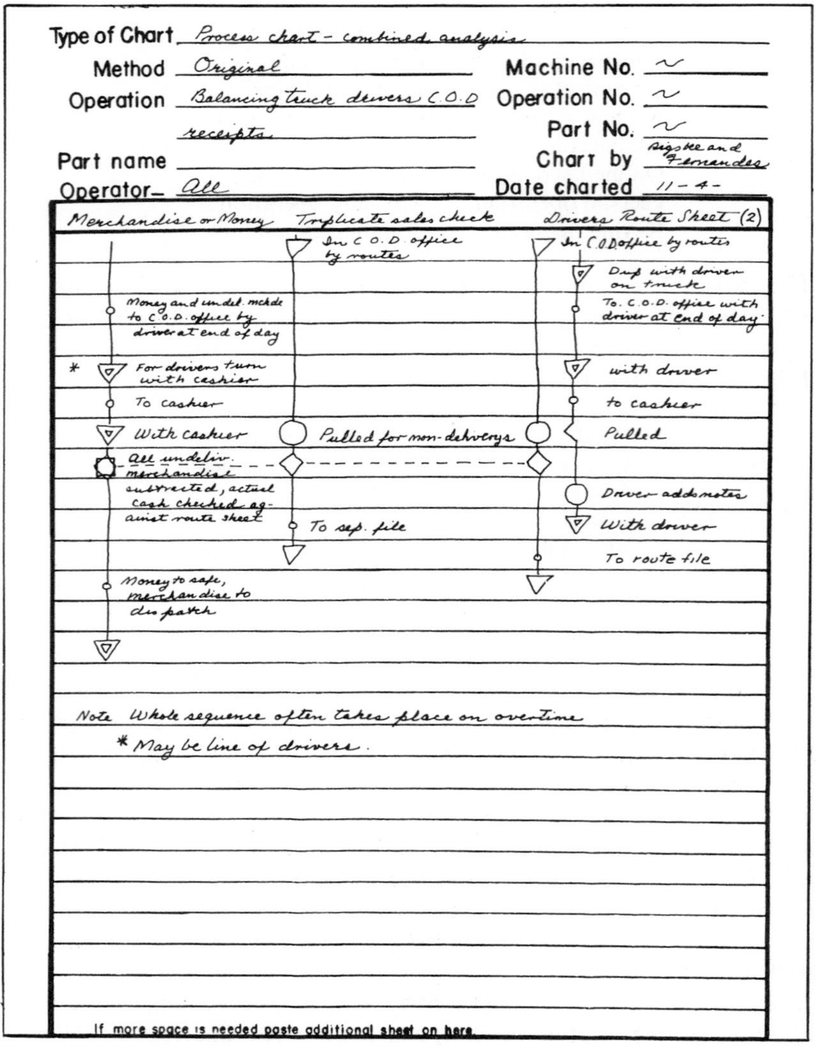

Type of Chart _Process chart - combined analysis_

Method _Original_   Machine No. ~

Operation _Balancing truck drivers C.O.D_   Operation No. ~

receipts.   Part No. ~

Part name _____   Chart by _Bigelow and Fernandez_

Operator _All_   Date charted _11 - 4 -_

Merchandise or Money	Triplicate sales check	Drivers Route Sheet (2)
	In C.O.D. office by routes	In C.O.D office by routes
		Dup. with driver on truck
Money and undel. mchde to C.O.D. office by driver at end of day		To C.O.D. office with driver at end of day
* For drivers turn with cashier		with driver
To cashier		to cashier
With cashier	Pulled for non-deliverys	Pulled
All undeliv. merchandise subtracted, actual cash checked against route sheet		Driver adds notes
	To sep. file	With driver
		To route file
Money to safe, merchandise to dispatch		

Note Whole sequence often takes place on overtime

* May be line of drivers.

If more space is needed paste additional sheet on here

Fig. 10.5 — Original process chart-combined analysis for checking in C.O.D. receipts and undelivered C.O.D. packages from delivery truck drivers in department store.

analysis was reviewed, using the check list for process chart-product analysis and the check list for process chart-man analysis, as well as the special check list for process chart-combined analysis given in this chapter.

CHECK LIST FOR PROCESS CHART—COMBINED ANALYSIS

1. Each step should be necessary. If not, eliminate it.
2. Each step should have an ideal place in the sequence. Where should it be?
3. Each step should have a reason for being by itself. Can it be combined?
4. Each step should be as easy as possible.
5. Each form should have a real purpose. Verify it. Is the form necessary? Can it be eliminated, combined with another form, or replaced by a copy of another form?
6. Each file should have a unique purpose. Does it? Avoid duplication. Avoid excess files. File by subject used to enter files. Check on manner of use.
7. If form is finally destroyed, perhaps it should never have been originated. What purpose did it serve?
8. Information going from one form to another suggests more copies in the first place. Are all information take-offs and readings necessary? If so, which are going to be given priority in the design of the form? Which were given priority?
9. Are all copies of a form getting equal use? Sharing the load may speed up the procedure.
10. Does someone sign all copies? How can this be avoided? Signers are often busy people.
11. Is there excess checking?
12. Where is the best place to check? Calculate the risk.
13. What would happen if the form was lost?
14. What equipment might help the job? (See commercial catalogues.)
15. Does one person handle too much of the procedure?
16. Are as many steps as possible given to the lowest classification of personnel?
17. Can travel of forms be advantageously reduced?
18. Can the form be kept in action, out of file baskets?
19. Does the information arrive in a timely fashion so that it may be acted upon?
20. Has the information display been reduced to understandable form? (There is a limit to the amount of detail that can be comprehended.)
21. Is the information accurate and reliable?

Step 4, *innovation*, was carried out by constructing the process chart-combined analysis shown in Figure 10.6. It entailed the following innovations:

1. Form 490, the route sheet for the new method, was the same as the original, but one copy was printed on a manila envelope and spot-pasted to the original. The duplicate envelope-copy served as both a report form and money container.
2. A night depository type of money safe was installed to receive the envelope-form 490, so that the contents could be left safely after the departure of the C.O.D. cashier.
3. A package chute arrangement was installed to enable the driver to deposit the undelivered C.O.D. packages in the C.O.D. office for redispatch the following morning.
4. Tables were placed near the C.O.D. office in the delivery center to enable the drivers to balance their route sheets.

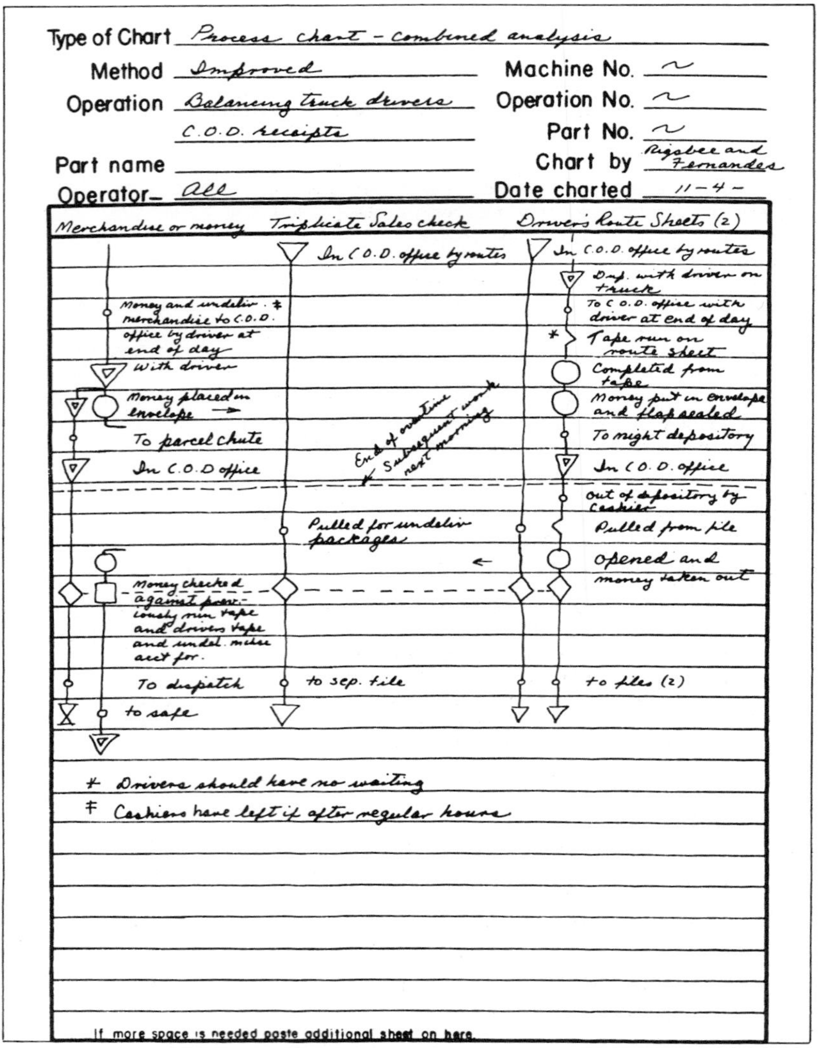

Type of Chart *Process chart – combined analysis*

Method *Improved*   Machine No. ~

Operation *Balancing truck drivers*   Operation No. ~

C.O.D. receipts   Part No. ~

Part name _____   Chart by *Rigabee and Fernandes*

Operator— *all*   Date charted *11-4-*

Fig. 10.6—*Improved process chart-combined analysis for checking in C.O.D. receipts and undelivered C.O.D. packages from delivery truck drivers in department stores.*

154

5. Several inexpensive listing-type adding machines were placed on these tables to facilitate balancing route sheets.

The improved method reduced the overtime of the two C.O.D. cashiers by approximately $1,200 per year, with the accompanying reduction of comparable overtime for a much larger number of delivery truck drivers.

SUMMARY — PROCESS CHART-COMBINED ANALYSIS

1. Uses:
   a. *For information leading to a Class 3, 4, or 5 change in information flow procedures when the aspect under study concerns:*
      1. *The flow of control information in relation to output flow.*
      2. *The flow of information where its relationship to man work is important.*
      3. *The processing and use of information for decision making, and so forth.*
   b. *For the design of a paperwork procedure.*
   c. *As an aid in the study of an organization.*
   d. *To assist in designing an effective organization structure.*
2. How made:
   a. *Following the instructions in Chapters 5, 8, and 10, as required, process charts are made of each person, product, form, or information item concerned. The steps with the product follow the breakdown of Table 1; use Table 2 for the man activity and Table 4 for the forms. In many cases it may be desirable to employ special steps and symbols more pertinent to the peculiarities of the process under study.*
   b. *A new chart, combining all pertinent information, is drawn with all the items on it so placed that a horizontal line drawn across the chart at any point passes through items that are happening at the same time. The chart may be drawn in several ways. Care should be exercised to select the format that displays the information most clearly. See Figures 10.5, 10.7, 10.8, and 10.9 for some examples of different formats.*
3. How used:
   a. *Each step of the process is questioned with the applicable check lists given in this chapter and in Chapters 5 and 8. With many charts of this type it is extremely desirable to consult the people concerned as early in the analysis as possible. It may be desirable to note their remarks directly on the chart at the place on the chart that is the subject of their comments.*
   b. *The design of each form involved may be reviewed.*
4. What then:
   a. *A process chart-combined analysis is drawn for a resulting suggested improved method in order to permit a final check and to provide a means of describing the proposed new procedure.*
   b. *A new form (or forms) may be designed to facilitate the work, although this is not always necessary.*

Supplemental Material

CASE III   ISSUANCE OF PRODUCTION ORDERS

This case merely introduces a more complex type of chart for analyzing more complex situations than have been discussed previously. Three methods of charting are given.

The subject of the charts is the following procedure, taken from a large manufacturing plant.

When a purchase order is received in the home office in New York City, it is checked by a sales agent. After initialing, he passes it to the office manager at the next desk who places it in the workbasket of one of four typists. After a sales order and duplicate are typed from it, the typist places the purchase order and the two copies of the sales order in her out-basket, whose contents are periodically taken by the office manager, who checks the typing and puts the original purchase order and original sales order into one out-basket for periodical filing by purchaser, and the duplicate sales order into another basket for eventual eveloping in a window envelope, which is sent to the proper manufacturing plant. One of these plants is in Gary.

At the Gary plant, the mail clerk routes such sales orders to the production order department. The production order clerk automatically types the information from the sales order onto a production order, making an original and three carbons, and assigns a production sequence number from her log. She checks her own typing. A batch of the first copies and the original related sales orders are sent to the plant manager's office. At the end of each day, the plant manager's secretary checks these against a telegraphic summary of orders sent from New York. The first copy and the sales orders are filed in the plant manager's office against the chronological sequence on the telegraphic summary.

The original production orders are sent in batches via plant mail to the accounting office, where they are held for the completion of the order, being filed by date of receipt in the accounting office.

Copy 2 of the production order is sent, in batches, to the materials control section, where a typist automatically makes three copies of a stores issue order and files the production order by its production sequence number.

Copy 3 of the production order is sent, in batches, to the forge shop foreman who holds it in an open (unorganized) file until copy 2 of the stores issue order comes to him. He matches production order sequence numbers and places the mated production orders and stores issue orders on the desk of the shop production control clerk.

After performing other duties, the foreman, once each day, checks the production control clerk's batch of production orders and stores issue orders against the copies of the production orders on the telegraphic summary in the plant manager's office.

The forms previously used for charting would obviously be inadequate to chart the numerous people and forms involved in this procedure. A ruled sheet, 17" × 23" with lines, six to the inch, as shown in Figure 10.7, is commonly used to chart situations of this complexity, although a blank sheet may be used. However, the rulings are of great assistance in keeping actions occurring at the same time horizontally aligned on the chart. The

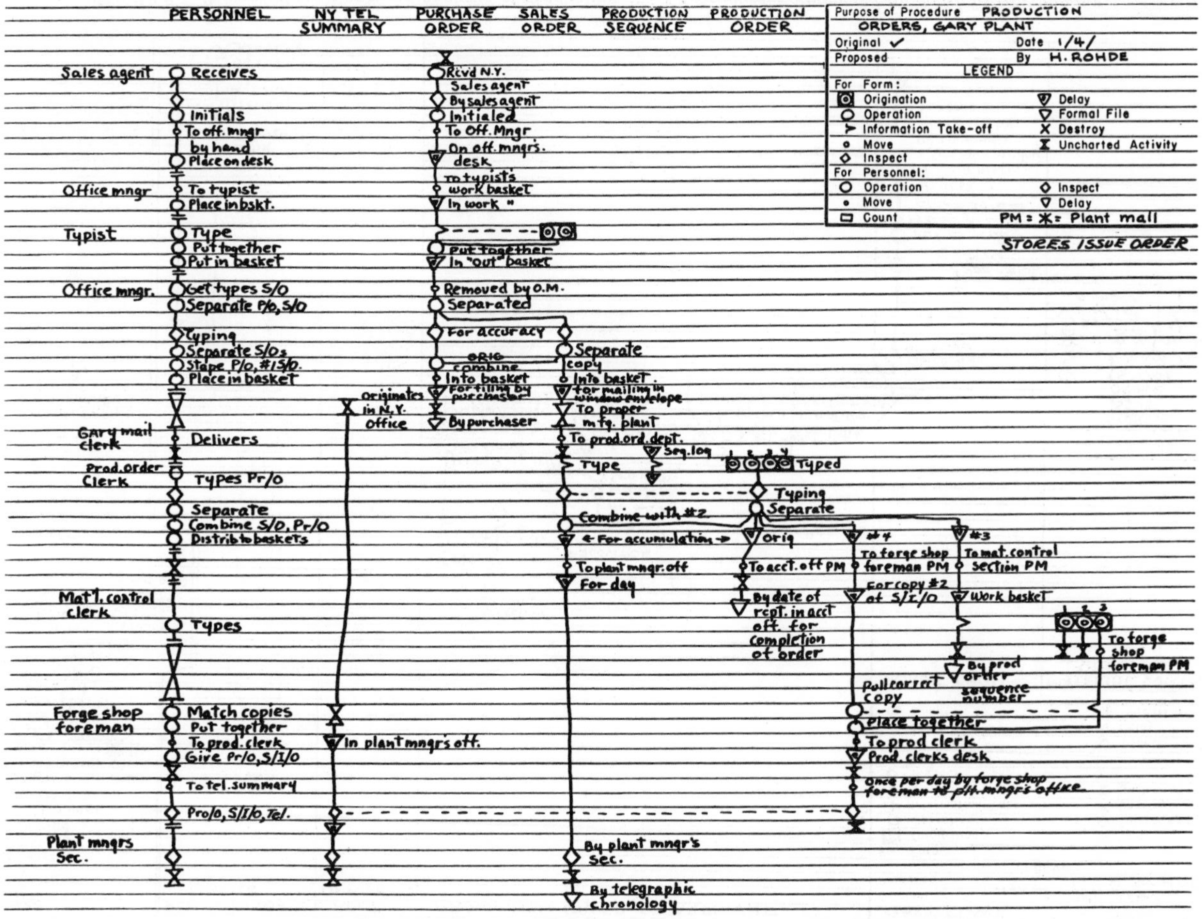

Fig. 10.7—Process chart-combined analysis of production order procedure, columnated by forms and with personnel column.

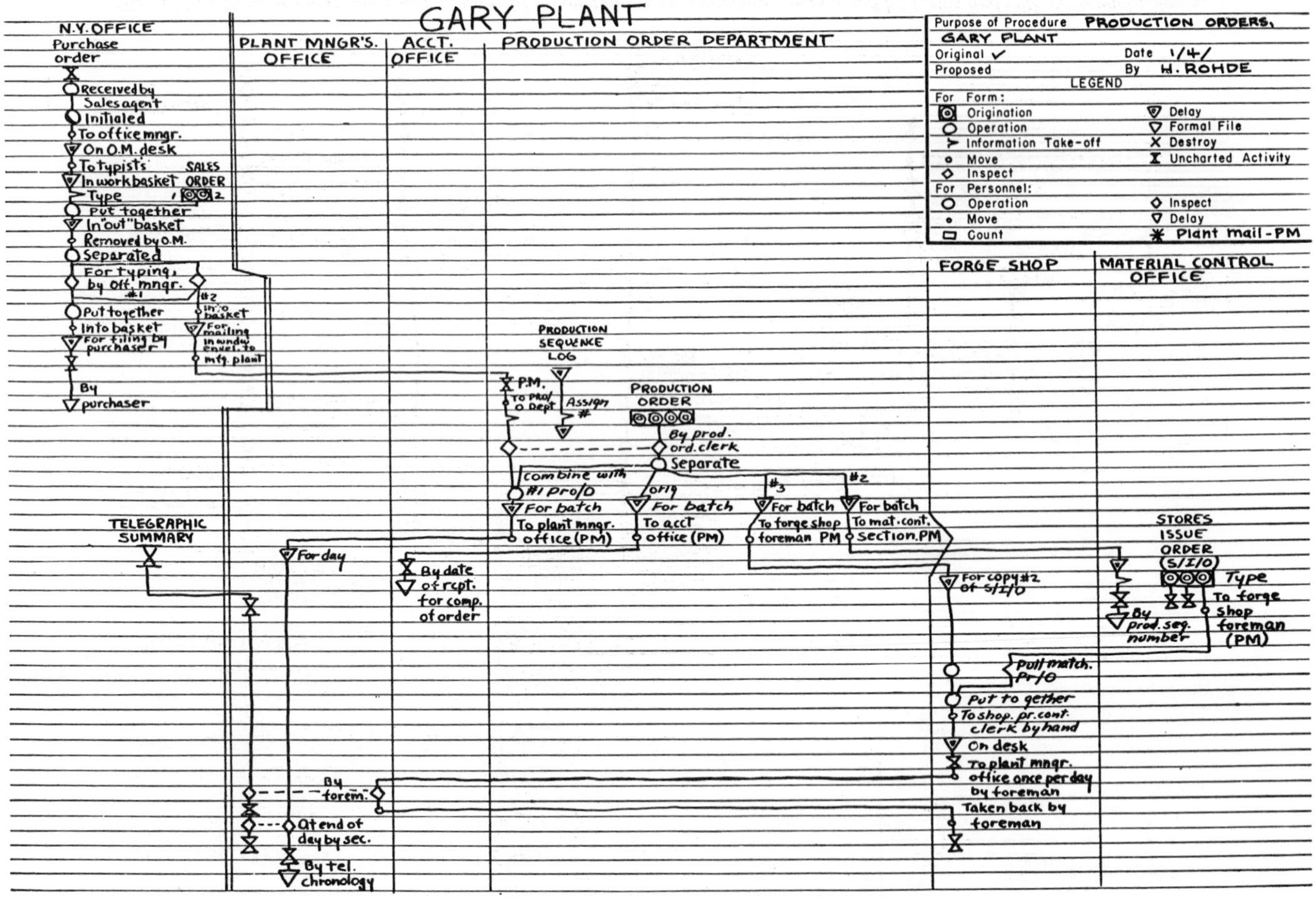

Fig. 10.8—Process chart-combined analysis of production order procedure, columnated by divisions of company.

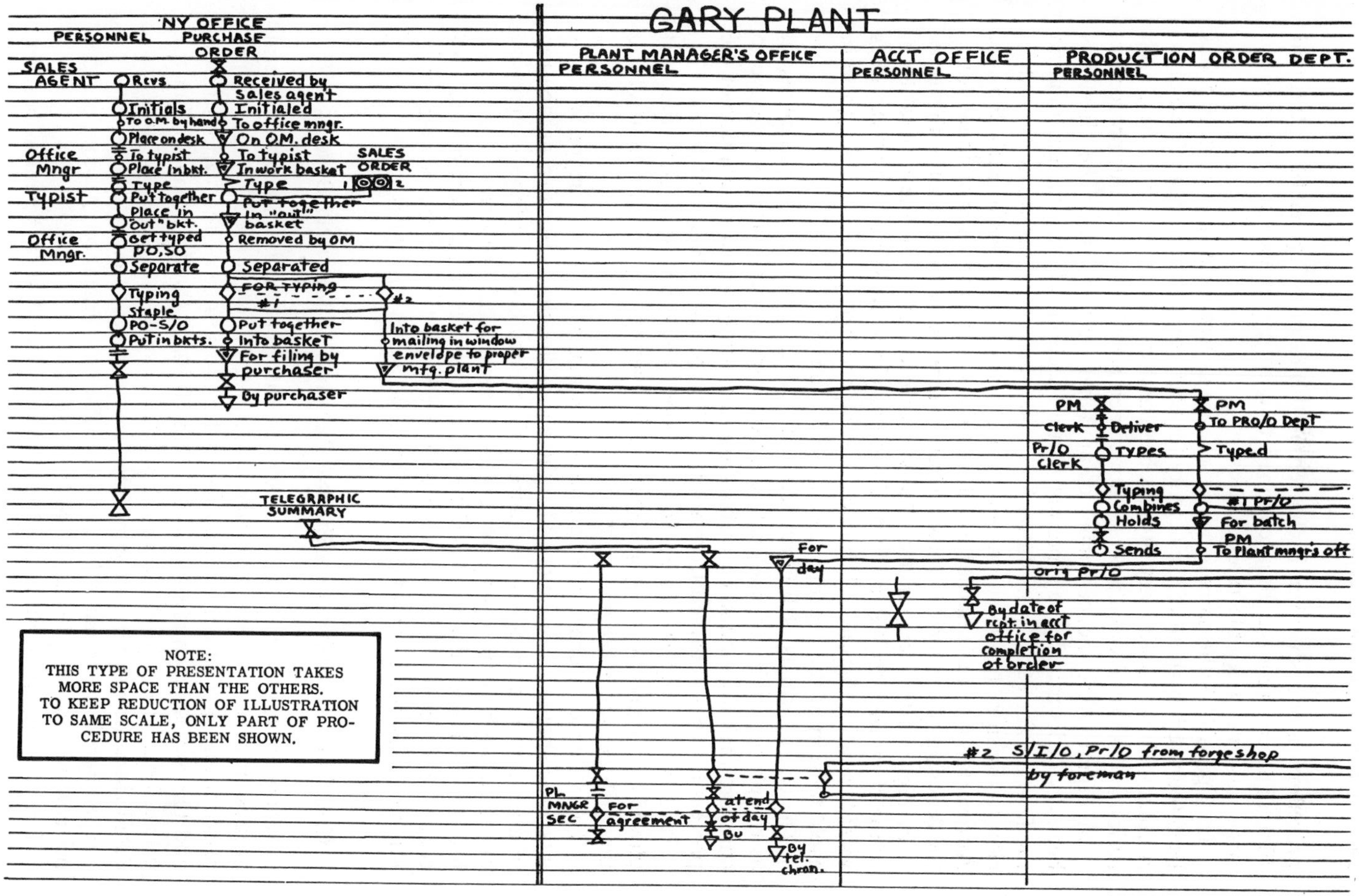

Fig. 10.9—Process chart-combined analysis for production order procedure, columnated by divisions of company and with personnel columns.

procedure previously given is charted on this form in Figures 10.7, 10.8, and 10.9. (The charting has been confined to a corner of the form to permit a larger and more legible reproduction.)

In Figure 10.7 the same general scheme as was used in Figure 10.5 has been followed, with all of the activity for each form kept in a single column. A column for personnel activity has been added to show who performs each action and what tasks each person concerned has in respect to this procedure.

In Figure 10.8, the personnel column has been deleted. The chart has been divided vertically to represent various sections of the organization and the flowline for each form shows how and when the form moves from division to division. It also shows what is done with the forms in each division. Although it is a little harder to follow all the steps for an individual form, the function of the form is usually shown more clearly in a chart of this type.

In Figure 10.9, personnel columns have been added to the general form of the chart used for Figure 10.8. Thus, this chart shows not only "who does what," as does Figure 10.7, but keeps clear the part played by each form in each division of the organization, as in Figure 10.8.

The chart formats of Figures 10.8 and 10.9 generally become more useful as the procedure being analyzed becomes more complex. It is instructive to compare the information derivable from the purely verbal description of the process to what is gained from study of Figures 10.7, 10.8, and 10.9.

It is with complex procedures that one may fully appreciate the part played by the graphic analysis technique in placing the information in a form that will permit intelligent study.

The value of a chart of this type for designing a procedure prior to its inception should be obvious. With the aid of the chart, effective partipation of all those concerned may be more easily gained because of the greater ease of indicating how their work relates to the total goal. The items in the check list may be more fully employed to assist in developing an economical procedure. Indeed, it is hard to imagine how an effective procedure with many ramifications can be designed without some aid of this type.

CASE IV   REPORTING ON ENGINE REPAIR AT A MILITARY BASE

When an engine is repaired, detailed information is routed to several groups in order to develop better preventive maintenance procedures, improve future engine design, and so forth. The source of the various forms and the routes taken is shown in Figure 10.10. It should be noted that the prime focus of this study was on Form 39. This form is charted with more detail than the other forms concerned in the procedure.

The chart is columnated by divisions of the organization, without personnel columns, as was Figure 10.8.

The proposed procedure, developed by a staff analyst of the unit concerned

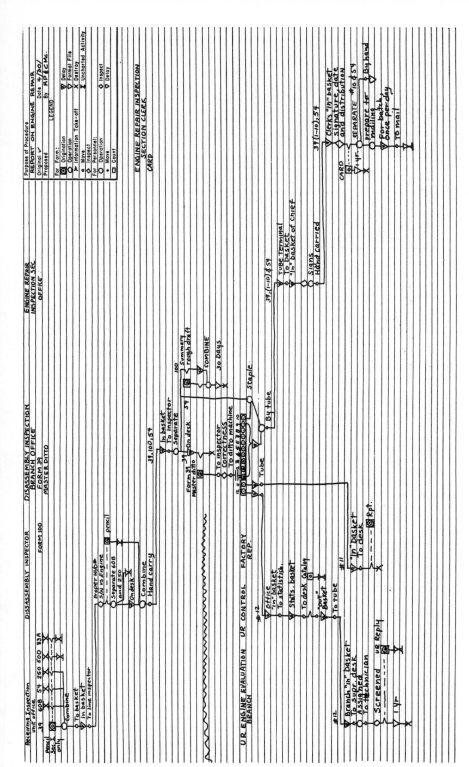

Fig. 10.10—Process chart-combined analysis of original method of reporting on engine repair at a military base.

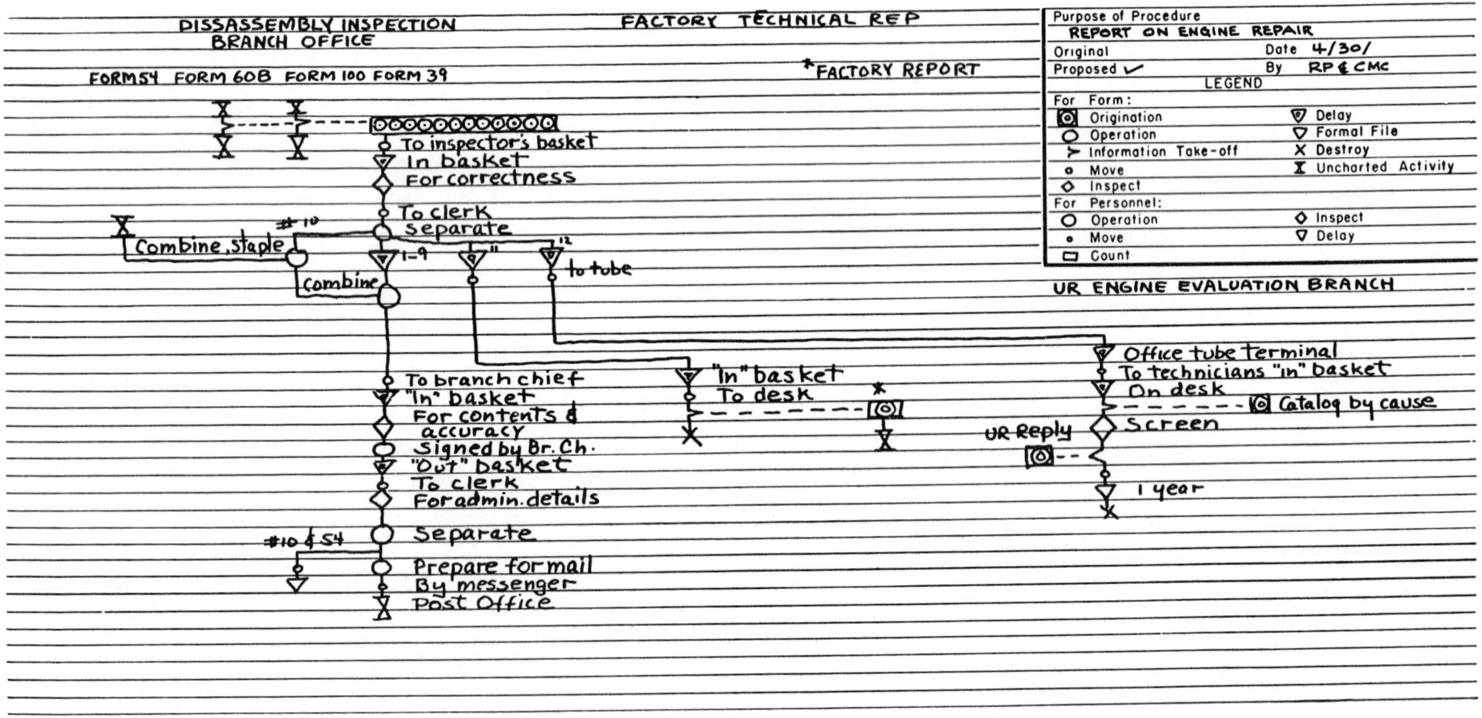

Fig. 10.11 — Process chart-combined analysis of improved method of reporting on engine repair at a military base.

with the repair work, is shown in Figure 10.11. (This is the format in which his proposal was actually submitted, together with supporting information.)

Use of the proposed procedure made possible the following economies:

1. Eliminated the first, handwritten original copy of Form 39 and its route. The information needed for the route served was already available on Forms 60B, 54, etc.
2. The duties of the UR statistician and the UR engine evaluation technician were combined, reducing personnel.
3. The number of people handling the information was reduced from 21 to 11, reducing the over-all workload.
4. Busy, higher-echelon supervisors were relieved of some work.
5. Rough draft by inspector was replaced by typed draft by clerk-steno, reducing value of time required.
6. Thin manifold copies of Form 39 eliminated need for machine reproduction, avoiding a bottleneck.
7. The procedure took less elapsed time to complete.

CHAPTER 11

Operation Charts

In many of the jobs in plants or offices, the persons doing them remain at one work station. Indeed, each large circle on any of the graphic presentations so far discussed usually indicates such a situation. In many cases, the jobs are important enough to warrant spending time on their design or improvement. In most cases, improvement is the result of a Class 1 or 2 change, although the higher classes may also be involved. Class 1 or 2 changes have the advantage, however, that they affect nothing other than the job under scrutiny, may be accomplished without disturbing other aspects of the work, and thus often may be achieved more quickly. When the objective of a work method problem involving but a single work station has been stated as a Class 1 or 2 change, the second step of the logical approach is still:

Analysis——The analysis of the work method into subdivisions or steps, pertinent to the job, appropriate to its scope, possessing known characteristics, or concerning whose performance information is already available.

Under the conditions given, operation charts are a common technique for the performance of this step.

An operation chart is a graphic means of portraying the separable steps of a person's body members when he is performing a job that takes place essentially at one location. It is a schematic model.

An operation chart is an analysis of the work performed by a person on any one operation on a process chart, either man, product, or combined analysis. It is a description of what the person does. It is used for the analysis of the work of individuals, not crews, and where the work of the machine, if any, is not the main controlling factor.

Operation charts are one of the most useful motion and time study techniques. No equipment is needed and significant results are possible. Not much time is necessary for the making of this type of analysis, and the results are often immediately installable. The more experience one has with methods improvement, the more useful this technique becomes. Almost anyone can use operation charts profitably. They are an ideal tool for designing the details of jobs in contemplated processes.

The operation chart usually involves a breakdown, into steps, of the work performed by each of the body members engaged in the task. This usually means the right and left hands. Where the feet or eyes are important factors, they may also be charted. The operation chart shows not only the sequence performed by each body member charted, but also their relationship to each other while working. It does not indicate the time or relative time for the steps.

The steps into which the work is commonly divided as well as the symbols used to represent these steps are given in Table 5. The symbols are similar to those used for process charts, but because of the difference in the scope of an operation, as opposed to a process, the symbols are used to represent different steps.

TABLE 5

Symbols for Operation Chart

Symbol	A.S.M.E. Symbol	Name	Used to Represent
◯	◯	Suboperation	Body member doing something at one place, such as taking hold, lining up, assembling, etc.
○	⇨	Movement	A movement of a body member toward an object or changing the location of an object.[1]
▽	◗	Hold	Body member maintains an object in a fixed position so that work may be done with or on it at that location.
▽	▽	Delay	Body member is idle or delaying for other body member.

[1] On very long operations the analyst may combine some of these steps into larger steps, using "get," in place of *reach for*, *take hold of*, and *bring* object to work area; "aside," meaning *move object* from work area, *let go of* object, and *return*. In such a case the chart is described as being made with "gross breakdown" and is considerably shorter than when made with the usual steps.

An operation chart is easily constructed from direct observation of the job. When the job is not yet being performed, such a chart may readily be used to set forth in detail the contemplated method. In either case, the analyst should first familiarize himself with the job cycle, i.e., all the movements required to bring a unit of the output to the stage of completion typical of the operation. It is most convenient to consider the cycle as starting with the first movement attributable to a unit of the output and ending with the last movement on that unit. This gives a more easily understood chart than one beginning and ending in the middle of the work on a part.

As with process charts-man analysis, four types of jobs, with the following characteristics, may be encountered:

1. The work has a single repeated cycle.
2. The work is cyclic, but there are several subcycles performed with different frequency.
3. The work varies from cycle to cycle.
4. The task has no regular cycle.

The method of handling these different types of jobs is essentially similar to the procedure used with process charts-man analysis, except that the work of the individual body members is studied rather than the worker as a whole.

Jobs of type 4 may be studied by means of a work activity analysis or a work sampling study (Chapter 9) or memomotion study (Chapter 15).

Four cases have been selected for discussion as typical of light and moderate work.

Case I is a simple mechanical assembly operation which was improved with a Class 2 change.

Case II is a job (performed at a machine) that was improved by a Class 2 change accompanied by a change from regular cyclic work to work with several subcycles performed with different frequency.

Case III shows a modified form of the operation chart used to detail jobs at an automobile plant prior to the start of the job.

Case IV shows some of the work done in connection with the planning of operation charts, prior to production, at a British plant.

Only Case I appears in the body of the chapter; the remainder are included in the Supplemental Material.

CASE I   HAND-HOLE COVER ASSEMBLY FOR
DIESEL-ENGINE CRANKCASE

A Class 1 or 2 change was indicated as desirable; the work was confined to one work station; hence, the analyst selected an operation chart as the most suitable man-analysis technique. The parts of the hand-hole cover are shown in Figure 11.1.

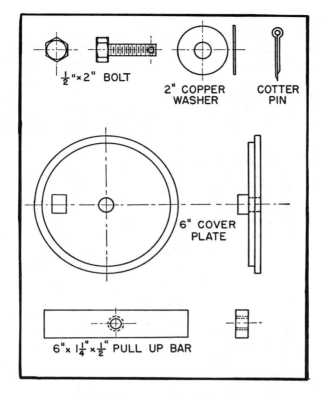

Fig. 11.1—Parts of hand-hole cover.

The analyst, after first familiarizing himself with the cycle, selected the busiest hand, in this case, the left, and classified the first step of that hand into the correct category from Table 5 and made an entry on a form such as used in Figure 11.2. He continued to analyze the complete cycle for that hand, showing the second step on the second line, and so on.

The charting of one hand completed, he similarly analyzed the other hand. Finally he checked his chart for correct simultaneity—that is, to see that items shown on one line happened at the same time. (In some cases corrections for this are necessary, and sometimes the charts must be redrawn before they are clear.)

A summary indicating the total number of lines of each type of step was placed at the end to indicate roughly the effectiveness of the method and for comparison with alternative methods. Note that a hold by one hand extending during several steps on the other is counted as if the symbol was repeated on each line, so that its importance is more adequately indicated than if it were only counted once. These quantitative figures should be used with care

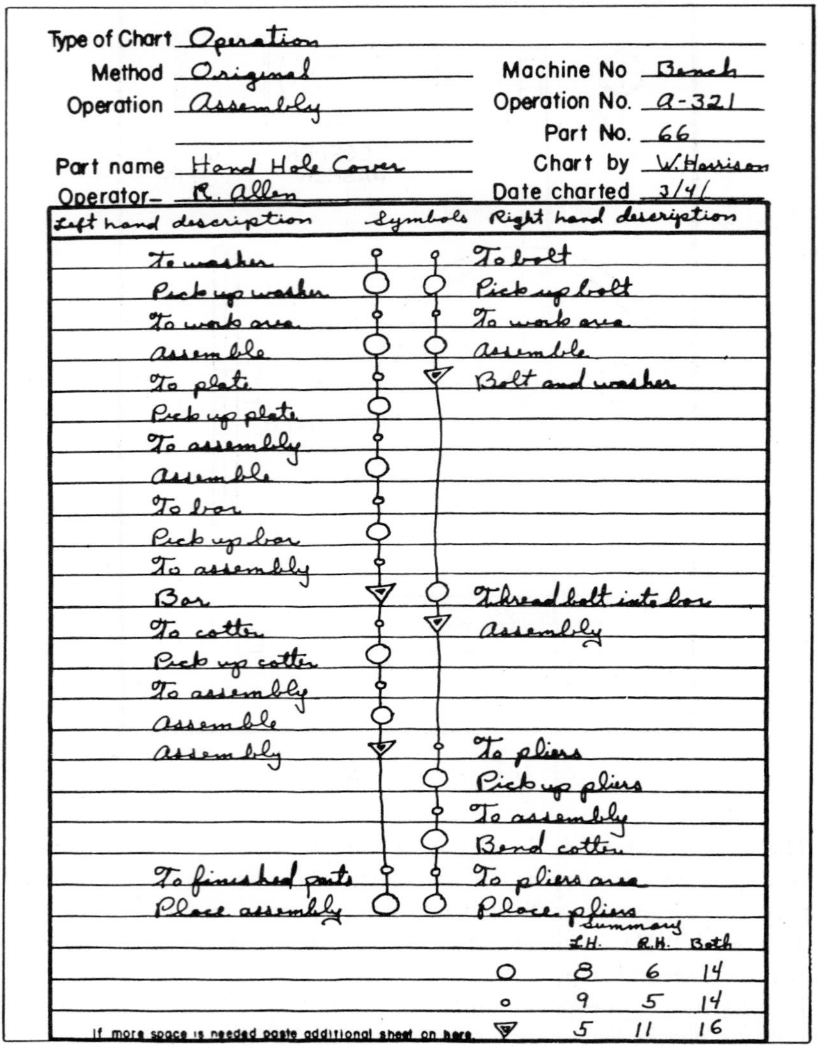

Type of Chart _Operation_

Method _Original_   Machine No _Bench_

Operation _Assembly_   Operation No. _Q-321_

                                          Part No. _66_

Part name _Hand Hole Cover_   Chart by _W. Harrison_

Operator- _R. Allen_   Date charted _3/4/_

Left hand description	Symbols	Right hand description
To washer		To bolt
Pick up washer	○ ○	Pick up bolt
To work area.		To work area.
assemble	○ ○	assemble
To plate	▽	Bolt and washer
Pick up plate	○	
To assembly		
assemble	○	
To bar		
Pick up bar	○	
To assembly		
Bar	▽ ○	Thread bolt into bar
To cotter	▽	assembly
Pick up cotter	○	
To assembly		
assemble	○	
assembly	▽ ○	To pliers
	○	Pick up pliers
	○	To assembly
	○	Bend cotter
To finished parts		To pliers area
Place assembly	○ ○	Place pliers

Summary

	L.H.	R.H.	Both
○	8	6	14
○	9	5	14
▽	5	11	16

If more space is needed paste additional sheet on here.

Fig. 11.2—Original operation chart for assembly of hand-hole cover.
(A form with a double row of preprinted symbols down the
center may be prepared and used if desired.)

inasmuch as the steps are seldom equal in time value. Numerical aspects of schematic models are only a guide to their understanding.

The analyst also made a sketch of the workplace layout as shown in Figure 11.3; this is usually a useful adjunct to the operation chart.

The general method of improving a job so analyzed is similar to that of

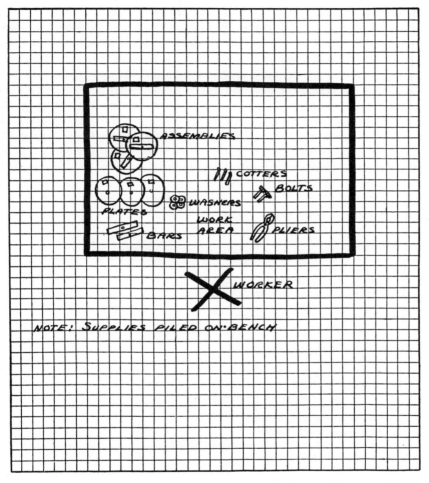

Fig. 11.3—Sketch of workplace for original method of assembly of hand-hole cover.

improving a job charted with a process chart–man analysis. The check list that is given is useful when carefully applied to each step on the operation chart.

The operation chart may be of an existing job or of a job that has not yet started. Both would still be subject to improvement.

Owing to the smallness of the separately identified steps, which in many cases are not unique to any one job or small group of jobs, the check list is more detailed than those previously given, and furthermore many of the items in it are experimentally verifiable in principle, apart from any job. Readings in the periodical literature will assist the reader in obtaining a more complete understanding of the principles of improvement. The reader should read not only articles dealing with his industry, but should read others as available, because many of the features of better methods are universally applicable to all types of work. The principles are sometimes more obvious when the work being done is not overly familiar.

CHECK LIST FOR OPERATION CHART

Basic Principles
A   Reduce total steps to minimum
B. Arrange in best order
C. Combine steps where feasible
D. Make each step as easy as possible
E. Balance the work of the hands
F. Avoid the use of the hands for holding
G. The workplace should fit human dimensions[1]

    1. Can a suboperation be eliminated?
       a. As unnecessary
       b. By a change in the order of work
       c. By a change of tools or equipment
       d. By a change of layout of the workplace
       e. By combining tools
       f. By a slight change of material
       g. By a slight change in product
       h. By a quick-acting clamp on jig, if jigs are used
    2. Can a movement be eliminated?
       a. As unnecessary
       b. By a change in the order of work
       c. By combining tools

[1] For information on human dimensions see: C. T. Morgan, A. Chapanis, J. Cook, and M. Lund (Eds.), *Human Engineering Guide to Equipment Design*. New York, N.Y.: McGraw-Hill Book Company, 1963; E. J. McCormick, *The Human Body in Equipment Design*. New York, N.Y.: McGraw-Hill Book Company, 1964; K. F. H. Murrell, *Human Performance in Industry*. New York, N.Y.: Reinhold, 1965; A. Damon, H. W. Stoudt and R. McFarland, *The Human Body in Equipment Design*. Cambridge, Mass.: Harvard University Press, 1966; H. Dreyfuss, *The Measure of Man: Human Factors in Design*. New York, N.Y.: Whitney Library of Design, 2nd Ed., 1967.

    d. By a change of tools or equipment

    e. By a drop disposal of finished material

       (The less exact the release requirements, the faster the release.)

3. Can a hold be eliminated? (Holding is extremely fatiguing.)

    a. As unnecessary

    b. By a simple holding device or fixture

4. Can a delay be eliminated or shortened?

    a. As unnecessary

    b. By a change in the work that each body member does

    c. By balancing the work between the body members

    d. By working simultaneously on two items

       (Slightly less than double production is possible with typical person.)

    e. By alternating the work, each hand doing the same job, but out of phase

5. Can a suboperation be made easier?

    a. By better tools

       (Handles should allow maximum flesh contact without sharp corners for power; easy spin, small diameter for speed on light work.)

    b. By changing leverages

    c. By changing positions of controls or tools

       (Put into normal work area—Figure 11.4.)

    d. By better material containers

       (Bins that permit slide grasp of small parts are preferable to bins that must be dipped into.)

    e. By using inertia where possible

    f. By lessening visual requirements

    g. By better workplace heights

       (Keep workplace height below elbow.)

6. Can a movement be made easier?

    a. By a change of layout, shortening distances (see Figure 11.4)

       (Place tools and equipment as near place of use and as nearly in position of use as possible.)

    b. By changing direction of movements

       (Optimum angle of workplace for light knobs, key switches, and handwheels is probably 30° and certainly between 0° to 45° to plane perpendicular to plane of front of operator's body.)

    c. By using different muscles

       Use the first muscle group in this list that is strong enough for the task: (See Figure 11.4 for visual items that may affect this order.)

       1. Finger (not desirable for steady load or highly repetitive motions)

       2. Wrist

       3. Forearm

       4. Upper arm

       5. Trunk (for heavy loads shift to large leg muscles)

    d. By making movements continuous rather than jerky

7. Can a hold be made easier?

    a. By shortening its duration

    b. By using stronger muscle groups, such as the legs, with foot-operated vises

The application of the check list to the job of assembling the hand-hole cover resulted in the improved method shown by the operation chart in Figure 11.5a and b, and in the new workplace layout shown in Figure 11.6. A chart form with preprinted symbols has been used in Figures 11.5a and b to show another common method of charting. This method was *tested*

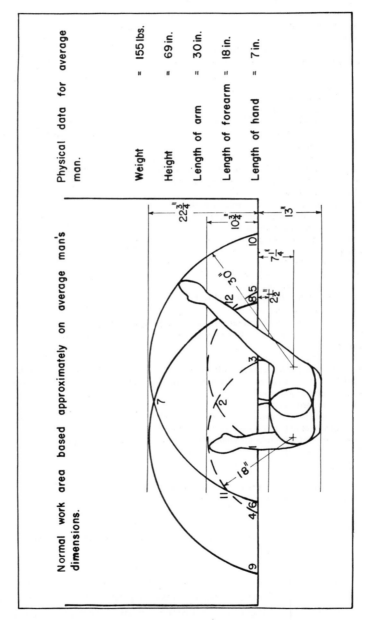

Fig. 11.4—Normal work area.

RIGHT AND LEFT HAND OPERATION CHART

of 2

Improved _____ Method   Bench Mach. No.
Assembly _____ Operation   Q-321 Opr. No.
_____   66 Part No.
Hand-hole Cover Part   W. H. Chart by
R. Allen _____ Operator   3/4/ Date

	SUMMARY /2	PER PC.				
	RIGHT HAND		LEFT HAND		BOTH HANDS	
	ORIG	IMP	ORIG	IMP	ORIG	IMP	SAVED
O	16		12		14	14	0
o	17		14		15.5		-1.5
▽	1		6		16	9.5	12.5
▽	0		2		0	1	-1
TOTAL	34		34		44	34	10

#	Left hand description	OPER. MOVE HOLD DELAY	DELAY HOLD MOVE OPER.	Right hand description
1	To bolt			To bolt
2	Pick up bolt			Pick up bolt
3	To work area			To work area
4	Assem. bolt to jig			Assem. bolt to jig
5	To washer			To washer
6	Pick up washer			Pick up washer
7	To assembly			To assembly
8	Assem. washer			Assem. washer
9	To cover plate			To cover plate
10	Pick up plate			Pick up plate
11	To assembly			To assembly
12	Assem. plate			Assem. plate
13	To bar			To bar
14	Pick up bar			Pick up bar
15	To assembly			To assembly
16	Fit and spin on			Fit and spin on
17	To cotter pin			To cotter pin
18	Pick up cotter			Pick up cotter
19	To right side assem.			To right side assem.
20	Right side assem			Assem cotter
21	To left side assem.			To left side assem.
22	Assem. cotter			Left side assem.
23	Left side assem.			To pliers
24				Pick up pliers
25				To assembly

Fig. 11.5a— Improved operation chart for assembly of hand-hole cover (continued).

RIGHT AND LEFT HAND OPERATION CHART

Improved _____ Method _____ Mach. No.

Assembly _____ Operation _____ Opr. No.

_____ _____ Part No.

Hand-hole Cover Part _____ Chart by

_____ Operator *3/4/* Date

SUMMARY						
	RIGHT HAND		LEFT HAND		BOTH HANDS	
	ORIG	IMP	ORIG	IMP	ORIG	IMP	SAVED
O						
o						
▽		*See sheet #1*				
▽						
TOTAL						

	Left hand description	OPER.	MOVE	HOLD	DELAY	DELAY	HOLD	MOVE	OPER.	Right hand description
1		◯	◦	▽	▽	▽	▽	◦	◯	Bend left cotter
2	To right side assem.	◯	◦	▽	▽	▽	▽	◦	◯	To right side assem.
3	Right side assem.	◯	◦	▽	▽	▽	▽	◦	◯	Bend right cotter
4	For right hand	◯	◦	▽	▽	▽	▽	◦	◯	To aside pliers
5		◯	◦	▽	▽	▽	▽	◦	◯	Place pliers
6	To left assembly	◯	◦	▽	▽	▽	▽	◦	◯	To right assembly
7	Pick up assem	◯	◦	▽	▽	▽	▽	◦	◯	Pick up assem.
8	To finished parts	◯	◦	▽	▽	▽	▽	◦	◯	To finished parts
9	Place assembly	◯	◦	▽	▽	▽	▽	◦	◯	Place assembly
10		◯	◦	▽	▽	▽	▽	◦	◯	
11		◯	◦	▽	▽	▽	▽	◦	◯	
12		◯	◦	▽	▽	▽	▽	◦	◯	
13		◯	◦	▽	▽	▽	▽	◦	◯	
14		◯	◦	▽	▽	▽	▽	◦	◯	
15		◯	◦	▽	▽	▽	▽	◦	◯	
16		◯	◦	▽	▽	▽	▽	◦	◯	
17		◯	◦	▽	▽	▽	▽	◦	◯	
18		◯	◦	▽	▽	▽	▽	◦	◯	
19		◯	◦	▽	▽	▽	▽	◦	◯	
20		◯	◦	▽	▽	▽	▽	◦	◯	
21		◯	◦	▽	▽	▽	▽	◦	◯	
22		◯	◦	▽	▽	▽	▽	◦	◯	
23		◯	◦	▽	▽	▽	▽	◦	◯	
24		◯	◦	▽	▽	▽	▽	◦	◯	
25		◯	◦	▽	▽	▽	▽	◦	◯	

Fig. 11.5b—(Concluded) *Improved operation chart for assembly of hand-hole cover.*

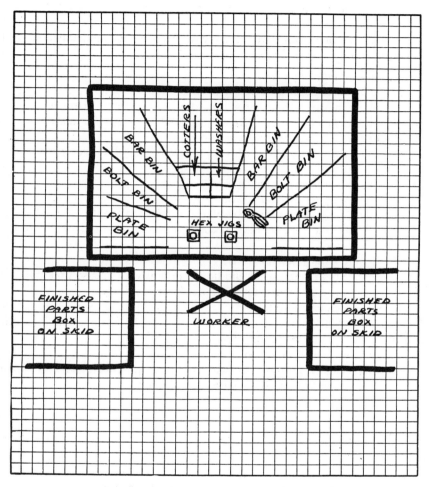

Fig. 11.6—Sketch of workplace for improved method of assembly of hand-hole cover.

by rechecking with the check list, and by discussion with the foreman. It was given *trial* in the shop; then standardized. Its *application* resulted in an increase in production of 82 per cent.

As with process charts–man analysis, the analyst should keep a file of solutions that he develops so as to provide a source of more detailed suggestions.

The check-list questions that helped with this job and the detailed suggestions that would be noted are as follows:

   3. Can a hold be eliminated?
      b. By a simple holding device or fixture
         Note: A hexagonal socket will hold a hex-head bolt firmly erect.
   4. Can delays be eliminated? (Removing the hold created a delay.)
      d. By working simultaneously on two items
         Note: It is possible to perform most tasks simultaneously with both hands.
   5. Can a suboperation be made easier?
      f. By lessening visual requirements
         Note: Small parts should be placed directly in front of the operator so that the eyes may direct both hands, and thus facilitate the work.
      d. By better material containers
         Note: Small material should be put in bins with lips, so that material may be picked up more easily and quickly.
      b. By changing leverages
         Note: Pull-up bar is easier to turn onto bolt than bolt into bar because bar gives more leverage.
      e. By using inertia where possible
         Note: Heavy pull-up bar will continue spinning onto bolt when given a start. Bolts with low inertia will not spin.

SUMMARY—OPERATION CHART

1. Uses:
   a. *For information leading to a Class 1 or 2 change on a job taking place at one location when the operator rather than a machine controls the flow of work.*
   b. *For designing the details of a job of the type indicated in a above.*
2. How made:
   a. *If the job is current, the chart is best prepared by actual observation of the worker. If the job has not yet started, it is prepared from a contemplation of the necessary work.*
   b. *The forms illustrated in Figure 11.2 and Figure 11.5a, or a blank sheet of paper, may be used.*
   c. *Although the chart may begin at any point in the work cycle, it is usually most convenient to begin with the hand that makes the first movement attributable to a unit of output.*
   d. *The first and last cycle of a work spell may be different from the other cycles. It is usually desirable to chart the most typical cycle.*
   e. *The first step of the hand that begins the cycle should be classified according to Table 5*

and an entry made, as on the first line of Figure 11.2. The symbols are usually drawn freehand, although forms with preprinted symbols are not uncommon.

 f. All of the steps of this hand should then be properly classified and plotted in order. It may be necessary to observe many cycles in order to accomplish this and check the completeness.

 g. The other hand should then be plotted, care being taken to place each step for this hand opposite the step of the other hand during which it occurs.

 h. Since step g often involves the squeezing in of lines and items to coordinate the chart properly, it is frequently necessary to redraw it so as to make it easily legible (Figure 11.2). However, since the chart is merely an aid to the understanding of the method, excess draftsmanship is a waste of time.

 i. A summary should be placed at the bottom of the chart.

 j. A sketch of the workplace is often a useful adjunct.

3. How used:

 a. Each step is questioned with the check list for operation charts. The dimensions of the workplace and the movements required should be studied with the aid of data on human dimensions.

 b. The general principles listed at the top of the check list are kept in mind as objectives.

4. What then:

 a. An operation chart is drawn for the resulting suggested method in order to permit a final check and to provide a means of describing the proposed new method.

 b. A revised sketch of the workplace is usually drawn, as well as drawings of the necessary tools, jigs, fixtures, bins, and the like.

Supplemental Material

CASE II   DRILL HOLES IN HINGE CHANNEL

Figure 11.7 is the original operation chart for drilling three holes in each of two ends of a hinge channel. The channel and two sets of holes drilled are shown in Figure 11.8. The workplace is shown in Figure 11.9, and a sketch of the workplace is shown in Figure 11.10. The checking of the original operation chart with the check list, with particular reference to those questions aiding in the application of principles B and C (at the top of the check list), resulted in the improved method shown in the operation chart in Figure 11.11 and in the sketch of the workplace in Figure 11.12. An air cylinder was attached to the drill press, an air jet was used to blow away chips, and the cyclic nature of the task was changed. Particular attention is called to the chart of Figure 11.11, which shows a task with several subcycles performed with different frequency. It should be noted that in this case the introduction of subcycles improved the task and was partly responsible for the increase in production of 138 per cent. Since, in other cases we have seen, the elimination of subcycles may be desirable, no general rule can be given.

CASE III   DETAILING JOBS AT AN AUTOMOBILE PLANT PRIOR TO PRODUCTION

The Oldsmobile Division of General Motors designs its operations before it begins to design tools. The workplaces and tooling are subsequently designed to facilitate the desired methods. A modified version of an operation chart

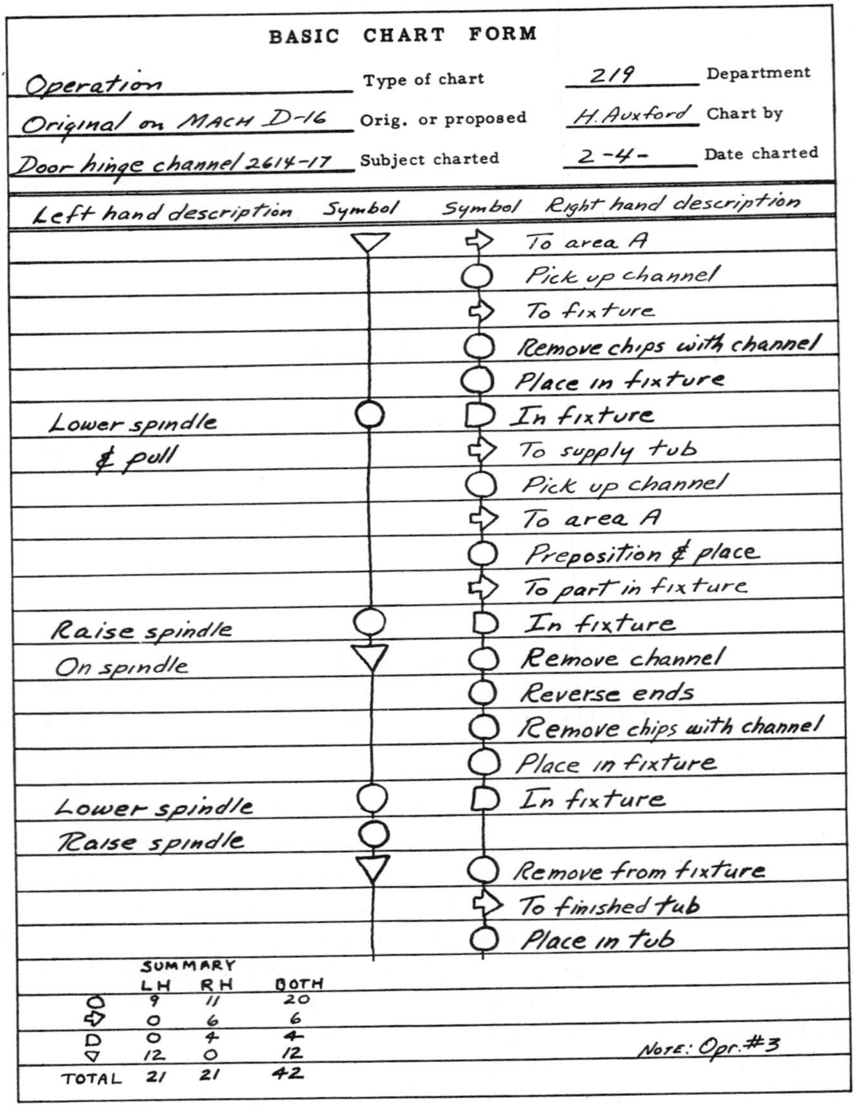

BASIC CHART FORM

Operation		Type of chart	219	Department
Original on MACH D-16		Orig. or proposed	H. Auxford	Chart by
Door hinge channel 2614-17		Subject charted	2-4-	Date charted

Left hand description	Symbol	Symbol	Right hand description
	▽	⇨	To area A
		◯	Pick up channel
		⇨	To fixture
		◯	Remove chips with channel
		◯	Place in fixture
Lower spindle	◯	D	In fixture
& pull		⇨	To supply tub
		◯	Pick up channel
		⇨	To area A
		◯	Preposition & place
		⇨	To part in fixture
Raise spindle	◯	D	In fixture
On spindle	▽	◯	Remove channel
		◯	Reverse ends
		◯	Remove chips with channel
		◯	Place in fixture
Lower spindle	◯	D	In fixture
Raise spindle	◯		
	▽	◯	Remove from fixture
		⇨	To finished tub
		◯	Place in tub

SUMMARY

	LH	RH	BOTH
◯	9	11	20
⇨	0	6	6
D	0	4	4
▽	12	0	12
TOTAL	21	21	42

NOTE: Opr. #3

Fig. 11.7—Original operation chart for drill holes in hinge channel.

178

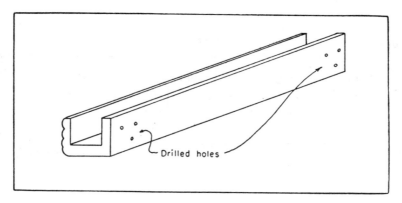

Drilled holes

Fig. 11.8 — Hinge channel.

Fig. 11.9 — Workplace for drill hinge channel.

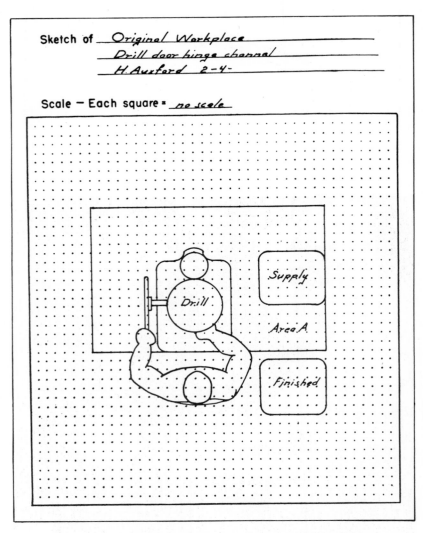

Fig. 11.10—Sketch of original layout of workplace for drill hinge channel.

BASIC CHART FORM

Operation _____ Type of chart _____2.19_____ Department

Proposed for Mach D-16 _____ Orig. or proposed _H. Auxford_ Chart by

Door hinge channel 2614-17 _ Subject charted ____2-4-____ Date charted

QUAN.	Left hand description	Symbol	Symbol	Right hand description
	For right hand	▽	⇨	To supply tub
1/pc 20 Times	To channel in fixture	⇨	○	Pick up channel
	Remove from fixture	○	⇨	To fixture
	To table	⇨	○	Place in fixture
	Turn end & place	○	D	Piece in fixture (Foot advances drill)
1/20 pcs. 1 Time	To area A	⇨	⇨	To area A
	Help R.H.	○	○	Pick up 20 channels
	To area B	⇨	⇨	To area B
	Help R.H.	○	○	Place 20 channels
	For R.H.	▽	⇨	To area B
1/pc. 20 Times	To channel in fixture	⇨	○	Pick up channel
	Remove from fixture	○	⇨	To fixture
	To 'finished' tub	⇨	○	Place in fixture
	Place in tub	○	D	Piece in fixture (Foot advances drill)

NOTE: OPR #3

SUMMARY & RECAP PER PIECE

	Improved			Original			Saved		
	LH	RH	BOTH	LH	RH	BOTH	LH	RH	BOTH
○	4.1	4.1	8.2			20			11.8
⇨	4.1	4.1	8.2			6			-2.2
D	0	2	2.0			4			2.0
▽	2	0	2.0			12			10.0
TOTAL	10.2	10.2	20.4			42			21.6

Fig. 11.11 — Improved operation chart for drill hinge channel.

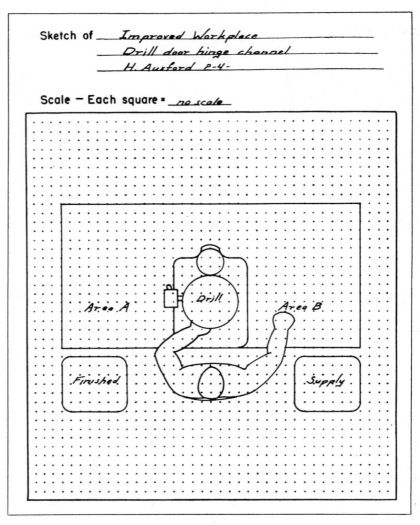

Sketch of ___Improved Workplace___
___Drill door hinge channel___
___H. Auxford 2-4-___

Scale – Each square = ___no scale___

Area A   Drill   Area B

Finished   Supply

Fig. 11.12 — Sketch of improved layout for workplace for drill hinge channel.

182

METHODS ENGINEERING DEPARTMENT   OLDSMOBILE DIVISION

OPERATOR INSTRUCTION SHEET

Part Name   Oil Pump Assembly   Part No. 555998   Dept. 6 - 21 Plant 7-23

Operation   10, Assemble gear and shaft, driv. gear, stub shaft to body Date 7-25-

WORK PLACE LAYOUT

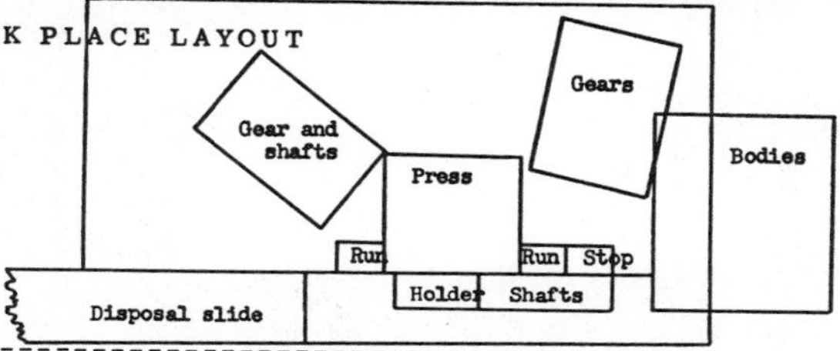

- Gear and shafts
- Gears
- Press
- Bodies
- Run
- Run Stop
- Holder Shafts
- Disposal slide

Step No.	WORK DESCRIPTION	
	LEFT HAND	RIGHT HAND
1	Get finished assembly from press and place in disposal slide open face up.	Get stub shaft from hopper
2	Get gear and shaft assembly from box and place in body	Place stub shaft through driven gear and place gear and shaft in body.
3		Get assembly from holder and place in press.
4	Press controls and cycle press.	Press controls and cycle press.
5		Get oil pump body from basket and place in wood holder during press cycle.

NOTE: If emergency occurs or ram does not return, press red "Stop" button to return ram.

PARTS ASSEMBLED
    555740   Gear and shaft assembly
    555736   Body
    444155   Driven gear

Approved by _____

Fig. 11.13 — Modified operation chart used for operator instruction sheet at workplace, Oldsmobile Division, General Motors.

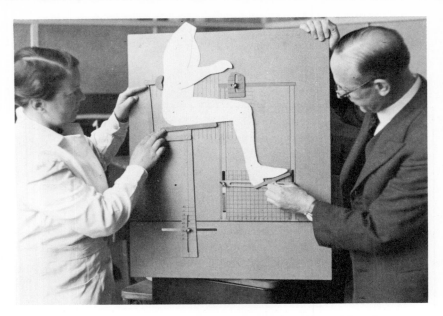

Fig. 11.14—Planning a workplace with an adjustable model work-place and a scale model worker, Lucas Ltd., Great Britain.

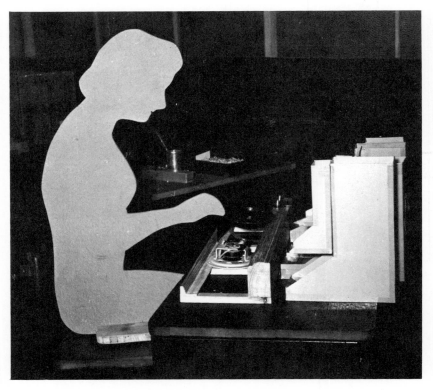

Fig. 11.15—Checking dimensions on a mock-up of a workplace, Lucas Ltd., Great Britain.

describing the method is eventually fastened to each workplace to serve as an operator instruction sheet. A gross breakdown (see footnote to Table 5) is used. Symbols are not employed inasmuch as "flagging" types of steps for improvement is not required for this use. The type of chart used is illustrated in Figure 11.13.

CASE IV   PLANNING WORKPLACES AT A BRITISH
PLANT

Lucas Ltd., British manufacturers of electrical parts for automobiles, design their methods and workplaces with great care, prior to production, in order to reduce costs and eliminate a large part of the problem of human resistance to change.

Figure 11.14 shows the late Mr. W. E. Smith, then head of the Methods and Time Study Department of Lucas, and one of his assistants planning a workplace with the aid of an adjustable model workplace and a scale model of a typical worker. Note that the heights of the fixtures, workplace, and chair are all being taken into consideration.

After the creation of an operation chart, a wood model of the workplace is constructed in full scale and checked with the aid of a full scale model worker as shown in Figure 11.15.

The final checking is done in an area separate from the production area. After all changes, the job is moved out onto the floor.

Through such a thorough approach, Lucas Ltd. has made enormous reductions in their cost of production and greatly increased their productivity, as noted in Chapter 1 (Figure 1.12).

CHAPTER 12

Multiple-activity Analysis— Man and Machine Charts

Multiple activity refers to cases where a man works with one or more machines, or where a group of men work coordinately with or without machines. The essential element of similarity in these cases is the requirement that any useful analysis show not only the sequence of steps on the two or more items charted but also the relative simultaneity of the steps of each. Multiple-activity analyses are usually used when the objective of the study is either to design the operation or to make a Class 1 or 2 change and where an analysis showing the relative simultaneity of the two or more items charted is required for a full understanding of the job. Like the preceding techniques, they are devices for aiding in performing the steps of the logical approach. The material on multiple activity is divided into two sections: man and machine analysis, treated in this chapter, and multiman analysis, treated in Chapter 13.

Man and machine charts are graphic means of portraying the separable steps of the work performed by a man and one or more machines and the relationship between the work of each. They are usually used when changes in the man and machine relationship will change productivity.

A simple type of man and machine chart, called a *man and machine operation chart*, is often used to analyze the work of one operator and one machine when the operator's work is done in one location. It is made like an operation chart, except that a third column is added for the machine. In this third column, the activity of the machine is classified into one of two categories. Hence, two symbols are used in the column for the machine: the symbol for suboperation when the machine is working, and the symbol for delay when it is idle.

The man and machine chart is usually made to obtain better utilization of the machine or the man. However, increased safety is also a common objective. The chart aids in determination of the most effective way of harmonizing the work of the individual with the machine. It may also be used to indicate how the machine might be altered to harmonize with the requirements of the individual.[1] If the chart technique is employed prior to the finalization of the machine's design, the requirements of the operator may be properly taken into account so that the machine may be designed for human use as well as for mechanical function.

As in the preceding chapters, the explanation of the details of handling this technique will be undertaken with the aid of examples. *Case I* will illustrate how the analysis technique was used to aid in the development of changes in the man work cycle to improve the rate of output, a Class 1 change. *Case II* will illustrate how the analysis led to increased output through changes in the machine cycle, a Class 2 change. Both of these cases concern simple cyclic jobs, although man and machine jobs may occur in any of the four basic forms of jobs described with both process charts-man analysis and operation charts. *Case III* shows a second version of man and machine charts wherein the operator's activity is handled in process chart type details rather than operation chart details, as a preliminary approach to examining the effect of alternative crew sizes for manning a machine. *Case IV* involves the same charting method as *Case III* but shows the application to a one-man multimachine type of problem. Only Case I appears in the body of the chapter; the remaining three cases are included under the Supplemental Material.

CASE I   An Analysis of the Operation of
a Centerless Grinder used on Engine Bearings

In the three columns of the man and machine operation chart shown in Figure 12.1 for the original method of centerless-grind engine bearing, the activities of the right and left hand of the operator and of the machine are charted in such a manner that a horizontal line drawn across the chart at any point passes through simultaneous actions. This chart was constructed by first making an operation chart in the usual manner and then adding the machine column to it in the same fashion as the analysis of the second hand was added to the analysis of the first. The work shown on the chart as "finish

[1] M. E. Mundel and R. C. Howell, "Applying Time and Motion Study Principles in Design," *Machine Design*, Aug. 1948, pp. 121–126; Earl D. Long, "Human Productivity and Tool Design," *Proceedings 17th Annual Institute, American Institute of Industrial Engineers*, 1966, pp. 12–20.

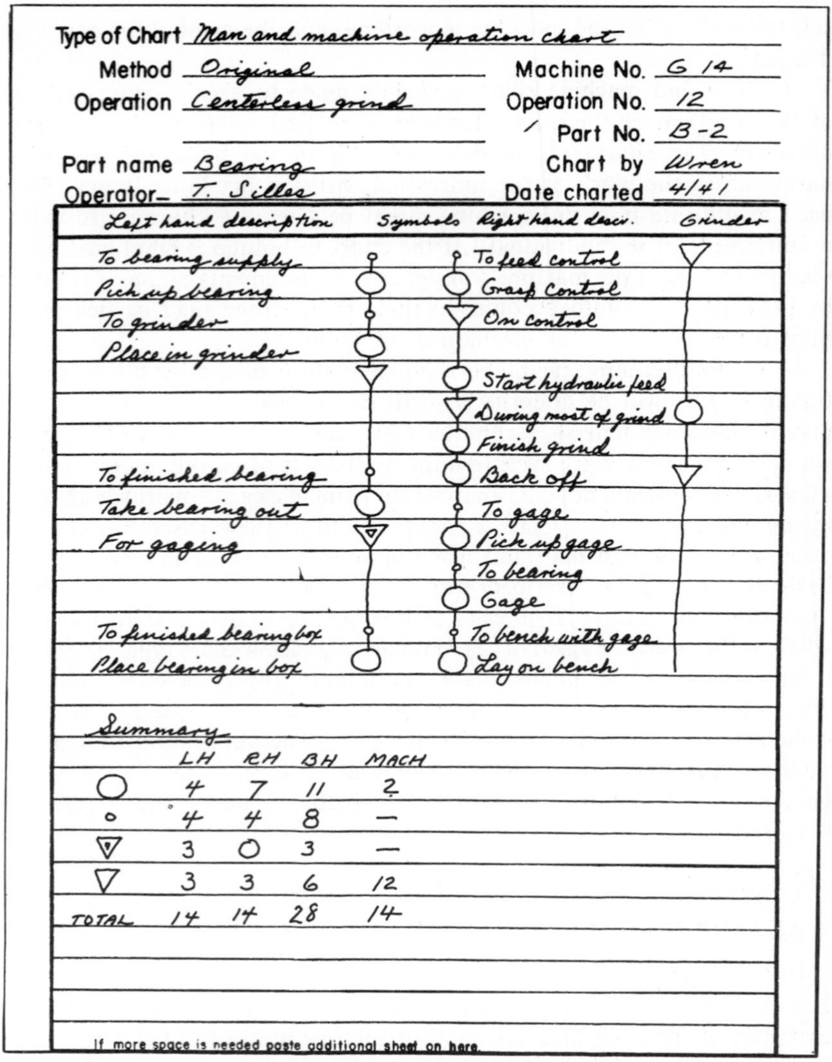

Type of Chart _Man and machine operation chart_

Method _Original_   Machine No. _G 14_

Operation _Centerless grind_   Operation No. _12_

_____   Part No. _B-2_

Part name _Bearing_   Chart by _Wren_

Operator _T. Silles_   Date charted _4/41_

Left hand description	Symbols	Right hand descr.	Grinder
To bearing supply		To feed control	
Pick up bearing		Grasp Control	
To grinder		On control	
Place in grinder			
		Start hydraulic feed	
		During most of grind	
		Finish grind	
To finished bearing		Back off	
Take bearing out		To gage	
For gaging		Pick up gage	
		To bearing	
		Gage	
To finished bearing box		To bench with gage	
Place bearing in box		Lay on bench	

Summary

	LH	RH	BH	MACH
◯	4	7	11	2
∘	4	4	8	—
▽	3	0	3	—
▽	3	3	6	12
TOTAL	14	14	28	14

If more space is needed paste additional sheet on here.

Fig. 12.1—Man and machine operation chart for original method of centerless grind engine bearing.

grind" was a hand manipulation of the controls, so as to be certain that all play in the feeding linkage had been eliminated and the part ground to size. The plant "process engineer" insisted on this.

The length of the chart, with this type of analysis, is not proportional to the time required for the job.

The original workplace layout is shown in Figure 12.2.

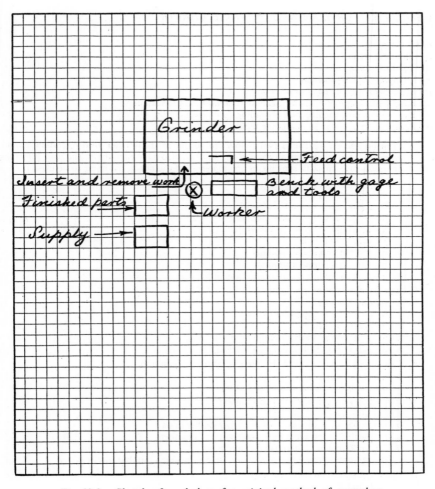

Fig. 12.2—Sketch of workplace for original method of centerless
grind engine bearing.

As with the preceding techniques, the third step of the logical procedure, *criticism*, is performed with the aid of a check list. A suitable one follows.

CHECK LIST FOR MAN AND MACHINE CHARTS

Basic Principles
A. Eliminate steps
B. Combine steps
C. Rearrange in best fashion
D. Make each step as easy as possible
E. Raise percentage of cycle of machine running time to maximum
F. Reduce machine loading and unloading to minimum
G. Raise machine speed to economic limit

> (The first seven questions that follow are similar to those used with operation charts, where more detail was given; hence, the reader is also referred to them. The bare questions are given here so as to provide, at one place, all of the check-list items to be used.)

1. Can a suboperation be eliminated?
   a. As unnecessary
   b. By a change in the order of work
   c. By a change of tools or equipment
   d. By a change in layout of the workplace
   e. By combining tools
   f. By a slight change of material
   g. By a slight change in product
   h. By a quick-acting clamp on the jigs or fixtures

2. Can a movement be eliminated?
   a. As unnecessary
   b. By a change in the order of work
   c. By combining tools
   d. By a change of tools or equipment
   e. By a drop disposal of finished material

3. Can a hold be eliminated? (Holding is extremely fatiguing.)
   a. As unnecessary
   b. By a simple holding device or fixture

4. Can a delay be eliminated or shortened?
   a. As unnecessary
   b. By a change in the work each body member does
   c. By balancing the work between the body members
   d. By working simultaneously on two items
   e. By alternating the work, each hand doing the same job, but out of phase

5. Can a suboperation be made easier?
   a. By better tools
   b. By changing leverages
   c. By changing positions of controls or tools
   d. By better material containers
   e. By using inertia where possible
   f. By lessening visual requirements
   g. By better workplace heights

6. Can a movement be made easier?
   a. By a change of layout, shortening distances
   b. By changing the direction of movements
   c. By using different muscles (see Figure 11.4)

Use the first muscle group in this list that is strong enough for the task :
1. Finger
2. Wrist
3. Forearm
4. Upper arm
5. Trunk
  d. Making movements continuous rather than jerky
7. Can a hold be made easier ?
  a. By shortening its duration
  b. By using stronger muscle groups, such as the legs, with foot-operated vises
8. Can the cycle be rearranged so that more of the handwork can be done during running time ?
  a. By automatic feed
  b. By automatic supply of material
  c. By change of man and machine phase relationship
  d. By automatic power cut-off at completion of cut or in case of tool or material failure
9. Can the machine time be shortened ?
  a. By better tools
  b. By combined tools
  c. By higher feeds or speeds

The first seven check-list questions are particularly useful for applying to the man activities during machine down time, since any reduction in machine down time increases the percentage of time the machine may be in operation. Because overhead costs often exceed direct labor costs, obtaining better utilization of the machine through reduction of down time is often an extremely valuable type of improvement.

In some cases, the machine running time provides a needed rest for the operator. It is worth noting that increasing production by reducing the machine down time through better hand motions may actually increase the amount of time per day that the operator may rest.

In the illustration given, production of engine bearings was being seriously hampered by the lack of centerless-grinding capacity in the plant. The expenditure for additional equipment would be of sufficient magnitude to warrant careful study. The application of the check list and the synthesis of a new method opened other avenues for more production. Output was increased by 23 per cent, the production bottleneck eliminated, and the amount of overhead and labor chargeable to each unit of the product was decreased by the installation of the procedure shown in the man and machine operation chart in Figure 12.3. The new workplace layout is shown in Figure 12.4. Note that this chart indicates only that this method will be faster, since some of the grinding is being performed during the gaging operation. This type of chart does not always permit estimation of the magnitude of the expected improvement. A normal summary like that used with operation charts may be misleading because it does not make possible an evaluation of the effect of such changes as removing the sixth step of the original method, during which both hands were idle for a considerable time. The

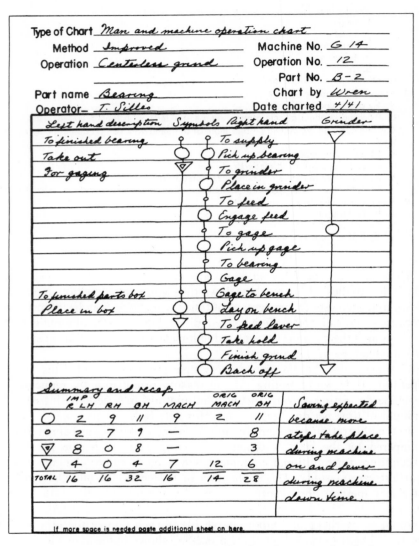

Fig. 12.3—Man and machine operation chart for improved method
of centerless grind engine bearing.

steps added to the improved method are performed in this interval, together
with several of the steps originally performed while the machine was down.
Close scrutiny of the chart will show that fewer steps are performed while
the machine is idle, which is a better measure of the desirability of the improved method than the total number of steps, because with the machine set

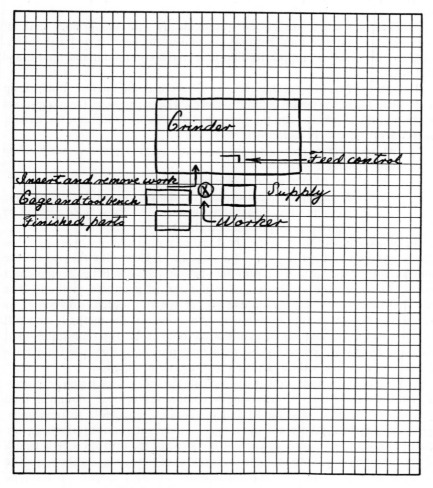

Fig. 12.4—Sketch of workplace for improved method of centerless grind engine bearing.

at optimum operating speed, the machine controlled part of the cycle is fixed and any improvement must affect idle or down time. It is worth pointing out, however, that optimum operating speed is frequently a subject worthy of study, although the available information is much too extensive to include here.

The bearings could not be fed automatically into the grinder without considerable complications, because one end of the bearing had a shoulder. In many other cases, hopper feeding may make continuous machine usage feasible.

As with the preceding techniques, for future use, the analyst should keep a classified file of the details of improvement. The useful item, from questions 8 and 9 of the check list, and the notes that were made to increase the ease of subsequent usage were as follows:

8. *Can the cycle be rearranged so that more of the handwork can be done during running time?*

   c. *By change of man and machine phase relationship*

      Note: If gaging of finished piece can be performed during machine running time, rather than during down time, the cycle will be shortened by just that much.

A slightly different form of the chart, called a man and machine operation time chart, can be used to great advantage in problems like this, where the time values for the various steps in the operation are available. Such a chart greatly facilitates the synthesis and evaluation of proposed methods. The required time values may be obtained roughly with a watch, stop-watch, or any of the motion picture techniques, or with any of the methods that will be described in the chapter on synthesized times. Since the time values used on these charts are primarily for analytical purposes, they need not have the accuracy of time values recorded for wage determination.

A man and machine chart that will indicate the time for each step graphically requires a new type of notation. A continuous vertical column is used instead of a column of symbols, and the column is scaled into time units. Since geometric symbols are no longer convenient, various shadings are used to indicate the nature of each of the steps of the operation. The length of each shading is used to indicate the amount of time spent on the step. The columns are kept in the same relationship to each other as with the first type of man and machine chart, except that the relationship is indicated much more accurately. A convenient system of symbols for man and machine operation time charts is given in Table 6. Man and machine time charts are still schematic models, but the charting of the steps on a scale of time makes them more complete models. The effect of shifting steps from one column to another may be more fully appraised and the consequences more carefully determined.

TABLE 6

Symbols for Man and Machine Operation Time Chart

Symbol[1]	Name	With Man Activities Is Used to Represent	With Machine Activities Is Used to Represent
■	Suboperation	Body member or operator doing something at one place.	Machine working ("on" time), machine paced.
▯	Suboperation	Not used.	Machine working ("on" time), operator paced.
▨	Movement	Body member or operator moving toward or with an object.	Not used.
▱	Hold	Boby member maintaining an object in a fixed position.	Not used.
▭	Delay	Body member or operator is idle	Machine is idle ("down" time).

[1] The amount of shading is chosen to suggest automatically the general usefulness of the step. The less shading, the probable greater undesirability of the step.

To gain additional insight into the method, the whole of the man and machine activity may be classified into three additional categories as follows: *independent man work*, when the man is working and his work neither controls nor is controlled by the machine, or when the man is idle and his idleness does not control the machine; *independent machine work* when the machine is working and is not controlled by the man; *combined work* when the man is operating the machine, loading the machine, or when the machine is waiting for the man.[2]

Consideration of the three categories suggested, which may be superimposed

[2] Suggested by Professor David B. Porter, New York University.

upon the usual time chart, should suggest in general that the combined work be reduced to a minimum to approach the minimum cycle time, the independent man work plus the combined work be reduced to a minimum to reduce the man-workload to a minimum, and so forth. Such an additional classification of the steps of the chart should assist in developing more effective work cycles.

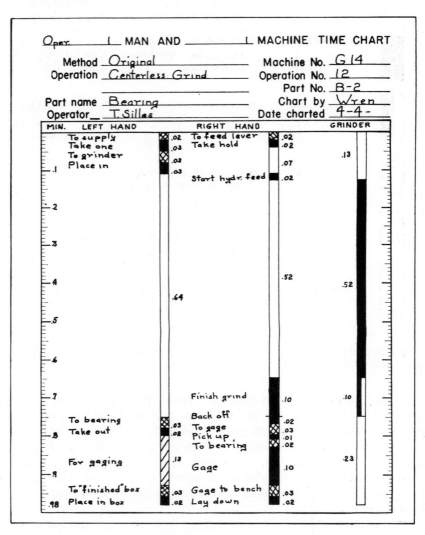

Fig. 12.5—Man and machine operation time chart for original method of centerless grind engine bearing.

A time chart facilitates rearrangement and balance of the work of the two hands and the man and the machine, and permits an evaluation of the magnitude of the probable effects of the change. Together with labor rates and overhead figures, this makes possible the determination, in a reasonably accurate fashion, of the economic desirability of installing a change, prior to its actual application. Through the use of time values from predetermined

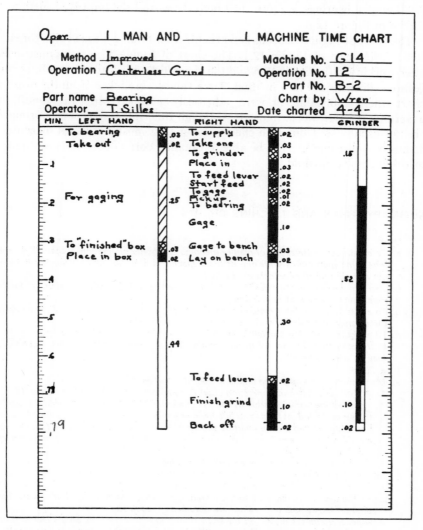

Fig. 12.6—Man and machine operation time chart for improved
method of centerless grind engine bearing.

time systems (commonly referred to as P.T.S.) discussed in later chapters, alternate designs of machines and their operating patterns may be compared, in terms of labor operating costs, while the machines are still in the drawing stage and the most preferable (depending on the criterion selected) design chosen.

The man and machine time chart for the original method of centerless-grind engine bearings is shown in Figure 12.5, and the improved method is shown in Figure 12.6.

The chart of Figure 12.5 was constructed after finding a time value for each step of the chart of Figure 12.1. The chart of Figure 12.6 was constructed after working with Figure 12.5 and the check list and, with the resulting suggestions, drawing the new method. Time values were taken from the original chart where applicable, or were judiciously modified when the conditions governing the step were changed. Although time standards for performance are not usually set from such charts, the analyst must still avoid inaccuracy as much as possible so as to be able to obtain a correct economic evaluation of the suggested method.

SUMMARY — MAN AND MACHINE CHARTS

1. Uses:
    a. To obtain better utilization of man or machine and better integration of the two on jobs where the man works with one or more machines and the interrelationship between the man and machine affects productivity.
    b. To aid in the selection of a desirable man and machine work pattern in view of production requirements and cost conditions.
    c. To assist in setting up a mathematical model of the man and machine relationship for the eventual determination of the true optimum arrangement.
    d. To assist in designing a machine for operation (as contrasted with function).
    e. In the simpler forms, to aid in determining where more detailed analysis techniques may be usefully applied.
2. How made:
    a. Man and machine operation charts are constructed as follows:
        1. A right- and left-hand operation chart is constructed as detailed in Chapter 11.
        2. The machine is then charted by the use of a procedure similar to that used for placing the second hand on right- and left-hand operation charts, with the machine information being placed on the chart as shown in Figure 12.1. Usually, only two symbols are used for the activities of the machine—the symbol for suboperation when the machine is working and the delay symbol when it is idle.
        3. A summary is placed at the bottom of the chart.
    b. Man and machine operation time charts are constructed as follows:
        1. A man and machine operation chart is drawn.
        2. By the use of the second hand of a watch, or a stop watch, or from film or standard time tables, sample time values are obtained for each step.
        3. A second chart is drawn on the form shown in Figure 12.5 or on a sheet of graph or cross-section paper, using the conventions established in Table 6. The length of each step on the chart is made proportional to the time involved. A convenient scale should be chosen by assigning to each line of the chart a time value such that the chart is of convenient size. The scale should be the same throughout the chart.

4. A summary may be placed at the bottom of the chart, although the length of the chart is, of itself, a rough summary.

c. Man and machine process time charts (see Supplemental Material) are constructed as follows:

1. A process chart-man analysis is constructed as described in Chapter 8, but the information is confined to half the chart, with the right half usually left blank.

2. The machines used are charted on the same sheet, as with man and machine operation charts, with the steps of the machines properly keyed into the process chart.

3. By the use of a watch, stop-watch, camera, or table of time values, the time is determined for each item on the chart.

4. By the use of a form similar to that used in Figure 12.12 or a sheet of graph or cross-section paper, the chart is redrawn, using the conventions of Table 7 and making each item of a length proportional to the time involved. A convenient scale should be chosen and a time value assigned to each line of the chart so that the chart is of a convenient size. The scale should be the same throughout the chart.

5. A summary may be placed at the bottom of the chart, although the length of the chart is, of itself, a rough summary.

3. How used:

Each step of the method analyzed may be questioned with the aid of suitable check lists.

With any man and machine task, the desired type of solution should be stated, so as to have a criterion on the basis of which to select a solution.

The time chart may be used to locate sections of the task that need more intensive study.

4. What then:

A proposed chart is either constructed or selected from the available solutions for the subsequent steps; or more detailed analyses, for further study, may be made of sections of the task.

Supplemental Material

CASE II   FORM SHEET-METAL BOX LINER
ON PRESS

Figure 12.7 shows the original man and machine operation time chart for the job of forming a sheet-metal box liner on a press. The sheet of metal was 5′ × 3′ and it was bent into a square-cornered U.

The time values on this chart were obtained from a motion picture film and, consequently, the units are much smaller than those used in the previous chart, the smallest time unit being one one-thousandth rather than one one-hundredth of a minute. Although, as will be seen in Chapter 14, measurements in thousandths of a minute are not a requisite with the use of film, it is frequently convenient to use such values, and is often easier than obtaining the less accurate stop-watch values.

The original workplace layout is shown in Figure 12.8.

The study of this analysis with the aid of the check list led to the following changes:

Two push buttons were installed at the height of the original safety button, and the machine was arranged to cycle automatically, eliminating the use of the three levers used in the original method.

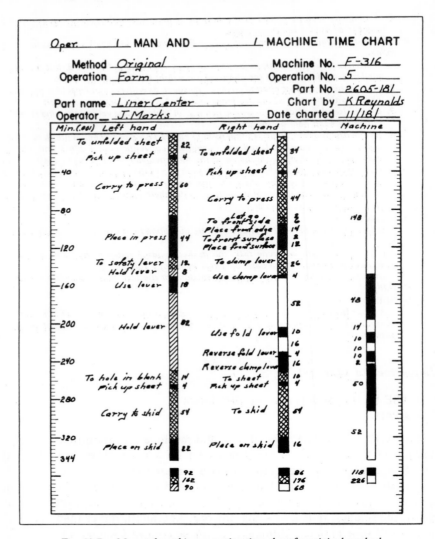

Fig. 12.7 — Man and machine operation time chart for original method
of form sheet-metal box liner.

The ram stroke of the press was speeded up by enlarging the air line feeding it. The improved time chart, shown in Figure 12.9, indicated that 35 per cent of the time was saved, which, on the basis of the production required in the plant where the job was located, amounted to an annual savings of $2,254 in direct labor.

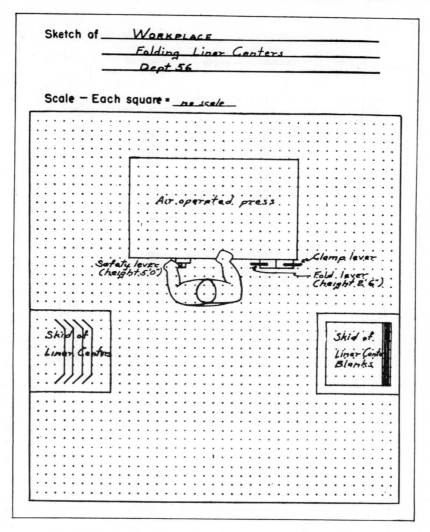

Fig. 12.8—Sketch of original workplace for form sheet-metal box liner.

CASE III   THE USE OF THE MAN AND MACHINE PROCESS TIME CHART

A simpler man and machine chart, *a man and machine process time chart*, may be used as the preliminary step in determining the most economical number of machines an operator might run or the most desirable number of workers that might be used as a crew.

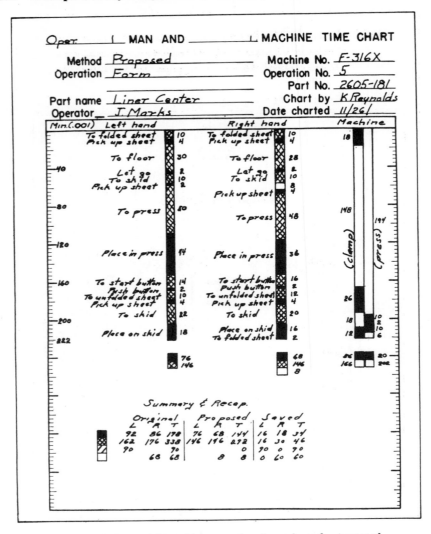

Fig. 12.9—Man and machine-operation time chart for improved method of form sheet-metal box liner.

To simplify the analysis, the man may be treated as with a process chart-man analysis, and the coding given in Table 7 is suggested. This will permit the time values to be graphically represented on the chart and will permit an easier approach to the problems encountered than that possible with geometric symbols.

Figure 12.10 is the man and machine process time chart for an operator running a radio-tube grid-winding machine and chopping and peeling the

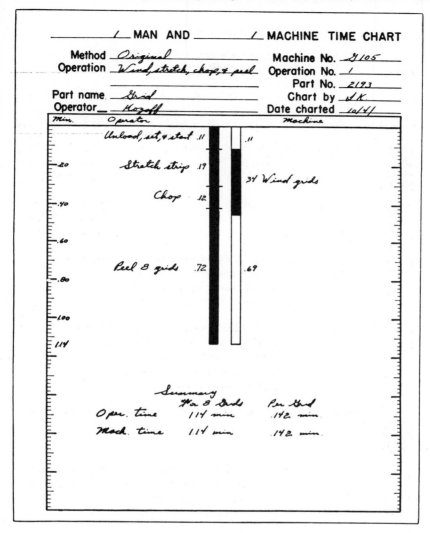

_____ ∠ MAN AND _____ ∠ MACHINE TIME CHART

Method _Original_   Machine No. _9105_
Operation _Wind, stretch, chop, & peel_   Operation No. _1_
                                Part No. _2193_
Part name _Grid_   Chart by _SK_
Operator _Kozoff_   Date charted _10/4/_

Min.   Operator   Machine

Unload, set, & start .11   .11

-.20   Stretch strip .19
                                   .34 Wind grids
          Chop   .12

-.40

-.60

-.80   Peel 8 grids   .72   .69

-1.00

1.14

                    Summary
                    For 8 Grids   Per Grid
          Oper. time   1.14 min   .142 min
          Mach. time   1.14 min   .142 min

Fig. 12.10—_Man and machine process time chart for one-man crew_
on winding, stretching, chopping, and peeling radio-tube
grids.

grids. The operator has been treated as a single unit without detailing any single body member. Since this job does not require the operator to move from the workplace, no movements appear in the breakdown of this job.

Radio-tube grids consist of a light wire wound spirally around two heavier and parallel support wires, as shown in Figure 12.11. Grids are usually wound in strips of from 6 to 16, depending on their length. Some extremely small

TABLE 7

Symbols for Man and Machine Process Time Chart

Symbol	Name	With Man Activities Is Used to Represent	With Machine Activities Is Used to Represent
	Operation	The doing of something at one place.	Machine working ("on" time), machine paced.
	Operation	Not used.	Machine working ("on" time), operator paced.
	Quantity determination	A special form of operation involving the person determining the quantity of an item present.	Not used.
	Inspection	A special form of operation involving the person comparing an attribute of a product with a standard, or verifying the quantity present.	Not used.
	Movement	A change in location; moving from one place to another	Not used.
	Delay	Idleness. Waiting or moving, provided the movement was not part of the job and the time could have been spent waiting.	Machine is idle ("down" time).

grids are wound with more grids to the strip. In the case cited here, 8 were wound in a strip. The winding machine automatically fastens the correct number of turns to the support wires, leaves a number of turns loose so that they may be peeled off to form the grids' legs, fastens those for the next grid, and so forth, all along the strip. It stops automatically at the completion of a strip. After the operator removes a strip of grids from the machine, she sets the machine ready to go again, starts it, and then again takes the finished strip of grids. She fastens the strip, by its ends, to a stretching device, brings the strip to its proper length, which automatically straightens it, and then,

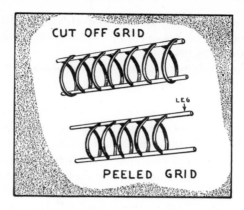

CUT OFF GRID

LEG

PEELED GRID

Fig. 12.11—Peeled and unpeeled radio-tube grid.

with a foot-operated chopper, chops the strip into individual grids. The loose turns on the ends of each grid are next peeled off by hand, and the loose length of wire snapped off by bending it back and forth. The grids are then placed in containers and are ready for further processing. Note that with one operator, as charted in Figure 12.10, the machine time chargeable to each grid is 0.142 minutes, and the operator time chargeable to each grid is 0.142 minutes. This type of analysis makes possible the determination of the effects of using a crew of two or more, as will be shown in the next chapter on multiman charts.

CASE IV   THE USE OF THE MAN AND MACHINE
PROCESS TIME CHART FOR THE ANALYSIS OF A MAN
AND MULTIMACHINE ASSIGNMENT

A more complex situation arises when one man must operate several machines and the job involves moving from machine to machine as well as working at each machine. Jobs of this type are usually most usefully analyzed with a time chart.[3] Here it is usually desirable to analyze the worker as

[3] In some cases a mathematical model may be evolved. See: W. D. Jones, "Mathematical and Experimental Calculation of Machine Interference Time," *The Research Engineer* (Georgia Inst. of Tech.), Jan. 1949, pp. 9–10; R. N. Fetter, "The Assignment of Operators to Service Automatic Machines," *The Journal of Industrial Engineering*, Vol. VI, No. 5, Sept.–Oct. 1955, pp. 22–30; R. F. Lomicka and J. M. Allderige, "Mathematical Man-Machine Analysis," *The Journal of Industrial Engineering*, Vol. VIII, No. 3, May–June 1957, pp. 157–164. (These last two articles have additional bibliographies.) See also: K. R. Baker, "Priority Dispatching in the Single Channel Queue with Sequence-Dependent Setups," *The Journal of Industrial Engineering*, Vol. XIX, No. 4, April 1968, pp. 203–206; C. R. Glassey, "An Algorithm for a Machine Loading Problem," *The Journal of Industrial Engineering*, Vol. XVIII, No. 10, October 1967, pp. 584–588. A single facility with a multiplicity of users problem is described in: J. Goldman and H. A. Knappenberger, "Simulation of Operating Room Scheduling Policies," *Proceedings 19th Annual Institute, American Institute of Industrial Engineers*, 1968, pp. 148–152.

a single unit to avoid confusing the data by overdetailing. Hence, it is customary to use one column for the operator, with a process chart type of breakdown, and one for each machine.

There can be four different objectives with problems involving the proper number of machines that an operator should run:

1. To arrange the method and number of machines so,as to reduce the operator's delays to the minimum required for rest and personal time. There may be considerable machine delay.

2. To arrange the method and number of machines so that the machine delay is reduced to the minimum required to provide the operator with rest and personal time, during which the machine may be unattended. There may be considerable other operator delay time.

3. To arrange the method and number of machines so that the combined operator idle time and machine idle time give the lowest cost of operation.

4. To arrange the method and number of machines so that both operator and machine idle time are reduced to the minimum required to provide the operator with rest and personal time.

Type 4, although usually desirable, is seldom feasible. The problem in most cases therefore becomes a matter of deciding which of the other types of solutions is the most desirable in view of existing conditions. If the plant has excess capacity, it is often best to keep actual costs to a minimum by reducing operator delays to a minimum—solution 1—although this may mean considerable machine delays. If the machine overhead is high and capacity is a limiting factor, an arrangement that keeps the machines busy but makes, perhaps, poor use of the operator's time may be desirable—solution 2. If the direct labor cost and machine overhead rates are somewhat similar, the third type of solution may be the same as one of the first two, although it may shift from one to the other as the cost picture changes. With complex cycles, it may be distinctly different from any other solution, and quite desirable, if minimum cost without maximum possible production from the equipment is a tolerable situation.

If a mathematical model of the man-machine situation is created, it may be used to find any of these solutions. A mathematical model permits the direct determination of the optimum arrangement after the nature of "optimum" is stated. The first three objectives which have been stated may be described mathematically. The fourth is a fortuitous situation. It should be noted that the logical procedure stated in Chapter 3 will still be followed although the step of analysis and the subsequent steps will be performed with a mathematical model as opposed to a schematic model. However, the schematic model or man and machine time chart may well be an important step in creating the mathematical model; further, in many cases, the schematic model is sufficient to permit the development of a satisfactory solution.

In all solutions, the most efficient integration of the man work cycle into the machine work cycle is usually desirable. The process chart-man analysis check list may aid in obtaining this. Preparation of loads and performance of inspection during machine running time, as in the case of the grinding of engine bearings, are also usually attributes of efficient man and multimachine

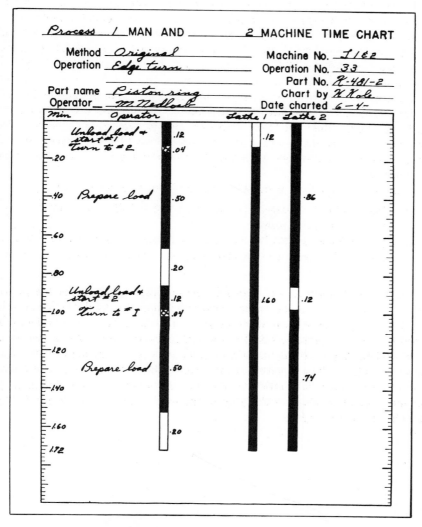

Fig. 12.12—Man and two-machine process time chart for edge-turn
piston rings.

setups. Easier methods of performing the hand part of the job done at each workplace, through Class 1 or 2 changes, are usually helpful, particularly when they affect what is done during machine down time. However, changes of this more detailed type are usually achieved through further analysis by other techniques of various steps in the sequence. This last statement should be carefully considered. Changes of this type are not suggested from a mathematical model of the situation, yet they may have a vital bearing on the final effectiveness of the man-machine arrangement. The analyst who proceeds to the more sophisticated techniques of mathematical models should ascertain that the model represents the embodiment of all reasonable Class 1 and 2 changes and that the work of creating the model is compatible with the economics of the problem. Waiting line or queuing problems involving machine servicing depend upon accurate values for "time to service." Certainly, all improvements possible through Class 1 or moderate Class 2 changes should be taken into account. In many cases, the economics of Class 2 changes which affect the "time to service" may be more fully evaluated with the aid of a queuing model. The two types of techniques, schematic and mathematical, compliment each other and should not be thought of as alternatives.

The man and machine process time chart is used to determine:

1. Where methods changes achieved with the aid of other analysis techniques would be of value.
2. What, in view of existing production requirements and cost relationships, is the most economical man and machine work pattern to follow.

Figure 12.12 is a man and two-machine process time chart for the job of edge-turn piston rings on lathe. Two machines are used for maximum machine output. A typical work cycle is charted. Note that considerable operator delay is present, but that the machines are kept busy all the time except when they are being unloaded or loaded. The only means of increasing production from these machines, other than higher feeds or speeds, or better tools, is through a facilitation of the machine unloading and loading. A detailed operation chart of this step in the work sequence would aid in the search for a better method.

CHAPTER 13

Multiple-activity Analysis— Multiman Charts

A study of those jobs on which a group of men work coordinately with or without machines requires a type of analysis that shows the relative simultaneity of the sequence of steps for all the men and machines.

Multiman charts are a graphic means of portraying the separable steps of the work of a crew, with or without machines, and indicating the relationships among them, when the work involves coordination of the crew.

When the work is done in sequence, it is often best analyzed by considering the work of each crew member separately. The aim is to distribute evenly the amount of work for each member of the crew, by breaking the sequence at the proper places, or else to improve the methods for the work of the crew members having the longest part of the sequence. Techniques that are used for the improvement of individual jobs are commonly employed in this area as well. In complex cases, mathematical models may be valuable.[1] Such work in sequence is not usually classified as "multiple activity."

[1] M. E. Salveson, "The Assembly Line Balancing Problem," *The Journal of Industrial Engineering*, Vol. VI, No. 3, May–June 1955, pp. 18–25; J. R. Jackson, "A Computing Procedure for a Line Balancing Problem," *Management Science*, Vol. 2, No. 3, April 1956, pp. 261–271; W. B. Helgeson and D. P. Birnie, "Assembly Line Balancing Using the Ranked Positional Weight Technique," *The Journal of Industrial Engineering*, Vol. XII, No. 6, Nov.–Dec. 1961; C. L. Moodie and H. H. Young, "A Heuristic Method of Assembly Line Balancing for Assumptions of Constant or Variable Element Times," *The Journal of Industrial Engineering*, Vol. XVI, No. 1, Jan.–Feb. 1965; F. M. Tonge, *A Heuristic Program of Assembly Line Balancing*. Englewood Cliffs, N.J.: Prentice-Hall, Inc., 1961; A. E. Gould, "Choosing a Method of Assembly Line Balancing," *Proceedings 16th Annual Conference and Convention of American Institute of Industrial Engineers*, 1965, pp. 211–213.

A watch, stop-watch, or motion-picture or video-tape camera (as will be seen in Chapter 14) may be used for studying the work of the coordinate crew. Since details of the interrelationships of the time that is spent by each of the members of the crew are frequently the key to rearranging the task, a type of chart involving a time scale is of the greatest value in most situations, although it is not a necessity. If the time values are obtained, however, they are also an aid in determining the economic desirability of any innovation, since they facilitate a reasonably accurate evaluation prior to the application of the change. The time values are for analysis only, and not for wage determination, so that extreme accuracy is not required. Also, as with man and machine analysis, predetermined time values, from tables, may be used to design crew jobs prior to the beginning of the actual work. Multiman charts are a desirable aid in developing such designs.

With coordinate crew work, the movements of the workers as units, particularly with heavy jobs, are of prime importance, and, therefore, a simple type of analysis, using the steps and conventions given in Table 7, is usually desirable. A coordinated right- and left-hand breakdown can be made of each worker, but for simplicity's sake it is better to make an analysis of the whole task, and left- and right-hand breakdowns only when parts of the job seem to warrant analysis in this detailed fashion.

Two cases will be examined.[2] *Case I* illustrates the use of multiman and machine charts for improving a job, and *Case II* shows the procedure for evaluating the desirability of changing the crew size on a job detailed as a one-man and machine task in the preceding chapter. Only Case I appears in the body of the chapter; Case II is in the Supplemental Material.

CASE I   CUT STUDS IN PREFABRICATED-HOUSE PLANT

The objective chosen from the possibility guide was a Class 1 or moderate Class 2 change. The choice was influenced by the use for many other jobs of the equipment used on this job—a fact that tended to rule out any highly specialized equipment. A standard overhead-track cut-off saw was used.

The decision to seek a Class 1 or moderate Class 2 change, the necessity (economic) of performing the job, the nature of the job (coordinate crew work), all indicated the desirability of a multiple-activity analysis—a multiman and machine time chart. Figure 13.1 is a plan view of part of the factory floor in a prefabricated-house plant, together with the paths of the three workers in the crew using the cut-off saw to cut 8-foot house studs from 14-foot mill-length $2'' \times 4''$ lumber. The work pattern of the crew and saw is shown in the multiman and machine process time chart in Figure 13.2. On this chart, one column has been used for each man and one column for

---

[2] The use of the *before and after* presentation in these cases should not cause the reader to lose sight of the use of the multiman chart as a design tool.

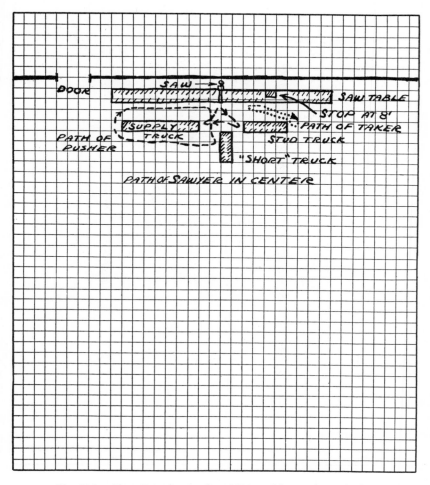

Fig. 13.1—Plan view of part of prefabricated house plant, showing location of material and equipment and path of three-man crew cutting studs, using original method.

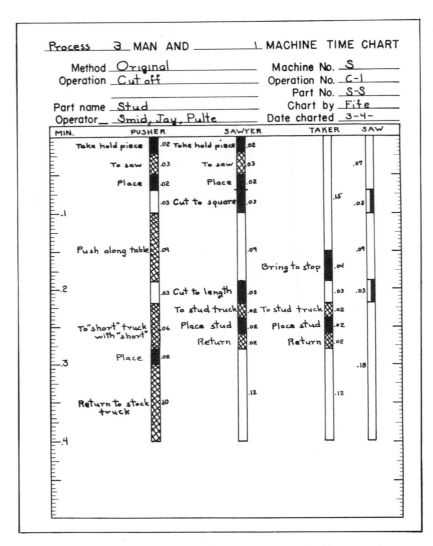

Fig. 13.2—Multiman and machine process time chart for original
method of three-man crew cutting 8-foot house studs from
mill length 2″ × 4″ stock.

the saw. The coding of the columns follows the standards given in Table 7.
The length of each section of each bar is proportional to the time spent on
that step of the task. As with previous charts, the columns are arranged so
that a horizontal line drawn through them at any place passes through simultaneous actions of the men and machines involved.

The chart was constructed by making a process chart-man analysis for each worker, roughly keying them together with the operation of the machine, obtaining rough stop-watch time values for each step, and adjusting these as the actions of the men indicated, so that they meshed properly as shown in Figure 13.3. For a person with considerable experience with the type of

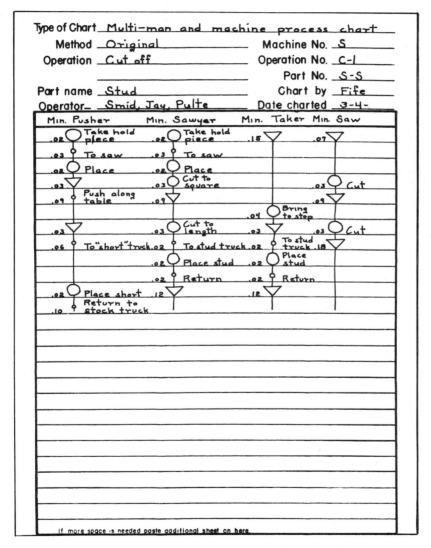

Fig. 13.3—*Multiman and machine process chart for original method of three-man crew cutting 8-foot house studs from mill length 2″ × 4″ stock.*

214   Multiple-activity analysis—multiman charts

work charted, this form of analysis may be sufficient, but the time chart form, even though it takes longer to prepare, is usually more productive. In the present case, the time chart shown in Figure 13.2 was drawn next. Note that all of these steps and time values may be obtained simultaneously from a motion-picture film or video-tape, thus greatly reducing the analytic work, particularly with large crews. (See Chapter 14).

Each item on the chart was criticized with the aid of a suitable check list like that shown here.

CHECK LIST FOR MULTIMAN AND MULTIMAN AND MACHINE PROCESS CHARTS

Basic Principles
A. Balance the work of the crew
B. If a machine is involved, consider increasing percentage of use
C. Ease the job of the most-loaded man
D. Eliminate steps
E. Combine steps
F. Make steps as easy as possible
   1. Can any operation be eliminated?
      a. As unnecessary
      b. By changing the order of work
      c. By new or different equipment
      d. By changes in the layout
   2. Can any movement be eliminated?
      a. By leaving out operations
      b. By shifting some operations to another job into which they fit more conveniently
      c. By changing equipment
      d. By changing the layout
      e. By changing the order of work
      f. By conveyors (Make sure they are economical.)
   3. Can delays be eliminated?
      a. By changing the order of work
      b. By changing the layout
      c. By new or different equipment
   4. Can countings or inspections be eliminated?
      a. Are they really necessary? What happens after they are done and the information obtained?
      b. Do they give unnecessary duplication?
      c. Can they be performed more conveniently by another person?
      d. Are they done at the best point in the sequence?
   5. Can operations be combined?
      a. By changing the order of work
      b. With new or different equipment
      c. By changing the layout
   6. Can movements be combined?
      a. By changing the order of work
      b. By changing the layout
      c. By changing the quantity handled at one time
   7. Can delays be combined?
      a. By changing the order of work

b. By changing the layout

c. If they provide rest, can they be grouped better.

8. Can countings or inspections be combined?

   a. By changing the order of work

   b. By changing the layout

9. Can any step be made safer?

   a. By changing the order of work

   b. By new or different equipment

   c. By changing the layout

10. Can any operation be made easier?

   a. By a better tool

   b. By changing positions of controls or tools

   c. By using better material containers or racks, bins, or trucks

   d. By using inertia where possible and avoiding it where worker must overcome it

   e. By lessening visual requirements (see Figure 11.4)

   f. By better workplace heights

   g. By using different muscles

      Use the first muscle group in this list that is strong enough for the task:

      q. Finger

      2. Wrist

      3. Elbow

      4. Shoulder

      5. Trunk

   h. By jigs or fixtures

11. Can any movement be made easier?

   a. By a change in layout, shortening distances

   b. By a change in the direction of movements

   c. By changing its place in the sequence to one where the distance that must be traveled is shorter

12. Can any delay of one crew member, caused by another crew member, be eliminated?

   a. By changing the number of the crew

   b. By changing the number of machines that the crew uses

      (One must again bear in mind the following four possibilities, which were listed previously in connection with man and machine charts.)

      1. Reduction of operator delays to the minimum required for rest and personal time. There may be considerable machine delay.

      2. Reduction of machine delays to the minimum required to provide the operator with rest and personal time, at which times the machine is unattended. There may be considerable other operator delay.

      3. Reduction of machine and operator delays such that they will provide the most economical balance.

      4. Reduction of both operator and machine delays to the minimum required to provide the operator with rest and personal time.

   c. By a redistribution of the work among the crew

   d. By changing the order of work of the crew

As a result of the application of this check list, the improved method shown in Figure 13.4 was devised and output was increased by 100 per cent. Saw usage was thus doubled. The changes in the workplace and the new pattern of movement of the crew are indicated in Figure 13.5.

The changes which made this new method possible were suggested by the following questions from the check list. The notes the analyst made for future reference are also given.

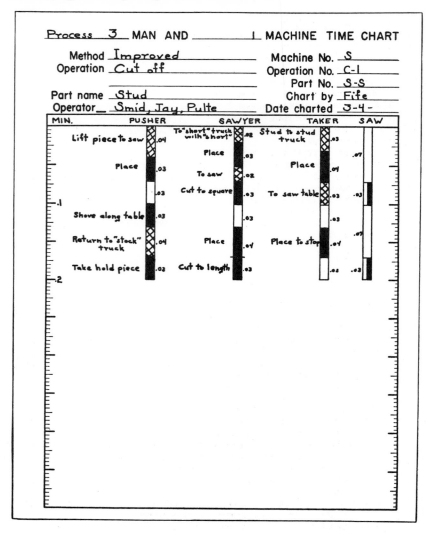

Fig. 13.4—Multiman and machine process time chart for improved method of three-man crew cutting 8-foot house studs from mill length 2″ × 4″ stock.

12. Can any delay of one crew member, caused by another crew member, be eliminated?
    c. By a redistribution of the work among the crew
        Note: Have the sawyer, instead of the pusher, place the shorts. Have the pusher place the stock on the table by himself.

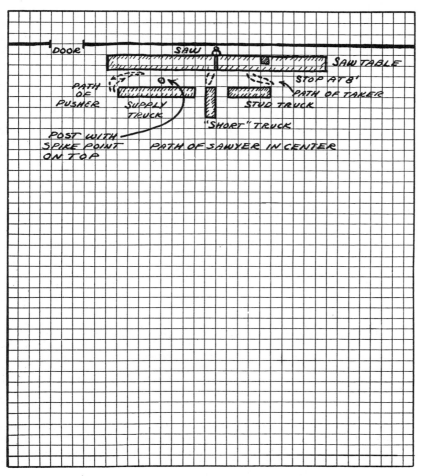

Fig. 13.5—Plan view of part of prefabricated-house plant, showing location of material and equipment and path of three-man crew cutting studs using improved method.

(This second would be impossible as the job was done, so further improvement was necessary.)

10. *Can any operation be made easier?*

    h. By jigs or fixtures

        Note: A post with a spike point on top (located as shown in Figure 13.5) makes it possible for a pusher to lift one end of the 14-foot stock, place its middle over the point, lift the opposite end onto the table by depressing and swinging his end of the board, and then lifting his end over onto the table, thus placing the stock on saw tables without help.

    d. By using inertia where possible

        Note: Instead of pushing material all the way down a saw table, it is possible to give it a thrust and it will slide to its destination.

SUMMARY — MULTIMAN CHARTS

1. Uses:
   a. *Arranging crew work for the best balance.*
   b. *Estimating the effect of crews of different sizes.*
   c. *Designing a crew task.*
   d. *As a basis for instructing the crew.*
   e. *Locating sections of the task where a detailed right- and left-hand analysis is needed to develop an improvement.*
2. How made:
   a. *A process chart-man analysis is constructed for one of the crew members. The information is confined, however, to one side of the chart. The classification of steps, symbols, and procedure is the same as with process charts-man analysis.*
   b. *The other crew members are charted, one at a time, in a similar fashion on the same sheet as in Step 1, care being exercised to place next to each other the symbols that indicate simultaneous activities.*
   c. *The machine or machines are analyzed next in a similar manner and placed on the same chart.*
   d. *By the use of an ordinary watch, stop-watch, motion picture, video-tape, or table of preapproximated performance times, the time is obtained for each item on the chart. If watches are used, the times will be collected from several cycles; hence some adjusting may be necessary to obtain comparable values. If films or tapes are used, steps a through d may be done on the same cycle of work.*
   e. *By the use of a form similar to Figure 13.2 or a sheet of graph or cross-section paper, the information obtained in the previous steps is recharted, using a time scale such that the chart is of convenient length. The conventions of Table 7 are used.*
   f. *A summary may be placed at the bottom of the chart, although the length of the chart is, in itself, a rough summary.*
3. How used:
   Each step of the operation is questioned with a suitable check list. The general principles listed at the top of the check list are kept in mind as objectives.
4. What then:
   A new multiman chart is drawn for the resulting suggested method (there may be several alternative charts if effects of variations in crew size are being examined) in order to permit a final check and to provide a means of describing the proposed new method.

Supplemental Material

CASE II   VARIATIONS IN CREW SIZE ON GRID
WINDING, STRETCHING, CHOPPING, AND PEELING

This job was originally described in the preceding chapter as a one-man
and one-machine operation. It is selected for re-examination in this section

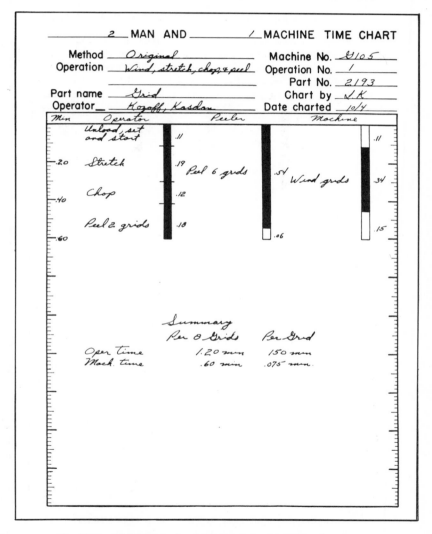

Fig. 13.6 — *Multiman and machine process time chart for two-man
crew on winding, stretching, chopping, and peeling radio-
tube grids.*

because it contrasts with Case I in size of parts involved and in work area, and illustrates how the technique described in this section may be used over the entire range of size of jobs.

Also, in Case I the objective was to improve the job by changing the details of doing the work; here the objective is to evaluate changes in the job with the changes restricted to variation of crew size (a Class 1 change). The details

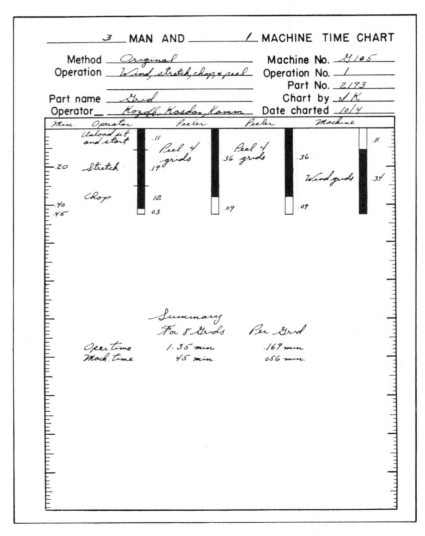

Fig. 13.7—Multiman and machine process time chart for three-man crew on winding, stretching, chopping, and peeling radio-tube grids.

of the steps of work are not to be affected in any way. They are merely to be redistributed among different numbers of workers.

Figure 13.6 is a two-man multiman and machine process time chart, and Figure 13.7 is a three-man multiman and machine process time chart for the job of winding, stretching, chopping, and peeling grids, previously shown as a one-man task in Figure 12.10. The method of charting is that used on the one-man chart. Attention is called to the manner in which the machine and operator time chargeable to each grid vary from method to method.

The most desirable solution is of course a function of the grid capacity of the plant, the amount of labor available, the demand for the product, and the cost relationships between machine time and labor time. Note, however, that this technique makes possible a good estimate of the effects of different-size crews, prior to actual testing of the different crews, and that it also provides the material for instructing the crew in the proper distribution of work, once the crew size is determined.

The solution that would be found most desirable in the case would be only for one type of grid and one set of values of the economic variables. All these may change from time to time. Also, since the winding time, chopping time, and peeling time are all functions of the size of grid, the size of wires, the number of turns per inch, and so forth, the best solution will vary from grid to grid, as well as with changes in the basic economic factors previously listed. However, the man and machine process time charts and the multiman and machine process time charts provide an easy means of comparing the possible solutions.

CHAPTER 14

Photographic and Electronic Data Recording Aids

The human eye, ear, and hand, when used in a real-time data recording system, impose a severe restriction with respect to the number of bits of information which may be recorded per unit of time. Further, they limit the number of aspects of a situation which may be maintained under simultaneous observation. In addition, the eye-ear-hand data recording system, when extended to its limit, is subject to errors of both observation and recording. There are many method study situations wherein some additional data-recording aid is needed in order to meet the requirements of effective analysis. Such situations are encountered when analysis requires the study in detail of all of the motions of a repetitive job, the path of motions with work involving a high level of skill, the relationships among a large and complex crew, or the simultaneous use of multiple communication channels in an information-flow procedure carried on in a restricted time frame.

In situations such as have been listed, a variety of photographic and electronic data recording aids have been used. These aids assist by recording data from real-time events and holding the information in a form permitting its transcription into a form serving the purpose of analysis. These aids serve as a time-buffer; they record within the time frame set by the events under scrutiny but may be transcribed, in a time frame imposed by human limitations, into a form suitable for analysis. The form of the analysis may be any one of the techniques discussed to this point or any of the approaches presented in the next chapter. The techniques of the next chapter follow this chapter because they are totally dependent upon the use of some aid; their use presumes data gathering at a level of detail beyond the capability of the unaided human data recording system.

The devices which have been found to be of assistance for gathering data are as follows:

1. Motion picture camera with timing device
   a. High speed photography
   b. Normal speed photography
   c. Slow speed photography
2. Video-tape recorder
3. Sound tape recorder
4. Special purpose still camera
   a. Cyclegraphic photography
   b. Chronocyclegraphic photography

The Motion Picture Camera and Video-tape Recorder

With the advent of relatively low priced, portable video-tape recorders, the motion picture camera and the video-tape recorder may be considered as almost interchangeable devices. They both employ a camera. The motion picture camera records on photographic film; the video-tape recorder on magnetic tape. They both can record visual and auditory information simultaneously. The speed of the motion-picture camera and of the video-tape recorder can be held constant with respect to a time-datum such as the frequency of the alternating current in use. The video record can be converted to a film record and vice versa. There are, however, some small differences which affect the desirability of employing one or the other of these devices in particular situations. These differences will be noted in the discussion which follows in the few places where pertinent. In most cases, that which is given as a characteristic of motion picture photography should be understood as applying equally to the use of the video-tape recorder.

As has been briefly discussed, the motion-picture camera (or video-tape) is merely an aid for performing the second step, *analysis*, of the scientific procedure. The motion-picture film (or video-tape) provides the means of obtaining as much detail as desired and possesses greater accuracy and flexibility than the human data recording system. Although motion-picture (or video-tape) aided motion study is taken by some to predicate the use of a camera and timing device to study, in great detail, the motions of a highly repetitive job performed at one location (and it is extremely useful in such cases), it should actually be thought of as an alternative means of observing and recording the work activities during any job, regardless of whether one man, a man and machine, a crew, or several men and machines are engaged, and whether the cycle is long or short. Indeed, it is usually the superior way to study long and complex cycles, particularly those with variable cycles and coordinated crew activities. The timing device may be a special time indicator included in the camera's field of view or a synchronous (constant speed) motor for driving the camera; the video-tape is taken at a known time rate.

The use of a motion-picture camera and film, or video recorder and tape, provides a permanent, complete record of the job method. The timing device provides a permanent time record on the film or tape for each step in the job, and the film or tape itself provides a record of the interrelationships among the men or machines involved. It is important to realize at the outset that motion pictures, or the electronic images on the tape, are merely a successive series of still pictures and that the time lag between successive pictures can and should be varied to apply conveniently to the job being studied. No other data-gathering method is as flexible in this respect. The size of the time values involved, which depends on the filming speed used, may be as large as or larger than those commonly associated with the breakdown on process chart-man analysis or smaller than those on the finest man and machine operation time chart. Even work sampling studies may be made with the aid of an intermittently operated motion-picture camera. Although small video-tape recorders of the type implicit in this discussion do not lend themselves to such radical changes in speed, the set used for analysis may be adjusted to present images on the screen of the image tube as if they had been taken at such slow speeds or random intervals; the set merely skips the information between the desired pictures.

With motion-picture or tape aided method study, a selected portion of the data recorded (usually a typical cycle of work, although in some cases a series of cycles or a selected period of time is used) is transcribed into form for analysis and criticism, first by film or tape analysis, and second by presentation by a suitable tabular or graphic technique. Any of the job breakdowns and accompanying graphic techniques that have already been described may be used as well as any one of the variety of techniques described in the next chapter.

The techniques described in the next chapter include one with a very detailed set of steps for analysis but the very detailed breakdown is used only when the physical conditions of the job require it; it is *not* a necessary part of motion-picture or tape aided method study. With some jobs the breakdown will resemble the *work activity analysis*. Whatever type is used, the essential feature is the use of film or tape to record the data as the event or job being studied occurs, with the subsequent analysis of the recorded data being the basis of dividing the task under study into appropriate steps, pertinent to the job and convenient to the objectives of the study.

Film for motion picture camera study costs approximately $0.16 to $2.50

per minute of record taken, depending on the speed of picture taking. A video tape may cost about $2.50 per minute of recording but the tape may be "wiped" and reused. Equipment for filming and film analysis may be assembled for approximately $600, although completely adequate and flexible equipment will run to about $2,000. The video-tape setup will also run about $2,000. However, if with the aid of this equipment costs can be reduced by only one-half of a man-year, the investment will be completely recovered. This should readily explain why the industrial use of the various forms of camera and video-tape study has been rapidly increasing.

If the work of a method study group is extensive enough to make considerable use of the equipment, the camera or video-recorder aided technique is, in many instances, the most economical means of analyzing many jobs. For example, it would be much easier to determine the interrelationships of a three-man crew, like those in the operation of cutting studs for prefabricated houses, described in Chapter 13, from a film or tape than from direct observation of the actual operation. The film or tape can be stopped, run backwards and forwards, and repeated as often as is necessary. As the work group increases in size and the task become more complex, the advantage of film or tape is even greater. A 40-man crew in a large foundry, which would normally have presented an almost insuperable problem, was studied by means of film with ease and accuracy.[1] The use of certain slow filming speeds has led to a much broader application of motion-picture films than may be generally realized and, as has been noted, tape may be used in a similar manner. The recording cost for the three-man stud-cutting job of Chapter 13 would have been about $0.20 (with pictures taken at 60 to 100 frames per minute as contrasted to the normal motion-picture speed of 960 frames per minute) for three cycles of work. It is worth comparing this with the probable cost of the analyst's time when obtaining the data by observation with paper, pencil, and watch. Such unusually slow picture-taking speeds, not used industrially until 1947, expanded the use of film and are referred to as "memomotion study."

Modern 16-mm film equipment, the size most commonly used,[2] have been brought to such a degree of perfection that the data recording usually requires no special preparation of the workplace and has little chance of failure. The equipment is reliable, sturdy, compact, extremely portable, and easy to use. The motion picture camera equipment is somewhat smaller than the tape equipment.

---

[1] Although the particular plant did not have enough work to make the purchase of filming equipment desirable, they could easily afford the analysis equipment. They hired an outside photographer to take their films, to obtain the use of superlative equipment.

[2] The introduction of Super-8 film and advances in the quality of film make it feasible to use this smaller size. However, the smaller film will not resolve as much detail as the larger 16-mm film and is somewhat harder to use if sound is also to be recorded.

Film recording and video-tape recording have the following advantages over other methods of gathering data:

1. *Permits greater detailing than eye observation.* Of course, the analyst should obtain from the record only that degree of detail best suited to his analysis requirements. However, with crew work or work with irregular cycles, the simultaneity of actions of the crew or the sequence, as it occurs, may be recorded with complete details by the camera or tape far beyond the capacity of any observer to observe and record without aids. For instance, a film study record taken at one frame per second (memomotion) of a pharmacist revealed that his prescription-filling time was consumed as follows:[3]

Description of Activity	Rank Importance	Per Cent of Time Used
Work on labels or prescription blanks	1	23.3
Work wrapping	2	10.5
Work putting material into prescription containers or with containers	3	10.1
Inspection of prescription blanks	4	7.4
Work applying labels	5	7.2
Travel to and from register	6	5.4
Work counting items	7	5.2
Travel to shelves or cupboards for material	8	5.0
Work with balance and accessories.................	9	4.3
Work getting down items........................	10	4.1
Work compounding	11	3.9
Work on drugs	12	3.3
Talking to customers	13	2.8
Work at cash register	14	2.3
Inspection of shelves...........................	15	2.0
Inspection of drug containers or contents...........	16	1.3
Travel to shelves or cupboards to put away	17	1.1
Work putting up items..........................	18	.6
Work with liquid measures	19	.2
TOTAL		100.0

Such data could have been gathered without film only with difficulty because the work pattern was highly irregular. This analysis almost automatically suggests steps that might be taken to facilitate the work. For instance, the time expended on the most time-consuming part of the work could be reduced

[3] Study made for "The Pharmaceutical Survey," of the American Council on Education.

with a special label-attachment on the platen of the typewriter; the next most time-consuming task could be facilitated through the use of a prescription bag (introduced later) such as shown in Figure 14.1.

Fig. 14.1—Prescription bag used to reduce wrapping time.

2. *Provides greater accuracy than pencil, paper, and watch techniques.* The time from picture to picture is approximately 0.001 minute when a 16-mm camera is used at the normal speed of 16 frames per second. Smaller time intervals may be obtained by running the camera faster. Slower speeds of 100 frames per minute (0.01 min. per frame), 60 frames per minute (1 sec. per frame) and 50 frames per minute (0.02 min. per frame) are often extremely useful and economical.[4] Of course, even larger time units may be used if desired. The man and machine operation time chart for the operation of folding sheet-metal box liners (Figure 12.7), was made from a film. Attention

[4] Speeds of 60 frames per minute appear to be just about right for maximum film economy and adequate detail, despite the disadvantage of using seconds instead of decimal minutes. In some industrial applications, however, the advantages of decimal minutes may outweigh the film economics, making 100 frames per minute preferable. In any case, the time value used should be selected by considering all of the requirements of the problem. Video-tape may be used in a similar fashion.

is called to the magnitude of the time units shown. These would be difficult to obtain by any other means except, perhaps, video-tape.

3. *Provides greater convenience.* The operation may be studied after a short run or after an experimental run. The film or tape can be stopped at will when being studied, so that each phase of the operation can be studied without bothering the operators. Even with such irregular jobs as building custom truck bodies, a single unit could be usefully studied by means of one-per-second films (or a video-tape used to produce equivalent data), developing data for better methods and better cost estimates on any other order that even partially resembled the one studied. Films or tapes also permit group observation without interrupting factory routine.

A more detailed example demonstrates the peculiar convenience of one form of film or tape aided study. The peeling of canning tomatoes was studied in Indiana during the winter of 1942–1943, with special tomatoes shipped ripe from Florida, to develop a better peeling method for the Indiana tomato canneries during the summer canning season of 1943.[5] The season generally lasts only from August until frost; hence, it would have been extremely difficult to develop and install any new method on a widespread basis during the season itself. This difficulty was increased by the small size

Fig. 14.2—Analyst using precision movie camera to make micro-motion film of expert tomato peeler. The workplace is a section duplicating the canning factory conveyor.

[5] M. E. Mundel, R. R. Fraser, and W. E. Luley, "An Easy Way to Peel Canning Tomatoes," *Purdue Extension Misc. Pub.* 23, 1943; also M. E. Mundel, R. R. Fraser, and W. E. Luley, "Work Simplification Applied to Tomato Peeling," *Factory*, Vol. 102, No. 5, May 1944, pp. 89–91.

and multiplicity of canning plants in the state. Moreover the job is extremely important, since over 9,000,000 man hours are spent peeling tomatoes each season.

Using the special tomatoes, films were made of short work spells with expert peelers from all over the state. Figure 14.2 shows one of the analysts filming a peeler with a precision spring-driven camera. A speed of 16 frames per second was used. In this case, the camera had a sufficiently constant speed to do away with the need for a separate timing device, although one may be desirable. Extremely detailed analyses were made of this job because of its importance. With simpler jobs, less detailed analyses are made. In the first phase of this analysis, the peeling cycle was divided into four major parts: (1) get tomato, (2) remove core, (3) peel, and (4) aside tomato. The study of many cycles by means of film revealed facts like those shown for "remove core," (part 2) in Figure 14.3, and for "peel," (part 3) in Figure

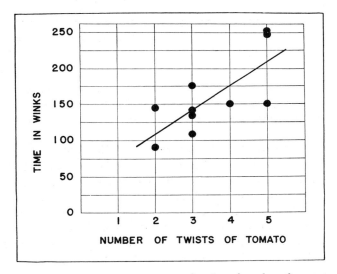

Fig. 14.3—Time to remove core as a function of number of separate twists of tomato. The number of twists is under the operator's control since the method of presetting the hands prior to inserting the knife controls this. (One wink equals 1/2000 minute. This term was introduced by the Gilbreths.)

14.4. Both magnitude and variation of time values are much smaller than could possibly be detected with a watch or any visual observation method. The films were also analyzed with the detailed breakdown that will be described in the next chapter. Such analyses of these films were instrumental in developing a method of peeling that permitted a group of new workers

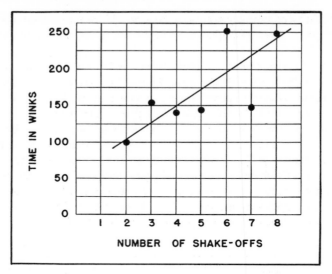

*Fig. 14.4—Time for peel as a function of the number of times the
peel is shaken off the peeling knife.*

finally to achieve a peeling rate 30 per cent faster than a similar group following ordinary factory methods. The group using the new method peeled 22
per cent more tomatoes in the five weeks studied (which included the training
period).[6]

4. *Provides a positive record.* The film or tape is without errors of the kinds
that may enter into pencil and paper records. This is particularly true of
complex jobs like crew tasks, where the recording of simultaneity depends
upon the ability of the observer. A pencil and paper record is, at best, partly
subjective, whereas a film or tape is an almost true record of what happened
and is available for re-examination at any time. With larger crews, it is almost
a necessity. For instance, to study a five-man extrusion-press crew in an
aluminum plant, the analyst has a choice of:

1. Observing each of the crew members in turn and attempting to make the
   tasks key in properly by "adjusting" the figures,
2. Getting four other observers to help him, so that all data come from the
   same cycles, or
3. Making a film or video-tape of the task, studying each crew member
   separately on the same recorded cycles, and combining these data
   afterwards.

[6] L. J. Havercamp, and L. S. Hardin, "Simplifying Tomato Canning Factory Operations," *Ind. Agr. Exp. Sta. Bul.* 528, Purdue Univ., 1948. (This bulletin includes a report
on an application of the method developed in the research previously footnoted.)

The ease of procedure 3 and the positive nature of the record it provides should be obvious. The slower (memomotion) speeds are commonly used in such applications.

5. *Aids in developing methods men.* Training in the use of film or video-tape aided method study, particularly with the detailed breakdown, tends to develop a "motion-mindedness" that almost invariably makes a person better able to develop more effective methods. It appears as though greater familiarity with the detailed movements of which jobs are composed helps one gain more facility for seeing possibilities of shifting them to achieve better methods. This is extremely important.

In addition to the above five advantages, films or video-tapes (or films made from tapes) are useful for preserving adequate records of job methods of intermittent jobs, for training, and for certain phases of time study work.

The main disadvantage of film study is the time lag between the taking of the data and its transcription into usable form. However, with developing facilities available in many cities to fill the needs of TV news films, films can usually be made available for study on either the same day or the day after taking. Video-tapes, of course, are usable immediately after taking. Although the cost of film is listed as a disadvantage, as compared with visual methods, there is in many cases an actual saving in the total cost of analysis, due to the reduced study time made possible by using film or tape for recording. It has been the experience of many plants that the recording equipment often more than pays for itself on the first job on which it is used.

Film or video-tape aided study involves three separate phases of activity for performing step 2, *analysis*, of the scientific method.

1. Recording
2. Transcribing (called *film analysis* or *tape analysis*)
3. Graphic presentation of the method for study, criticism, and improvement

Sound Tape Recorder

Reference was made in Chapter 10 to a special set of steps which might be recognized in an analysis of a mixed-means communication system. Such systems arise in the operation of an aircraft, the aircraft control-tower relationship, a missile launch site, and so forth. The recording of data in a form suitable for real analysis is beyond the limits of the human data recording system. However, a multichannel tape recorder (or a number of tape recorders, one on each channel, and cross-cued for a time datum base) may be employed. These tapes may later be transcribed in the same manner as dictation records, and the time obtained by one of two methods. For one method, the tape may be replayed, after being transcribed and the sequential times for each sequential transmission may be determined by a stop-watch. As an alternative, for somewhat greater accuracy, the tape may be played to an oscillograph and the length of the oscillograph tape measured later to obtain both the time of the inception of the transmission and its duration. Various types of time charts may be used to present such data for analysis.

The U.S. Federal Aviation Authority, as a routine procedure, tapes communications between aircraft and control towers so as to provide an aid in analyzing any undesirable events which may transpire. The aim is to assist in designing remedial measures.

Sound tapes may also be used to record visually observed data; the use of tape decreases the limitations of the eye-ear-hand recording system. In many cases such data may be presented for analytical consideration by any one of the analysis techniques described in preceding chapters.

Special Purpose Still Camera

Some tasks performed at one location are of such a nature that details of the motion path are of primary importance and concern. This is particularly true of short-cycle skilled operations for which the operator must be taught a motion path as well as a sequence of motions. It is also true of motions in space, like folding flatwork in a laundry, or parts of jobs containing similar motions. For the study of such tasks F. B. Gilbreth developed two techniques, cyclegraphic and chronocyclegraphic analysis. He was still perfecting these when he died in 1924.[7]

A *cyclegraph* is a photographic record on still film of the path of motion of a body member taken with a light attached to the body member. A long shutter opening is usually used, equal to the time for a motion cycle.

A *chronocyclegraph* is a similar photographic record except that the light is caused to flicker with a nonsymmetrical peak of brilliance[8] so that both speed and direction of movement may be determined.

Gilbreth used a stereoscopic (three-dimensional) camera so as to record fully the true motion path; subsequent analysts have, for the most part, done likewise. In some cases, however, to expedite the availability of data, a Polaroid Land (60-second development) camera has been used with a simple

[7] The techniques reported here have not been used extensively in the United States. However, they appear to have their place of use and are described here to make available this additional approach to the determination of the "one best way." The writer is indebted for much of this material to Miss Anne G. Shaw of Cheshire, England. Miss Shaw, who studied under Lillian Gilbreth, has taken a leading role in applying motion study into Great Britain.

[8] The same result may be obtained by rotating a photographic wedge in front of the film, a method proposed by Miss Shaw and developed by Professors Connolly and H. C. Wiltshire at the College of Aeronautics, Cranfield, England.

two-dimensional presentation.[9] However, converting such a camera to three-dimensional recording is relatively easy.

In the past these techniques received but little use in the United States, probably because of the scant literature available concerning them, the lack of experience with them, and the lack of simple commercial equipment. However, in England, under the direction of Miss Anne G. Shaw, these techniques have been used extensively and appear to represent another valuable approach to the selection of a preferable way of doing a job. The photographs on pages 233 and 234 were supplied by Miss Shaw, who wrote, concerning Figure 14.5,

Fig. 14.5 — Chronocyclegraph of original method of collating sheets of a duplicated five-page report. (Photograph courtesy of Miss A. G. Shaw.)

as follows (the job being studied was the collating of a report of five pages):

When the . . . chronocyclegraph [Figure 14.5] is examined as a whole, three points are immediately obvious:

1. The right hand is moving each sheet a considerable distance and the spacing and shape of the spots shows that the speed of movement varies

[9] Gerald E. Clark, "A Chronocyclegraph That Will Help You Improve Methods," *Factory*, Vol. 112, No. 5, May 1954, pp. 124, 125. This article describes a photographic wedge slightly different from Connolly and Wiltshire's.

along the path followed in picking up each sheet of paper. The round, closely spaced spots indicate how the movement begins slowly as the sheet is picked up. They then spread out and elongate as the hand gains speed, contracting as it slows down to allow the left hand to take the paper. As the hand travels down to pick up the next sheet they become long and thin, showing that this is the fastest part of the movement.

2. The left hand moves in jerks and the congestion of spots shows that it travels much more slowly than the right hand.

3. Both hands travel over a considerable distance from the moment when they pick up the first sheet to the point at which they shake the sheets together before the right hand puts them down and moves back to pick up the next sheet.[10]

In her discussion of this chronocyclegraph,[11] Miss Shaw points out how the motions might be shortened and the task of the left hand, which merely accompanies the right hand and acts as a holding device, eliminated, thus freeing it also for picking up sheets. She goes on to indicate that a method like that shown in Figure 14.6 permits both hands to move more freely and pro-

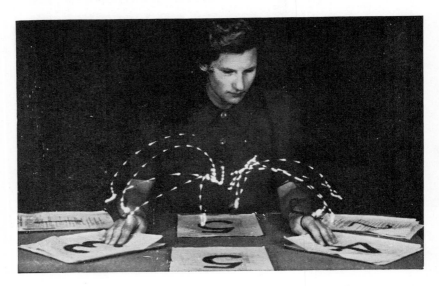

Fig. 14.6 — Chronocyclegraph of improved method for task of Figure 14.5. (Photograph courtesy of Miss A. G. Shaw.)

ductively. Note the more regular and more widely-spaced dots. (The finished reports, piled directly in front of the operator, are separated from one another

---

[10] A. G. Shaw, *The Purpose and Practice of Motion Study*. Buxton, Derbyshire, England: Columbine Press (Publishers) Ltd., 1960, 2nd edition, p. 106.

[11] *Ibid.*, pp. 78, 79.

by causing sheet 5 to project somewhat from the other four.) In addition, Miss Shaw points out that this method is immediately available, although a fixture might further facilitate it. She goes on to note that the conclusions (quoted previously) were drawn from a general examination of the chrono-cyclegraph without counting the spots; further, that in a simple task like this an experienced analyst would probably not need a record of this type. She adds, however, that in many cases a proposed method may be conveniently tested with this technique and additional sources of savings found or operator faults detected and corrected.

Supplemental Material

A description of the three phases of recording, transcribing, and graphic presentation, using film or video-tape recording follows. The description is general; no particular level of detail and no particular graphic presentation is predicated.

Filming. The following equipment is needed for making motion picture films:

1. *Sixteen-mm camera* (super 8-mm film may be used in many cases) with an $f1.5$, 1-inch lens or better, or an $f1.2$, wide-angle (12-mm) lens. The wide-angle lens is used most frequently. The camera should have a good spring motor and variable speed for taking pictures. However, a motor drive is preferable to a spring motor. The camera should have a shaft to which the motor drive can be attached. A suitable camera, attached to a motor drive, is shown in Figure 14.7.

The ideal setup includes a synchronous motor drive for the camera which provides speeds of 60, 100, 1000, and 1440 (sound speed) frames per minute, with a gear shift for rapid change from speed to speed This is shown already attached to the camera in Figure 14.7.

2. *Tripod for camera.* A tripod helps get better pictures for little extra money It does away with jerkiness often caused by unsteady hands. If a tripod is used, it should have a pan-and-tilt head.

3. *Exposure meter.* Any of the electronic exposure meters presently available are suitable for assisting in determining the proper exposure. A regular exposure meter, rather than one specially set up for ciné work, is to be preferred because of the odd exposure intervals used with memomotion speeds.

4. *Timing device* (optional). This may be a clock like the one shown in Figure 14.8, with 100 divisions on its face and a large hand making 20 rpm or 10 rpm, and a small hand making 2 or 1 rpm, depending on the speed of the large hand. Since slow-motion pictures at 32 frames per second are sometimes necessary instead of the normal 16 frames per second, the faster clock is

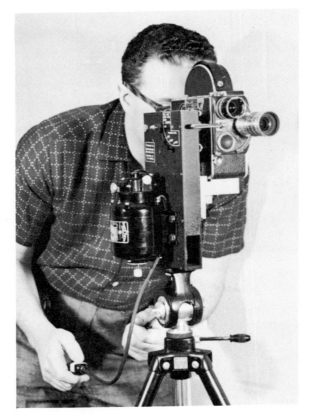

Fig. 14.7—Bolex H-16 camera equipped with f1.2, 12 mm lens and commercial gear-shift, four-speed, synchronous motor drive. (Courtesy Sullivan-Becker Machine Co., Kenosha, Wis.)

desirable. The clock is usually referred to as a microchronometer. If an electric-drive camera with a synchronous (constant-speed) motor is used instead of a spring-driven camera, the microchronometer may be dispensed with, although it may be left in the picture in order to:

a. Be sure the workers know that time is recorded. Values surreptitiously obtained have no advantage and create mistrust.
b. Be proof of the continuousness of the film.
c. Identify, at any future time, the speed of picture taking.
d. Measure the length of any missing section if the film is inadvertently damaged in use.

Current practice attempts the use of motion pictures with as little dis-

Fig. 14.8 — Microchronometer.

turbance of normal work conditions as possible. Since the placement of a timing device on the workplace can be a distraction, the use of these devices is decreasing.

5. *Synchronous motor drive.* An electric drive with a synchronous motor not only permits taking a longer series of pictures without pausing to rewind, as with spring-driven cameras, but permits the elimination of the timer from the work place. This contributes to a more casual use of motion pictures by reducing the distractions, and also makes it possible to use memomotion speeds.

Since the introduction of modern high speed lenses and films, lights are not required for micromotion filming. Indeed, modern lenses and films permit the making of good quality motion pictures in almost any location where there is enough light for the worker to see what he is doing. The use of high-intensity photographic lights in the factory is a source of great disturbance. The glare is not only annoying to the operator, but it makes the operator the focus of attention. Certainly, the conditions filmed are different from normal. The employment of available-light photography also reduces the set-up time for picture taking. Equipment without lights greatly reduces the bulk which must be brought to the job, making it possible for one man to carry, set up and employ the equipment. Figure 14.9 shows one man taking motion pictures using available light. All of the equipment in use is shown.

Filming for data recording involves only six simple rules:

1. Obtain the cooperation of the operator and his foreman. It is often worthwhile to notify them a day ahead, so that the operator may dress accordingly if so inclined. On the other hand, with available-light photog-

Fig. 14.9 — Micromotion filming with available light.

raphy, the use of motion pictures may become so routine that this procedure may be abandoned as attaching undue importance to the films. In a union shop it may be worthwhile obtaining the cooperation of the steward. No one should have anything to fear from pictures, since they are merely a more reliable means of studying what would otherwise be visually studied with less accuracy. When filming large crews, subsequent analysis of the film may be much easier if the workers are issued inexpensive T-shirts with large numbers on the front and back. If so, adequate explanations for the shirts should be made well beforehand and all questions answered.

2. Place the camera as close to the action of the job as possible, but be sure the view of the camera includes all the activities wanted for analysis. Set the lens focus and check the view through the finder. It should be borne in mind that the films are to gather data and not to represent an artistic effort; they should be taken with as little fuss as possible.

3. Select the speed of picture-taking and set the camera speed control or motor drive accordingly.

4. Get the best exposure possible. Quality films are not a requisite, but better exposures make the analysis easier. With modern high-speed films, surprisingly little light is required. Exposure instructions accompany both camera and exposure meters and are also published in book form by Eastman Kodak.[12] Basically, the length of exposure is controlled by the number of frames per second, in a manner explained in the instruction book accompanying the camera. Usually 8 frames per second give an exposure of 1/15 sec.; 16 frames, an exposure of 1/30 sec., etc. Only a few cameras are at all adjustable in this respect, and the adjustment usually permits cutting down the exposure but not increasing it. The exposure meter has a calculator attached to it that takes into account:
   a. The exposure interval.
   b. The sensitivity of the film, which is given either on the film carton or on a folder in the film carton.
   c. The amount of light on the subject. (Pictures for data should usually be exposed for the darkest part of the picture *in which detail is wanted.*) The use of available light is usually accompanied by more uniform lighting than with photographic lighting; this simplifies the exposure problem.

   The calculator on the exposure meter is used to determine the correct lens aperture for any condition of these three variables.
5. If you use a microchronometer, make sure it is in the picture as much as possible. (It is preferable that it be in all the time; otherwise the counter on the projector will have to be used to interpolate.) However, the use of a synchronous motor drive without a microchronometer means one less feature of the workplace to fuss with. This contributes to faster filming.
6. Make a record of exposure data and pertinent job information. This record permits discovery of the reasons for poor exposures, if they occur, and the application of corrective measures on future films. It also provides a place, identifiable against the film, to record important job information that does not appear on the film.

Video-tape recording. Video-tape recording differs little from film recording. A special camera is used and this camera is connected to a special tape recorder.[13] The equipment is handled in a manner similar to that used with film. A tripod and exposure meter are necessary, and all of the human problems remain the same.

[12] Eastman Kodak Company, *How to Make Good Movies.* Rochester, New York: Eastman Kodak Company (undated and frequently revised).
[13] I have not given make or model numbers of suggested equipment because of the extreme rate of change and improvement taking place in commercially-available equipment. M.E.M.

Film analysis. The films must be processed after they are taken. Inasmuch as motion-picture film processing is available on a one-day or same-day basis in most major cities, the film is rapidly available for analysis. Plants located in cities without processing service can usually arrange for mail service from the nearest processer; a three-day turn-around time is usually the maximum. (When time was of the essence, the author obtained 45-minute service.)

A projecter used for film analysis must have specific features somewhat different from the conventional projector. The optical system must have heat filtering sufficient to permit prolonged examination of single frames. A frame-by-frame advance of the film, forward or backward, must be convenient; the projector should also have a built-in frame counter. A suitable commercially-available projector is shown in Figure 14.10. All of the commercially-available analysis projectors have been specially designed for motion and time study work and each offers specific advantages.

Fig. 14.10—The Eastman Analyst converted into the "Industrialist"
for motion study film analysis by the L-W Photo-products
Co., Los Angeles. This projector features a push-button
advance and a reverse switch for push-button reverse
indexing. It has a frame counter at the rear and may also
be run as a regular projector. The optical system permits
a very bright picture.

Data used with any of the analysis methods described in the preceding chapters may be taken from the film. Obtaining the exact relationship between the two hands or the members of a crew is much easier with film than with actual observation, since the film can be stopped and the action held still from step to step during the analysis. Each frame may be individually examined and notes made of the method and the time for each step. The analysis is usually made with a portable shadow box, as shown in Figure 14.11. With

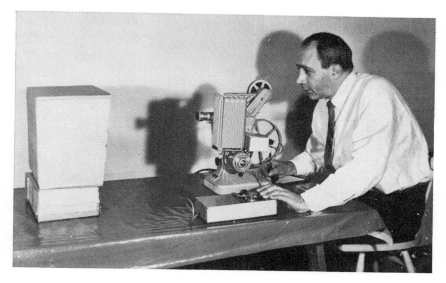

Fig. 14.11—Film analysis in daylight with a portable shadow box.

some repetitive skilled jobs a complex breakdown of the sort described in the next chapter is extremely useful.

Tape analysis. Video-recorder tape is analyzed in a manner similar to motion picture film but, instead of a projector, a closed-circuit television set is used. The tape controls must give a "stop-motion" capability and an ability to select positions for "stop-motion" at desired time intervals, as well as the ability to hold such pictures on the picture tube. All such sets provide the feasibility to change the brightness and the contrast of the image at will over a wide range; this is a feature which is superior to the motion-picture-camera-film system. All of the required equipment is commercially available.

Graphic presentation. Subsequent to film analysis or tape analysis, any of the graphic or tabular methods given with the man-analysis techniques already discussed may be used, as well as specially designed presentations. The one chosen will depend on how the film or tape is analyzed; this will depend upon the objective and the nature of the problem.

CHAPTER 15

Micromotion
and Memomotion Analysis

The data recorded on a motion picture film or video-tape may be transcribed into a form suitable for presentation by any of the graphic techniques given in previous chapters. However, it may be preferable to take advantage of the peculiar characteristics of the data record and transcribe a greater variety of facts, or greater detail, if doing so will assist in the development of a better method. One of the advantages of a tape or film record is that a tentative transcription of the data may be made from the film or tape. If the details of the transcription fail to suggest alternatives leading to improvement, then other transcriptions at other levels of detail or with other types of details may be made; the raw data remains on the film or tape for reuse as often as necessary.

Two basic methods of film or tape analysis have evolved. One is a detailed breakdown called micromotion analysis; the other is a "family" of grosser breakdowns called memomotion analysis.

The detailed breakdown with film or tape study is designed principally for routine application to short-cycle jobs which mainly involve hand motions. Cases will arise where the motions of other body members (the leg, trunk, or eyes) are also worth analyzing. However, an analysis of the activities of the two hands is the most common case. When other body members are also involved, the procedure is still similar.

Long-cycle jobs should be analyzed first with one of the grosser techniques until these procedures have provided all the improvements they can suggest, since a detailed micromotion analysis of the whole original long cycle often provides an overwhelming amount of detail. However, in competent hands a large number of valuable suggestions can be developed, and a detailed analysis is often exceedingly effective. Suggestions for a whole series of jobs may come from a detailed analysis of one. The selection of this analysis technique requires discretion and careful weighing of the time at the analyst's disposal for profitable application to the job. However, as will be explained later, familiarity with this type of analysis has several by-products of extreme importance that make a familiarity with this technique almost a necessity for fully effective method and time study work.

Memomotion analysis is the name given to the analysis of the special forms of film or video-tape study in which pictures are taken at unusually slow speeds. (With tape, as was noted, the shift to the equivalent of slow speed is obtained by manipulation of the analysis set.) Sixty frames per minute (one per second) and one hundred frames per minute are the speeds most commonly used. Like all film or tape study, it is primarily another means of performing the second step of the logical method, *analysis*, with man activity, and requires three phases: filming, film analysis, and graphic presentation. Memomotion may also be used to study the flow of material or the use of materials-handling equipment in an area, or to study simultaneously the man work, equipment usage, and flow of material.[1] In such cases, if a time-shortened visual presentation is desired, film must be used or a special film made from the tape record. In this way, one hour of activity can be viewed in about four minutes. The information contained on the film may be analyzed in numerous ways and alternative presentations of the data in graphic form are possible, depending on the objectives of the study. The development of an adequate basis of analysis will be discussed later in this chapter.

Micromotion Analysis

The detailed breakdown requires analyzing the activities of the hands (and other body members if desirable) into 17 separate categories. These categories are called *therbligs* (Gilbreth backwards), after Frank B. Gilbreth, pioneer in motion and time study, who, together with his wife, Lillian M. Gilbreth, first identified these categories and developed the film-analysis technique.[2] Originally 17 were identified and another was added later, but one original category, *find*, has been dropped from the list given here, since

---

[1] See W. J. Richardson, "Memomotion and Fork Truck Time Standards," *Modern Materials Handling*, Vol. VIII, No. 4, April 1953, pp. 67–70; B. F. Coggan, "Why Not Try Area-Wide Camera Studies?" *Modern Materials Handling*, Vol. VIII, No. 12, Dec. 1953, pp. 74–76.

[2] Edna Yost, *Frank and Lillian Gilbreth, Partners for Life*. New Brunswick, N.J.: Rutgers University Press, 1949.

it never occurs by itself, has no duration, and is really the end point of *search*, which is included in the 17 given. These 17 therbligs are common to all human activity and provide a most convenient set of categories for the classification of all physical acts and for use as a framework for the classification of basic ways of improving these acts.

Since time is plotted on simo-charts,[3] which are the usual graphic means of presenting the sequence of therbligs in a task and the simultaneity of the body members involved, a space type of symbol must be used, as with the time type of man and machine charts. Since 17 categories of motion are involved, black and white shadings of the sort used with the previous time techniques would be confusing. Hence, colors are used. Names, definitions, letter symbols, and colors used to represent the therbligs on the simo-chart are given in Table 8. For ease of recognition, each therblig is defined by its beginning point, its content, and its end. The therbligs are grouped by colors in such a manner that even a quick glance at a simo-chart will give an idea as to the over-all effectiveness of the method. There are five color groups and the order of appearance in Table 8 roughly indicates the order of desirability of the groups.

Familiarity with therbligs and their characteristics facilitates three other aspects of motion and time study work:

1. Therbligs may be used to increase clarity in writing job descriptions for time studies or training material. They provide a descriptive terminology for jobs in terms of what the worker must do, rather than describing only what happens to the material. In addition, as will be seen in later chapters, the time for many tasks may be approximated prior to the inception of the task from tables of therblig times. Designing a job in terms of therbligs (when such detail is appropriate) facilitates dimensioning it in terms of time.

2. Since all jobs consist of various combinations and amounts of therbligs, they provide a convenient and extremely effective framework for the thinking of the method analyst or time study man. They are sufficiently small so that information gained in improving the therbligs on one job is frequently directly applicable to another job to a greater extent than with any of the breakdowns of the analysis techniques previously discussed.

3. After a moderate amount of training with film or tape analysis, the analyst is usually able to perceive a job (where such detail is appropriate) in terms of therbligs and can transfer his knowledge of ways of improving the performing of therbligs to the job being studied visually with significant results.

Any one of these three aspects would be sufficient reason for becoming familiar with the technique of micromotion study and therbligs.

[3] Gilbreth's short name for *simultaneous motion cycle charts*.

TABLE **8**

Therblig Definitions and Symbols

Color Group and General Characteristics	Therblig	Symbol	Color	Eagle Pencil [1]	Dixon Thinex Pencil	Definition
	Grasp	G	Lake red	744	369	Begins when hand or body member touches an object. Consists of gaining control of an object. Ends when control is gained.
	Position	P	Blue	741	376	Begins when hand or body member causes part to begin to line up or locate. Consists of hand or body member causing part to line up, orient, or change position. Ends when body member has part lined up.
	Pre-position	PP	Sky blue	740½	418	Same as position except used when line up is previous to use of part or tool in another place.
Red-blue— terminal therbligs	Use	U	Purple	742½	396	Begins when hand or body member actually begins to manipulate tool or control. Consists of applying tool or manipulating control. Ends when hand or body member ceases manipulating tool or control.
	Assemble	A	Heavy violet	742	377	Begins when the hand or body member causes parts to begin to go together. Consists of actual assembly of parts. Ends when hand or body member has caused parts to go together.
	Disassemble	DA	Light violet	742	422	Begins when hand or body member causes parts that were integral to begin to separate. Consists of taking objects apart. Ends when hand or body member has caused complete separation.

[1] The colors of some of these pencils vary somewhat from the standard colors. They have been selected to match the standard as closely as commercial pencil colors allow.

TABLE 8 (Continued)

Color Group and General Characteristics	Therblig	Symbol	Color	Eagle Pencil	Dixon Thinex Pencil	Definition
	Release load	RL	Carmine red	745	383	Begins when hand or body member begins to relax control of object. Consists of letting go of an object. Ends when hand or body member has lost contact with object.
Green— gross movement therbligs	Transport empty	TE	Olive green	739½	391	Begins when hand or body member begins to move without load. Consists of reaching for something. Ends when hand or body member touches part or stops moving.
	Transport loaded	TL	Grass green	738	416	Begins when hand or body member begins to move with an object. Consists of hand or body member changing location of an object. Ends when hand or body member carrying object arrives at general destination or movement ceases.
Gray-black— hesitant movement therbligs	Search	SH	Black	747	379	Begins when hand or body member gropes or hunts for part. Consists of attempting to find an object. Ends when hand or body member has found location of object.
	Select	ST	Light gray	734½	399	Begins when hand or body member touches several objects. Consists of locating an individual object from a group. Ends when the hand or body member has located individual object.

TABLE 8 (Continued)

Color Group and General Characteristics	Therblig	Symbol	Color	Eagle Pencil	Dixon Thinex Pencil	Definition
Yellow-orange— delay therbligs	Hold	H	Gold ochre	735	388	Begins when movement of part or object, which hand or body member has under control, ceases. Consists of holding an object in a fixed position and location. Ends with any movement.
	Unavoidable delay	UD	Yellow ochre	736	412	Begins when hand or body member is idle. Consists of a delay for other body member or machine when delay is part of method. Ends when the hand or body member begins any work.
	Avoidable delay	AD	Lemon yellow	735½	374	Begins when hand or body member deviates from standard method. Consists of some movement or idleness not part of method. Ends when hand or body member returns to standard routine.
	Rest for overcoming fatigue	R	Orange	737	372	Begins when hand or body member is idle. Consists of idleness which is part of cycle and necessary to overcome fatigue from previous work. Ends when hand or body member is able to work again.
Brown— accompanied by thinking	Plan	PN	Brown	746	378	Begins when hand or body members are idle or making random movements while worker decides on course of action. Consists of determining a course of action. Ends when course of action is determined.

TABLE 8 (Continued)

Color Group and General Characteristics	Therblig	Symbol	Color	Eagle Pencil	Dixon Thinex Pencil	Definition
	Inspect	I	Burnt ochre	745½	398	Begins when hand or body member begins to feel or view an object. Consists of determining a quality of an object. Ends when hand or body member has felt or seen an object.

To facilitate an examination of this technique, part of a film of a repetitive job is reproduced, frame-by-frame, in this chapter. Only enough of the film appears in the body of the chapter to permit the reader to check a few steps of the analysis. For those who wish to check more steps, the remainder of the film of the work cycle is included in the supplemental material appended after the chapter. A simple job has been selected so as to make the presentation as compact as possible. The task used for discussion is an assembly operation in which three parts of a medicine-bottle dropper top are preassembled prior to sterilization. The parts are shown in Figure 15.1.

The analysis, transcribed from the film, is shown in Figure 15.2.

In the section of the film shown in Figures 15.3a, b, c, and d, the supply bins are cut away and only a few parts are shown to overcome the lack of clarity caused by the reproduction method required for printing. The large hand on the clock in the pictures was turning at 20 rpm; each division

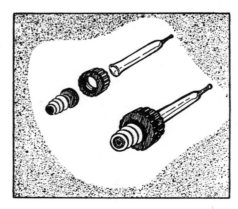

Fig. 15.1—Parts of medicine-bottle dropper top and assembled dropper top.

RECORD OF FILM ANALYSIS

Film No: 3
Date filmed 2/16/43
Analysis by J. Ross
Date 2/22/

Operation Assemble
Operator Armstrong-151
Part name Bottle dropper-top
Part No. 27

1 Sheet of 1
Dept. Tops-92

Clock reading	Subtracted time	Therblig symbol	Left hand description	Right hand description	Therblig symbol	Subtracted time	Clock reading	Notes
116	8	TL	Finished part to tray	To rubber tops	TE,G	20	116	
124	2	RL	Dropper top into tray	Rubber top	G	10	136	
126	16	TE	To bakelite caps	To work area	TL	12	146	
142	8	G	Bakelite cap	To bakelite	P	8	158	
150	4	TL	To work area	" "	A	6	166	
154	2	P	For assembling	Rubber top	RL	2	172	
156	18	H	"	To top end of rubber	TE	4	174	
				" " " "	G	2	178	
174	2	P	For RH to grasp rubber	Pull rubber thru	A	8	180	
176	1+	H	" " " pull "	Rubber	RL	2	188	
				To glass rods	TE	6	190	
190	+	P	To receive glass	Glass rod	G	8	196	
194	32	H	"	" " to cap	TL	8	204	
				" " " "	P	2	212	
				" " " "	A	10	214	
				" " " "	RL	2	224	
226	X	TL	Finished part to tray	To rubber tops	TE	X	226	
176	110					116	110	
110	OK					110	OK	

Fig. 15.2 — Film analysis using therblig breakdown for film in Figure 15.3.

249

Fig. 15.3a — Print of a movie film for original method of assembling medicine-bottle dropper top (continued).

Fig. 15.3b — Print of movie film for original method of assembling medicine-bottle dropper top (continued).

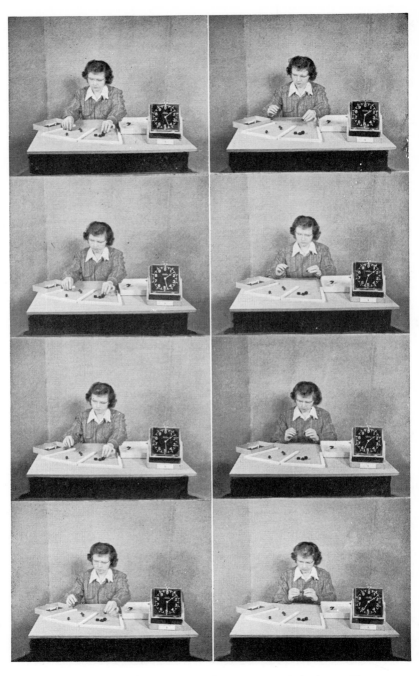

Fig. 15.3c — Print of movie film for original method of assembling medicine-bottle dropper top (continued).

Fig. 15.3d—Print of movie film for original method of assembling medicine-bottle dropper top (continued). (*Remainder of film in Supplemental Material.*)

represents 1/2000 minute. It is suggested that the reader check each step of the analysis given against the pictures of the film, for the short section of film which is shown, using the procedure which follows.

In making a film analysis with the therblig breakdown, it is usually desirable to use the following steps in connection with a form for film analysis (Figure 15.2) or a sheet of ruled columnar paper.

1. The data at the top of the sheet are obtained from the film or tape data sheet, so that the information is properly identified for future reference.
2. The entire film or tape is viewed, and a typical whole cycle is selected from those available on the film.[4] A cycle is considered to be the complete series of motions required to bring a unit of output to the degree of completion characteristic of the operation. As with the previous techniques, it is usually most convenient to select a cycle starting with the first motion connected with the production of a unit and ending when the same motion is repeated with the next unit.
3. The actual recording of the therbligs usually begins with the busiest body member, following it entirely through the cycle, and repeating the procedure for each body member being analyzed. The film or tape is examined frame-by-frame.[5] The beginning time (clock or counter reading for the first frame or picture in which the therblig appears), the letter symbol, and the explanation for the first therblig of the cycle are noted on the first line of the analysis sheet. The second notation for the cycle is made for the first frame in which the next therblig appears. The explanation should assume that the therblig is the verb, and should tell what and where the action is. Actual therblig times may be obtained later by successive subtractions. For therbligs like RL, which can take place in the interval between two pictures and thus not appear on the film at all, the time interval itself is usually arbitrarily assigned, e.g., at 16 frames per minutes, approximately 0.001 minutes. On the form given, space is provided for the two hands, and the column headed Notes is for the analysis of any other body member (eyes, feet using pedals, and so forth). This is the most common type of analysis. Special forms may be designed for more complex analyses.

Some analysts prefer to construct the simo-chart directly from the film or tape without recourse to the analysis sheet, but most will find it more convenient to use this intermediate step. Some, after making the analysis, have a clerk construct the simo-chart.

---

[4] In some cases, a considerable number of cycles or all of the film covering a selected period of time may be analyzed, depending on the nature of the task and the objectives of the study.

[5] When using tape a convenient interval between "stop-motion and hold" points must be selected.

It is regretted that printing economies do not allow the presentation of the simo-charts in color. The colors would normally appear in the graduated bars on the charts. The reader will find it worthwhile to color the charts while studying them, to see what they actually look like.

The colors are quickly and easily learned since they are in groups, and the colors and patterns representing undesirable and desirable job characteristics are soon recognized. In general, their desirability follows the order of their groups as given in Table 8. The understanding and improvement of the entire job pattern are aided considerably by the colors.

The simo-chart for the operation of assembling the medicine-bottle dropper top is given in Figure 15.4. Each hand has been charted in a separate column. The two columns are so aligned that a horizontal line drawn through them at any place would indicate simultaneous action of both hands. A clock scale appears on both sides of the chart, to facilitate construction and comparison with the film, and a cumulative time scale appears in the center. The scale used on simo-charts is usually adjusted to give a convenient length to the chart. Each space may represent any time unit, as long as the same scale is used throughout the chart. Since the 20 rmp microchronometer appeared in this film. the basic time unit on this chart is 1/2000 minute. To fit this operation onto a single sheet, each space on the simo-chart was used to represent two winks.

In the case being discussed, the simo-chart represents the final phase of performing the *analysis*, the second step of the logical procedure.

To perform step 3, *criticism*, each therblig in the job is questioned with the proper check-list questions from the check list for therbligs, together with the eight important basic rules that appear at the head of the list, in Table 9. The check list is much more detailed than any previously given, since detailed analysis permits the checking of many more possibilities of improvement.

A suggested improved method, developed by trying to utilize as many check-list suggestions as possible for this operation, is shown in simo-chart form in Figure 15.5, which was synthesized. The time values were taken, where possible, from the original method. The experience of the analyst was used to supply the missing ones. The chart was made to check the desirability of the improved method prior to its application. With considerable micromotion experience, this may be done with a reasonable degree of accuracy.

The proposed method was then rechecked against the check list. Subsequently, a sample application was made.

The new workplace that was used is shown in Figure 15.6. The new method made possible a 64 per cent increase in output.

It is probably obvious that the check list for the right- and left-hand operation charts may also be used with simo-charts. On the other hand, the body

SIMO-CHART

Method *Original* Film No. *A-6-CC*
Operation *Assembly* Operation No. *DT27A*
  Part No. *27*
Part name *Bottle dropper top* Chart by *Ross*
Operator *Armstrong – 157* Date charted *2/22/*

LEFT HAND DESCRIPTION	Symbol	Time	Total time in seconds	Time	Symbol	RIGHT HAND DESCRIPTION	Clock
Finished part to tray	TL	8	0				120
	RL	2		20	TE / UO	To rubber tops	130
To bakelite cops	TE	16	20				
				10	G	Rubber tops	140
Bakelite cap	G	8					
To work area	TL	4		12	TL	To work area	150
	P	2	40				
				8	P	To bakelite	160
For assembling	N	18		6	A		170
				2	RL	Rubber tops	
For RH to grasp top	P	2	60	4	TE	To top of rubber	
				2	G	Top of rubber	180
For RH to pull rubber top	N	14		8	A	Pull rubber thru	
				2	RL		190
For gloss	P	4		6	TE	To gloss rods	
			80	8	G	Gloss rod	200
For assembly of gloss	N	32		8	TL	To cop	210
				2	P		
			100	10	A	Insert gloss	220
			110	2	RL		230

L H Summary

	Symbol	Time
58.2%	H	64
14.6%	TE	16
11.0%	TL	12
7.2%	G	8
7.2%	P	8
1.8%	RL	2

R H Summary

Time	Symbol	
24	A	21.8%
20	TE	18.2%
20	G	18.2%
20	TL	18.2%
10	P	9.1%
10	UO	9.1%
6	RL	5.4%

Fig. 15.4—Simo-chart for original method of assembling dropper bottle tops.

member activities involved in each step of a right- and left-hand operation chart are usually more clearly understood by the analyst with some micromotion training. The therblig check list can then be profitably applied to right- and left-hand operation charts, without recourse to film analysis. The analyst will find it useful to add to the check list from time to time as he finds suggestions that are peculiar to his industry.

TABLE 9

Check List for Therbligs

Basic Principles

1. Try to have both hands doing the same thing at the same time or balance the work of the two hands.
2. Try to avoid the use of the hands for holding.
3. Keep the work in the normal work area. (See Figure 11.4.)
4. Relieve the hands of work whenever possible.
5. Eliminate as many therbligs or as much of a therblig as possible.
6. Arrange the therbligs in the most convenient order.
7. Combine therbligs when possible.
8. Standardize method and train worker.

			Examine		
Therblig	Design of Product	Tools	Jigs	Workplace Layout and Equipment	Motion Pattern
G	Easy to pick up No hazard	Combine Pre-position Assign place Design for grasp In holder	Easy to take parts from or self-ejecting If portable, design for grasp	Ejecting bins Lip bins Slide bins PP boxes No barriers to vision Tool holders Tweezers or tongs	Avoid hand to hand grasp PP parts Slide parts Use bins to advantage Use best type of grasp

TABLE 9 (Continued)

Therblig	Design of Product	Tools	Jigs	Workplace Layout and Equipment	Motion Pattern
			Examine		
P and PP	Less weight Maximum tolerances Bevel holes Round tops of pins Bevel screw ends Make parts for easy line-up Easy access Remove burrs	Self-guiding or locating Easy grip Good leverage Pre-position in holders	Hold parts at convenient angles Receive parts from convenient TL path Stops, guides, funnels Maximum tolerance in jig Large locking motion Self-locating for parts	Paint for seeing Maximum PP of tools and material Arrange for easy TL to place of P and PP	Natural, free motions with accuracy supplied by stops Combine P with TL Combine several P's into one
U, A, and DA	Minimum tool work Reduce screw lengths Easy to get at Combine parts Subassemble Remove burrs	Power Ratchets Combined tools PP tools Design for task Easy to use Best leverage Utilize momentum	Allow free action of tools Guide tools Bevel bushings Bullet top on locating pins Hold parts firmly Uniform type of fastening, preferably clamp levers At convenient height and angle Rotatable Few fastenings	Not in way of tools Tool holders Convenient height	Natural motions Lightest muscle group able to do job Proper leverage Proper posture Back brace on chair Combine U's and A's

TABLE 9 (Continued)

				Examine		
Therblig	Design of Product	Tools	Jigs	Workplace Layout and Equipment	Motion Pattern
RL	Droppable Easy to let go of	Suspended or in PP holder at all times	Easy to fit parts into Will automatically locate parts Kick, blow, drop, slide, or spring parts out	Chutes for RL near work area or in TL path Self-counting trays	As soon as possible Foot ejector As part of TL Without P
TE and TL	Fewer parts Less weight	Within easy reach Light Easy to hold Balanced Counterbalanced Self-returning Foot control	Near parts Chutes and drops Make following P less exacting Attach levers, wheels, and wrenches	Arrange parts for natural sequence Get parts and tools close to point of use	Use smooth continuous motions, circular paths, avoid backtracking Co-ordinate with use of eyes Use both hands systematically Use smallest amount of body required Two or more parts at once provided this does not interfere with subsequent P

TABLE 9 (Continued)

			Examine		
Therblig	Design of Product	Tools	Jigs	Workplace Layout and Equipment	Motion Pattern
SH and ST	Standardize parts Make nontangling Color code	Not tangle with other tools Minimum number Special eyeglasses Combine Paint in contrasting color Pre-position Definite location	Fixed in place Levers or wrenches attached Paint controls in contrasting color	Lip bins Definite places for tools and materials Label or color bins Bins contrast with parts Illuminate workplace Paint workplace for seeing	Use eyes to do work Use uniform motion pattern Use bins or trays of material systematically
H, UD, and AD	See basic rules. These therbligs are undesirable. Balance work with machine cycle if machine is used.				
R	If other therbligs are improved this will be reduced to a minimum. Rest is preferably provided by a rest pause rather than as a regular element in the cycle. If it occurs as part of a machine operation, it should take place during machine running time.				
PN	See basic rules. This therblig is undesirable. Balance work with machine cycle if machine is used.				
I	Easy reference points Minimum requirements	Easy reading Go-no-go Optical Rugged Combined gages	Minimum number of fastenings Uniform fastenings Light Built-in gages Easy reading	Good light, free of glare and flicker; of proper color, direction, and contrast	Fixed and definite pattern even for eyes Arrange so part is stationary when being viewed

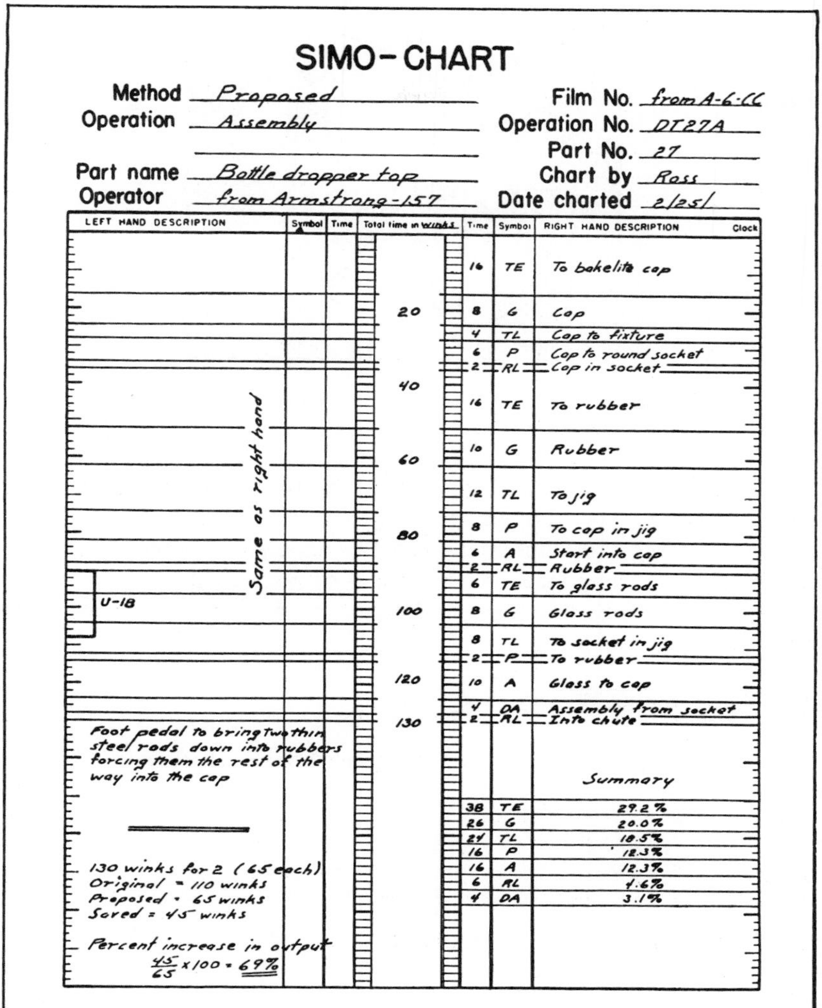

SIMO-CHART

Method __Proposed__ Film No. __from A-6-CC__
Operation __Assembly__ Operation No. __DT27A__
  Part No. __27__
Part name __Bottle dropper top__ Chart by __Ross__
Operator __from Armstrong-157__ Date charted __2/25/__

LEFT HAND DESCRIPTION	Symbol	Time	Total time in 1/2000	Time	Symbol	RIGHT HAND DESCRIPTION	Clock
				16	TE	To bakelite cap	
			20	8	G	Cap	
				4	TL	Cap to fixture	
				6	P	Cap to round socket	
				2	RL	Cap in socket	
			40	16	TE	To rubber	
			60	10	G	Rubber	
				12	TL	To jig	
			80	8	P	To cap in jig	
				6	A	Start into cap	
				2	RL	Rubber	
				6	TE	To glass rods	
U-18			100	8	G	Glass rods	
				8	TL	To socket in jig	
				2	P	To rubber	
			120	10	A	Glass to cap	
			130	4	DA	Assembly from socket	
				2	RL	Into chute	

Same as right hand

Foot pedal to bring two thin
steel rods down into rubbers
forcing them the rest of the
way into the cap

Summary

			Summary		
38	TE	29.2%
26	G	20.0%
24	TL	18.5%
16	P	12.3%
16	A	12.3%
6	RL	4.6%
4	DA	3.1%

130 winks for 2 (65 each)
Original = 110 winks
Proposed = 65 winks
Saved = 45 winks

Percent increase in output
$\frac{45}{65} \times 100 = 69\%$

Fig. 15.5—Simo-chart for improved method of assembling dropper
bottle tops.

Micromotion study with the detailed breakdown is particularly advantageous in reorganizing jobs to fit handicapped workers. Here the aim is not only to improve the whole method, but also to locate and eliminate required movements of crippled or missing body members or joints. Conversely, for therapeutic work, the aim may be to increase the movements involving affected body members or joints. Since micromotion study with the therblig

Fig. 15.6 — Workplace for improved method of assembling dropper bottle tops.

breakdown analyzes the task in terms of body movements, it is a highly effective tool for both of these special uses.[6]

Right- and left-hand operation charts may also be drawn in terms of therbligs without using films by using the symbols indicated in Table 10, and placing the proper therblig symbol alongside of each operation chart symbol on the chart.

TABLE 10

Symbols for Operation Charts with Therblig Breakdown

Symbol	A.S.M.E. Symbol	Used with Therblig
◯	◯	G, P, PP, U, A, DA, SH, ST, RL, I
○	⇨	TE, TL
▽	⟩	H
▽	▽	AD, UD, R, PN

---

[6] The Gilbreths also pioneered in these applications. See F. B. Gilbreth and L. M. Gilbreth, *Motion Study for the Handicapped.* London: George Routledge and Sons, Ltd., 1920.

However, the time values will not be available, and an accurate evaluation of the possibilities inherent in a proposed method requires much more experience on the part of the analyst than is needed with a simo-chart.[7] Making a right- and left-hand analysis in therbligs from observation also requires a high degree of familiarity with micromotion and a discerning eye, but a well-trained analyst may readily make such an analysis and find it very useful.

Memomotion Analysis

Memomotion analysis finds its primary field of use with any of, or any combination of, the following:

1. Long cycles.
2. Irregular cycles.
3. Crew activities.
4. Long period studies.

It is used for the following reasons:

1. It will record interrelated events more accurately than visual techniques. In addition, it facilitates studying tasks which consist of irregular sequences of events that cannot be predicted in advance and for which records of both method and time are desired.
2. It reduces film cost to about 6 per cent of the cost with normal film speeds, and consequently reduces the amount of film to be analyzed without reducing the period covered.
3. When film is used, it permits rapid visual review of an extended period of performance. When a film taken at one frame per second is projected at the normal speed of 16 frames per second it permits viewing a film of an hour of operation in four minutes. In addition to saving time, viewing with a compressed time scale frequently brings to light novel aspects of the subject being studied which are often instrumental in developing new ideas for better methods.
4. It has all the other usual advantages of film or tape study.

Memomotion study has been applied with advantageous results to activities like the following:[8]

1. Gas company street work.
2. Twenty-four-man steel casting mold line.

---

[7] Time values may be supplied from one of the predetermined time systems described in a later chapter.

[8] The list cited is not exhaustive but merely indicates the wide range of activities to which the technique may be usefully applied. See M. E. Mundel, "Memomotion," *Time and Motion Study*, Vol. VII, No. 3, March 1958, pp. 32–43. (A film showing samples of the actual films taken for the first nine applications in the list is available from the author.)

3. Prefabricated house section manufacture.
4. Railroad car humping in a classification yard.
5. Aircraft service on the ramp at a commercial airport.
6. Dry-salt meat packing line.
7. Stripping at the delivery end of a cutting press.
8. Package handling at a packing-house sorting center.
9. Two-man welding crew on water heater assembly line.
10. Municipal garbage handling.
11. Dental activity.
12. Household activities.[9]
13. Department store clerks.
14. Fifty-man paper-making machine repair crew.
15. Ice-house crew.
16. Railroad car loading crew.
17. Auto and passenger pattern at airport passenger terminal entrance.

The equipment required was shown in Chapter 14. A clock is seldom used, since a large area is often covered with the camera—either by getting far enough away from the area of activity or by "panning" around it, thus making it extremely difficult either to obtain a large enough image with the typical microchronometer or to keep a clock in view. Therefore, to avoid possible misunderstanding, it is extremely important that the workers be apprised of the fact that the memomotion camera (or video recorder) records time values as well as motions and that it is being used.

Memomotion study also offers a vehicle for time study, which will be discussed later in this book.

The paticular graphic technique chosen to present the data obtained by memomotion study is a function of the nature of the problem. Any of the preceding techniques may be used. Indeed, even a therblig breakdown (treating the man as a unit instead of separating the individual body members) is often possible and convenient. Special groupings are frequently desirable.

To appreciate the advantages more fully and to demonstrate the manner of using and analyzing memomotion films (or making a memomotion analysis from tape), let us consider the case of the pharmacist referred to in Chapter 14.

First, memomotion study was an ideal technique for studying this activity, since the sequence of activity was not predictable in advance. Visual recording of the events while they took place would have been extremely difficult and of doubtful accuracy. Second, using this technique the activities of the pharmacists in a drugstore were studied over a period running from 7:00 A.M. to 2:00 A.M. the next morning. Approximately 1,900 feet of film were used, instead of the 27,010 feet that would have been required at normal film

---

[9] See "Easier Homemaking," *Life*, Sept. 9, 1946.

speeds, yet every second of the pharmacists' time could be grouped into activity categories that meaningfully explained their use of time. Third, a "bird's-eye" view of the activities could be gained from a rapid review of the film. Fourth, the method of analysis could be determined from a study of the film, permitting study at leisure.

The manner of using the memomotion film was predicated upon the definition of *analysis* given earlier in this book: *to break the work down into subdivisions or steps, pertinent to the job, appropriate to its scope, possessing known characteristics, or concerning whose performance information is already available.* The purpose in this study was to improve the performance of the job in terms of time without lessening the quality of the work. Therefore, in this case, it should be apparent that the steps into which the work was to be analyzed had to separate each part of the work related to a different type of accomplishment (output-oriented), as well as separating each type of man activity.

A preliminary study of the part of the film dealing with the preparation of prescriptions indicated the pharmacist worked with the following:

1. Ingredients.
2. Tools (scales, liquid measures, etc.).
3. Finished prescriptions.
4. Labels and prescription orders.
5. Wrappings.
6. Cash.
7. Customers.

The basic information on man activity indicated that in working with the items listed a man would:

1. Work at one place.
2. Scrutinize or inspect.
3. Move from place to place.
4. Talk to customers.

Compounding these two groups of categories into a single one, together with a cursory review of the film, yielded the following categories into which the work shown on the film was then analyzed (the column on the left shows the mnemonic symbol used to facilitate recording):

WRL	work putting items back on shelves
WQ	work with liquid measures
WCA	work at cash register
WD	work on drugs (pulverizing, taking out of jar, etc.)
WLA	work applying labels
WB	work with balance and accessories
WL	work on labels or prescription blanks

WR	work wrapping prescriptions
WA	work putting material into prescription containers or work with prescription containers
WC	work counting items
WG	work getting down items (from shelves)
WCP	work compounding
IC	inspection of drug containers or contents
IP	inspection of prescription blanks
IS	inspection of shelves
TR	travel to and from cash register
TL	travel to shelves or cupboards to put material away
TE	travel to shelves or cupboards for material
VC	talk to customers

While this is not the only set of categories into which this work could be divided, any basis of analysis, considering the particular objectives of this study and the nature of the work, would closely resemble the list given here, although minor differences are possible.[10]

After the development of this list of categories, a large accounting-type work sheet was prepared. The first column was designated for a short description of the work observed, the second column for the film-analysis projector counter reading corresponding to the first frame of film of that activity, a column for the subtracted time, and a column for the symbol assigning the activity into one of the previously determined categories. To facilitate tabulation and checking, the rest of the columns of the work sheet were used to extend the subtracted times into columns for individual categories. A section of such a sheet is shown in Figure 15.7.

One of the first results of this analysis was the table shown on page 226, resembling a work activity analysis summary. This table was extremely valuable in suggesting improvements in the task.

It is worth noting that prescription activity occupied only 28 per cent of the drugstore manager's time. The part of the study thus far discussed was only a subproject within the main study concerning 100 per cent of the time. The main study required a determination of what a drugstore manager did during the day to permit:

1. The development of suggestions concerning alterations in the activity pattern to lead to more profitable operation.

---

[10] It should be noted that a list somewhat different from the one given here was used when the analysis began. As the film analysis progressed, the list was modified in view of the details actually encountered on the film, and the list given here was the one finally used. Such a change is almost impossible if one is recording directly from observation of the actual activity. Even where the analysts have considerable experience, they usually do not anticipate all activities that will be encountered; film is of great assistance in allowing the backtracking necessary to adjust to the new groupings.

Sheet 3 of 9 — Pharmacist — Film C-1-17-W

DESCRIPTION	COUNTER	TIME	SYMBOL	WRL	WQ	WCA	WD	WLA	WB	WL
Take phenobarb back to shelf	79307	3	TL							
Put phenobarb on shelf	79310	2	WRL	2						
To elixir of m.	99312	5	TE							
Take elixir off shelf	79317	3	WG							
Take elixir to bench	79320	3	TE							
Measure reqd. amount	79323	17	WQ		17					
Put elixir away	79340	4	TL							
Put elixir on shelf	79344	3	WRL	3						
Back to bench	79347	3	TL							
Pour elixir into Rx	79350	10	WA							
Type label, number label of Rx	79360	122	WL							122
Paste label on bottle	79482	15	WLA					15		
Wrap bottle	79497	137	WR							
To cash reg. for customer	79634	11	TR							

Fig. 15.7 — Section of memomotion analysis sheet of film of pharmacist's activity.

2. The determination of typical duties, as practiced, in order to assist in:
   a. Selecting potential managers with respect to job requirements.
   b. Advising schools supplying supporting curricula of actual job characteristics.
3. An analysis of the effect of store layout and merchandise arrangement.

In order to achieve these objectives, a second group of categories was employed in the analysis of the memomotion film. It appeared to the analysts that the desirable major groupings would result from a compounding of the accounting divisions of the business and the basic man activities. Consequently, the separable parts of the work were divided into the following man activities:

O	do work at one place
T	move from place to place
I	inspect
U	unavoidable delay
A	avoidable delay
V	talk to people

These man activities were further classified as attributable to one of the following:

Selling	Customer relations
Administration	Phone
Stock control	Prescriptions
Fountain and lunch counter	Personal

The data from an analysis of three stores and their managers are given in Figure 15.8.

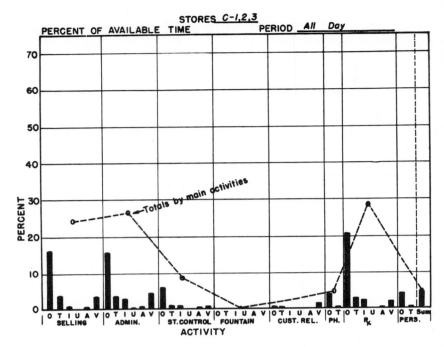

Fig. 15.8 — Summary of distribution of working time for pharmacist-managers of three drug stores.

An examination of another memomotion study will further illustrate the development of special categories in the performance of *analysis*. From its records a public utility found that the time to install a gas service renewal averaged 64 man-hours, although some crews consistently took only 24 man-hours. (A nine-man crew was used on the job although only three or four were employed on a single site at any one time.) A memomotion study was made of one of the superior crews to determine the method that made this low-cost performance possible. A view through the memomotion camera of the first phase of the operation is shown in Figure 15.9.

The analysis categories were created by compounding the phases of the work (*preparing the site, opening the excavations, making the connections, closing the excavations*) with the basic man activities (*do, move, inspect, wait*) and with the tools and equipment used (*shovel, air drill, torch,* etc.). Typical categories were:

> **WPB**   work preparing barricades for traffic
> **WOD**   work opening excavation with air drill
> **MPA**   move air compressor to location

Fig. 15.9 — View through memomotion camera of gas service renewal crew beginning street excavations.

The analysis revealed that the quick performance was due primarily to the organization of the work and not to the speed of working. In addition, numerous ways of making the task easier and less costly were found. In this respect, particular attention was paid to the most time-consuming activity categories. A summary of the analysis categories and a multiman chart (with only the major steps) were produced to use both as training aids and as a guide to supervision. These led to a considerable reduction of costs.

The foregoing two examples have been cited to illustrate further the wide range of applicability and the manner of developing a procedure for analysis of memomotion films for tasks different from ordinary repetitive production operations.

Supplemental Material

Micromotion analysis. In order to facilitate the paging, the continuation of Figure 15.3 (the micromotion film) is appended at the end of this section as Figures 15.19a, b, c, and d.

Memomotion analysis. The following three cases were chosen from widely separated areas of activity to show the scope of this technique. The first case is from a large steel foundry; the second, from a large metropolitan hotel; and the third, from a dental operatory.

CASE I Three-man Crew Running Heavy
Castings through a "Rotoblast"

A possibility guide had indicated that a Class 1 or 2 change was desirable, and a study of the process chart-product analysis suggested that the operation, shot-blast casting in "Rotoblast," was necessary. This completed step 1, *aim,* of the logical approach. For convenience and accuracy, step 2, *analysis,*

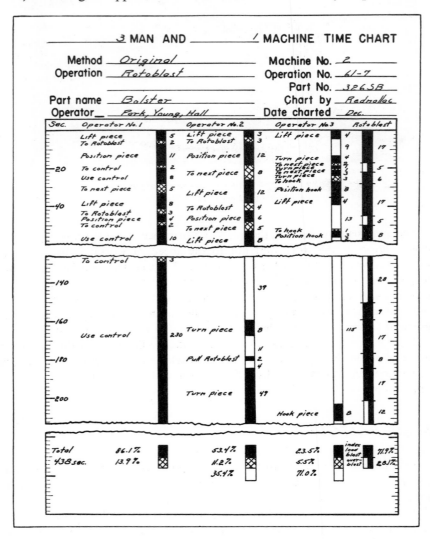

Fig. 15.10 — Sections of chart showing original method of "Rotoblast."

was performed with a memomotion camera.[11] Sufficient light from the building monitor penetrated even the murky foundry interior to do away with the need for any supplementary lighting. The crew, aware that they were being photographed, were filmed at work. An analysis was made of the film in order

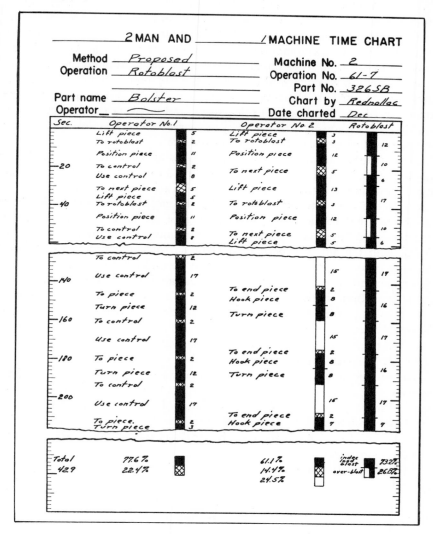

Fig. 15.11—Sections of chart showing proposed method of "Rotoblast."

[11] An Eastman Ciné Special and motor drive were used.

to obtain data with which to construct a multiman and machine process time chart.

The analysis was made with a projector equipped with a frame counter. A typical cycle was selected from those available on the film. Since the selected cycle was 439 seconds long (7.3 minutes) and there are 40 frames per foot on 16-mm film, the selected section was only 11 feet long. At normal speeds the cycle would have occupied almost 200 feet of film. The reduction in analysis time by using the memomotion film should be obvious. The selected cycle was identified for future examination by placing an ink spot on the beginning frame. The film was analyzed by noting the beginning counter reading, together with a process chart-man analysis symbol and a description for one operator, on the first line of a ruled sheet, and indexing the projector until the first frame showing a new activity appeared; thereupon noting again the counter reading, process chart-man analysis symbol, description, and so forth. This procedure continued until all the activities of the operator were detailed for the whole cycle. The film was then returned to the starting point and the second operator's activities analyzed. In this case, the film was studied four times, once for each worker and once for the machine. Sections of the chart of the original method are shown in Figure 15.10. The sections on the chart marked "overblast" could not be determined from the film, but were found with the aid of experimental data on the minimum required shot-blasting time. In drawing the chart, these experimental data were used to determine unnecessary blasting, which was labeled "overblast." The chart could have been made without film, but the use of film assured obtaining data on all men from the same cycle, was quicker, gave greater accuracy, and provided a record to use in checking the analysis. It also helped in discussions with foremen and workers, because they needed but a short time away from their job to review a rather lengthy period of work.

The proper multiman check list was used on this foundry chart, and the new method, parts of which are shown in Figure 15.11, resulted. The improved method saved 35 per cent of the man-minutes of work per unit while increasing hourly production by 2 per cent. The new method did not require the crew to work faster, but made for a better distribution of the work and provided a more effective work pattern.

The memomotion film was later used in the discussions prior to the successful installation of the new method.

CASE II   Maidservice in a Hotel

A large Chicago hotel experienced difficulty in getting its maids to clean and make up a sufficient number of rooms; hence, costs were excessive. Maid service cost this hotel approximately $130,000 in the year prior to study.

Visual recording and timing of such a task was extremely difficult, since the routine varied from maid to maid and from room to room.

The first step in reducing costs on this operation involved setting up reasonable quality requirements (Class 4 changes) and adequate scheduling (Class 3 changes). To obtain information from which to develop Class 1 and 2 changes, a memomotion study was made of the maids' activities. The area covered in the work was large, but no one spot permitted photographing from a fixed location. Consequently, a portable setup was used (Figure 15.12),

Fig. 15.12—Portable filming equipment.

which enabled the observer to carry the camera and motor drive and follow a maid.

The analysis of this film permitted the flow path of the work to be studied, as well as the time for and nature of each step. Part of the graphic presentation of the method most frequently observed is shown in Figure 15.13, together with part of the flow path, which was also taken from the film.

Discussion of this analysis by the hotel staff and study of the method with

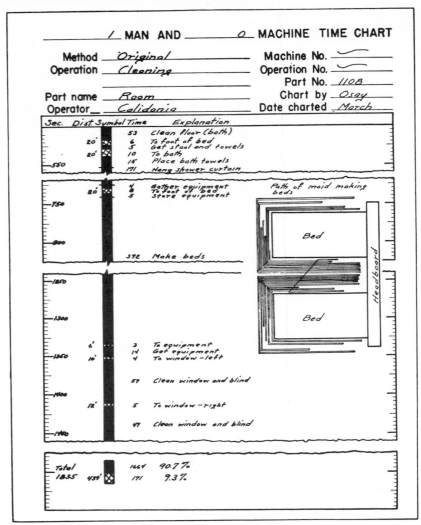

Fig. 15.13 — Sections of chart showing original method of maid cleaning hotel room.

the check list for process chart-man analysis led to the development of a
proposed method that promised to save 34 per cent of the time. Part of this
proposed method is shown in graphic form in Figure 15.14.

A trial application proved successful. Subsequently, a training manual and
a training film were prepared, and the maids, in small groups, were trained
in the new method and properly equipped. The memomotion film was not
used in training.

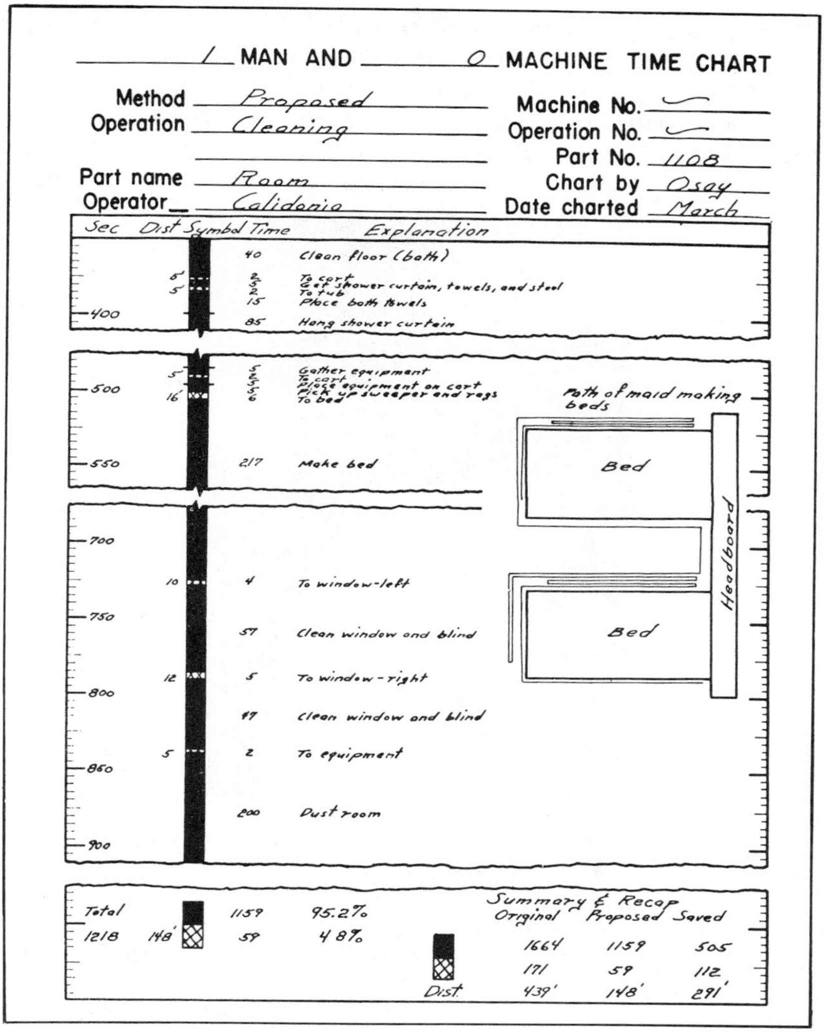

Fig. 15.14—Sections of chart showing proposed method of maid cleaning hotel room.

CASE III A STUDY OF A DENTAL OPERATORY

A work sampling study was made by a group of dentists. The study indicated that the major portion of time was spent in the operatory, and that the largest single category of work was restorative dentistry. A technique that preserved a record of the flow of work and gave the movements of the dentist as a whole, together with the activities of the assistant, seemed most appropriate for making a more detailed study. The variety and rapidity of the activity and the lack of a repetitive pattern made it impossible to expect to record the events directly from visual observations. Therefore, a memomotion study was made of a one-hour period of restorative dentistry.

The camera and motor drive were placed high in the corner of the operatory, as shown in Figure 15.15. The camera was started before the patient

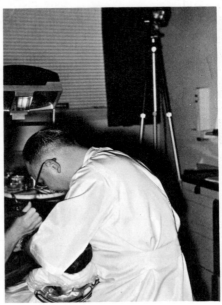

Fig. 15.15 — Memomotion camera unobtrusively placed in the corner of a dental operatory.

entered the operatory and allowed to run unattended. The path of the dentist is shown by the solid line and that of the assistant by a dotted line on the plan view of the operatory in Figure 15.16.

It should be obvious that most of the enormous amount of time- and energy-consuming travel was caused by the poor placement of equipment. The operatory, laid out as was customary for one-man operation, was inefficient for a two-man team.

The operatory was rearranged as shown in Figure 15.17. The travel of the dentist and the assistant are again shown. These new travel lines were taken from a second memomotion film of a case of restorative dentistry requiring almost the same amount of work as that in the first film.[12] The change is so great that quantification is not needed.

[12] A film showing the "before" and "after" as memomotion films is available from the film library of the American Dental Association and is titled, "Motion Study in the Dental Operatory."

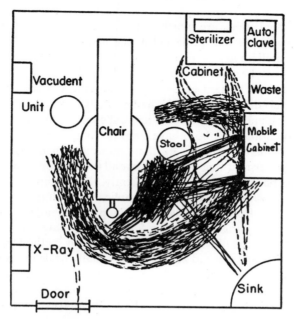

Fig. 15.16 — Original layout of operatory with travel paths of dentist and assistant.

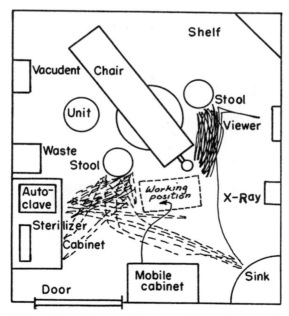

Fig. 15.17 — Improved layout of operatory with travel paths of dentist and assistant.

Two additional items are worth noting. First, the dental study group[13] began by viewing the film projected at the normal speed of 16 frames per second, as a preliminary to detailed analysis. The actual detailed analysis was not necessary because the distortion of the time scale made the defects in layout and work pattern exceedingly apparent, and the changes needed were immediately discerned. Second, had an analysis been made, the similarity between this job and the gas service renewal cited in the body of the chapter would have been marked; both have steps of "preparing the site," "opening the excavation" and so forth. Further, improved methods in both cases show similar patterns, if one will look beyond the difference in physical scope of the jobs. As has been mentioned frequently, the principles of improvement embodied in the various check lists are applicable to all types of work.

As can be seen from the preceding examples, memomotion is merely a convenient way of using film or tape for gathering data on certain types of jobs. The memomotion film facilitates analysis by any method that might have been used if the actual job had been studied visually while in operation, keeps filming costs down, provides a quick overview, retains all the advantages of films, and is an extremely useful tool when properly applied to jobs that require it. Tape also provides all of these advantages, except the ease of quick viewing.

[13] The Milwaukee Dental Research Group.

Fig. 15.18a—Print of movie film for original method of assembling medicine-bottle dropper top (continued).

Fig. 15.18b—Print of movie film for original method of assembling medicine-bottle dropper top (continued).

Fig. 15.18c—Print of movie film for original method of assembling medicine-bottle dropper top (continued).

Fig. 15.18d—(Concluded) *Print of movie film for original method of assembling medicine-bottle dropper top.*

CHAPTER 16

Motion Economy

The preceding twelve chapters have been devoted to a discussion of details of formal techniques for improving jobs. A logical procedure was suggested for employing these techniques. The results obtained by applying these techniques have been illustrated with jobs varying greatly in physical scope and representing a wide variety of activity. The making of the analysis, fundamental in the use of a logical procedure, has entailed learning many ways of dividing tasks into steps or subdivisions. If one has followed the details of the numerous illustrations, worked problems from Appendix E, and also applied these techniques to some actual jobs, using the appropriate check lists to assist in developing improved methods, surely his way of look-ing at jobs must have undergone changes. These changes certainly include the following:

1. It is no longer possible to look at tasks without seeing them (a) as falling into a category most readily studied with the aid of a particular tech-nique, and (b) as a series of steps related to this technique.
2. Certain basic improvements are suggested from even a casual observa-tion of a job; the check lists are automatically applied.

It is the purpose of this chapter to aid in summarizing the check lists from the various techniques, to strengthen the second item from the preceding list, and to assist in making possible a more complete approach to improving work. It is not the intent of this chapter to replace the formal analysis tech-niques with a quick visual method, but to provide a check list of general principles for the analyst who has learned to see jobs in terms of these analyses.

These general principles of improvement have considerable historical background. Frank B. Gilbreth first listed the variables in the work situation under several headings, two of which follow:[1]

Variables of the Surroundings, Equipment and Tools.
1. Appliances.
2. Clothes.
3. Colors.
4. Entertainment, music, reading, etc.
5. Heating, cooling, ventilating.
6. Lighting.
7. Quality of material.
8. Reward and punishment.
9. Size of unit moved.
10. Special fatigue-eliminating devices.
11. Surroundings.
12. Tools.
13. Union rules.
14. Weight of unit moved.

Variables of the Motion.
1. Acceleration.
2. Automaticity.
3. Combination with other motions and sequence.
4. Cost.
5. Direction.
6. Effectiveness.
7. Foot-pounds of work accomplished.
8. Inertia and momentum overcome.
9. Length.
10. Necessity.
11. Path.
12. "Play for position."
13. Speed.

Gilbreth went on to discuss each of these, to give specific examples and to generalize from these examples, thus creating general principles of improvement. He elaborated on these in *Fatigue Study* (written with Lillian Gilbreth),[2] and finally developed a set of "Rules of Human Motions."[3] These rules were rearranged and amplified by Barnes[4] as "Principles of Motion Economy,"

[1] F. B. Gilbreth, *Motion Study*. New York, N.Y.: D. Van Nostrand, 1911; reprinted in W. R. Spriegel and C. E. Myers, *The Writings of the Gilbreths*. Homewood, Ill.: Richard D. Irwin, Inc., 1953, pp. 152–153.

[2] F. B. and L. M. Gilbreth, *Fatigue Study*. New York, N.Y.: Sturgis and Walton, 1916.

[3] F. B. and L. M. Gilbreth, "A Fourth Dimension for Measuring Skill for Obtaining the One Best Way," *Bulletin of the Society of Industrial Engineers*, Vol. 5, No. 11, Nov. 1923, pp. 6–7.

[4] R. M. Barnes, *Motion and Time Study*. New York, N.Y.: John Wiley & Sons, 1937, pp. 110–178.

and also given as "Laws of Motion Economy and their Corollaries" by Lowry, Maynard, and Stegemerten.[5]

However, it has been generally recognized, according to R. N. Blair, that

these various listings do not represent the principles of motion economy in any fundamental sense, but simply provide some useful rules, of varying significance and of unequal importance. These range from basic points of general applicability, such as the preferability of smoothly continuous motions over motions involving sudden and sharp changes in direction, to very specific suggestions of the type describing a good kind of handle for large screwdrivers.[6]

Professor Blair goes on to reclassify the material into a new list of 15 items.

The individual check lists given in previous chapters were derived from the basic Gilbreth material amplified by experience with the analysis techniques. They were an attempt to present these principles without the ambiguity of generalities, yet avoid the mixing of specifics phrased for different scopes of work. However, the general principles of improvement are presented now as a means of summarizing the various check lists for those familiar with the details of analysis. (The material is phrased primarily in respect to the work of an individual. It should be noted, however, that, in many cases, references to "the hand" could also refer to crew members in group work.) These general principles should be of great value in helping to discern potential job improvements and to select an analysis technique compatible with the potential gain. Further, the list of principles may be used as a summary check list after the job analyzed has been questioned with the aid of one of the detailed check lists. It may also be used as a summary check list on new jobs, once the initial work pattern has been "roughed out."

A final word of caution might be appropriate at this point. The list of general principles is directed primarily at the mechanical aspects of jobs. This is not meant to imply that the reaction of the worker is mechanistic. Indeed, as was indicated much earlier in the book, the worker's reaction is anything but. Therefore, to maintain the proper perspective, this summary chapter might well be accompanied by a rereading of Chapter 2, The Human Factor.

General Suggestions for Improving Jobs

A. *Elimination*
1. Eliminate all possible jobs, steps, or motions. (This applies to body, leg, arm, hand, or eye.)
2. Eliminate irregularities in a job so as to facilitate automaticity. Provide fixed places for things.

[5] S. M. Lowry, H. B. Maynard, and G. J. Stegemerten, *Time and Motion Study*. New York, N.Y.: McGraw-Hill Book Co., 1940, pp. 95–112.

[6] R. N. Blair, "A Fresh Look at the Principles of Motion Economy," *The Journal of Industrial Engineering*, Vol. 9, No. 1, Jan.–Feb. 1958, pp. 3–5.

3. Eliminate the use of the hand as a holding device.
4. Eliminate awkward or abnormal motions.
5. Eliminate the use of muscles to maintain a fixed posture.
6. Eliminate muscular force by using power tools, power feeds, etc.
7. Eliminate the overcoming of momentum.
8. Eliminate danger.
9. Eliminate idle time unless needed for rest.

B. *Combination*
1. Replace with one continuous curved motion short motions which are connected with sudden changes in direction.
2. With fixed machine cycles, make a maximum of work internal to the machine cycle.
3. Combine tools.
4. Combine controls.
5. Combine motions.

C. *Rearrangement*
1. Distribute the work evenly between the two hands. A simultaneous symmetrical motion pattern is most effective. (This frequently involves working on two parts at the same time.) With crew work, distribute the work evenly among members of the crew.
2. Shift work from the hands to the eyes.
3. Arrange for a straightforward order of work.

D. *Simplification*
1. Use the smallest muscle group capable of doing the work, providing for intermittent use of muscle groups as needed.
2. Reduce eye travel and the number of fixations.
3. Keep work in the normal work area.
4. Shorten motions.
5. Adapt handles, levers, pedals, buttons, etc., to human dimensions and musculatures.
6. Use momentum to build up energy in place of the intense application of muscular force.
7. Use the simplest possible combination of therbligs.
8. Reduce the complexity of each therblig, particularly the "terminal" therbligs.

TO

DEPT.

FROM

94B - 10/68

CHAPTER 17

Time Study— Introduction

In Chapter 1 the relationships between the cycle of managerial control and the techniques of motion and time study were discussed. Subsequently, the objectives of the motion study techniques and then the details of the techniques were examined. The discussion included an examination of the factors that affected the choosing of a specific technique in any particular situation.

This chapter will examine in greater detail the objectives for using the time study or work measurement techniques. The words *time study* and *work measurement* will be used synonymously. The relationship to the cycle of managerial control will be examined. This chapter will also examine some basic measurement problems and some basic facts relating to these problems as preliminary to a study of the actual techniques. The aim is twofold. First, the objectives for using a set of techniques are fundamental to really understanding the techniques. Second, it is commonly thought that there are large areas of activity which cannot successfully be subjected to work measurement and thus cannot be brought under real managerial control; this chapter is designed also to demonstrate that this is not so.

Time study (or work measurement) was originally defined in Chapter 1 as *a set of procedures for determining the amount of time required, under certain standard conditions of measurement, for tasks involving some human activity.* The result of such a measurement is called a *standard time*. The first and fundamental use of a standard time is to assist in the operation of the management cycle, as the cycle was described in Chapter 1. The standard time is used as *a numerical coefficient for converting a quantitative statement of the workload (step 3) to a quantitative statement of the required manpower resources (step 4).* If the time-use of other resources is concomitant with the use of manpower, the amount of these other required resources may also be computed from the standard time. Planned or standard costs will also be computed at this point from these same data. Standard times, as has been noted in the chapters dealing with time charts, also play a role in the design of methods. Standard times also provide a basis for the comparison of the actual and the planned used of manpower (step 7 of the cycle of managerial control).

In more detail, standard times have the following uses:

1. *To determine labor and equipment requirements.* Any managerial plan for the production of outputs must be tested for feasibility. Feasibility is examined by converting the desired quantity of outputs to a statement of required resources and determining whether this amount of resources is within the allowable limitations. (In industrial enterprises such limitations are economic, viz., outputs must be profitable; in government enterprises they are substantive, e.g., number of men, space, money.) If the plan is not feasible, either the amount of the desired outputs must be altered or the factors affecting the need for resources must be altered. (This second area of change was the area of impact of the motion study techniques described in the preceding chapters.) Labor and equipment requirements expressed as their money cost when added to materials and overhead costs give standard costs. The need for standard times for these basic uses in the cycle of managerial control is so fundamental that some sort of standard time must be generated, no matter how informal are the techniques used. Even in situations where managers may deny the feasibility of work measurement, some alternative of technique is being used. It is one of the purposes of this book to describe procedures which are more effective than these informal techniques so as to improve the results obtained by the exercise of managerial control. Standard times, for these basic uses, must either reflect expectable performance, or the ratio for converting to such performance must be known.

2. *To assist in developing effective methods.* (As was noted in Chapter 1, the motion study aspect and the time study aspect are not fully separable; this is an area of great overlap.)

a. *To determine the number of pieces of equipment a person may run.* As was seen with man and machine charts, time values for the human parts of the cycle are important factors in setting up the job method. Here, the time standards should be such that they are attainable by most of the workers if good machine utilization is to be expected.

b. *To balance the work of crews, co-ordinate or in sequence.* Efficient crew work demands an even distribution of work among the members of the crew. It is the crew member with the longest job who determines the output of the crew. Office processing sequences, assembly lines, and most crew activities usually achieve higher production and lower cost than individuals doing complete operations. Lower cost is achieved because of the greater automaticity possible with the smaller tasks, the specialized tooling and workplaces possible, and the reduction in training time and cost. However, an unequal distribution of work among the crew members can more than offset these gains. With an eleven-man work sequence, or production line, if the task of one worker requires 10 per cent more work than the next longest job, the work of at least one whole worker may well be lost. (The relative ability of the worker with longest task may increase or decrease this figure.) Whether the standard times are easy or difficult to achieve does not matter so long as all standard times are of equal ease or difficulty. Consistency of the standard times is the sole requirement for this application.

c. *To compare methods.* As can easily be seen, a standard of consistent difficulty is required to provide an unchanging yardstick for the comparison of two or more methods of performing the same work. In this case the relationship of the standard time to possible performance is immaterial.

3. *To constrain the use of manpower.*

a. *To set schedules.* Production (or work accomplishment) schedules are a vital necessity for any organization. They are used to control the rate of using resources. They also serve as a basis for planning sales programs for profit-motivated organizations; for planning accomplishment programs for government or service organizations. They should permit proper coordination of staff departments, operations, purchases, and delivery or sales, and so forth. Production schedules, if they are to be reliable guides, must be based on measures bearing a known relationship to the expected rate of output. Any standard time that is greater or less than that which may be actually expected as typical performance needs a known correction factor for use in schedule making, but is still quite usable. Scheduling is greatly facilitated if the correction factor for computing typical performance is the same for all standards in use in the organization.

b. *To set labor standards.* This does not necessarily refer to wage incentives. Labor standards can be the levels of individual or group production deemed satisfactory, and may be applied without financial incentives. The standard times used for this purpose should be readily attainable, by the type of worker who is expected to be average for the job, in order to avoid either making "substandard performance" typical or creating a frustrated feeling on the part of the workers. The importance of this can hardly be overstressed. Labor standards, properly determined and properly understood, are an asset to both management and labor, since they fix a level of satisfactory activity and protect the interests of both groups.

c. *To determine supervisory objectives.* A foreman or supervisor is supplied with a mix of men, materials, space, machines, tools, and methods. The mix will vary greatly, depending upon the nature of the outputs. It is his job to supervise the coordination of this mix to achieve an expected result. Time standards for this use should indicate the rate at which he is expected to coordinate his facilities in order to meet schedules and produce outputs within the standard costs. Such time standards will also help the foreman or supervisor to select workers who need additional training, who are misplaced, or who have unusual aptitudes or apply themselves with unusual diligence. Time standards for these uses should indicate typical expected performance, or some known proportion of it, so that an individual's performance may be evaluated against such standards.

d. *To provide a basis for the setting of piece prices or incentive wages.* Incentive wages are a means of automatic financial supervision for both labor and management. They tend to reward the more productive worker in proportion to his output. They also give rise to worker insistence on management's keeping a steady flow of work during the working day and on eliminating sources of work stoppage such as poor maintenance. To keep production up to the desired level, the standards at which incentives begin must be more than attainable and worth exceeding. They must also be consistent so as to provide equal incentive opportunities from job to job and thus avoid inequities within labor grades or the upset of established job hierarchies. There must also be a sufficient difference between base pay and the pay at a reasonably possible level of performance so as to provide an incentive that will stimulate production. Hence, if the wage incentive is calculated on the basis of the work done in excess of standard performance, then the standard time should be greater than that needed by the average worker, as well as being expressed in relatively consistent units.

4. *To assist in comparing performance with plans with respect to workload and resource usage.* An organization, if profit motivated, usually prices its merchandise prior to manufacture. To do this it must predict how much labor or production-center time will be expended on each phase of the work, and must have a means of continuously comparing actual performance to predicted performance. For performance predictions, as with schedule setting, the standard times are usable if they bear a known relationship to the time that will actually be required. Standard times for each operation are used for detailed cost checks on operations and in the determination of the exact places for the application of corrective action. They assist in "pinpointing" jobs that are not being performed as expected. For non-profit activities such as government agencies, the same continuous comparison of plans with performance must take place so that corrective actions may be taken, when needed, to obtain the maximum possible conformance of events with plans. For this use, the time standards must have the same basic characteristics as given above.

From the foregoing, one conclusion may be reached; the concept of standard time may vary somewhat with the intended use. Hence, the particular technique chosen for a particular problem will be a function of (among other factors) the use to be made of the standard time.

To continue, a standard time, it was noted, is a numerical coefficient for converting a quantitative statement of workload to a quantitative statement of the required manpower resources. This statement raises two questions:

1. In what units is workload expressed?
2. In what units are manpower resources expressed?

These two questions are worth examining in great detail in that practically all the difficulty which has been encountered in attempting to serve managerial needs with standard times can be traced to a failure to satisfactorily answer these two questions; a failure which is often caused by a lack of realization of the full implications and ramifications of these questions.

Let us examine first the problems of quantifying workload. In industrial organizations, where the output is substantive, such as home appliances, shoes, clothing, and so forth, the problem of quantifying the workload with respect to direct labor has been looked upon, quite properly, as a minor problem. Little difficulty has been encountered. However, with the indirect work of such organizations and with service type organizations or with government agencies, poor methods of quantifying the workload have frequently frustrated work measurement efforts, leading many to conclude that real work measurement and consequently, real managerial control is not possible. For instance:

> "The (Army) Corps (of Engineers) had, over a period of years, attempted to develop a comprehensive work measurement system. Based on the frustrations of these attempts, the agency contended that its heterogeneous mix of work had, and would, defeat such efforts."[1]

Almost any service type output has an important difference as compared with substantive outputs. Substantive outputs can be represented by an engineering drawing; service type outputs cannot be so represented. Because of this, substantive outputs are easily converted to a quantitative statement of workload but service type outputs present a more difficult problem.

For instance, an organization making home appliances has no difficulty in recognizing that there are different workloads connected with the production of each of their different appliances, such as their washing machines, dryers, and dishwashers. In the process of quantifying workload, each type

---

[1] U.S. Department of Army, Corps of Engineers, "Chronology of Actions Taken by the Corps of Engineers on Work Measurement." Report prepared by the Manpower Management Division, Office of Personnel Administration, Office of the Chief of Engineers, August 1963, as described in: John R. Hadd, "An Investigation of the Feasibility of Agency-wide Work Measurement in the United States Army Corps of Engineers," M. A. Thesis, George Washington University, February 1966.

of appliance must be counted separately. Further, each type of appliance, such as a washing machine, can be represented by an engineering drawing of the total assembled unit. The washing machine assembly drawing may be replaced by a set of part drawings, one for each part. Each part drawing and the information concerning how many of the parts are needed for each assembly may be supported by a material requirement statement and by a process chart-product analysis or other presentation of the production sequence for the part. Each step in the production sequence is readily identified; the requisite equipment may readily be specified. Each task in the workload of producing a part may easily be identified. How often the task must be performed per washing machine may readily be forecast; the relationship of the task to the consumption of manpower per washing machine is obvious. Hence, it is obvious that work measurement can and should be used to provide a standard time for each task in the production sequence for each part. A "roll-up" may then take place. The manpower resource for each task may be multiplied by the number of that part required per assembly; the total manpower for all parts may be obtained by adding the values for all parts. If these are added to the manpower for the readily identified tasks of assembling, painting, testing and packing (which are applied to all parts), the manpower resources required per unit washing machine can be obtained. If the manpower resource required per unit washing machine is multiplied by the anticipated number of washing machines per week, month, or year, the total manpower resource required for that period of time can be determined. If we want to know the manpower resources for a different number of washing machines, we merely change the final multiplier. It is important to note the relatively fixed relationship (for a given method and process) between the number of units of final product (washing machines) and the tasks on the parts. Of course, if a large number of different models of different kinds of appliances are made, the preceding calculations may involve much detail. Make versus buy decisions must also be made, and so forth, but difficulties will not be encountered with respect to what to count; a convenient procedure is obvious and direct. However, with many indirect service or government activities there is no substantive output. Consequently there is no engineering drawing to assist in determining what to count, although the manpower resources are usually a larger portion of the required resources than with substantive outputs and, hence, an even more important problem for managerial control. Further, as will be shown later, there is seldom as direct a relationship between what appears to be the final outputs and the manpower or tasks required. All too often heterogeneous outputs are added to give a meaningless measure of outputs; a measure whose relationship to manpower required cannot be determined in other than a delusive, empirical fashion. Some additional analytical aids are needed to assist in deciding what to count and how to summarize.

A method for solving the problem of quantifying the workload with non-substantive outputs may be found by examining the procedures used with the washing machine (or any substantive output) and identifying the basic features which make the procedure workable. If these basic features are expressed in terms which do not predicate a substantive output, we will have a procedure for solving the problem of quantifying workload which will also cover service and government activities. We shall have a general procedure rather than a specialized one limited to use with the production of substantive (or hardware) type outputs.

Let us examine the real underlying concepts of the procedure outlined for use with washing machines. The appliance manufacturer had an *objective*; he wanted certain results. These results were most probably described in terms of money profit. A given total number of appliances were planned as a *gross output* consisting of a number of washing machines, a number of dryers, a number of dishwashers, and so forth. The unit of output in each group was, naturally, one machine. Each machine had a parts list. Each part had a list of tasks. This was the planning framework used within the cycle of managerial control.

Let us reduce this specialized, hardware-oriented concept to general terms. The concept must not predicate a substantive output. Let us introduce a concept involving a *hierarchy of work-units*. A work-unit is *any amount of work or the results of such work which is convenient to use as an integer when quantifying work*. We may have large and small work-units, large ones divisible into smaller ones and small ones aggregative into larger ones; thus, we have a *hierarchy of work-units*. Let us further define some specific sizes of work-units, starting with large ones and proceeding to small ones.

Let us give different typical sizes of work-units names and numerical designations to facilitate discussion, without thinking of this as other than a guide; it is not to be taken as a strict taxonomy. In a particular situation, more or fewer orders of work-units may be more convenient. The set of classifications given in Table 11 has proved useful in a wide variety of situations ranging from government agencies to industrial purchasing departments:

To apply the concept and terminology to the appliance manufacturing situation:

The eight-order work-unit is:
  The desired profit

The seven-order work-unit is:
  The total output of appliances (number of units)

The sixth-order work-units are:
  6-1. All washing machines produced
  6-2. All dryers produced

TABLE 11[1]

Name	Numerical Designation	Definition
Results	Eighth-order work-unit	What is achieved because of the outputs of the activity.
Total output	Seventh-order work-unit	The total of end products or completed services of the working group.
Program	Sixth-order work-unit	A group of like outputs or completed services representing part of the seventh-order work-unit but which are a more homogeneous sub-group.
End product	Fifth-order work-unit	A unit of final output; the units in which a program is quantified.
Intermediate product	Fourth-order work-unit	A part of a unit of final output; the intermediate product may become part of the final output or merely be required to make it feasible to achieve the final output.
Task	Third-order work-unit	All of the activity associated with, and all of the things associated with the performance of a unit of assignment by either an individual or a crew, depending on the method of assigning.
Element[2]	Second-order work-unit	The activity associated with the performance of part of a task which it is convenient to separate to facilitate the designing of the method of performing the task or the determination of some dimension of the task.
Motion	First-order work-unit	The performance of a human motion. This is the smallest work-unit usually encountered in the study of work. It is used to facilitate job design or dimensioning and never appears in control system above this level of use.

[1] Adapted from: M. E. Mundel, *A Conceptual Framework for the Management Sciences.* New York, N.Y.: McGraw-Hill Book Co., 1967, pp. 166–167.

[2] First- and second-order work-units never appear in the control systems of an enterprise. They have been included here because they do appear in some work measurement techniques and they do complete the hierarchy of work-units.

6-3.   All dishwashers produced

The fifth-order work-units are:
  6-1.1.   A washing machine produced
  6-2.1.   A dryer produced
  6-3.1.   A dishwasher produced

The fourth-order work-units are, for each end product, the lists of the following:
  a. Parts produced
  b. Services applied to all parts, such as assembled, packed, and so forth
  c. Indirect services such as personnel administration provided (usually distributed to the parts or end units as an overhead charge)

The third-order work-units are specific to each of the fourth-order work-units and consist of the task lists.

The second-order work-units are the constituent parts of each of the tasks. (The basis of separating these parts will be discussed in Chapter 18.)

The first-order work-units are the therbligs (described in Chapter 15) which make up each of the parts of each task.

This particular listing of work-units has three useful properties, which may also be described as the criteria for a useful hierarchy of work-units. These three properties are:

1. They provide a clear hierarchy of countable, convertible units of quantification from the objective to the workload; the resources required for the larger or higher orders of work-units may be divided into that needed for the smaller or lower orders of work-units; the resources required for the smaller ones may readily be aggregated into the resources needed for the larger work-units.
2. They permit a meaningful forecast of the workload to be made in terms related to the required manpower, or convertible to such terms.
3. At one or more levels it is obvious that a firm relationship of the work-unit to required manpower resources can be established; that at these levels a work count (the number of times a work-unit is to be performed or produced) is a meaningful number with respect to required resources.

These work-units and their place in the management cycle are shown in Figure 17.1. The major points of impact of method study and its subpart, procedure design (see Chapter 10), as well as the steps affected by time study or work measurement, are also indicated.

Let us examine a practical application of the preceding concepts to the problem of quantifying service type outputs with the aid of data from an effort undertaken by the Meat Inspection Activity of the Consumer and Marketing Service, U.S. Department of Agriculture. (The actual facts have been simplified in this presentation so as to reduce the complexity of the example without altering the nature of the problem or its solution. The actual, com-

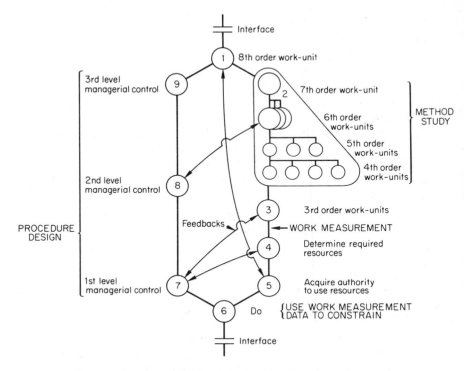

Fig. 17.1—The management cycle showing where the various orders of work-units would appear. The major points of impact of method study and its subpart, procedure design, as well as the steps affected by time study or work measurement are also shown.

plete work-unit hierarchy appears in Appendix A.) Previous to this effort, budget planning procedures (steps 1 through 5 of the cycle of control) were based on either an empirical relationship between total agency staffing and the number of meat packing plants needing service, or an empirical relationship between total staffing for the agency and the total number of pounds of all types of meat inspected. Needless to say, these two methods did not produce compatible answers. Neither method led to a management control system; neither method represented a procedure for accounting for all of the factors affecting the required manning and funding. Further, and this is most important, although "meat inspected" is one dimension of the output, and perhaps the most obvious one, it has been found that the workload of inspection, as a total, is relatively *independent* of the amount of meat produced and inspected. "Meat inspected" is an obvious but not a useful way to describe the outputs when one is concerned with determining manpower requirements.

To apply the analytical approach which has been developed:

The objective (eighth-order work-unit) of the agency is:

> To assure the American public of a safe, wholesome, and properly labeled supply of meat and meat products in the channels of interstate commerce and to facilitate the export of meat and meat products by giving the foreign purchaser similar assurance.

The seventh-order work-units were described as:

1. Official meat packing establishment inspection services provided for one year.[2] (Paid for by public funds.)
2. Non-official meat packing or meat products establishment inspection services provided for one year. (A reimbursed activity.)

Outputs within each of these two work-units were more homogeneous than when not separated because they are funded differently. This is the beginning of a replacement for the natural division supplied by the engineering drawings of the hardware-producing organization. To continue with the analysis:

> The programs (sixth-order outputs) or groupings of like outputs were listed as follows: (The first digit identifies the seventh-order work-unit to which the output belongs; the lower case letter is the sixth-order identification.)
>
> 1-a. Inspection services provided for one year where the plant workload requires less than one inspector.
> 1-b. Inspection services provided for one year where the plant workload requires exactly one inspector.
> 1-c. Inspection services provided for one year where the plant workload requires more than one but less than six inspectors.
> 1-d. Inspection services provided for one year where the plant workload requires six or more inspectors per establishment.[3]
> 2-a. Government product specification examinations performed.

Within each of the sixth-order work-units 1-a through 1-d, the natural fifth-order work-unit becomes "A plant (of that type) serviced," but, of course, these quantities cannot be added from program to program to give a number with a fixed relationship to manpower required.

Further division is desirable in this case. This additional, needed subdivision is encountered with many government work-unit hierarchy problems. The list of Table 11 was given only as a guide, not as a limiting list. In this case, the fifth-order work-units of program 1-a, "Inspection services provided for one year where the plant workload requires less than one inspector," can be usefully divided into two subgroups (sub-fifth-order work-units) as:

[2] Note the use of the past tense verb to assist in reducing the confusion of outputs with activities.

[3] This division is not arbitrary. Each group of plants requires a different amount of manpower per plant. Further, the number of plants in each group is changing independently and responds differently to economic factors; each sixth-order work-unit needs a different forecasting system.

1-a.1. Inspection services provided for one year where the workload requires less than one inspector but the plant is in an isolated location where no other work exists for the inspector, or where because of the nature of the work the inspector cannot leave during the working day.

1-a.2. Inspection services provided for one year where workload requires less than one inspector but the plant is of such a nature or so located that the plant may be combined with other plants into a multiplant assignment, using one in-plant inspector.

The fourth-order work-units, the intermediate products required to produce "a plant (of a type) serviced," will be a mix from the following list (which is the equivalent of the "parts list" in manufacturing; the situation resembles "custom" manufacturing).

4-1. Cattle slaughter inspected in-plant

4-2. Hog slaughter inspected in-plant

4-3. Sheep slaughter inspected in-plant

4-4. Sausage manufacturing maintained in compliance in-plant

4-5. Cured product manufacturing maintained in compliance in-plant

4-6. Inspection supervision provided

4-7. Inspection results appraised

4-8. Inspection methods designed

4-9. Laboratory support provided, and so forth

(The above list has been greatly shortened for simplicity's sake. A complex service may have many more "parts" than a washing machine.)

Let us review what has been done. We have developed a clear trail from the objective of the agency to a work-unit breakdown of the outputs. The equivalent of the bill of materials of the manufacturing plant has been established. We are now knowledgeable with respect to what to count and what to measure to determine required manpower resources. The three criteria of a useful work-unit hierarchy have been met.

Some of the subsequent work measurement activity is extremely simple and only the roughest type of standard times will suffice. For instance, let us suppose that all that is known about the standard time for work-unit 4-2, "Hog slaughter inspected in-plant," is that experience indicates that a man should be able to inspect between 100 and 150 hogs per hour. Obviously, such a poorly defined standard cannot be given full use, but let us consider inspection service provided to a plant slaughtering only 50 hogs per hour; an output of type 1-a.1.

Outputs of type 1-a.1 permit the simplest type of work measurement to be used to determine the manpower resources for the 4-2 component of the output, the in-plant "part." It is obvious that one man-year of a competent inspector is needed plus an additional amount of capability to allow for sick and annual leave. The records of the inspection service show that this is 14 per cent. Hence, each output of fourth-order work-unit 4-2 in a 1-a.1 type fifth-order output requires 1.14 man-years of manpower. Such a simple calculation will cover almost 10 per cent of the total agency manpower and, hence, is an important application of work measurement.

Other fourth-order work-units, of course, will require more complex techniques, as will borderline cases of 1-a.1. However, the discussion of each technique used to accomplish work measurement in this example would be quite lengthy. A separate presentation of the techniques will be made in subsequent chapters, as more appropriate. However, the presentation of the whole work-unit hierarchy in Appendix A also indicates which work measurement technique was used for each fourth-order work-unit.

The important conclusion from the preceding discussion is that if an analytical method is used to assist, one can determine what to count and what to measure, even with service type outputs. The mix of work does not preclude the useful application of work measurement. The conclusion of the U.S. Army Corps of Engineers, quoted earlier, should be phrased to read: "An attempt to apply work measurement without an analytical aid for solving the problem of what to count and what to measure has little chance of success." However, this should surprise no one; wrong approaches seldom succeed.

An additional example from a diverse field of endeavor seems desirable to show that meat inspection is not a special case. The Office of the Solicitor, Department of the Interior, presents a work measurement problem with totally different details but which may be solved by the same general approach. The Office of the Solicitor provides legal services to the Secretary, the Deputy, and Under-Secretaries and the program Bureaus and Offices of the Department. It is divided into 11 subject-matter offices located in Washington and nine area offices and 20 subarea offices. Hence, it operates in 29 locations in the United States. It employs approximately 210 professional employees. Services are provided to all 36 program Offices and Bureaus of the Department of the Interior in their dealings with the private sector, the Indians, the States, the Congress, the Executive Office, and in certain foreign problems dealing with fish, water, and so forth. Typical of the program Bureaus served are the Bureau of Mines, the Office of Oil and Gas, the Bureau of Indian Affairs, the National Park Service, and the Bureau of Commercial Fisheries.

The eighth-order work-unit of the Office of the Solicitor is the same as the eighth-order work-unit of the Department of the Interior; the Solicitor only serves to facilitate it.

The seventh-order work-unit is the totality of advice, opinions, briefs prepared, and so forth, as characteristic of the output of lawyers.

It seems convenient to think of the sixth-order work-units as being 36 in number with each described as: "A (specific Office or Bureau of the Department) served for one year."

Note, it is the Bureaus or Offices which produce the real outputs of the Department; the Solicitor only serves to facilitate these outputs in a variety of ways. Hence, it seems appropriate that the workload forecasting and work measurement system of the Office of the Solicitor should be related to the individual Offices and Bureaus that generate the workload. Also, service functions are frequently undermanned. If the required resources of the Office of the Solicitor were computed from the total of the individual workloads generated by the Offices and Bureaus, then any over-all shortage of legal manpower could be reacted to by changing the allocations of legal manpower to the program Offices or Bureaus, with some ability to anticipate the consequences.

The selection of the fifth-order work-units presents a special problem. Legal assistance takes many forms, such as undocumented advice, aid in negotiating, reviewing for legality, or documented assistance such as interpretations, opinions, drafts, and so forth. However, if the outputs were divided by kind of service, the residual mix of subject matter in any of these fifth-order work-units would constitute a heterogeneous mix which would be difficult, if not impossible, to relate to the variety of outputs of each Office or Bureau served. Hence, the fifth-order work-units were defined as "All matters (of a specific subject variety) processed." (A *matter*, briefly, is a document or other communication requiring a formal professional legal response.)[4]

Fifty-nine varieties of matters were separately identified *by subject* so as to allow relating matters to the variety (caused by the external society) in the mix of outputs for the Offices and Bureaus served. These fifty-nine categories were devised as a result of many discussions between the analysts and the attorneys. Numerous test periods were used to make certain that the selected categories were such that matters could be so classified, and that the list of categories was all inclusive and mutually exclusive, a basic requirement for classifications of outputs. All inclusive means that all matters could be classified; mutually exclusive means that a matter would not be counted in more than one category. When the work-unit structure was completed (with the work-unit structure being defined as the hierarchy of work-units from objective to tasks) a special work measurement procedure was designed and applied and the standard times used for all of the uses indicated at the beginning of this chapter.[5]

In summary, with both the Meat Inspection Activity and the Office of the Solicitor, the same general approach derived from an examination of that used with substantive manufacture was used. However, the details differed greatly. Also, as will be seen in later chapters, the work measurement tech-

[4] "Cases completed" might appear to be the obvious output, but if legal aid is effectively applied, cases may not even develop, matters will. Further, cases constitute too heterogeneous a mix; some last for 100 years. Large cases have many matters; small cases few. Hence, matters seemed a more appropriate and convenient concept for counting.

[5] See: "Workload Analysis Reporting System," Office of the Solicitor, U.S. Department of Interior, 1967.

niques were different. Purpose came first, followed by an identification of "what to measure." "How to measure" was subsequent.

Both of these efforts demonstrate a procedure for extending the area in which work measurement may be usefully employed to assist management with respect to decisions related to manpower resource management, an area where facts are frequently hard to come by if traditional technique-oriented thinking is followed. It is contended that the management of any activity may be aided by appropriate work measurement; that the sequence is to determine why to measure, then what to measure, then how to measure. In other words, the specification of the nature of the work-units and how to count them comes first. The selection of the work measurement technique must follow rather than precede these steps.

Now let us turn our attention to the second basic question given earlier, "In what units are manpower resources expressed?" To answer this by saying "man-hours" or "man-years" is to miss many important aspects. Implicit is the need to state *what kind of a man* (ability-wise), and *how fully he is to exert his ability.* We need to state the *rate* of work-input implicit in the time use of manpower embodied in the standard time. We need to state to the extent appropriate, the method, conditions of work, equipment, type of individual, and degree of exertion of such an individual's capabilities.

As with physical measurements, to avoid chaotic results a standard must be defined in such a manner that consistent, reliable measurements may be made, sufficient for the purpose for which the measurement is made. If, in a machine shop, each worker's micrometer had different graduations on it, product control would be extremely difficult and inefficient, if not impossible. Similarly, if no adequate standard of human performance is defined, managerial control will lack effectiveness. However, garments are not made to micrometer type measurements. Such meticulous accuracy would be inappropriate. In many cases of human performance, non-micrometer type measures may also be appropriate.

However, in many work measurement problems an adequate verbal description of the unit of measurement is not enough. It must also, for the most effective use, be embodied when possible in some physical form as are other standards. For example, the metric unit of length, the meter, was originally defined verbally as one ten-millionth of the distance on the earth's surface from the pole to the equator. Imagine trying to apply this standard consistently with this statement as the sole guide! Before the meter was of any use as a measuring unit it had to be reduced to physical forms, like rulers or gage blocks. The fact that the meter, as thus finally defined by an objective embodiment, was somewhat at variance with its verbal definition did not greatly hinder its ultimate usefulness. While such a discrepancy between verbal and objective definition would not be entirely inconsequential in the case of time study, as will be seen later, it is of less consequence than the need for consistency. Consistency is also of prime importance with most other measuring units or standards. Also, the need for adequate objective representation of the standard is frequently just as great with work measurement as with other types of measures.

Inasmuch as the following chapters of this section deal with various aspects of work measurement or with various techniques, it is desirable at this point to examine some fundamental facts concerning the factors relating to the "rate of work input." These data will provide a background for understanding some of the procedures examined later.

With any human physical attribute (and the ability of a person to do work is, in the final analysis, a function of physical attributes), the ratio between the best and the worst, excluding highly unusual people, is seldom greater than 2 to 1, with few cases of these extremes. Ralph Presgrave, analyzing data developed by Hull,[6] Wechsler,[7] and Barnes,[8] suggests that for practical purposes range of human capacity may be taken as being between 1:2 and 1:2.5. He suggests the reasonable dependability of a 1:2.5 range, although he states, "In fact a range of 1:2 in practice is extremely unusual and very often includes examples that any competent observer would refuse to take into account, even though, as a matter of courtesy, or in an attempt to assist poor operators, he might take a study."[9] Undoubtedly the actual range of 1:2.5 is reduced to the limits of 1:2 by even rudimentary worker selection.

The nature of the distribution of capacities is such that with each trait the greatest number of people tend to possess an average amount, with the number diminishing as the extremes are approached. This is the so-called "normal" distribution.

Consequently, for any job on which a large number of people work, or on a group of jobs with consistent time standards, the distribution of workers and performance (if all workers worked at their jobs at the maximum pace they could maintain on such jobs without harmful exertion) would be as shown in Figure 17.2.

It is worth noting that a change in the ratio between standard time and time at typical performance will alter the scale of the abscissa shown in Figure 17.2, change the scale value at the mid-point, and shift the position of the line indicating the division between substandard and below average workers. With the upper end of the curve shown in Figure 17.2 always bearing a value equal to twice the lower end, it can be seen that when the ratio of standard

[6] C. L. Hull, *Aptitude Testing*. Yonkers, N.Y.: World Book Company, 1928.

[7] D. Wechsler, *The Range of Human Capacities*. Baltimore, Md.: Williams & Wilkins Co., 1935.

[8] R. M. Barnes, *Motion and Time Study*, 2nd Ed. New York, N.Y.: John Wiley & Sons, 1940, p. 271.

[9] R. Presgrave, *The Dynamics of Time Study*. Toronto, Canada: University of Toronto Press, 1944, p. 108.

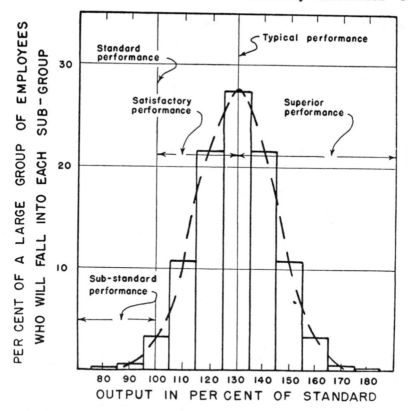

Fig. 17.2—Distribution of performance of a large group of workers with typical performance denoted as 130 per cent of standard. (Designating typical performance as 130 per cent of standard is common industrial practice.)

time to time at typical performance reaches 100/100, the line below which we find substandard workers lies at the mid-point and half the workers are "substandard," but when the proportion is 150/100, the substandard line lies at what is, for all general purposes, the bottom of the curve, and we have (excluding unusual cases) no "substandard" workers.

It should also be apparent that, in most cases, there will be workers who will not, even with the proper training, reach the level of standard performance. They are on the wrong job and, in most cases, the sooner they are shifted to other tasks for which they are more suited, the more advantageous it will be for the management and the worker. There will also be workers who will greatly exceed the standard level of performance. With the variation in human capacity, this is to be expected. This represents the ideal condition of a worker properly fitted to a job, provided the standard time is consistent with the definition it embodies, although, our mores being what they are, an extreme case may cause considerable disturbance with a wage incentive system.

It is to be noted that well-performed worker selection, pacing by limits of equipment, and group work will tend to reduce the spread of the curve shown in Figure 17.2. Figure 17.3, an actual curve for the hours worked in

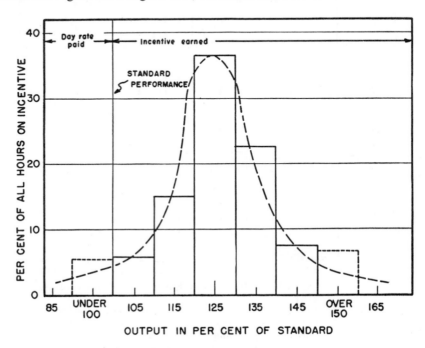

Fig. 17.3—Per cent of hours worked on incentive vs. per cent perform-
ance for one week. (Courtesy of C. J. Allen, Chief
Industrial Engineer, Patrick Cudahy, Inc., Cudahy,
Wis.)

one week by 1100 workers at a plant with an incentive system, displays some increased central grouping because of extensive group work at this plant. On the other hand, it clearly displays the basic characteristics of the theoretical curve of Figure 17.2. The incentive system in this plant is based on standard times designed so that the average worker may make 25 per cent incentive.

It may also be seen that both the selection and application of a rate of work input for use in the standard time must take into account the uses intended and the social aspects of the situation. These are matters that require careful consideration and frequently introduce difficult problems. However, consideration of its common uses should indicate the vital necessity of adequate work measurement to the effective management of an enterprise; hence the need to solve such problems.

We may now reach some conclusions with respect to time study or work measurement.

Time study or work measurement was defined, in two compatible ways, as being:

1. A set of procedures for determining the amount of time required, under certain standard conditions of measurement, for tasks involving some human activity.
2. A set of procedures for developing numerical coefficients for converting a quantitative statement of the workload (step 3 of the cycle of managerial control) to a quantitative statement of the required manpower resources (step 4).

The problems of determining *why to measure* and of selecting *what to count* and *how to count it* were shown as basic problems. It was further indicated that in a service activity or government agency, the problem of counting outputs or workload in a fashion which is related to manpower usage is not as simple as with substantive outputs, but is feasible. A general theory of a hierarchy of work-units was evolved and used as a substitute for the natural framework of the engineering drawings and process designs of the substantive outputs.

Also, it was shown that the relationship of a "standard time" to real-world expectancy could vary, depending upon the use to be made of the standard time. As will be shown in later chapters, different uses also affect the desirability of using a particular time study or work measurement technique. Further, it was shown that work-units vary greatly both in magnitude and nature. As will be shown, the characteristics of the work-unit under study must also be taken into consideration when selecting an appropriate time study or work measurement technique.

The next seven chapters will describe a variety of time study (or work measurement) techniques, or aspects of techniques. The situations examined will vary greatly. The nature of the standard time (ST) will vary considerably. The techniques will vary greatly. However, all will be directed at serving the greatest possible number of uses of time study as given at the beginning of the chapter. The presentations, as with the motion study techniques, will be directed at the problem of serving objectives rather than at techniques for their own sake.

In all cases the discussion of the techniques will concern the effects of different purposes, different ways of selecting a work-unit, different ways of obtaining a work count (the number of times a work-unit is performed), and different ways of obtaining a work time (the time associated with the work count). Differences will also be found in the way numerical modifiers are obtained and used to alter the above data so as to change its relationship to real-world times, and in the amount of additives used. However, in all cases, the basic relationship may be expressed by the following equation:

$$ST = \left(\frac{W/T}{W/C} \times M\right) + A$$

where

ST = standard time.
(1) W/T = work time.
(2) W/C = work count associated with W/T.
(3) M = a modifier used to adjust the meaning of W/T with respect to the real world.
(4) A = an additive used to adjust the ST to real people.

In each chapter in which a technique is discussed, the variations in procedures and the significance with respect to these four aspects will be discussed as well as the effect or limitations imposed by circumstances surrounding the time study effort, e.g., intent, or peculiarities of the work-unit.

Supplemental Material

The supplemental material of this chapter is divided into two sections.

1. An examination of the industrial definition of standard time.
2. Statistical interfaces between work-units. This second subject concerns a phenomenon which has probably been at the root of many difficulties encountered in attempts to apply work measurement to organizations with non-substantive outputs.

The Industrial Definition of Standard Time

In the body of the chapter it was shown that the term *standard time* could have many meanings. In much industrial practice however, a single specific meaning is attached to this term and this definition represents an agreement between labor and management. This supplemental material examines some fundamental aspects of potential definitions which should be considered to achieve a satisfactory definition.

Earlier, a standard time was defined as indicating how long a given rate of work input must be maintained to produce a unit of output. The factors or conditions concerned in a standard time were suggested as:

1. *Unit of output (work-unit)*
2. *Rate of work input*

    a. Method
    b. Conditions of work
    c. Equipment
    d. Type of individual
       1. Skill
       2. Aptitude
    e. Degree of exertion of the specified type of individual

Consequently, a standard time may be more fully defined as follows:

DEFINITION—*A standard time is a function of the amount of time necessary to accomplish a unit of work:*
    1. using a given method and equipment,
    2. under given conditions of work,
    3. by a worker possessing a specified amount of SKILL *on the job and a specified* APTITUDE *for the job,*
    4. when working at a pace that will utilize, within a given period of time, the maximum physical exertion such a worker could expend on such a job without HARMFUL EFFECTS.

Within this definition, the following word meanings are intended:

skill—the ability to do a job in the proper manner; the ability to repeat a definite muscular pattern. Other worker characteristics being constant, the higher the skill, the faster the possible pace before the muscular coordinations fail.

aptitude—physical fitness for the job.

harmful effects—the results of excessive physical and mental activity, caused by the work, which are not dissipated during the typical usage of the interval between work days.

It should be noted that this last item has a primarily sociological basis. Consider the two heavy horizontal lines of Figure 17.4. The upper line, the physiological maximum, may be defined as the fastest an average man could work, day after day, using the time between work spells for rest, without physical deterioration. Such a pace is not attained in modern industry. This concept is not compatible with a democracy in which men work to live, rather than live to work. The physiological maximum would connote a slave population with no energy to engage in family activity, leisure time, or civic pursuits. The lower, heavy line is the physiological minimum, the slowest pace at which work could be performed without increasing the rate of expending energy. This is likewise practically never encountered, and is certainly not compatible with a high standard of living based on high production.

For an organization to operate profitably within the economic environ-

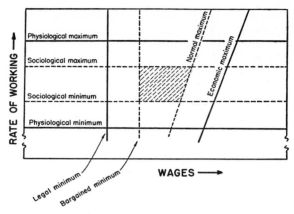

Fig. 17.4—Wages vs. rate of work and the area in which the actual
work-pace lies.

ment, the work pace must be at least at or above the broken horizontal
line labeled *sociological minimum*. For workers to accept this required rate
of exertion as reasonable and proper (consistent with their concept of their
society), the work pace cannot exceed the upper broken horizontal line labeled
sociological maximum. However, the situation is complicated further by economic aspects. Leisure energy without sufficient income for comforts considered reasonable in the society is not satisfactory. Therefore, the two vertical
heavy lines have been added to the chart to indicate, as do the first two heavy
lines, conditions which are factually determinable but not always socially
acceptable. The legal minimum wage is fixed by law for the most part. The
economic maximum wage, the point where the organization would make zero
per cent profit, a level economically determinable, is certainly not acceptable
to the owners. Therefore, the two vertical broken lines have been added.
The bargained minimum is the wage level above the legal minimum attained
by virtue of the scarcity of skills, the desire of management to pay a good
wage, or the pressure of collective bargaining. The line labeled normal
maximum is the most the organization can pay, still making a reasonable
profit and not pricing itself out of the market.

The four broken lines enclose a *wage vs. rate-of-work* area within which the
point denoting the actual conditions in an actual plant lies. Reference to Chapter 2 will suggest that the diagram of Figure 17.4 is only a rough representation of two of the many variables affecting the situation. As will be seen in
later chapters, a means of defining this point on the *rate-of-work* scale is
feasible. However, the reader should recognize that the phrase *maximum
physical exertion* (in the definition of standard time) refers to this sociologi-
cally-determined point and not to a true, physiologically-determinable condition.

To make the general definition of standard time usable, it is necessary to replace the word *function* with a numerical value and to replace with a definite adjective each use of the word *specified,* thus defining a particular standard performance.

Many concepts or units of standard time are possible.

Some definition of this general type is usually found in collective bargaining contracts or in a statement of policy by management, although in many cases the detailing of the standard unit of performance is not carried out completely.[10]

The following three examples are taken from union-management contracts:

I. The production standards shall:
  1. Be established for a specific set of conditions.
  2. Reflect the production requirements as related to a fair day's work for a fair day's pay and shall enable the normally skilled employee to increase his incentive earnings approximately 25 per cent above the occupational hourly rate for his occupation in effect (date) without unreasonable effort.[11]

II. Guaranteed piecework prices shall be set so that a normal employee or group of employees, possessing normal skill and training, working under normal conditions, may, by normal incentive effort, after making an honest effort to attain incentive earnings over a reasonable trial period, have an opportunity to earn per pay period approximately 50 per cent above his piecework base rate or their piecework base rates.[12]

III. Standards shall be set so that an average employee using the prescribed method, working under the prescribed conditions, and producing satisfactory work, shall be able to earn 25 per cent above the evaluated rate after he has had sufficient opportunity to become familiar with the job, has the required skill and ability to properly perform the job and works at the incentive pace. It is understood, however, that there is no guarantee that every employee will achieve a performance under which he will earn not less than 25 per cent above the evaluated rate. Nothing herein contained shall be construed as imposing ceilings on earnings.[13]

A consideration of the uses of standard times enumerated in this chapter and their requirements will show that it is desirable that the unit of measurement used in standard times should, for widest use, meet, if possible, the

[10] B. Gottlieb, "A Fair Day's Work Is Anything You Want It To Be," *Proceedings 19th Annual Institute and Convention,* May 1968, pp. 155–163. (This article also contains an extensive bibliography of related articles.)

[11] Agreement between American Steel Foundries and United Steelworkers of America, East St. Louis Works.

[12] Articles of Agreement Between Servel, Inc. and United Electrical, Radio & Machine Workers of America.

[13] Agreement between Cudahy Brothers Company and United Packinghouse Workers of America, C.I.O.

following three criteria, on the basis of which a convenient standard unit of measurement may be established:

1. Consistent with respect to difficulty of attainment. (See all uses listed.)
2. Representative, regardless of the job, of a performance that can be bettered by a constant amount by the average worker.[14] (See number 3 of the list of uses.)
3. If for incentive use, providing an attainable differential of adequate size. (See number 3d of the list of uses.)

The first criterion may be fulfilled by: setting up any definite set of specifications for the measurement or time study; adhering to these specifications in the determination of standard times; and, in addition, defining the *function of the amount of time* as that which would be taken by working at a pace requiring an expenditure of *some fixed proportion of the maximum physical exertion possible on the job*.

The second criterion suggests two things: (1) Wherever the word *specified* appears in the basic definition, as concerns the type of worker, it must be replaced with an adjective denoting the average worker, and (2) *the function of the amount of time* "that would be required with the maximum physical exertion such a worker could expend on the job without harmful effects," be set as some definite proportion greater than unity,[15] so as to permit such a worker to exceed standard performance by a fixed amount.

The third criterion suggests that the *function of the amount of time* be set so that the proportion of time allowed for standard performance, as compared to the time at maximum exertion, is sufficiently more than unity to permit the worker to exceed standard performance by an adequate amount. What is "adequate" poses a real problem and is a function of the use to be made of the standards. If no wage incentives are involved, any amount is adequate inasmuch as the sole purpose in such a case is to avoid the frustration arising from an unattainable "standard." If the standard time is to be used also as a basis for wage incentives, or if this may eventually be contemplated, then the problem is more complex. An incentive in the general sense may be considered an incentive only when it is so regarded by the person to whom it is applied. Hence, in a particular plant the adequacy of size of the

---

[14] With some incentive plans, incentive payment begins at some fraction, less than unity, of standard performance. In such a case this criterion would need to be restated, but the implication would not change.

[15] If an incentive plan that starts the incentive below standard performance is used, then the proportion of the time at maximum exertion that will be allowed may be set at unity and the point at which incentive begins placed at the point necessary to meet this second criterion and also the third, which follows. This is a less common situation, inasmuch as the method of expecting incentive to begin at standard allows wages to be in direct relationship to the percentage of standard performance, which appears to be more easily explained to working groups whose usual ability with mathematics is not high.

average attainable differential is a function of such factors as customs, and attitude toward standards and the incentive system. In the contract definitions cited earlier, the amounts were 25, 50, and 25 per cent. The common range is 20 to 50 per cent, with 30 per cent being a commonly effective value. Since most present-day incentive systems pay wages in direct proportion to output, the attainable differential in production should equal the adequate incentive increment.

Consequently, on the basis of all the comments on the criteria involved, the following definition is suggested for general use, since, in the author's opinion, it best meets the requirements given. (Reference should also be made to the definitions of terms laid down earlier.)

DEFINITION—*The standard time for a job will be 130/100 of the amount of time that will be necessary to accomplish a unit of work:*
  1. *using a given method and equipment,*
  2. *under given conditions,*
  3. *by a worker possessing sufficient skill to do the job properly,*
  4. *as physically fit for the job, after adjustment to it, as the average person who can be expected to be put on the job,*
  5. *and working at the maximum pace that can be maintained on such a job day after day without harmful effects.*

If the third criterion is interpreted differently, then the proportion of the time at maximum pace required for standard performance (doing the job in the standard time) can be altered accordingly; that is, in the sample definitions from labor contracts which were cited earlier, the proportion would be 125/100, 150/100 and 125/100, respectively.

It should be noted that the use of standard times together with incentives in shops where the work is not entirely manual is accompanied by additional problems relative to the criteria given for standard times. Let us assume that the standard time for a manual job, Job *A*, set according to the recommended definition, is 1.0 minute. An average incentive worker may be expected to perform this job in 0.77 minute. In another job, Job *B*, where a man feeds an automatic machine whose fixed cycle time is 1.0 minute, the standard time for the manual work of feeding the machine while it is running is also 1.0 minute. The incentive worker who performs this work in 0.77 minute will still produce only one piece in 1.0 minute. (The range of jobs between *A* and *B*, with part of the cycle controlled, present the same problem to a lesser degree.) The standard time of Job *B* does not violate any of the criteria established; it is the work situation which does not permit production to be solely a function of how hard the worker exerts himself. This may be thought of as an inequity which may be remedied with additives to be included in the job standard.

There may be some who feel that the recommended definition is cumbersome and unnecessary. However, they should realize that time studies give time standards for human performance, on the basis of which equipment and manpower requirements, schedules, cost controls, supervisory objectives, prices, and even wages are often set. These areas of activity are vital to adequate managerial functioning. As was noted in the body of the chapter, the concept of standard time, like any standard of measurement, must eventually be placed in some usable, concrete form. This will be discussed in later chapters, but the determination of what concept is to be embodied is certainly a vital first step. It should be reasonable to suggest that this first step, on which all of these managerial activities are based, be performed in a manner that will make possible an approach to real measurement, adequate for the intended use.

Statistical Interfaces Between Work-units

In the washing machine illustration cited in the body of the chapter the work-units could be aggregated in a simple fashion. It was noted that some parts were used in quantities greater than one per unit washing machine, but this was hardly a complex relationship. An allowance for scrap parts or loss might be needed, but this also could hardly be called complex information. A somewhat more complex but still simple relationship will be found between the typical second- and third-order work-units. For instance, let us examine the third-order work-unit, *make screw on automatic screw machine*. Note, *screw* is singular. The second-order work-units will be such as:

2–1. Set up machine for this particular screw.

2–2. Run test piece and adjust machine.

2–3. Load machine with stock.

2–4. Check output periodically.

2–5. Load output into tote pan.

2–6. Fill out production report for lot.

Obviously, the time for second-order work-units 2–1 through 2–6 cannot be added to obtain the time for "make screw." We can, however, in this case, express the relationship between the time for the third-order work-unit and its constituent second-order work-units by means of the following formula:

$$\text{Third-order work-unit time} = \frac{T(2\text{-}1)}{L} + \frac{T(2\text{-}2)}{SL} + \frac{T(2\text{-}3)}{N}$$
$$+ \frac{T(2\text{-}4)}{CL} + \frac{T(2\text{-}5)}{L} + \frac{T(2\text{-}6)}{L}$$

where

$T(2\text{-}1), T(2\text{-}2)$ = time for each performance of each second-order work-unit

L = lot size; normal number of the particular screw made under one manufacturing order

SL = sublot size; the number of screws made between adjustments of the machine

N = number of screws obtained per bar of stock

CL = check-lot size; the number of screws made between successive checks of the machine

The information represented by the values of L, SL, N, and CL could be called the statistical interface between the second- and third-order work units. It has seldom been dignified by such a name; the process of attributing the time for the second-order work-units to a third-order work-unit has usually been described as a *pro rata allocation.* With direct work on substantive outputs, the relationship is seldom complicated. The most complex relationship is usually between the second- and third-order of work-units; the relationship at higher orders, as was noted, is usually extremely simple. There may also be a need to allow for scrap or loss, but this is seldom a complex type of information.

However, when dealing with service outputs, the relationship between successive orders of work-units is seldom as clear-cut and as simple. The relationship is frequently sufficiently complex that the term *statistical interface* is far more descriptive than the term *pro rata allocation.* The interfaces are not limited to second- and third-order; they frequently occur between many of the orders. They seldom are simple. The work-units which are chosen for a non-substantive output organization must be selected so as to make it feasible to obtain quantitative information describing these statistical interfaces. It is worth noting that if one of the outputs for the Meat Inspection Activity, described in the body of the chapter, had been "Meat Inspected," the statistical interface between this output and the lower orders of outputs would have been so complex that it is doubtful that a satisfactory quantitative description of the causal factors of this interface could be obtained.

If the criteria of an effective hierarchy of work-units is reviewed, it will be noted that implicit in the criteria is the need to select the work-units such as to make feasible the obtaining of quantitative information concerning the statistical interface between successive orders.

CHAPTER 18

Direct Time Study— Intensive Sampling

Direct time study—intensive sampling is a procedure in which the performance of a task is observed directly and continuously for a limited period of time. Data are recorded concerning the work time and the associated work count, together with an appraisal of the performance in comparison with the standard concept of performance. An allowance for non-work time is usually added in conformance with policies which have been established by the organization. All these data are used to compute a standard time. In much of the literature the procedure is called either "stop-watch time study" or "direct time study." In that recording devices other than stop-watches are often used, the term "stop-watch time study" seems misleading. Also, there are other methods of time study in which direct observations are made, but the method of sampling is different; hence, a compound name is used here to fully identify the general technique.

As an alternative definition, using the terms of the equation for a standard time given in Chapter 17, direct time study—intensive sampling may be defined as a procedure wherein:

1. W/C. Obtained, usually with details concerning the method, by a direct and continuous observation of a period of performance. The period is limited and fully watched. It is an intensive sample.
2. W/T. Obtained by direct observation with a stop-watch, motion-picture camera, video-tape recorder, or time study machine or portable computer.

3. *M*. An appraisal of the performance in comparison with the standard concept of performance; a mental evaluation is made by the observer.
4. *A*. An increment added to allow for non-work time; usually determined by policy; the value may vary with the type of work and with the purpose of the standard time.

The results of direct time study—intensive sampling are sometimes referred to as "engineered standards." The term "engineered standard" is used when the value for W/T contains only actual work time and when the values for M and A are obtained systematically and the basis of M is known. However, as will be seen in later chapters, there are other means of obtaining so-called engineered standards. It will also be seen that there are situations which preclude the setting of engineered standards. However, in such situations, other techniques may be used to obtain standard times which satisfy all the requirements for such values. Hence, the term "engineered standard" does not in all cases denote a preferable type of value.

Direct time study—intensive sampling is most frequently employed when the task for which a standard time is sought is repetitive. Repetitive work is work with a cyclic pattern which is repeated over an extended period of time much greater than the period required for the sample or observation period. Repetitive work is usually a third-order work-unit as defined in Chapter 17. The technique may be used when the work has a single repeated cycle, subcycles, or a limited variety of cycles. If a large variety of cycles are employed, which are not repeated in a limited time, other techniques which are described later, such as *direct time study—extensive sampling*, may well be preferable.

The use of the technique is limited to work which is actually being performed; the technique may not be used to set a standard prior to the start of work. However, a short experimental run may suffice to provide the necessary data.

Much industrial production work and routine office work will exhibit characteristics which allow this technique to be employed. Of course, as will be seen later, other techniques may also be used, but all techniques must be understood if the most preferable technique is to be chosen. This chapter will examine pertinent details of alternative methods of employing direct time study—intensive sampling.

There are five distinct steps in the setting of a standard time by means of direct time study—intensive sampling. They are:

1. Defining the standard of measurement so as to provide a basis for determining the modifier M. This definition needs to be established only once for all studies in a plant.
2. a. Recording the standard practice, describing the work-units and their relationship to the next higher order of work-unit.

 b. Observing and recording the work time taken by a particular operator, together with data concerning the associated work count.

 c. Rating or relating performance to the standard; determining the modifier M.

 d. Application of allowances; the determination of the adjustment factor A.

Each of the steps under 2 must be performed for each job studied.

Step 1, the defining of the standard of measurement, is the basis (as was noted) for the determination of the modifier M. With direct time study— intensive sampling, this modifier is determined toward the end of the work measurement process. Therefore, it seems convenient to delay the discussion of step 1 and the modifier M until its natural place in the sequence of actions, given under 2 above, is reached. The discussion which follows will examine the steps given under 2, in the order given.

Recording the Standard Practice

The recording of the standard practice requires that the units in which the output is to be counted (the fourth-order work-unit), the method, the equipment, and the conditions of work be made a matter of record. The carrying out of this step results in what is commonly called a "written standard practice."

Any time study predicates either the previous existence of, or the creation of, a written standard practice. This is one aspect of motion and time study where the motion study phase and the time study phase are hard to separate. Certainly any plant where the production is such that formal motion study techniques would be used could hardly afford to be without formal time study.[1] Consequently, it would seem obvious that the final statement of a job method design should be put into a form suitable for use in conjunction with the subsequent time study of which it will be a necessary and integral part. Furthermore, in many plants, because of the lack of trained personnel or a lack of realization of the possible benefits, there is no formal motion study activity, but only time study activity with informal or casual method design, which is performed by line supervisors, tool engineers, workers, and time study men. In such cases, the written standard practice must be prepared during the carrying out of the time study function. We must also realize that production exigencies will frequently necessitate starting a job (and perhaps

---

 [1] This was the case, however, with U.S. Government Arsenals and Depots from 1917 to 1947 because of restrictions placed upon them in Congressional appropriation bills. The above statement in the text summarizes the testimony offered the Armed Forces Appropriations Committee of the U.S. Senate by a group of engineers interested in performing a public service.

even completing the run) with a method designed "on the spot," and even accompanying it with a standard time set long before any formal methods analysis for the determination of the optimum method is made. Indeed, many cases will exist where it would be uneconomical to use any but the most cursory procedures for method design, as in adapting past practice on somewhat similar operations to the requirements of the new job. All these items considered, it seems desirable to place the text material on "written standard practice" in two places: first, in this section on direct time study intensive sampling, so that it may be studied in context, since some features of the best method of recording a written standard practice are designed primarily to facilitate the time study of the job and, second, in a summary in the section on the application of motion and time study data (Chapter 25).

Before any other phases of the measurements for standard time are made, the method, equipment, and conditions should be recorded in sufficient detail so that the job and the conditions surrounding it may be reproduced or examined at any time in the future exactly as they were at the time of study. This is the guiding principle for preparing an adequate written standard practice.

An adequate record of standard practice also increases the value of the time study for the eventual determination of time values for synthesized standards based on "standard data." (This aspect will be covered later in this chapter.) Experience has also shown that, if the standard practice is not adequately recorded, the standard time that is determined will eventually become "wrong." The actual practice is not static and, as time passes, almost invariably changes. Without an adequate description of what was timed, there is no means of evaluating a change. It should be obvious, therefore, that if the standard time is to have any real significance it must be accompanied by a reliable record of what this time allows for or what actions are involved. In addition, without a good description of the job, an undesirable plant attitude is developed. Standard times become associated with amounts of production rather than with amounts of physical work that are called for from the worker. This brings about resistance to changes that lead to higher amounts of production, even though they may call for the same amount of physical work. The cry of "speed-up" is often raised. We must separate "speed-up" into two categories: The speeding up of workers may or may not be justifiable, depending on the original pace; speeding up production without increased exertion, although it raises certain other personnel problems, is a vastly different proposition from increasing the exertion, and the two must not be confused.[2] An adequate method record helps differentiate these.

---

[2] Increased exertion may also take two forms: raising the exertion to the level called for in the definition of standard time, or exceeding this level. Although only the second variety is theoretically improper, the first also raises definite problems in the maintenance of satisfactory industrial relations.

It is also vital in the maintenance of union relations. Clauses like the following are frequently found in labor contracts:

> Once an incentive rate has been established and has been given a fair trial under normal operating conditions, no change in rates shall be made during the life of this Agreement, except as follows:
>
> (a) If a change of design, methods, equipment, tools, job duties, or material makes a difference in the time required to perform the job, a revision may be made in the piece rate. If the change clearly affects definite elements in the existing job, only the elements affected will be changed. However, if a job has been so completely changed that a comparison between the old job and the new job is not reasonably possible, a re-study of the entire job may be made to establish the rate.[3]

The need for an adequate method record for proper operation within such an agreement should be readily apparent.

Motion-picture film or video recorder tape is sometimes used to make a partial record of the method. It provides an extremely accurate record of that which may be seen and is often an economical aid, since it may also be used as an aid in future training of operators. It is particularly valuable on important but intermittent jobs or on jobs so complex that written descriptions would be almost impossible, i.e., boning-out a veal carcass in a meat-packing plant. As will be noted in the section of this chapter which deals with timing, the motion-picture camera or video tape recorder may be used to combine the two steps of recording the method and timing. However, speeds, feeds, tools, and the like must usually be manually recorded.

Before recording the standard practice, the time study analyst should first make the method as effective as can be conveniently accomplished. The experienced motion and time study analyst is often able to suggest several Class 1 changes in a job after a simple visual inspection. A trained motion study analyst should be able to regard a job in terms of steps such as are used in constructing process charts-man analysis, operation charts, man and machine charts, and so forth. He should be sufficiently familiar with the basic principles of improvement so that desirable changes are obvious to him. Sufficient practice with the analysis techniques will develop this attitude, often referred to as "motion-mindedness." As was noted earlier, a cursory analysis during time study is sometimes the economical limit of analysis. This is one of the reasons for placing much of the material on written standard practices in this chapter.[4] If more complex changes are possible, it may still be desirable to determine the standard time for the job, as it exists, and revise the standard when the changes are installed. In some plants, though, it may be desir-

---

[3] Agreement between Aluminum Goods Mfg. Co. and Aluminum Workers International Union together with International Association of Machinists, Manitowoc, Wisconsin.

[4] Written standard practices may exist for process or operation. Only the latter are considered in this chapter.

able to hold off the determination of the standard time until the job is fully improved. The individual plant situation will determine which is preferable.

The first step in recording the standard practice is to identify the work-unit or end-product of the job, usually a fourth-order work-unit. Usually several alternatives are possible, although, in most cases, one is preferable. For example, in operating a screw machine, the preferable unit may be a *piece* (or some number of pieces); alternatives would be *per bar of stock* or *per foot of stock*. For the operation of washing the oil off the pieces produced by the screw machine, the preferable work-unit may be a 100-pound basket of stock; an alternative would be pieces.[5] It should be noted that in most cases the work-units are interconvertible. After taking a time study in terms of one, it may be desirable subsequently to convert to another. Whatever work-unit is selected, it should be adhered to in the preparation of the standard practice so as to produce record that will relate to the standard time finally obtained. In general, the work-unit for direct time study should be selected so as to be:

1. Directly related to the work-input.
2. Suitable for forecasting the workload.
3. Convenient to time.
4. Easily identified.
5. Convenient for scheduling and recording production (if it is the final, reported work-unit).

In actually describing a job for time study, it is usually found desirable to break down the job into steps referred to as *time study elements*. These are second-order work-units. The use of an element breakdown, as will be seen subsequently, facilitates timing, comparison of the times with the times from other tasks, evaluation of the data, and later use of the times for the development of standard elemental data for synthesized standards.

The elements, which will be timed separately, should be chosen in accordance with the following requirements:[6]

1. *Easily detected and definite end point.* This will facilitate timing because the well-defined end point is easier to note accurately. The most desirable type of end point is one which permits some means of anticipating its occurrence so that the time study man many prepare to read his watch at the correct instant. For example, it is easier to determine the instant a lathe chuck key is laid upon a bench than the instant the worker is finished tightening the chuck preparatory to removing the key. However, a compromise is sometimes necessary when this requirement conflicts with one of the others which follow.

---

[5] Substantive outputs have been given as examples. Direct time study-intensive sampling is not usually applicable to service type outputs.

[6] This aspect of written standard practices is further reason for including their first treatment in this section.

2. *As small as is convenient to time.* When stop-watches are used, the smallest practical unit is about 0.04 minute, or three seconds. Even this, however, requires skill on the part of the time study man. If motion-picture films or video-tapes are taken and later analyzed or if time study machines involving constantly moving paper tapes are used, a smaller time unit is possible. Some hand operations involving highly repetitive performance with highly skilled operators can be much more adequately studied with these finer discriminating techniques.

3. *As unified as possible.* The element should consist of a well-unified group of motions such as reach for, take hold of an object, move it, and place it (in terms of therbligs, TE, G, TL, P, A, and RL), rather than part of a series of movements with one object and part of another series with another object. The worker usually tends to perform such activities as a pattern, rather than as a series of acts; hence, the motions should be timed as a group and should not be divided at an odd place. Also, an operator may possess different amounts of the different skills required by the various steps of the job; thus his performance on each step is best judged when separated. In addition, breaking the job down into elements involving only manipulative ability, visual perception, strength, and so forth, facilitates the subsequent job of rating.

4. *Hand time should be separated from machine time.* Hand time is subject to the control of the operator; machine time, with automatic feeds or fixed speeds, is not. Even where hand feeds are used, the proper time for the machine work is determinable with a long established, highly mechanistic form of experimentation.[7] Machine time also permits a high degree of standardization and cross-checking from study to study. Hand time is much more variable and harder to determine precisely. Hence, these two types of times should always be separated.

5. *Internal time should be separated from external time.* Handwork done while the machine or process controls the total elapsed time (internal time) should be separated from handwork done while only the handwork controls the total elapsed time (external time).

6. *Constant elements should be separated from variable elements.* The act of starting a machine is usually independent of the piece being worked on. The act of setting aside a given type of material box is often independent of the nature of the pieces in it, within limits,[8] and is usually independent of the operation performed. Elements of this type should be kept separate from those involved in the actual handling of the piece, which will probably vary with the size, shape, and weight of the individual piece, its location, orientation, and how easily it may be handled.[9] For instance in small assembly work, the

[7] H. Rossmoore, "A New Tool for the Time Study Engineer," *Modern Management*, Vol. IX., No. 1, Jan. 1949, p. 14.

[8] Weight, roughness with which it may be handled, distance, etc.

[9] Although these are somewhat the same variables as affect box handling time, there is more likelihood, in the case of handling the piece, that they will vary from job to job.

getting and placing of a nut may be a function of the size, bin, destination, or nature of assembly—a variable from job to job. If the assemblies move progressively in standard boxes, the box handling may be a constant from job to job. The separation of these two types of times aids in the development of standard elemental data, and in cross-checking between studies. The standard elemental data aspect will be discussed more fully later in this chapter.

7. *Regular and irregular elements should be separated.* Elements that do not occur in every cycle should be kept separate to facilitate proper prorating. Often, considerable observation is required to find them, but they are a valid part of the job.

With all types of work it is essential to record, for the actual time study, in addition to the standard practice, the following items:

1. The name, clock number, and work location of the operator observed.
2. The date and time when the time study is made.

The essential criteria of the adequacy of the accompanying written standard practice are:

1. Does it contain everything the worker has to do?
2. Could the job be reproduced from it?

The following items must be included to meet these criteria, and are also the requirements of a written standard practice when it is made following the motion study phase, even if no time study is to be made. These items may be called the requirements for recording a method design.

1. The department in which the job is.
2. Job number.
3. Work-unit identification.
4. Product, material specifications, and identification as related to the operation and work-unit.
5. Workplace layout[10] and dimensions.
6. Equipment description and its condition; if abnormal, so noted.
7. Tool descriptions.
8. Feeds and speeds of machines, welding currents used, and so forth.
9. Surrounding environmental conditions.
10. Services in the way of machine and tool maintenance and delivery and material handling rendered to, or required of, the worker.
11. A description of the actual manual details of the job.
    a. The seven requirements of good time study elements should be observed as far as possible in this description.
    b. The type of terminology used in the description of the elements varies with the nature of the job. For heavy work involving moving from place to place, a description of the activities of the person as

---

[10] A Polaroid camera may be employed advantageously to assist in making this part of the record.

a whole is most suitable. For heavy work with crews, the activities of the individual crew members as well as their coordination must be indicated. For heavy and moderately heavy work, done mainly at one place, the activity of the individual as a whole is sufficient, unless the coordination of the body members of the worker is a critical factor, in which case the activities of each body member should be detailed and the coordination indicated. This latter is the preferable procedure with light work. Where the time study man is familiar with the therblig breakdown, he will find this a useful terminology to use in his descriptions, particularly with small handwork. Where the therblig time studies are shown to men who are unfamiliar with the terminology, the use of the therbligs may be undesirable, as they will be an unintelligible shorthand and may be subject to mistrust, depending on plant attitude. However, more and more plants are wisely undertaking training programs in motion and time study for foremen and supervisors, and therbligs or equivalent first-order work-units are constantly coming into more common use. Also, they form a good shorthand to use on this record, which may be expanded for instructional material later.

In some cases, a single time study sheet is sufficient for the recording of the standard practice. In other cases, it is necessary to attach drawings of the tools, and so forth. In still others, the written standard practice may run to several pages. No one form has yet been devised that will handle the problems of all plants satisfactorily.

The preparation of the description of the manual details of the job (item 11 of the preceding list) may be done most easily in two steps:

1. List a rough outline of the elements and check these against the previously given requirements for time study elements, adjusting the elements as necessary.
2. Detail the descriptions of the elements one by one.

For example, with the job of filling fountain pens in a pen factory inspection department, preparatory to inspection by use, the following elements would be suitable. (This job is chosen for use as an example here because probably everyone is familiar with the parts. The work-unit is *a pen filled.*)

Element Number	Preliminary Description
1	Dispose of last pen to "writing" inspector and get pen
2	Prepare for filling
3	Fill with ink
4	Wipe point and partially reassemble

The detail on the first step would be as follows. (The terminal point of the element is underlined. This is a desirable way of indicating when the watch [or time study machine or film or tape] is to be read as the job is actually timed.)

Element Number	Left-Hand Description	Right-Hand Description
1	Aside pen in "writing" inspector's ready rack, <u>point</u> <u>down</u>, <u>release</u>	Get pen from tray

In terms of a therblig breakdown, this would be:

Element Number	Left-Hand Description	Right-Hand Description
1	TL pen to "writing" inspector's ready rack, PP and <u>RL</u> <u>pen</u> <u>into</u> <u>rack</u>	TE to pen tray, G pen from tray

A complete sample time study sheet ready for time study, with the entire written standard practice included on it, is shown with an ordinary detailed breakdown in Figure 18.1, and with a detailed therblig breakdown in Figure 18.2.

Figure 18.3 is a time study sheet prepared for use in a machine shop. Note the summary under each element. It is given in therbligs to aid in accurately defining the motions. Note also the columns for feeds and speeds as well as the special boxes for items commonly associated with the machining operations in this shop.

Figure 18.4 is part of a standard practice (or method description) for a job in a steel mill. Two separate studies are required here: one of the operator, and one of the helper. The descriptions are of such size that they are kept on sheets separate from the time study. The time study sheets merely refer to these elements by number.

Figure 18.5 is a written standard practice prepared in great detail, as is necessary for this type of work, for the grid-peeling job mentioned in previous chapters. The total of all of the elements shown is about 0.08 minutes. In this case, a regular-speed movie film, a video tape record, or a time study machine tape would be required to obtain the times for these elements. A time study sheet, if used to record the values from the film, tape, or time study machine, would merely refer to these elements by giving the number that

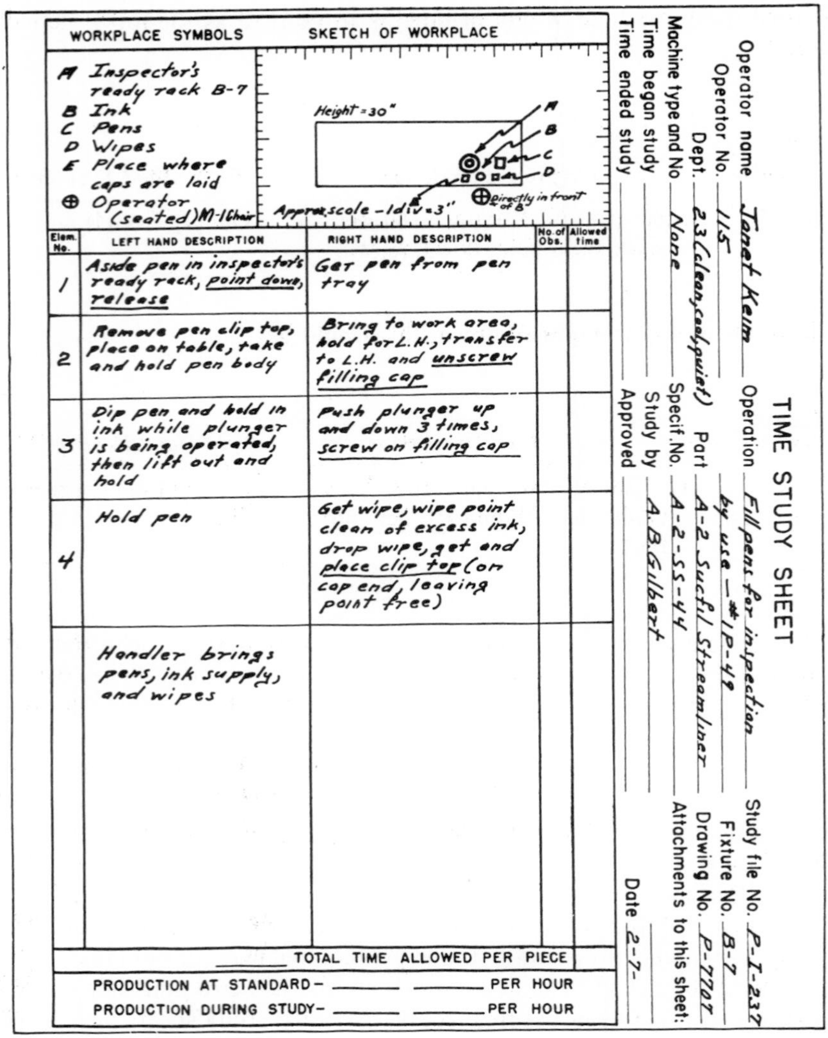

TIME STUDY SHEET

WORKPLACE SYMBOLS	SKETCH OF WORKPLACE

A Inspector's ready rack B-7
B Ink
C Pens
D Wipes
E Place where caps are laid
⊕ Operator (seated) M-16 chair

Height = 30"

Approx. scale - 1 div = 3"   ⊕ Directly in front of B

Operator name _Janet Keim_   Operation _Fill pens for inspection_
Operator No. _115_   _by use — #1P-48_
Dept. _23 (clean, cool, quiet)_   Part _A-2 Suctil Streamliner_
Machine type and No. _None_   Specif. No. _A-2-55-44_
Time began study _____   Study by _A.B.Gilbert_
Time ended study _____   Approved _A.B.Gilbert_

Study file No. _P-I-237_
Fixture No. _B-7_
Drawing No. _P-7707_
Attachments to this sheet: _____
Date _2-7-_

Elem. No.	LEFT HAND DESCRIPTION	RIGHT HAND DESCRIPTION	No. of Obs.	Allowed time
1	Aside pen in inspector's ready rack, _point down_, _release_	Get pen from pen tray		
2	Remove pen clip top, place on table, take and hold pen body	Bring to work area, hold for L.H., transfer to L.H. and _unscrew filling cap_		
3	Dip pen and hold in ink while plunger is being operated, then lift out and hold	Push plunger up and down 3 times, screw on _filling cap_		
4	Hold pen	Get wipe, wipe point clean of excess ink, drop wipe, get and place clip top (on cap end, leaving point free)		
		Handler brings pens, ink supply, and wipes		
	TOTAL TIME ALLOWED PER PIECE		_____	

PRODUCTION AT STANDARD - _____ _____ PER HOUR
PRODUCTION DURING STUDY - _____ _____ PER HOUR

Fig. 18.1 — Front of time study sheet with method description for filling fountain pen for writing inspection.

WORKPLACE SYMBOLS	SKETCH OF WORKPLACE		

WORKPLACE SYMBOLS

A *Inspector's ready rack B-7*
B *Ink*
C *Pens*
D *Wipes*
E *Place where caps are laid*
⊕ *Operator (seated)(MI Chair)*

SKETCH OF WORKPLACE

Height = 30"

Approx. scale – 1 div = 3"   Operator in line with B

TIME STUDY SHEET

Operator name *Janet Klein*   Study file No. *P.I-237*
Operator No. *115*   Operation *Fill pens for inspection*
Dept. *23 (clean, cool, quiet)*   by use – *#1P-49*   Fixture No. *B-7*
Machine type and No. *None*   Part *A-2 Curtis Streamliner*   Drawing No. *P-7707*
Time began study _____   Specif. No. *A-2-55-44*   Attachments to this sheet: _____
Time ended study _____   Study by *A. B. Gilbert*
Approved _____   Date *2-7-*

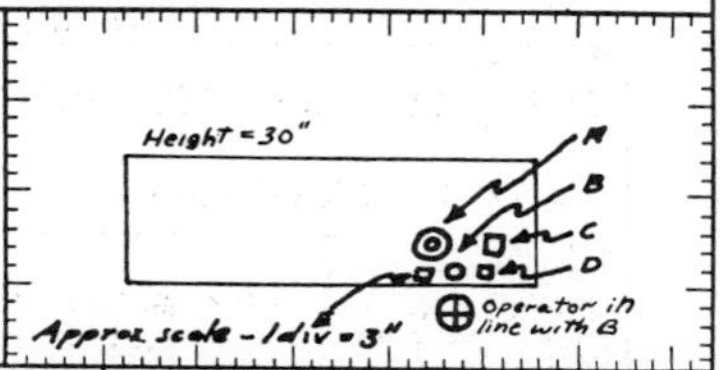

Elem. No.	LEFT HAND DESCRIPTION	RIGHT HAND DESCRIPTION	No. of Obs.	Allowed time
1	TL pen to ready rack, PP point down, RL into rack	TE to pen tray, G pen from tray		
2	TE to work area, G clip top, DA, TL and RL clip top on table, TE, G and H pen	TL pen to work area, H for left hand, RL to left hand, TE, G and DA filling cap		
3	TL pen to ink, P in ink, H while plunger is being operated, TL from ink	U plunger 3 times, A filling cap, RL cap		
4	H pen	TE to wipe, G, TL to point, U to remove excess ink, RL wipe, TE to clip top, G, TL, P and A onto cap end leaving point free, RL clip top		
	Handler brings pens, ink, and wipes			

_____ TOTAL TIME ALLOWED PER PIECE

PRODUCTION AT STANDARD – _____ _____ PER HOUR

PRODUCTION DURING STUDY – _____ _____ PER HOUR

Fig. 18.2—Front of time study sheet with method description in terms of therbligs for filling fountain pen for writing inspection.

TIME STUDY SHEET

SHEET _1_ OF _1_

DATE _10-30-_

PART NO. _31-13642_

PART NAME
BODY FOR #4 SYLPHON ATTACHMENT

OPERATION
TAP (3) 5/16" -18 HOLES

MATERIAL
IRON CASTING

DRG. NO.	38309

DEPT.	OPER. NO.
32	6

ORDER NO. 337295

QUANTITY 150

ATTACHMENTS

SKETCH ☐
PHOTO ☒
PHOTO IN FILE ☐
OBSERVER _R. DUCHIN_
FOREMAN _A. GAULKE_
APPROVED _L. Piel_

OPERATOR NAME CHAS. URANOV	CLOCK NO. 2250	SEX M	TOOL NO. 5/16"-18 TAP	GAUGES 5/16"-18 thr'd plug gage
MACH. NAME NATCO	MACH. NO. 363-364		H.S.S.	
STOCK ☒ TRUCK ☒ ORDER	STOCK ☒ TRUCK ☒ ORDER			WORK UNIT BODY (1)
RECEIVED ☐ PAN ☐ RANDOM	REMOVED ☐ PAN ☐ RANDOM			

NO.	FEED	SPEED	DESCRIPTION OF OPERATION BY ELEMENTS		NO. OF OBSERV.	BASE TIME
			L.H.	**R.H.**		
1			Idle, help position pc & hold pc.	Pick up pc. from truck at right, help position under spindle, pick up brush in oil, can at right, oil taps, return brush to can while right foot moves to pedal and engages feed		
			(UD-TE-G-P-M)	TE, st., G, TL-P-RL-TE G, TL, U, TL, RL		
2		1196	Tap (3) 5/16"-18 Holes with machine on automatic UD, TE	UD, TE		
3			Remove pc, dispose in truck at left G, TL, P, RL	Help remove pc, idle G TL RL		
4			Pick up pc from truck, hold pc, return pc to truck TE, st, G, TL, M, TL, P, RL (1 piece/50)	Pick up plug gage from bench, gage (3) 5/16"-18 holes, return gage to bench TE, G, TL, (P, A) 3x, TL P, RL		

REMARKS: _Element 4 too long to be internal._

TOTAL TIME ALLOWED _____

HOURS PER 100 PCS _____

PIECE PER HOUR _____

SET-UP _____

Fig. 18.3 — *Front of time study sheet for tapping operation.* (Courtesy of L. Piel, Chief of Time Standards, Johnson Service Co., Milwaukee, Wis.)

Element No.	Operator	Element No.	Helper
1	Stop machine and walk from control lever to coiler	1	Pick up 4 pieces of wire from holder, place 4 pieces of wire 90 degrees apart on top of finished coil on skid and step to coiler
2	Inspect last end of coil, pick up snips from machine framework, cut off last end of coil and lay end and snips on machine framework	2	Remove handwheel and front plate, pulls coil a little away from back plate and slip on coil clamp
3	Walk from coiler to spare reel		
4	Index swivel reel, pick up end of coil on spare reel and feed thru Burr Roller to feed rolls		
5	Walk from feed rolls to coiler		
5a	With helper lift coil off coiler and place on skid	3	With operator lift coil off coiler and place on skid
6	Walk from coil on skid to control lever	4	Remove core from coil on skid and place on coiler
7	Start machine and feed end of coil thru feed rolls and past coiler and stop machine	5	Delay
8	Walk to coiler		
9	Inspect first end of coil, pick up snips from machine framework, cut off first end of coil and lay end and snips on machine framework		
10	Walk from coiler to control lever	6	Rethread coiler, take up slack and replace front plate and handwheel
11	Delay		
12	Start machine and walk from control lever to spare reel	7	Step to coiled strip on skid
13	Unscrew reel handwheel from reel shaft and lay on floor out of way	8	Pick up one end of wire under finished coil on skid, make 1 wire tie around coil by hand, twists wire tight around coil with pliers, and bends ends flat on coil
14	Pull reel front plate from reel shaft, roll to support and lean front plate against support	9	Repeat No. 8
		10	Repeat No. 8
15	Pick up hook, pull coil about 8" off pile on skid and lay hook down	11	Repeat No. 8

Fig. 18.4 — Part of a method description for two-man burr roll (would be accompanied by machine drawing).

SM6658G

STANDARD METHOD FOR PEELING GRID 6658 - 4/18/

GRID DATA

TPI 56   **TT** 45½   Oval OD .130   CC .320   Sup. .025 Nickel Homo

Lat. .0032 Moly   Length 1.072   Legs .063   .196, .125

ELEMENT NO.	Left Hand Description	Right Hand Description
1	Dispose of grid into tray (deep tray, grids on end)	Lip grasp one grid with T and #1F Delay for L.H. dispose
2	Move to work area	Move to work area with grid
3	Grasp grid - Hold; one support V'd into V formed T and #2 F in opposition, other support on and parallel to #1 F ball.	Slide off grid and pull loose turns off. Stroke supports with T and #1F balls as drawn off grid to get loose turns off. Usually only one stroke needed. Unusual cases two strokes, only rarely three.
4	Hold - turn if necessary so that support wire, that last turn is fastened to, is toward other hand.	Grasp wire, balls of T and #1F about ½ to 3/4" from where fastened to support wire and rotate till wire breaks — 3 or 4 times.
5	Remove #1F from contact with grid and slip thumb toward center of "flat" of grid.	Push top support wire clock-wise with thumb and thus help rotate unpeeled end into position.
6	After grid is rotated, relax all fingers momentarily and return to holding position; one support V'd into V formed by T and #2F; other support on and parallel to #1F ball.	Place #1F on top of second support as grid comes around and slip off along supports with balls of T and #1F to get loose turns off. Usually only one stroke is made. Unusual cases take two, only rarely three.
7	Hold grid, proper support is already in position.	Grasp loose wire, balls of T and #1F about ½ to 3/4" in from where fastened to support wire and rotate till wire breaks — 3 to 4 times.

Fig. 18.5 — Method description for peeling radio-tube grid, showing elements requiring filming or time study machine. (Detailed workplace layout record would be made on a separate sheet.)

328

identifies the standard practice sheet and the element number. The method would not usually be transcribed in detail onto the time study sheet but would be attached to it, and a note indicating this would be made in the "attachments" space.

Observing and Recording the Work Time

This section concerns the recording of time values from an actual operator and the reduction of these figures to values representative of the actual performance observed.

Time values for a time study may be recorded in the following three ways:

1. *Stop-watch*—The most common type is represented by the decimal minute watch in Figure 18.6.

Fig. 18.6 — Decimal minute stop watch. Side arm starts and stops watch; pressure on crown returns hand to zero.

2. *Motion-picture camera and film analysis*—Until the introduction of available light photography and video-tape recording, the cost of using motion pictures was usually too high, but this aspect has been vastly altered as indicated in Chapter 14.

3. *Time study machine*—This usually consists of a set of finger-actuated markers working on a constant speed paper tape, and, as will be seen, possesses certain novel and worthwhile features. Equipment with punched tape output or punched card output units also has been devised, permitting the

data obtained to be processed directly by electronic data processing equipment.[11]

Of these three methods, the use of the stop-watch is the most common but under certain conditions, as will be seen, the use of photographic or electronic recording is preferable.

1. Stop-watch Procedure

Three[12] commonly used methods of operating stop-watches for the taking of time studies are the following:

1. Continuous timing.
2. Repetitive or snap-back timing.
3. Accumulative timing.

1. *Continuous timing.* In continuous timing the watch runs continuously throughout the study. The watch is started at the beginning of the first element of the first cycle being timed, and is not stopped until the study is completed. At the end of each element the time is recorded. The individual element times are obtained by successive subtractions after the study is completed. This is one of the most commonly used methods. A typical time study board with watch is shown in Figure 18.7.

2. *Repetitive timing.* In repetitive, or snap-back, timing, the watch is started at the beginning of the first element of the first cycle being timed, and is simultaneously read and snapped back to zero at the completion of this, and each subsequent, element. This allows the element times to be entered directly on the time study sheet without the need for subtractions. Consistent over- and under-reading of the watch will cause cumulative errors with this method but would not affect the continuous method. Also, considerable

---

[11] G. R. Ewing, "Automeasurement," *Proceedings 7th Annual Conference of American Institute of Industrial Engineers*, Columbus, Ohio, May 1956, pp. 12–1 thru 12–10.

[12] A fourth method of stop-watch timing, called *cycle timing*, is frequently described in motion and time study and industrial-engineering literature. This method consists of timing the elements in groups of one less than the number of elements in the cycle. It is followed by a mathematical procedure for the determination of the individual element times. This method involves the assumption that the average value for each element computed on the basis of a small sample of cycles will be the same as the average value for each element computed on the basis of a sample $(X - 1)$ times the size of the original sample, with X equal to the number of elements in the cycle. Chance alone, in each use of this method, would control the relative validity of this assumption and hence the accuracy of the results. The assumption would only be valid with an enormous number of readings obtained from a stable performance. In practice, such a large number of readings would not be from a stable performance and hence new random variations would be introduced because of variations in the work pace. An introduction into time study measurement of inaccuracies such as are caused by cycle timing is not desirable, and this method is not recommended.

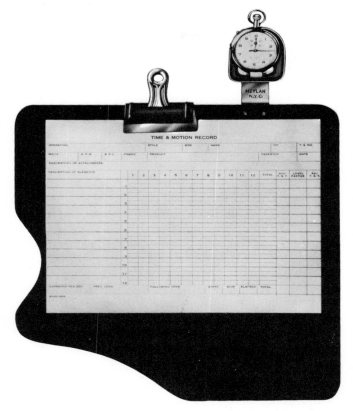

Fig. 18.7—A typical time study board as used with continuous or repetitive timing.

manipulation of the watch is required. Many labor groups look upon the repetitive method as being highly liable to error. With extremely short elements, any errors which occur may represent large percentages of the elements. Some time study men use another watch to accumulate the total time so as to check these errors. However, in competent hands the repetitive method is successful enough to make it widely used.

3. *Accumulative timing.* Accumulative timing is a method involving either two or three watches. In one method, two watches are mounted in a special holder with a mechanical linkage between the watches. For continuous timing, the linkage is manipulated so that at the end of each element one watch is stopped and the other restarted. The stopped watch is read, and element times are obtained later by subtracting alternate readings. For repetitive timing, the stopped watch is returned to zero after being read and element

times are read directly. An effective three-watch accumulative mechanism is also used and is shown in Figure 18.8. The watches used on this board function as follows: The first press on the crown returns the watch to zero, the second press starts it running, the third press stops it at the reading. On the board in Figure 18.8 each watch is one step out of phase with the others.

Fig. 18.8—Three-watch, accumulative time study board called "Quick-Click" produced by the Meylan Stop-Watch Co., New York.

Each press on the lever, which presses the crowns of all three watches, stops one watch, returns one to zero and starts another watch running. In this fashion, the time for each element may be read, without subtraction, directly from a stopped watch. For short elements the board is very useful. A fourth watch is sometimes added as a check on the total elapsed time.

A study of the errors in reading stop-watches, with both the continuous and the repetitive method, has been made by Irwin Lazarus.[13] He analyzed the readings made by 37 time study men familiar with the repetitive method and 13 time study men familiar with the continuous method. The standard deviation[14] of the errors, about the mean error, made with the continuous method was 0.0081 min., and 0.0081 min. with the snap-back method. The average error with the continuous method was +0.000097 min., and −0.00082 min. with the snap-back method. We may conclude that in competent hands either of these two methods is satisfactory, inasmuch as the error is not large enough to influence any of the subsequent calculations.[15]

For recording the time values with a stop-watch, the form shown in Figure 18.9 is convenient. Many variations of this form are used with equally good results. It is often printed on the back of the form used to record the standard practice illustrated in the last chapter. It should never be used without an adequate written standard practice. As in the example shown, in the small description column for each element should be written the end point of the element after which the time is to be recorded, as an aid in timing. (This is the part of the element description that was underlined in some of the examples given earlier in this chapter, and this small reference to the element should not be confused with an adequate description.)

Space is provided on this form for recording 15 cycles of 15 elements. If more elements or cycles are to be recorded, two or more sheets may be used. If the study has less than eight elements, two sets of lines may be used, thus allowing space for 30 readings of each element. If the use of two sheets is a common occurrence, a larger form should be designed and printed. For each element of each cycle, two boxes are provided in columns labeled R and T. The R column is for "readings" when continuous timing is used, as in the example shown. The subtracted times, which are the time values for each element, are placed in the T, or "time," column. A colored pencil for this keeps the R and T values separate and facilitates correct calculations later. If repetitive timing is used, the values will be placed immediately in the T column, or a form with T columns only may be drawn up. On some forms

---

[13] Irwin P. Lazarus, "Nature of Stop-Watch Time Study Errors," *Advanced Management*, Vol. 15, No. 5, May 1950, p. 15. Mr. Lazarus provided, by means of a modified telegraph code signal generator, a series of warning and reading stimuli, one series auditory and one series visual, so as to provide a controlled situation that approximated the actual time study situation. The data on which these statements are based were obtained with experienced time study men, using their own watches, in their own plants, using the method they were accustomed to, but reading visual signals from Mr. Lazarus' equipment.

[14] This is the error probably not exceeded 68 per cent of the time. Twice this value would probably not be exceeded 95 per cent of the time, and three times this value would probably not be exceeded 99.7 per cent of the time.

[15] While the difference in the average error was of statistical significance (not ascribable to chance), it was not large enough to be of practical significance. Differentiation between these two concepts of significance is vital in interpreting time study research data.

Fig. 18.9— *Continuous timing of operation of filling fountain pen for writing inspection (see Figures 18.1 and 18.2).*

ELEMENTS

CYCLES

No.	TERMINAL POINT	1 R	1 T	2 R	2 T	3 R	3 T	4 R	4 T	5 R	5 T	6 R	6 T	7 R	7 T	8 R	8 T	9 R	9 T	10 R	10 T	11 R	11 T	12 R	12 T	13 R	13 T	14 R	14 T	15 R	15 T
1																															
2																															
3																															
4																															
5																															
6																															
7																															
8																															
9																															
10																															
11																															
12																															
13																															
14																															
15																															

RECAPITULATION

ELEMENTS	1	2	3	4	5	6	7	8	9	10	11	12	13	14	15
Amount of body															
Foot pedals															
Bimanualness															
Eye-hand coordination															
Handling requirements															
Weight or resistance															
TOTAL TIME IN___															
NUMBER OF OBS.															
PRO-RATE DIVISOR															
AVERAGE PER CYCLE															
RATING															
RATED TIME															
PER CENT OF CYCLE															
I+ ADJUSTMENTS															
BASE TIME															
I+ ALLOWANCES															
ALLOWED TIME															

SYMBOLS USED

C-Extra unnecessary motion
D-A.D. Dropped part
F-Unnecessary fumble
H-Unnecessary hesitation
P-Includes personal time
R-Made reject by improper work
X-Deviation from std. routine

ALLOWANCES

Personal _____%

TOTAL _____%

LOOP VALUES

334

the letter *C* (for clock) is used instead of *R* and the letter *I* (for interval) instead of *T*. It is usual practice to time enough cycles to obtain a representative sample of performance.

What constitutes a representative or reliable sample may be mathematically determined. It is well worth pointing out that this is not a substitute for rating but merely a means of determining if the value to which the rating is to be applied is reliable. We must realize that there is almost invariably some variation from reading to reading for any element, even if the worker is not attempting to vary his pace. This variation will be caused by the following random variations, among other causes:

1. In operator movements and pace.
2. In the positions of the parts worked with.
3. In the position of the tools used.
4. In the slight errors in watch reading.

For any observed pace of performance, timings of ten cycles will tend to produce a more stable average than readings of five cycles; the average of 15 timings will tend to be better than that of ten, and so forth. It should also be understood that two sets of 15 readings on the same element will seldom, if ever, in practice, produce an identical average, even though the pace may be the same in both cases, and thus result in the same performance ratings. Hence, without a control on the number of readings, an error may creep into our standards. A study of this possible error shows that it frequently is of considerable magnitude.

To limit the number of readings it would be reasonable to require enough to make the chances 95 out of 100 that we are within ±5 per cent of the true average for the element for the pace at which it was performed.[16] Some may prefer a looser criterion of 95 chances out of 100, ±10 per cent. In this latter case, the odds may be restated as 68 out of 100 of being within ±5 per cent.

If the time studies are to be used for incentive wages, either of these criteria would seem to be reasonable minimum reliabilities, since ±5 or 10 per cent usually approximates a bargainable increment in wages. Errors of more than this magnitude are to be avoided.[17]

Measures have been developed by mathematical statisticians for determining the probable accuracy of a sample. These may be adapted to fit this time study problem conveniently.

A relatively simple procedure, based on formula (A) which follows, is particularly suitable for application on the shop floor while the study is being

[16] The reliability of the sum of the elements will be better than the individual elements. If the time values are to be used only in a single standard it will be less important that all elements meet this criterion. For combined tolerance see any book on statistical quality control. On the other hand, if the elemental values are to be used in constructing standard data, meeting the criterion given will simplify subsequent work with these data.

[17] William Gomberg, *A Trade Union Analysis of Time Study*. Englewood Cliffs, N.J.: Prentice-Hall, 2nd Ed., 1955, p. 36.

made. Formula (A) gives a measure of the variability of the data about its average. The variability is represented by σ, the standard deviation, which is expressed as follows:

$$\sigma = \frac{\bar{R}}{d_2} = \frac{\overline{H - L}}{d_2} \qquad (A)^{18}$$

$\bar{R}$ = average range; average difference between the highest and lowest values in a series of samples of readings of correct performances of an element.

d_2 = a constant based on sample size (see any text on statistical quality control).

H = highest value in a sample of readings of correct performances of an element.

L = lowest value in a sample of readings of correct performances of an element.

$\overline{H - L}$ = average of differences between high and low values in samples of correct readings of an element.

Note: $H - L = R$ for a single sample; R is an estimate of $\bar{R}$.

Further, $\bar{X}$, the average, may be estimated as follows:

$$\bar{X} = \frac{\overline{H + L}}{2} \qquad \text{(for a series of samples)} \qquad (B)$$

$$\bar{X} = \frac{H + L}{2} \qquad \text{(for a single sample)} \qquad (C)$$

If we assume that σ, as computed, may be used to represent the variability of a huge group of similar readings from the parent population (a commonly tenable assumption), another measure $\sigma_{\bar{x}}$, the standard error of the mean (or average) may be computed by (D). The value computed by (D) indicates the probable variability of the averages of groups of N values of X about the obtained $\bar{X}$.

$$\sigma_{\bar{x}} = \frac{\bar{R}}{d_2\sqrt{N}} \qquad (D)$$

Setting 5 per cent of $\bar{X}$ equal to $2\sigma_{\bar{x}}$,

$$.05\frac{\overline{H + L}}{2} = 2\frac{\overline{H - L}}{d_2\sqrt{N}}$$

Rearranging the terms so as to make N into N', a variable, so as to determine the number of required readings to meet the criterion:

$$\sqrt{N'} = \frac{4\,(\overline{H - L})}{.05d_2\,(\overline{H + L})} \qquad (E)$$

and N' is a function of $\overline{H - L}/\overline{H + L}$

---

[18] The σ here is only an estimate of the sample σ which is only an estimate of the population σ. However, as will be shown, a quick estimate has considerable utility.

All expectable values of $\overline{H - L}/\overline{H + L}$ for samples of five and ten readings of an element have been used with equation (E) and the answers for N' are presented in Table 12, page 338.

To use Table 12, $H - L$ from one sample may be used as an estimate of $\overline{H - L}$ and $H + L$ from the sample used as an estimate of $\overline{H + L}$. Using this procedure, the time study man, by inspection, takes the H and L values from either the first five or ten readings of an element, as available, and computes the value $(H - L)/(H + L)$. (It is to be noted that ten values form a good basis for using Table 12 in order to determine the appropriate number of readings, although ten readings are seldom an adequate sample on which to base the final average.) Entering the table with this value and going across the table to the proper column, corresponding to the sample size, the time study man may find an estimate of the required number of readings without further computation.

For example, let us assume the element readings were 6, 7, 6, 8, 7, 5, 6, 8, 7, 6, 7, 6, 6, and 7 (all in 0.01 minute). Taking the first ten values, we find:

$$H = 8$$
$$L = 5$$
$$\frac{H - L}{H + L} = .23$$

For this value, based on a sample of 10, Table 12 indicates 36 readings as required. [This is somewhat higher than the number which would be indicated as necessary by a more rigorous form of computation (as given in the supplemental material appended to this chapter). However, the value errs on the safe side and the number indicated is not an excessive number in most situations. The conclusion from the quick computation is that 14 readings are insufficient; they do not give a sufficiently reliable average. The study must be continued until at least 36 readings are obtained.]

As an alternative procedure, the readings may be divided into samples of 5, and $\overline{H - L}/\overline{H + L}$ used to enter the table. For the illustration given, the results would be as follows:

First 5   6, 7, 6, 8, 7; $H - L = 2$, $H + L = 14$,
Second 5   5, 6, 8, 7, 6; $H - L = 3$, $H + L = 13$,

$$\overline{H - L} = \frac{2 + 3}{2}$$
$$\overline{H + L} = \frac{14 + 13}{2}$$
$$\frac{\overline{H - L}}{\overline{H + L}} = \frac{5}{27} = .18$$

and $N' = 38$ (from Table 12, samples of 5). This compares with the $N' = 36$ obtained from the use of the ten readings as one sample of 10.

TABLE 12

Number of Readings Required for ±5 Per Cent; 95/100 Probability[1]

$\dfrac{H-L}{H+L}$	Data From Sample of		$\dfrac{H-L}{H+L}$	Data from Sample of		$\dfrac{H-L}{H+L}$	Data From Sample of	
	5	10		5	10		5	10
.05	3	1	.21	52	30	.36	154	88
.06	4	2	.22	57	33	.37	162	93
.07	6	3	.23	63	36	.38	171	98
.08	8	4	.24	68	39	.39	180	103
.09	10	5	.25	74	42	.40	190	108
.10	12	7	.26	80	46	.41	200	114
.11	14	8	.27	86	49	.42	210	120
.12	17	10	.28	93	53	.43	220	126
.13	20	11	.29	100	57	.44	230	132
.14	23	13	.30	107	61	.45	240	138
.15	27	15	.31	114	65	.46	250	144
.16	30	17	.32	121	69	.47	262	150
.17	34	20	.33	129	74	.48	273	156
.18	38	22	.34	137	78	.49	285	163
.19	43	24	.35	145	83	.50	296	170
.20	47	27						

[1] For ±10 per cent, 95/100 probability, divide answers by 4.

Note that this method, based on R, is sensitive to extreme readings, particularly with short elements. Further, since the use of a single sample R as an estimate for $\bar{R}$ is only an approximation, the results have a limited validity. However, it may be used immediately, while the time study is being made, as a guide to subsequent action. In questionable cases, one may check the estimate, using a more rigorous procedure (see Supplemental Material), after the time study has been taken back to the office.

The time study man should have the time study form clipped to a clipboard and hold the watch in such a way that it is directly in his line of vision to the job. He should stand slightly to the side and to the rear of the operator, if possible, so that his motions do not disturb the operator (a proper position is shown in Figure 18.10). The worker should be aware that a time study is being taken. The main requirement is to hold the watch so that the hands of the watch can be kept in view while the job is being studied. The watch may then be read by refocusing the eyes, without hunting for the watch and with little loss of time. It is important to watch constantly the performance of the

Fig. 18.10 — A correct position for taking a stop-watch time study.

operator to be sure that the time entries made represent valid performances of the elements as the method description defined them.

Such occurrences as the following may be noted:

1. A fumble during an element.
   a. Due to lack of operator skill.
   b. Inherent in the job.
2. A false movement.
3. A personal movement, such as scratching. (Note that time will be allowed for this in the allowance for personal time, but that this is not part of the element being timed.)
4. A minor machine adjustment or repair.
5. Faulty work due to low skill or faulty movements.
6. Faulty work due to poor material.

Any element containing any such variation or any variation from the prescribed pattern of motions should be marked so as to identify it on the time study sheet. (See Symbols Used in Figure 18.9.)

The unusual occurrences should be handled as follows:

1. If it is not a necessary part of the job, as the job is set up, or if it represents wrong movements or work improperly done, the recorded time value should be discarded and have no influence on the final result.
2. If it is inherent in the element—e.g., fumbles with tangled material— it should be allowed to remain in the study.

3. If it is an irregular occurrence—e.g., faulty material or a machine adjustment—it should be evaluated separately and added to the final time standard in proportion to its rate of occurrence. If, on a sewing machine operation, the thread tends to break once every fifty cycles, one fiftieth of the time required to rethread, after evaluation to standard performance level, will be added to the standard total cycle time.

The actual element times for each element are added and the total entered

	C/I																
ADDITIONAL SIMILAR PARTS										TIME STUDY STARTED		2:30 Pm					
1 Engage feed	C																
	I	20	27	23	27	27	23	22	24	25	22	23	21	24	23	23	23
2 Tap out of pc.	C																
	I	10	8	11	10	10	10	9	9	9	10	9	9	9	10	10	10
3 RL pc. in truck	C																
	I	5	5	6	6	5	7	7	6	6	6	6	5	6	6	6	6
4 RL gage on bench	C																
	I																
1	C																
	I	25	25	24	22	F	23	24	23	27	27	25	24	27	20	21	24
2	C																
	I	9	9	10	9	10	9	9	9	9	8	10	9	10	9	9	9
3	C																
	I	6	7	6	6	5	7	6	6	5	6		5	5	6	6	6
4	C																
	I											143						
1	C																
	I	22	21	26	23	20	18	24	20	20	20						
2	C																
	I	9	9	9	9	10	9	9	9	9	9						
3	C																
	I	6	6	7	5	6	5	6	7	5	6						
4	C																
	I																

RECAPITULATION

ELEMENT NO.	1	2	3	4	5	6	7	8	9	10	11	12
AMOUNT OF BODY												
FOOT PEDALS												
BIMANUALNESS												
EYE-HAND COORD.												
HANDLING REQUIRE.												
WEIGHT												
TOTAL TIME IN HOURS	0952	0391	0241	0143								
NUMBER OF OBS.	41	42	41	1								
PRO-RATE DIVISOR	1	1	1	50								
AVERAGE PER CYCLE	00232	00093	00059	00029								
RATING												
RATED TIME												
PERCENT OF CYCLE												
1+ ADJUSTMENTS												
BASE TIME												

SYMBOLS USED IN STUDY

C. EXTRA UNREQUIRED MOTION
D. UNNECESSARY DROPPING OF PART
F. UNNECESSARY FUMBLE
H. UNNECESSARY HESITATION
P. INCLUDES PERSONAL TIME
R. PRODUCED REJECT BY IMPROPER WORK
X. DEVIATION FROM STANDARD ROUTINE

112	00	91
85	81	71
65	55	49
45	41	37

Fig. 18.11 — Repetitive timing of tapping operation (see Figure 18.3).

in the proper total box, in the columns at the bottom of the form. The number of observations included in this total is entered in the box under the total, and the arithmetic average found and entered in the box in the appropriate box. The average is the total divided by the product of the number of observations and the prorate divisor, so as to indicate the time to be charged to each cycle. The units of time used—seconds, decimal hours, or minutes—should be noted on this row. The statistical reliability should be calculated and used to decide whether to proceed further with the calculations.

The arithmetic average is suggested (instead of other values such as median, mode, and so forth, used by some time study men) because it is the only figure that is representative of the total sample of observations. It is simple to compute and includes both high and low values, which, if they represent valid performances of the elements, most certainly should be included in the representative measure. Also, the representativeness of this measure may be, as was shown earlier, evaluated.

Figure 18.9 is a continuous time study, made with a stop-watch, of the operation of filling fountain pens for inspection, the method for which is described in Figures 18.1 and 18.2. Figure 18.11 is a complete repetitive timing, made with a stop-watch, of the machining job, the method for which is described in Figure 18.3.

2. Memomotion procedure[19]

Memomotion study used for the setting of time standards may be applied in two ways. Both procedures offer the advantage of providing an objective record, which may be reviewed later by anyone, including the worker, and which is not "interpreted data" as with a stop-watch record. Different element breakdowns may be made at any time, as the need arises. In addition, more smaller elements may be timed, a decided advantage as will be seen later. Also, a whole crew may be timed simultaneously. The necessary data may be recorded on the film or tape more rapidly and more completely than with stop-watches. Indeed, most of the advantages given for photographic or electronic aids over visual method study techniques apply here also.

It is particularly suggested that disputed rates subject to a grievance or arbitration procedure may be most ideally studied with the full-camera technique as a more accurate and reliable record, since the objectiveness of the process safeguards the interests of both management and labor, if they are both concerned with accuracy, as they should be. Furthermore, rates set with this data may be discussed more factually and many grievances may be avoided. The two procedures are:

[19] M. E. Mundel, "Memomotion Study Technique Simplifies Work Analysis," *Factory*, Vol. 107, No. 6, June 1949.

1. Partial use of camera (motion picture or video recorder).
2. Full use of camera.

With either method, as with stop-watch studies, the worker should be aware that a time study is being made. Also, all the usual data taken prior to a stop-watch time study should be recorded, except the motion pattern, which may later be taken from the film or tape. No microchronometer need be used, but the worker should be fully aware that time is being recorded.

1. *Partial use of camera.* In this method, the camera is used only at the one per second speed or at the 100 frames per minute speed; hence the camera is used only to record method and time.[20] However, once set up, it does this automatically, leaving the observer free to devote his attention fully to the task, and provides a much better opportunity to formulate a rating than when using a stop-watch. This method, however, only begins to make use of the full potentialities of the camera.

The film when developed and ready for analysis is put into a hand crank or automatic indexing projector with a frame counter and, using a time study sheet, the data (which would have been recorded while the job was observed if a stop-watch was used) is entered in the blanks in a similar fashion—counter readings instead of stop-watch values being used, and an initial reading instead of the implied 0 of the stop-watch being made at the beginning of the first element. This is placed above the first *R* box. Otherwise, the procedures are identical. However, the record may be made at the analyst's own pace, small elements, down to 1 or 2 seconds identified and recorded, and the film later re-analyzed and the elements changed if this is found desirable. The data of the film are permanent and accurate. All calculations are made in a fashion identical with stop-watch calculations. A short section of memomotion time study film and its relationship to the time study sheet are shown in Figure 18.12 for the job of "tube cut-off". This illustration includes the data related to the modifier *M* and the additive *A*.

A twenty-five man molding crew at the American Steel Foundries plant at Granite City, Illinois, was time-studied with the aid of memomotion camera timing. Because of the extreme area involved, the men were given numbered jerseys to wear so as to increase the ease of identifying them on the films. The gang was filmed in six sections as indicated in Figure 18.13. The films were taken at 100 frames per minute in order to obtain values similar to those obtained by stop-watch methods. The advantages of using films rather than direct observations have been summarized by Mr. C. H. Walcher, Works Manager, American Steel Foundries, Granite City, Ill., as follows:[21]

> The pictures were taken as a result of a grievance. The pictures gave us
> a very adequate coverage and enabled us to show all concerned parties

[20] As was noted in Chapter 14, a video-tape record may be used in an equivalent fashion.
[21] Letter to author.

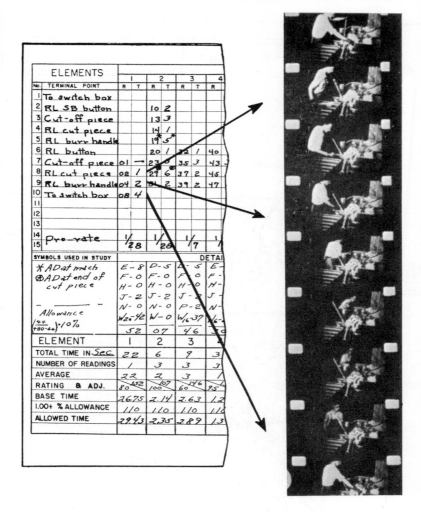

Fig. 18.12—Short section of memomotion film and time study recordings made from it for operation of tube cut-off.

exactly how the rate was determined. Because the time study men were not involved in recording elemental break-downs, much more attention was given to pace determination which resulted in better leveling factors. The pictures proved that the present rate on this job was not tight. All men on the unit were covered in one day which represents a tremendous reduction of in-shop time to obtain the necessary information.

Mr. L. Randolph, the Chief Industrial Engineer at the plant, reports that the pictures taken have been used continually as reference points for methods

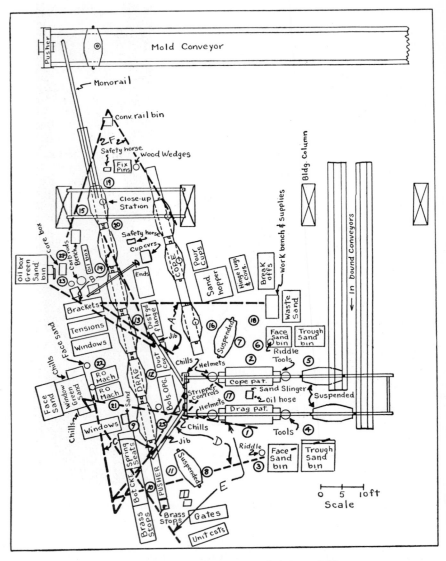

Fig. 18.13—*Layout of mold floor showing locations of 25-man crew (small numbered circles) and six memomotion camera locations and views (broken angles A-F), for time study timing.* (Courtesy L. Randolph, Chief Industrial Engineer, American Steel Foundries, Granite City, Ill.)

descriptions. They have also, he reports, been used for method instruction with the old as well as with new employees.

2. *Full use of camera*. This is the same as the partial procedure except that either during the study or immediately after it, the gear shift on the drive is used to obtain some footage at 1,000 frames per minute so as to record a reviewable version of the pace exhibited by the operator during the study.[22] This will be used for rating, as will be explained later. Provided care is taken to see that what is filmed at 1,000 frames per minute is similar in pace to what was filmed at one per second, this procedure should aid time study work as follows:

1. Allow others to check the rating.
2. Provide a record of the pace.
3. Facilitate actual rating.
4. Provide material for discussion rather than grievances.

These features will be more obvious later in this chapter, but they all improve what is the most difficult phase of time study.

The Consumer and Marketing Service of the U.S. Department of Agriculture used the full film technique in order to set standard times for all of the in-plant slaughter inspection outputs produced by the Service. (Some of these outputs were mentioned in Chapter 17.) A small team from the central staff office in Washington, D.C., visited selected, representative slaughter establishments in all sections of the United States. They made a film record (at 1000 frames per minute because of the rapidity of the operation) of selected inspectors. The inspectors were selected from among those who performed the work correctly and maintained adequate standards of inspection. The use of the full film technique gave the following advantages:

1. Field time and the expenses associated with field time were reduced to a minimum. This more than offset the cost of the film.
2. The methods could be reviewed in detail by all staff members concerned, to make certain that standards were set on effective and adequate methods of inspection. As a by-product, several worthwhile method changes were introduced.
3. The determination of the modifier M (to be discussed later in this chapter), could be a joint effort of the entire staff. The film constituted a record of the pace of the worker and was available for review at any time.

The standards times set for slaughter inspection were used in budget formulation for manpower resource determination, and for the detailed allocation of manpower to slaughter plants serviced by the Consumer and Marketing Service.

---

[22] When an extensive series of time studies are being taken on film, some plants have found it economical to employ a second camera to do the 1000 frame per minute sampling.

3. Time Study Machine

A time study machine is a sort of compromise between a stop-watch and a camera. One version uses finger-actuated markers on a constant-speed paper tape and produces a record such as shown in Figure 18.14, which is

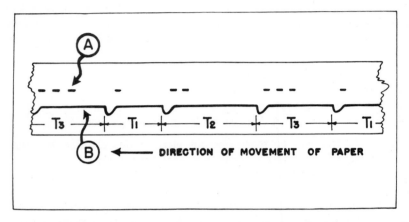

Fig. 18.14 — Section of tape from time study machine on three-element task.

a record on a three-element time study. The marks on line *A* identify the elements that took place between the marks on *B*. The circled letters have been placed on the figure for purposes of illustration and are not made by the machine. The dimension lines underneath line *B* have likewise been added to aid in this explanation. Each jog in line *B* indicates the end of an element, and measurement of the distances T_1, T_2, etc., with a properly calibrated rule, permits accurate determination of the element times. In use, the time study observer stands as with a stop-watch but is free to observe the job continually, two fingers being used to operate markers *A* and *B*. This is the chief advantage, as it leaves him free to watch the pace, which is a desirable feature, as was mentioned when discussing memomotion timing. Also, smaller elements may be timed, since the task of looking at, interpreting, and writing down the watch reading is eliminated. Special marks may be made on the tape to denote unusual occurrences. The only disadvantage is the measuring of the paper tape, and this is but a minor drawback. On the other hand, this record is an interpreted record, and not by any means as objective as the film.

Other than using the paper tape to obtain the time values, the procedure with the aforementioned time study machine is the same as the procedure used with stop-watches.

Time study machines with punched tape or punched card outputs may reduce the work load on the time study man in another way. The tape or cards may be used to list the times with tabulating equipment and obtain averages and so forth without further manual activity.

The stop-watch method is still the older and more common, and the camera and machine procedures the newer. Both the time study machines and the camera offer considerably more opportunity for accuracy, particularly with small elements. Also, both have the tendency to ease the most difficult phase of time study, that of rating, by reducing the amount of attention required for recording the time values. However, as has been demonstrated, in competent hands even seemingly complicated stop-watch methods produce results of satisfactory accuracy on elements of typical size.

Rating or Relating Performance to Standard

Since it is obvious that in practically all real situations the observed operator is neither of the type specified by the definition of standard, nor working at the pace required for standard performance, two questions remain: (1) how to evaluate the performance observed as compared with the requirements given in the definition of standard used as the basis of the measurement, and (2) how to reduce this evaluation to a mathematical value (the modifier M) that will allow the adjusting (if necessary) of the representative time values actually obtained, so as to determine a base for the standard time. These are the aims of rating.

The result of the adjustment made by rating still will not include a pro rata proportion of the time during which the operator will be away from the workplace in order to attend to personal needs or for performing such activities as final, daily workplace clean up, and the like (the additive A), as required for the *standard time*. Hence, the time values after being adjusted by ratings are commonly called *base times*.

Many time-study rating procedures have been proposed. Indeed, this is one of the major areas of controversy in present-day time study. Many of these rating procedures have been in wide use with varying degrees of success depending on the inherent relative validity of the procedures, the ability of the time study men who use them, and the plant attitude toward standards. This last is particularly important. Many standard times in plants may appear to function well, even though they are incorrect in that they are either inconsistent with each other or with the concept of standard they purport to represent, because the workers have learned that it is advantageous to have them function as if they were correct. The workers may vary their exertion on the different jobs to produce at all times in some relatively fixed relationship to standard, thus covering up time study inconsistencies. They may complain sufficiently on the standards that are difficult to achieve so that the standards are revised, and restrict their output on the easy ones so that the inaccuracy there is undisclosed. The men may even set up a system such that a consistent differential is maintained between individuals.

Indeed, the "game" may become even more complex, particularly when good labor relations exist. Most workers may feel that the standard times in use are fair, and in a time study situation may more or less honestly attempt to give their concept of a fair performance. The time study man may be generally aware of this. While certain workers may not be in the "game," being inclined either to slow down or speed up abnormally when being studied, the time study man may know who these workers are and tend to avoid them. Hence, the observed time represents almost by tacit agreement the correct rated time. The time study men may, by rating, adjust this value a small amount, almost at random, to complete the study. This "game" often continues until, (1) somebody not "in on the game" becomes part of a study, or (2) a new type of work enters the system and the workers' original concept of what is a fair output is grossly in error, or (3) until the standards which are, in reality, a heterogeneous group of concepts of standard (representing essentially many workers' concepts) are subjected to real pressure, either for wages through incentives because of external economic changes, or for sociological reasons. The subsequent demonstration of the inconsistencies of the standards creates many problems.

These practices, encouraged by past rate cutting, are sufficiently widespread so that many of the poorly conceived systems of rating or leveling often appear to be functioning properly.[23] Almost inevitably, in such cases, costs become out of line with profitable operation, or labor unrest develops. Certainly, the relationship between management and labor is deleteriously affected and morale suffers. Good labor relations are hard to build when one group feels it must continually deceive the other.

It should be realized at the outset that time study measurement is not an absolute measurement, nor for that matter, are most measurements. Measurement is usually characterized by a residual error or inherent variability, which can be demonstrated by repetition of the measurement. The important question is, as with all measuring techniques, "Is the size of the residual error, in the procedure to be used, such that the measurement is satisfactory for its purpose?" This, however, is not the sole criterion with which either the student, the practicing industrial engineer, technician, or the industrial supervisor can select the time study rating procedure he intends to study. In the first place, through the force of circumstances of industrial employment, he may be confronted with a procedure neither embodying the best of available techniques nor based on the most tenable theory.[24] Whether he is in a posi-

[23] O. Collins, M. Dalton, and D. Roy, "Restriction of Output and Social Cleavage in Industry," *Journal of Applied Anthropology*, Fall, 1946.

[24] This may not, of course, have been the situation when the procedure was instituted at the particular plant.

tion wherein he has no choice but to acquiesce or whether it is possible for him to suggest or introduce change, it is still necessary, if he is to plan his actions on an intelligent basis, that he understand the actual procedure in use, its underlying theory, and its limitations. In the second place, most proposals have been made in an attempt to avoid specific shortcomings inherent in what was previous practice; hence they require some knowledge of previous procedures for a complete understanding.

Further, knowledge about a time study rating procedure does not automatically confer skill in its use. Practice is necessary in all cases. A procedure for developing skill at rating is described in the Supplementary Material appended at the end of this chapter.

Commonly employed time study rating procedures can be divided into three main groups:

1. Mathematical.
2. Requiring judgment, unanchored; *subjective rating*.
3. Requiring anchored judgment; *objective rating*.

1. *Mathematical procedures.* The mathematical plans require a statistical sorting out, on the basis of the time recordings alone, of the effect of the operator's skill, aptitude, pace, relative rate of exertion, capriciousness, and so forth, from normal job variation. These must be separated in order to obtain a measure that would be relatively the same, regardless of whatever conditions of the above-mentioned parameters were in existence at the time the data were recorded. It is not surprising that this has never been done successfully. Any other mathematical method would require the existence of an outside reference point from which the variation of the particular observations obtained could be measured. The only reference point usable for such a purpose would be the standard time, but if this were known there would be no reason for the rating.

An apparently ingenious solution to this dilemma was proposed by Professor R. L. Morrow and designated "synthetic leveling."[25] Mr. Morrow proposed to take data on body-motion times assembled by other researchers in the field, and, for those elements of the study under consideration to which these times were applicable, develop a synthesized standard time, and thus obtain a reference point. He proposed to use this reference point by computing the ratio of the synthesized time for the element to the average observed time for the element, and subsequently multiply the remainder of the average observed element times by this ratio in order to adjust them to base times.

The application of Morrow's procedure implies (among other presuppositions) an assumption that, within limits, all manually controlled elements of a study are affected equally by variations in operator skill, aptitude, pace, exertion, attitude, and the like. An extensive investigation of the validity of

[25] R. L. Morrow, *Time Study and Motion Economy*. New York: The Ronald Press Company, 1946.

that assumption was made by P. W. Schwab, who used motion-picture films to time accurately industrial operators of different proficiency performing various light manual industrial jobs in an actual plant.[26] This study indicated that (at least under these conditions) this assumption was not even remotely tenable and that the residual error with such a procedure had limits too wide for acceptance.

2. *Procedures requiring judgment, unanchored; subjective rating.* Many rating systems involving judgment have been proposed and used. These, for the most part, involve a procedure that meets the following definition: "Rating is that process during which the time study man compares the performance of the operator under observation with the observer's own concept of normal performance."[27]

For the most part, the procedures which have been proposed involve the same basic routine because of the inference, inherent in the usual interpretation of this definition, that the time study man must perform two separate steps in rating, which are as follows:

1. He must judge the difficulty of the job and form a mental concept of what the performance of the job under observation would look like if it met the requirements of standard performance as defined by the definition the observer is working with.

2. The observer must appraise the actual performance under observation as compared with the concept formed in step 1 and place a numerical value on this appraisal.

This is the essence of the rating procedures proposed by Barnes,[28] Carroll,[29] Lowry et al.,[30] Myers,[31] Presgrave,[32] and Shumard,[33] to mention only a few workers in the field and to suggest a few representative procedures, although the discussion in this chapter is not confined to these few, but covers current subjective rating procedures.

[26] P. W. Schwab, "An Investigation to Determine the Proportionality of Element and Therblig Times at Typical Levels of Factory Activity," *M. S. thesis*, Purdue University, 1948.

[27] "Report of Committee on Rating of Time Studies," Society for the Advancement of Management, *Advanced Management*, Vol. 6, No. 4, July–September 1941, p. 110.

[28] R. M. Barnes, *Motion and Time Study*, 4th ed. New York, N.Y.: John Wiley and Sons, Inc., 1958.

[29] Phil Carroll, Jr., *Time Study for Cost Control*, 2nd Ed. New York: McGraw-Hill Book Co., Inc., 1943.

[30] S. M. Lowry, H. B. Maynard, and G. J. Stegemerten, *Time and Motion Study*, 3rd Ed. New York, N.Y.: McGraw-Hill Book Co., Inc., 1940.

[31] H. J. Myers, *Simplified Time Study*. New York, N.Y.: The Ronald Press Company, 1944.

[32] R. Presgrave, *Dynamics of Time Study*. New York, N.Y.: McGraw-Hill Book Co., Inc., 1945.

[33] F. W. Shumard, *Primer of Time Study*. New York, N.Y.: McGraw-Hill Book Co., Inc., 1940.

In all of these procedures, the guide usually recommended for learning to perform step 1 is actual practice, controlled experience (rating under the supervision of an experienced time study man), observation and rating of films of operations for which acceptable rating values have been previously established, or a combination of these.

Variations exist in the details given for performing step 2 with respect to (1) the number of subfactors into which the second step is divided, (2) the terms used to describe the basis of the comparison between the performance observed and the concept formed in step 1,[34] (3) the numerical scales employed, and (4) whether bench-mark jobs are suggested. None of these variations radically alters the basic nature of the procedure as previously outlined.

The number of subfactors into which the performance of step 2 is divided varies from one[35] to as many as six.[36]

The terms used to describe the basis of the comparison between the performance observed and the concept formed in step 1 include *speed, effective speed, tempo, effort, pace, speed of movement, skill, conditions, consistency, attitude, application, mental-physical coordination,* and so forth. In some cases, several of these are given as synonymous.

Various descriptive terms such as *excellent, good,* and *fair,* or more elaborate phrases,[37] are frequently provided as guides to various typical numerical values to be determined in step 2. These numerical values are intended for use as a rating or leveling factor by which the final representative values for the observed element times are to be multiplied so as to adjust them to *base times.* If one numerical adjustment is to be used for all manual elements, then the remarks made with respect to Morrow's synthetic leveling factor apply. If developed separately for each element, then the procedure is more reasonable. In all the procedures, of course, a machine-controlled element is assigned a rating essentially equivalent to unity inasmuch as this is not subject to operator-caused variation, other than by deviation from the standard practice.

In some references, however, it is implied that deviations from the proper method are also taken into account in step 2, although this greatly increases the difficulty of the practical application of the procedures.

The actual numerical scales suggested by the various authors vary considerably, but this neither increases nor decreases the validity, nor does it greatly affect the relative ease or difficulty of application. The two scales in general

[34] Not only do the terms used differ, but the same term may be used with different meanings in the different procedures.

[35] Presgrave, *op. cit.*

[36] C. A. Hoke, "A New Method of Leveling Time Studies by Attribute Analysis," *Proceedings 1946 Annual Time and Motion Study Clinic.* Chicago Ill.: Industrial Management Society, 1946, pp. 125–130.

[37] Particularly in Lowry, Maynard, and Stegemerten, *op. cit.*

use employ either a 60 base[38] or a 100 per cent base. The base value is related to some definite concept of standard. The authors employing the 60-base system give their appraisals of performance, or ratings, as a ratio to 60, as 50/60 or 55/60, and so forth, if slower, and 65/60 or 70/60, and so forth, if faster. Those employing the 100 base give their ratings as decimals; that is, .90, .95, and so forth, if slower, and 1.05, 1.10, and so forth, if faster. This is the form of the rating used as a multiplying factor for the observed times in order to adjust them to a base time, although the 60-base ratings are usually recorded (the line labeled "rating" in Figure 18.9 would be used) as, for example, 50, 55, 60, or 65, and the 100-base ratings as, for example, 90, 95, 100, or 105. As was indicated in Chapter 17, the typical top and bottom limits of the scale reached in practice will be affected by the concept of standard employed, where this concept stands in relation to typically expectable performance, and by the numerical value assigned to this concept.

It is to be noted that Presgrave's presentation differs markedly from the others in that he was the first to offer bench-mark jobs, which are easily performed; namely, card dealing and walking, together with accompanying standard times so as to provide two fixed points in the area of the first judgment required. This provides convenient opportunities for practicing step 2, but these do not alter his inherent procedure from the general form previously outlined.

In a shop where most jobs are relatively similar in nature (and this can be the case), such judgment procedures as have been described may well be feasible. Where a variety of jobs is encountered and the appearance of the job performance, as conceived in step 1 of the procedure, changes from job to job, these common rating methods employing fully subjective judgment place a tremendous burden on the time study man, whose consistency may then well be questionable, particularly if his training is inadequate or there is no periodic check or evaluation of the quality of his ratings.

Where incentive plans are in use, such procedures have given rise to a most peculiar situation. Management and labor, especially organized labor, may bargain for suitable wage rates, as a function of the nature of the jobs, and for a statement defining standard performance. In many cases where labor is highly organized, such negotiations may be rather extended. When all of this is done, the medium of exchange, the amount of work expected per hour for the agreed base wages, is still unsettled and is subject to the daily decision of the time study man, who compares the performance he observes to his concept of adequate performance on each job. This is the essence of the conventional procedure. From the viewpoint of the time study man this is a monstrous responsibility; from the viewpoint of management, the results may be very variable; from the viewpoint of labor, this could negate the

[38] The 60 base was originally intended to convey the concept of 60 minutes worth of performance in an hour.

results of their protracted bargaining. Certainly it is a situation that may easily give rise to grievances for all three groups.[39]

The details of using subjective procedures, commonly called *effort rating*, appear in Appendix B.

3. *Procedures requiring anchored judgment; objective rating.* Objective rating is the name given to a procedure wherein the two steps of the rating procedure are performed in the reverse order of the usual subjective procedure. As will be shown later, this permits anchoring, to external standards, of the judgments used for both steps. The procedure was first used in an industrial plant in 1939. The first publication describing it appeared in 1944,[40] and it first appeared in a text in 1946.[41] Subsequent research developed refinements to the procedure and made all of the necessary materials readily available. It is in current use in many plants throughout the world. The design of the objective rating procedure evolved from the following interpretation of the available facts.

We must recognize that rating is relating observed performance to standard by means of judgment. The judgment, to be of real significance, should be on some observable, demonstrable basis. The procedure should be such that the judgment is explanable by other means than mere recourse to "experience." The basis must be concrete. Such a basis would permit real agreement between labor and management on at least the measuring unit involved, or in other words, the concept of adequate performance. Whether unions are involved or not, it is likely that any group of workers will cooperate more fully if they understand the procedure of rating time studies, provided that the procedure is sound. Further, such a basis would make for more effective cooperation between all the parties involved in a time study and, if a single objective standard of reference could be substituted for the usual multiplicity of mental concepts, we could expect to reduce the error of measurement.

---

[39] It is small wonder that many time study systems have been proposed in the constant effort to reduce the variables or improve the judgment in the time study situation. It is unfortunate that some of these are sometimes intended to "confuse if they cannot explain." It is also unfortunate that in some cases some of the three parties involved are neither openminded about new proposals nor apparently educationally equipped to evaluate them.

In one rating system, the average element time is obtained in the usual fashion. Then a "good" time is determined for each element by guess or wishful measurement (namely, the time study man selects for each element an element time that looks "good" to him). The average for an element is divided into its "good" time to obtain the efficiency, and the average is then multiplied by this efficiency to obtain the rated time. This would be the "good" time, except that the use of loose arithmetic leading to the introduction of additional decimals makes the method look much more exact. Such procedures would be amusing if they were not in use.

[40] M. E. Mundel, "An Analysis of Time Study Rating Systems and Suggestions for a Simplified Systematic System," *Industrial Engineer*, April 1944.

[41] M. E. Mundel, *Systematic Motion and Time Study*. Englewood Cliffs, N.J.: Prentice-Hall, Inc., 1946.

The judgment made must involve the evaluation of the observed performance, as compared with that required by the definition of standard performance in use, so as to permit the computation of the standard for the job. For any given job, the primary objective phenomenon from which all inferences concerning performance are made is the pace or rapidity with which the parts of the job are performed. The actual pace of performance observed must be understood to be a function of the skill, aptitude, and exertion of the operator, but these variables are neither separately identifiable nor is a separate appraisal pertinent.

The operator's *skill* determines how rapidly he may do the job properly: less skill showing up in a slower maximum pace, more skill in a faster maximum pace, provided that the method remains constant. Hence, with a given method, skill may be reflected in pace. If the worker does not possess sufficient skill to perform the job in the proper manner, even at a slow pace, then the job cannot yet be time studied. It should be obvious that no consistent set of units exists with which to measure deviations in method; consequently, even the first step of expressing method as a function of time (entailed in rating method) is not yet feasible. However, in most cases, even partially trained people can perform a job in a prescribed manner if allowed to work at a suitable pace.

The operator's *aptitude* determines how fast a pace he can maintain, or how long a period it takes him to acquire the skill required for a rapid pace. Other things being equal, poor aptitude permits but a slow pace, and high aptitude permits fast pace, provided that the proper method is followed. Hence, both aspects of aptitude are also reflected in pace.

The *exertion* of a given operator is a function of two items: the difficulty of the job and pace. Hence, exertion, which determines the physical effect of the work upon the operator, is also reflected in pace.

Consequently, it may be seen that the evaluation or rating of performance (as is correctly done in many rating procedures) may be reduced to a judgment of not more than two items: (1) observed pace, and (2) job difficulty. In the typical time study procedure, the time study observer first judges (2), job difficulty, in order to form a concept of the appearance of adequate performance for the job (as required by the definition of standard time he is using), and then judges (1), observed pace, against this imagined concept. This was discussed with respect to subjective rating, and while it is theoretically correct, the practical difficulties were enumerated.

What makes a more reliable time study rating procedure possible is, first of all, the realization that the difficulty of the job and its effect on maximum possible pace does not need to be judged but may be reduced to objective terms, based on observable phenomena, and reduced to tabular form as a function of strength required, amount of body used, degree of dexterity, and the like. Thus, the sole remaining phenomenon to be judged in rating is observed pace, or rate of activity, or actual speed of movement as compared with a pace required for standard performance. Although the desired pace is implied in the definition of standard time, this is still subject, if left in this form, to subjective variation. As will be seen later, the procedure may be altered so that standard pace may be set up in objective form so that the two items that the time study observer must compare can be concrete and any number of observers may make an appraisal of performance as related to standard, without recourse to an imagined concept. This produces a remarkable increase in the reliability of the time standards.

What is proposed is again a two-step rating procedure, but the steps are in the reverse of the conventional order. This is called *objective rating* and consists of the following steps:

1. The rating of observed pace against an objective pace-standard, which is the same for all jobs. This standard is embodied in a film. (See Appendix C.) In this rating, no attention whatsoever is paid to job difficulty and its limiting effect on possible pace; hence, a single pace-standard may be used instead of a multiplicity of mental concepts.
2. The use of a *difficulty adjustment*, consisting of a percentage increment, added after the application of the numerical appraisal from step 1 has been used to adjust the original observed data. This percentage increment is to be taken from experimentally determined tables of the effect of various observable factors that control the exertion required at a given pace. Such tables have been developed and appear in Appendix C.

Experimentally verified (as described in Appendix C), such a procedure offers a vastly improved probability that time studies rated with this procedure will more consistently represent a single concept of standard time than those adjusted by conventional procedures.

The application of such an improved procedure requires some preliminary activity before any time studies are made. However, this preliminary activity need be performed but once, and the subsequent details of taking time studies are less complex than with conventional rating procedures.

Application of Allowances

Time as computed by the procedures given thus far does not include three additional groups of additives (A) that must commonly be included in the standard time. These are:

1. Allowance for personal time.
2. Allowance for irregular occurrences that may not have been time studied or that cannot be prorated.
3. Allowance for machine time.

Each of these will be discussed separately. These allowances differ from the difficulty adjustments[42] in three respects: first, they are usually applied similarly to every element in the task; second, they may, in some categories, actually represent a block of time that may be accumulated from a large number of cycles to eventually provide an interval in the work spell during which the worker will not be working; and third, they relate to factors external to the job.

1. *Allowance for personal time.* This category is not to be confused with the catchall term *fatigue allowance*, which is frequently found in the literature and which, because of the manifold interpretations placed on the term *fatigue*, has led to a great deal of misunderstanding. It should be borne in mind that after the time study observations have been adjusted either by subjective or objective ratings (in the latter case, including difficulty adjustments), the result is supposedly a time value that would permit the operator to produce work in this time, or less, throughout the normal work spell, as far as the internal work of the operation is concerned. No allowance could be devised which would prevent the operator from becoming *fatigued* (in the common sense of the word) from the day's work, but if the concept of normal, which was used in rating, was reasonable, the fatigue (in this sense) is reasonable. The use of an additional allowance would, in subjective rating, imply that step 1 of the rating procedure was done improperly and in objective rating, that the difficulty adjustment was inadequate.

However, no attention has been given to personal needs (among other items) or to the effect of the external conditions of the operation upon personal needs.

It is not usual that a person can work through a normal industrial work spell without attending to personal needs. The amount of time required for these will be affected by the conditions surrounding the work; less in comfortable quiet surroundings, and more when they are hot, dusty, or noisy.

Many plants follow a practice of providing for personal time during the working day in accordance with a schedule as given in Table 13.

A means of correctly reducing the time values given in Table 13 to a percentage figure for proper pro rata addition to the base times will be discussed later in this chapter.

In many plants, to replace most personal time taken at will, rest pauses of various lengths are introduced into the work spells at definite intervals. An appropriate amount of time will have to be introduced into each standard so as to apportion this time to all the jobs the worker may work on during the day. In such cases, the value that would otherwise be selected from Table 13 is replaced with the total time of these rest pauses.

---

[42] Whether the difficulty adjustment is made mentally as with subjective rating or from tables as with objective rating, is not of concern. Allowances will be appropriate in both cases.

TABLE 13

Allowance for Personal Time[1]

Condition	Reference Letter	Time in Minutes for an 8-Hour Work Spell Divided by a Lunch Period into Two 4-Hour Work Spells
Comfortable	S	23
Warm or slightly disagreeable....	T	30
Hot, dusty, noisy, etc.	U	50
Special or unusual..............	SP	As required

[1] When rest breaks occur in the work spell, these may be in lieu of all or most of the personal time.

A few examples of "special or unusual" conditions may be of interest. In one plant manufacturing dye transfer carbons (hectograph material), the maintenance of satisfactory industrial and public relations (indeed, lawsuits could easily be involved) requires that sufficient time for washing be allowed, so that the workers do not inadvertently carry away any of the exceedingly transferable dye on their persons or clothes when leaving the plant. As a result, as much as two hours or 120 minutes out of a 480-minute day may be allowed for changing clothes when entering and for thorough washing and rechanging when leaving.

For another example, the operator of a process furnace in a pipe plant may easily be able to perform the motions of the cycle of his task in 0.25 minutes, but the heat of the furnace, radiating to his body, may force him to remain idle, away from the furnace for 30 minutes out of each hour, or 240 minutes out of an eight-hour work spell.

Such allowances, as can readily be seen, are quite reasonably subject to collective bargaining. However, if wage incentives are in use, care should be taken that negotiations for such allowances are not confused with wage negotiations, which are something quite different. These may easily be confused if the allowances are raised beyond the point of fulfilling their purpose and instead so increase the allowed time per unit as to permit considerably more incentive increment than could be anticipated with the concept of the standard in use. This is far beyond the conceived purpose of the allowances.

2. *Allowances for irregular occurrences.* Although it is desirable to study and rate all irregular occurrences and prorate these so as to apportion them properly to each cycle, some occurrences are of such a nature as to make this

extremely difficult. For example, let us assume that a sewing-machine opera-tor must clean his or her machine at the end of the day. Perhaps this takes five minutes. It is hardly proper to charge this solely to last job of the day, nor is it feasible to prorate this to a time value addible to each cycle if the machine operator works on several jobs each day (as is not uncommon) and each job has a different total cycle time, although the cost of this five minutes should be distributed among the jobs. Consequently, an adjustment must be made such that a total of five minutes is accumulated during a day as part of the standards.

Allowances may be made for tool and machine maintenance and the like. A mechanical or electrical recorder may be placed on the machine and the foreman or worker may note, in an accompanying log, the reason for each delay. These two records may later be analyzed to provide a basis for allow-ances for irregular elements.

It is strongly suggested, however, that where the irregular work may be directly attributed to a specific job, and a rate of occurrence during that job determined, that the time value be handled as an irregular element. Otherwise these allowances for irregular elements may well get out of hand and eventually lead to sizable inconsistencies in the comparative difficulty of different standards. Extended time studies may be made in the course of which the work is divided only into productive work and delays. These may be made with a stop-watch or a memomotion camera. The camera offers the advantage of being able to observe more than one machine at a time, with no loss of accuracy. Using such studies as a basis, the allowances may be determined.

Figure 18.15 is a *production study* made, at a large printing plant, of the operation of a combiner, a machine for pasting a printed sheet to cardboard. To make this study, the time study man was at the machine before the shift began. The foremen and workers had been notified, on the previous day, that such a study would be made. The study was made with a stop-watch. The record was made in the following manner:

1. The basic information at the head of the sheet was entered prior to the starting of the shift.
2. The observer started his stop-watch when the shift began and recorded the following:
   a. The ending time of each period of productive work.
   b. The units produced during each period of productive work.
   c. The ending time of each delay.
   d. The reason for each delay.
3. The watch was allowed to run throughout the entire shift and all events were recorded.
4. The actual production and delay times were obtained subsequently by subtraction, and the values at the bottom of Figure 18.15 were computed.

PRODUCTION CHECK STUDY (All time in minutes, readings are ending times)

Page __1__ of __1__
Dept. _16_
Product and No. _1272 PUZZLE_   Study date __3/3/__
Operation _COMBINE_   Opr. and No. _PINE 817_
Machine and No. _COMBINER #7_   Work unit _SHEET_
                                       COUNTER ZEROED AT EACH DELAY

Units made	TIME Begin 8.00		TIME			Explanation of delays (why or what done)
Count	R	T	R	T	x = Allowable	
327	805.35	5.35	806.85	1.50	X	SHEET JAMMED
740	819.16	12.31	821.16	2.00		PERSONAL
982	837.49	16.33	837.77	.28	X	OVERSIZED BOARD
544	846.83	9.06	847.39	.56	X	GLUE DRIP
163	850.10	2.71	853.82	3.72		PERSONAL
415	900.73	6.91	901.22	.49	X	SHEET FOLDED
1782	930.93	29.71	931.51	.58	X	OIL PICK UP ARMS, SQUEEKING
694	953.96	11.54	958.12	4.16		PERSONAL
603	1008.17	10.05	1008.60	.43	X	TORN SHEET
659	1019.58	10.98	1019.84	.26	X	BAD SHEETS
1019	1036.83	16.99	1037.68	.85	X	ADD GLUE
575	1047.27	9.59	1048.18	.91	X	ADJUST GLUE ROLL
256	1052.44	4.26	1053.70	1.26	X	THIN GLUE WITH WATER
694	1105.25	11.55	1107.11	1.86	X	" " " "
585	1116.86	9.75	1117.40	.54	X	SHEET JAM
283	1122.12	4.72	1124.57	2.45	X	NO PICK UP - ADJUST CUPS
169	1127.39	2.82	1128.87	1.48	X	SHEET ON GLUE ROLLER
85	1130.28	1.41	1133.45	3.17		PERSONAL
456	1141.06	7.61	1141.91	.85	X	ADJUST GUIDES TO NEW BATCH SIZE
1084	1200.00	18.09				LUNCH TILL 1 PM
337	105.62	5.62	106.45	.83	X	THIN OUT GLUE
1022	123.47	17.02	125.65	2.18		PERSONAL
675	136.88	11.23	137.60	.72	X	CARDBOARD MISFEED
332	143.14	5.54	144.62	1.48	X	ADD GLUE
1482	209.32	24.70	210.13	.81	X	ADJUST GLUE ROLL
688	221.56	11.43	222.32	.76	X	SHEET JAM ON PRESSURE ROLL
892	237.19	14.87	238.10	.91	X	REPLACE WORN PICK UP CUP
711	249.93	11.93	251.46	1.53	X	ADD GLUE AND THIN
664	302.52	11.06	303.78	1.26	X	ALIGN LOOSE GLUE GUIDE
814	317.36	13.58	321.48	4.12		PERSONAL
585	331.22	9.74	331.47	.25	X	TORN SHEET
880	396.10	14.63	347.09	.99	X	CLEAN LINT FROM PICK UP
1078	405.03	17.94	405.76	.73	X	SHEET ON PRESSURE ROLL
261	410.11	4.35	411.76	1.65	X	ADD GLUE
2618	454.30	42.54	500.00	5.70		CLEAN FOR 2nd SHIFT

1 _25,762_ Total production count
2 _427.95_ Total production time *Min*.
3 _60.2/MIN._ Rate of production, unadjusted (1 ÷ 2)
4 _27.00_ Allowable delay time
5 _56.6/MIN._ Adj. rate of production [1 ÷ (2 + 4)]
6 _25.05_ Unallowable delays (Personal time and clean up allowed elsewhere)
7 _53.5/MIN_ Observed rate of production

Fig. 18.15—Production study in printing plant.

Following the study, a delay percentage was computed for delays too small to be punched out and normally expectable in the work. Breakdowns or other delays not a regular part of the work would not, by company policy, be charged to productive time and therefore were not included in the delay allowance. Production studies are of considerable assistance in aiding in the determination of why an operator or group of operators are not performing at standard. Inasmuch as production studies are a continuously observed, intensive sample, the exact events may be examined and the reasons for sub-standard performance determined. Indeed, they are more effective for this latter purpose than for determining delays inasmuch as delay studies, in many cases, should be taken over longer periods than can be economically studied by means of production studies.

As a preferred procedure, the use of work sampling may assist in deter-mining accurately the rate of occurrence of irregular events or delays and may more readily be extended over the necessary period of time. This pro-cedure is also described in the literature as "Ratio-Delay Study." This approach, described in relation to methods study in Chapter 9, requires recording the events taking place during random observations of an operation and computing the percentage occurrence of any type of event as the percen-tage of the total observations. If the number of observations is great enough to reduce the probable sampling error to tolerable limits, then the percentage computed may be taken as representing the percentage required for this activity.

The details of making a work sampling study were described in Chapter 9. When making such a study in order to determine delay or other allowance percentages, there will be only two differences from the procedure previously given. These differences are:

1. The categories into which the observations will be classified must be appropriate to the concept of allowances or delays.
2. The sample size must be enough to provide an accuracy suitable for performance standards.

Table 3, Chapter 9, page 132, would be used to determine the size of the required study. The use of Table 3 is very simple. Let us say we wished to determine the actual per cent of time spent in tool replacement on a machine. A rough estimate places this at 5 per cent. Let us further assume that ± 1 per cent accuracy with 95/100 probability is sufficient. Table 3 indicates that 1,900 readings are necessary. Let us assume our random method of recording is estimated as giving us 50 recordings a day. Thus, 38 days will be required to obtain sufficient data. (It should be noted that these readings will not be other than a miscellaneous duty of the individual obtaining them unless a considerable number of work sampling projects are in progress, of which this is only a part.) To continue, let us say that at the end of 38 days we have 1,950 readings and the percentage indicated, for the event under study, is 6. Table 3 indicates that we must continue to accumulate readings until we have 2,260, at which time we will again check. A similar procedure would be followed with the other limits.

As an alternate procedure, the cumulative percentage may be graphed with the study continuing until a stable value is reached. The accuracy of this cumulative percentage may be checked by daily computation, as follows:

$$E_{95/100} = 2\sqrt{\frac{\bar{p}(1-\bar{p})}{N}}$$

where:

$E_{95/100}$ = the value to be added and subtracted from the value of $\bar{p}$ to indicate the limits within which we have 95 chances in 100 that the true value of $\bar{p}$ lies.

$\bar{p}$ = the percentage of observations of any one type.

N = the total number of observations made in the study.

Both of the two preceding procedures are based on an assumption that the activity being observed is relatively stable with respect to the manner in which working time is used. This may not always be true. Indeed, the continued sampling may of itself affect the activities of the operators. Heiland and Richardson list four sources of instability, as follows:

1. Mixture [of behavior patterns or circumstances].
2. Cyclic effects.
3. Trend effects.
4. Stratification effects.[43]

The presence of such factors may be detected with the aid of a control chart for daily posting of each p from each day's sample.[44]

The formulas for the standard deviation of p (σ_p) were given in Chapter 9. The analyst may plot a control chart with $2\sigma_p$ or $3\sigma_p$ upper and lower control limits,[45] depending on the sensitivity desired, and thus detect the possible occurrence of assignable causes of fluctuations or shifts in $\bar{p}$. These control charts would be interpreted in the standard manner. Certainly it is not desirable to use an allowance percentage based on a mixture of two conditions, one of which is not a normal condition. On the other hand, if p stays in control, the values from Table 3 may be used to set limits for the study.

Work sampling may also be made with the aid of a memomotion camera, particularly in cases where the categories of activity may be determined without interrogation of the worker or workers being observed. The camera, in

[43] R. E. Heiland and W. J. Richardson, *Work Sampling*. New York, N.Y.: McGraw-Hill Book Co., 1957, p. 106.

[44] For a complete discussion of such a use of the control chart see *op. cit.*, pp. 101–118.

[45] To compute these limits the p used would be the $\bar{p}$ from the first 5 to 10 days and the N would be the daily number of observations rather than a cumulative N.

this case, is operated intermittently by means of a program timer which operates the camera for short periods at various intervals during the working day. The program timer of Figure 18.16 is set to operate the camera for ten-second runs at each five-minute interval during a ten-hour period. In this

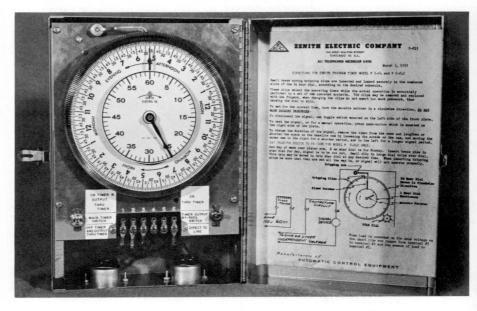

Fig. 18.16—Program timer for memomotion work sampling.

manner, the timer, which operates the camera, may be set at odd intervals such as 7:54 A.M., 8:01 A.M., 8:06 AM., 8:11 A.M., and so forth, and allowed to operate for three days on one 100-foot roll of film. To randomize the data further, the clock of the timer may be displaced again after each work shift. The ten-hour program readily overlaps both ends of the nine-hour work day (including the lunch hour). The 24-hour movement of the timer automatically starts the unit in operation before each shift begins, minimizing the labor of taking the study. A lesser number of camera circuit actuators may be placed, if desired, in the timer program, giving greater randomization to the study and allowing a longer period to be sampled with each 100-foot roll of film.

After the film is processed, it is analyzed with a film analysis projector as described in Chapter 14. A specific frame of film of each sequence, i.e., the fourth, is classified into the proper category of the sampling study, the frames preceding and following this selected frame being used to make this classification.[46]

---

[46] A single picture is insufficient to determine status in most cases.

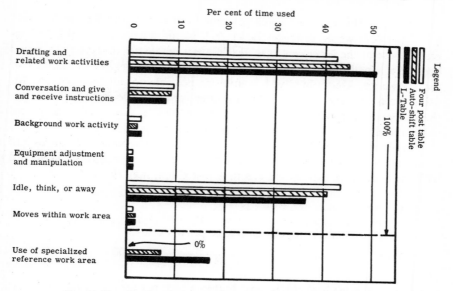

Fig. 18.17 — Results of memomotion work sampling of 105 draftsmen in ten companies, showing effects of different types of drafting furniture.

Figure 18.17 gives the results of a sampling study made, in a number of different companies, for the Hamilton Mfg. Co. of Two Rivers, Wisconsin, by means of memomotion sampling. A considerable number of draftsmen could be observed simultaneously by the camera, and the drafting departments were not continually disturbed by the presence of a strange observer walking through the room.

This is an appropriate place to examine a suitable way of making an adjustment to the base times so as to allow for the accumulation of the blocks of time required to provide for the first two allowance categories which have been discussed.

Let us assume that the allowances for a sewing-machine operator for personal time and irregular occurrences not prorated to each job are as follows:

Personal-reference S	23 min.
Irregular—daily cleanup	5 min.
Total time to be distributed	28 min.

In other words, if the work day is 480 minutes, it will be made up of 28 minutes of allowances and 452 minutes of work. Consequently, each expenditure of time in work must allow the worker to accumulate $[(28/452) \times 100]$ per cent more time for expending in the manner implied by the allowance categories. In this case this is 6.2 per cent.[47] In actual practice, in this case, 6 or 7 per cent would probably be used. It would appear reasonable to suggest the use of the 7 per cent (the next highest whole per cent) in such a case because it is within the range of accuracy and does not imply a diminution of the allowance. Undoubtedly, it would be possible to advance reasons for using the 6 per cent value. This is a matter for policy decision inasmuch as the inherent reliability of time study could hardly support, on a logical basis, the use of a decimal percentage allowance.

As a general procedure, to combine personal and irregular allowances into a per cent value for addition to base time, the following equation, in accord with the procedure used in the example just given, may be used.

Let A = minutes per work day.

B = minutes personal allowance per work day.

C = minutes irregular allowance per work day.

Then   per cent allowance $= \dfrac{B + C}{A - (B + C)} \times 100$

It is also suggested that the nearest higher whole per cent be used unless the calculation gives a whole number.

3. *Allowance for machine time.* This third category raises certain questions that must be carefully examined. For discussion, let us say the definition of standard time in use is: "130/100 of the amount of time required, assuming method and condition, for the typical operator expending maximum exertion on the job."

The effect of the factor of machine control in such circumstances might best be understood by examining four sample jobs, as follows:

Job A 100 per cent hand time,   0 per cent machine controlled
Job B 60 per cent hand time,   40 per cent machine controlled
Job C 30 per cent hand time,   70 per cent machine controlled
Job D 0 per cent hand time, 100 per cent machine controlled

In all of the foregoing cases we may further assume that the operator is idle during the machine time, except in case D, where his work may be a feeding of the machine—work which makes but a slight demand upon him. Of course, such jobs should be considered a challenge to the method designer, who should attempt, in most cases, to find some useful activity for the otherwise idle time, but this is not always possible. Further, the desirability of maximum machine utilization or the desirability of continuous attention to the machine may outweigh the desirability of maximum labor utilization. There-

---

[47] See D. Anderson and A. H. Hansen, "The Right and Wrong of Time Study Computations," *Iron Age*, August 17, 1944. This article appears to be the first to propose this obviously correct procedure.

fore, it does not appear unreasonable to assume that we may encounter valid instances of such jobs as have been listed.

In case A, if the actual standard time represented the recommended definition of standard time, the typical operator on the job would be able to exceed standard performance by 30 per cent.[48]

In case B, the effect of the rest has been found to be such that it will usually permit the operator to increase his pace sufficiently, on the hand or operator controlled part of the cycle, above that expectable on job A. (In this case also, the expectable incentive increment would be 30 per cent without excessive exertion, provided that the pace concept used to rate the job was the same pace against which job A was rated.) To make this obvious, let us further assume that job A at the given pace (with adjustments added if objective rating was used) was 1 minute long and that job B involved the identical 1 minute of work plus 0.667 minutes (40 per cent of total cycle) of rest while a machine operated.

A comparison of case A and case B yields some significant observations.

1. The maximum pace, taking into account the effect of machine enforced rest, is lower for job A than job B even if the actual handwork is identical.
2. It is unlikely that step 1 of subjective rating will take into account the effect of the intermittent rest. To do so would require an infinite multiplicity of mental concepts. Hence, the operator will obtain the full benefits of the intermittent rest.
3. Objective rating will not differentiate between the two jobs inasmuch as all jobs are compared to a single, standard pace. The operator will obtain the full benefits of the intermittent rest.

As will be shown later, the effect of the rest, if the operator obtains the benefit, is such that expectable production increment on job B will be the same as on job A. Hence, the standard time set by normal procedures will meet all of the criteria given in Chapter 17.

Case C raises fully the problem of machine control. In this case the operator will again, without undue exertion, find it possible, because of the larger rest, to increase his pace above even that expectable with job B. However, the fixing of 70 per cent of the cycle time will not allow him to exceed standard by 30 per cent, even if the pace required for standard was the same as on job A. This condition ensues as soon as more than 45 per cent of the cycle is machine controlled.[49] Therefore, the indirect adjustment made, when the same pace as was used to rate job A is used to rate job C, will not fully adjust

---

[48] With a different version of standard in use this per cent and all others in the following discussion would change, but the implications would remain the same.

[49] The data supporting this statement appear in the supplementary material appended to this chapter.

the time for job C to match the definition of standard time represented by the time standards of cases A and B.

Case D is the extreme situation. This gets no benefit from any indirect adjustment, and the observed time is the minimum time.

The expectable production increment over standard is greater on jobs A and B than with job C and is greater with jobs A, B, and C than with job D. What should be done, if anything, about these differences, depends upon

TABLE 14

Allowance Table

Category	Reference Letter	Condition	Time in Minutes in 8-Hour Work Spell[1]	Per Cent
1-Personal[2]	S	Comfortable	23	
	T	Warm or slightly disagreeable	30	
	U	Hot, dusty, noisy, etc.	50	
	SP	Special or unusual	As required	
2-Irregular (Clean up, tool, etc.)	Use name	Evaluate	Suitable	

To reduce the total of time from categories 1 and 2 to a per cent value, use an equation in which: A = minutes per work day; B = minutes personal allowance per work day; C = minutes irregular allowance per work day.

$$\frac{B + C}{A - (B + C)} \times 100 = \text{per cent allowance}$$

3—Per cent of base time of cycle controlled by the machine	V followed by per cent controlled by machine and per cent internal manual work	Depends on policy chosen	

[1] Divided into two 4-hour work spells by a lunch period.

[2] If rest spells are used, use total time of rest pauses instead of this if rest pauses are meant as substitutes for personal time taken at will.

the use to be made of the standards and upon the concept of equity held; a policy decision is required.

Three basic types of solutions are possible:

1. Make no adjustment.
2. Adjust the standards so that the probable production increment over standard is related to the per cent of manual work in the cycle.
3. Adjust the standard so that the expectable production increment over standard is the same for all jobs.

Some alternative solutions are examined in the supplementary materials appended at the end of this chapter.

At this point, let us summarize with respect to allowances:

Allowances are added to all elements equally. Table 14 is suggested with the understanding that either because of the nature of the allowance or the meagerness of data, as fits each case, some of the items of such a table may need to be recomputed or may well be negotiated before being used in an actual application.

Summary Example

A time study completed with allowances, and with the final calculations made and transferred to the front, is shown in Figure 18.18a and b. Note the two calculations at the bottom of the front of the sheet, which are designed to summarize the effect of the ratings and allowances for the time study supervisor. The "production anticipated at standard" is computed on the basis of the allowed cycle time. The "production during study" is computed on the basis of the total average time (with irregular elements prorated as necessary). These two values sum up the relationship between the observed performance and anticipated performance and are often of great aid in indicating when unusual or difficult situations may arise from the installation of the standard.

Supplemental Material

The supplemental material of this chapter is divided into three parts.

1. Computing the required number of readings for a time study. (A more rigorous mathematical treatment than that included in the body of the chapter is discussed. Some examples are given.)
2. A procedure for developing skill at time study rating. (Experimental material from studies of trained time study raters is examined and discussed. Means of conducting suitable training sessions are described,

ELEMENTS

No. TERMINAL POINT	1 R	1 T	2 R	2 T	3 R	3 T	4 R	4 T	5 R	5 T	6 R	6 T	7 R	7 T	8 R	8 T	9 R	9 T	10 R	10 T	11 R	11 T	12 R	12 T	13 R	13 T	14 R	14 T	15 R	15 T
1 Release ring	07	7	33	6	62	7	86	7	15	7	43	6	71	7	98	6	24	6	50	6	79	7	76		44	7	71	6	98	7
2 Pick up assembly	16	9	43	10	70	8	96	10 M	52	9	80	9	07	9	32	8	59	9	99	10	25	9	53	9	80	9	08	10		
3 Let go of weight	22	6	50	7	77	7	03	7	32		59	7	86	6	13	6	37	7	66	7	95	6	32	7	59	6	86	6	15	7
4 Let go of lever	27	5	55	5	82	5	08	5	37	5	64	5	92	6	18	5	44	5	72	6	00	5	37	5	65	6	91	5	20	5
5 Return from Stockroom					110	98																								
6																														
7																														
8																														
9																														
10																														
11																														
12																														
13																														
14																														
15																														

RECAPITULATION

ELEMENTS	1	2	3	4	5	6	7	8	9	10	11	12	13	14	15
Amount of body	C-2	C-2	C-1	C-2	C-8										
Foot pedals	E-O	F-O	F-O	F-O	F-O										
Bimanualness	H-O	H-O	H-O	H-O	H-O										
Eye-hand coordination	J-2	J-2	J-2	J-2	I-O										
Handling requirements	N-O	N-O	N-O	N-O	N-O										
Weight or resistance	O-O	O-O	N-15	8-8	14-15										
TOTAL TIME IN MIN.	.91	1.28	.92	.78	.99										
NUMBER OF OBS.	14	14	14	15	1										
PRO-RATE DIVISOR	1	1	1	1	100										
AVERAGE PER CYCLE	.065	.091	.066	.052	.0098										
RATING	110	110	108	105	90										
RATED TIME	.0715	.1001	.0712	.0595	.0088										
PER CENT OF CYCLE															
1+ ADJUSTMENTS	1.04	1.04	1.19	1.12	1.23										
BASE TIME	.074	.104	.085	.061	.0108										
1+ ALLOWANCES	1.04	1.04	1.04	1.04	1.04										
ALLOWED TIME	.077	.108	.088	.064	.011										

SYMBOLS USED

C–Extra unnecessary motion
D–A.D. dropped part
F–Unnecessary fumble
H–Unnecessary hesitation
P–Includes personal time
R–Made reject by improper work
X–Deviation from std. routine
M–Missed reading

ALLOWANCES

Personal 15 min ___ %
Clean up 3
18/450–18 = ___ 4 %

TOTAL ___

LOOP VALUES		
141	132	120
120	83	82
74	67	53
44	40	36

Fig. 18.18a — Completed rear of time study form for task of assemble saxophone pad (continued).

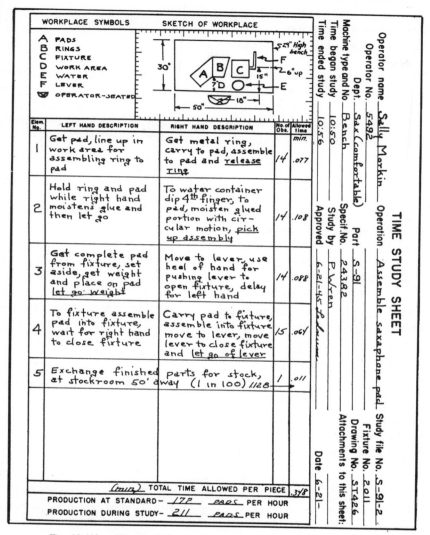

WORKPLACE SYMBOLS — SKETCH OF WORKPLACE

A PADS
B RINGS
C FIXTURE
D WORK AREA
E WATER
F LEVER
☺ OPERATOR-SEATED

TIME STUDY SHEET

Operator name Sally Markin
Operator No. 5492
Dept. Sax (comfortable)   Part S-91
Machine type and No. Bench   Specif. No. 24382
Time began study 10:50   Study by P. Wren
Time ended study 10:56   Approved 6-21-45
Operation Assemble saxophone pad. Study file No. S-91-2
Fixture No. 2.011
Drawing No. ST426
Attachments to this sheet:
Date 6-21-

Elem. No.	LEFT HAND DESCRIPTION	RIGHT HAND DESCRIPTION	No. of Obs.	Allowed time
1	Get pad, line up in work area for assembling ring to pad	Get metal ring, carry to pad, assemble to pad and release ring	14	.077
2	Hold ring and pad while right hand moistens glue and then let go	To water container dip 4th finger, to pad, moisten glued portion with circular motion, pick up assembly	14	.108
3	Get complete pad from fixture, set aside, get weight and place on pad let go weight	Move to lever, use heel of hand for pushing lever to open fixture, delay for left hand	14	.088
4	To fixture assemble pad into fixture, wait for right hand to close fixture	Carry pad to fixture, assemble into fixture move to lever, move lever to close fixture and let go of lever	15	.061
5	Exchange finished parts for stock, at stockroom 50' away (1 in 100) 1128·		1	.011

(min.) TOTAL TIME ALLOWED PER PIECE .318

PRODUCTION AT STANDARD— 172 pads PER HOUR
PRODUCTION DURING STUDY— 211 pads PER HOUR

Fig. 18.18b—(Concluded) Completed front of time study form for task of assemble saxophone pad.

as well as means for examining the data from such training sessions in order to evaluate the skill developed.)

3. Allowances for machine time. (Relevant research is examined. The results of the alternatives mentioned in the body of the chapter are compared. Data is provided for computing an appropriate allowance with a variety of policies.)

Computing the Required
Number of Readings for a Time Study

This application of sampling theory is based on the assumption that chance or random causes control the variation from reading to reading for a given element in a time study. In most cases this is a tenable assumption.

Formula (A)[50] gives a measure of the variability of data about its average. The variability is represented by σ, the standard deviation, which is expressed as follows:

$$\sigma = \sqrt{\frac{\Sigma d^2}{N}} \tag{A}$$

$d = X - \bar{X}$ computed for each reading of the element separately before squaring and then summing.

X = individual readings of an element.

$\bar{X}$ = mean or average of all readings of an element.

Σ = sum of like items.

N = number of readings of an element.

This equation may be expressed for machine computation (Friden, Monroe, Marchant, etc.):

$$\sigma = \sqrt{\frac{\Sigma X^2}{N} - \left(\frac{\Sigma X}{N}\right)^2} = \frac{1}{N}\sqrt{N \Sigma X^2 - (\Sigma X)^2}$$

From this, assuming it to represent the variability of a huge group of similar readings or the parent population (a commonly tenable assumption), another measure $\sigma_{\bar{x}}$, the standard error of the mean (or average), may be computed, by (B), which indicates the probable variability of the averages of groups of N values of X about the obtained $\bar{X}$.

$$\sigma_{\bar{x}} = \frac{\sigma}{\sqrt{N}} \tag{B}$$

The property of this last measure is such that 95 per cent of the probable values of $\bar{X}$ (average for the element) will lie within $\pm 2\sigma_{\bar{x}}$ of the true average.

Hence, if $2\sigma_{\bar{x}}$ is equal to or less than 5 per cent of $\bar{X}$, we may say the chances are at least 95 out of 100 that our average for the element, to which the rating will be applied, is within ± 5 per cent of the true average representing the performance we observed. If the 10 per cent criterion is used, then the above may be restated by the reader, using "10 per cent" in place of "5 per cent."

---

[50] A very early suggestion of a somewhat similar mathematical procedure was suggested for use without a performance rating in: Elmer B. Royer, "How Many Observations Are Necessary in Setting Wage-Incentive Standards?" *Personnel*, May 1937, pp. 137–139.

As was explained earlier, neither of these would seem to be an unreasonable minimum criterion to apply to our time studies.

If these conditions are not met, we may work formula (B) backwards, using the σ we first obtained, setting $2\sigma_{\bar{x}}$ equal to 5 per cent of $\bar{X}$, and solving for N', which will indicate the number of readings that will probably be needed.

Indeed, it is this last property that makes this test feasible, easy, convenient, and economical to use after some additional mathematical manipulation of the formulas.

Combining formulas (A) and (B), we may state:

$$\sigma_{\bar{x}} = \frac{\frac{1}{N}\sqrt{N\Sigma X^2 - (\Sigma X)^2}}{\sqrt{N'}}$$

and setting 5 per cent of $\bar{X}$ equal to $2\sigma_{\bar{x}}$, we get

$$0.05\,\bar{X} = \frac{\Sigma X}{20N} = 2\frac{\frac{1}{N}\sqrt{N\Sigma X^2 - (\Sigma X)^2}}{\sqrt{N'}}$$

$$\frac{\Sigma X}{20} = \left(\frac{2\sqrt{N\Sigma X^2 - (\Sigma X)^2}}{\sqrt{N'}}\right)$$

and

$$N' = \left(\frac{40\sqrt{N\Sigma X^2 - (\Sigma X)^2}}{\Sigma X}\right)^2 \tag{C}$$

where N' is the required number of readings.

This equation may be easily handled even by one who is not familiar with the mathematics of its derivation.

If the analyst prefers to set his limits as 95 chances out of 100 of being within ± 10 per cent, then

$$N' = \left(\frac{20\sqrt{N\Sigma X^2 - (\Sigma X)^2}}{\Sigma X}\right)^2 \tag{C'}$$

Equations (C) and (C') are the important ones. A desk calculator such as a Friden, Monroe, or Marchant may be used to obtain ΣX and ΣX^2 simultaneously, and $N\Sigma X^2 - (\Sigma X)^2$ quickly thereafter. The square root of the value under the radical may then be extracted with a slide rule to give an equation of the form $(AB/C)^2$, which is also rapidly solved on a slide rule.

Furthermore, since the units in which the element times are recorded occur in both the numerator and denominator of the expressions (C) or (C'), the decimal place of whatever unit is used in timing may be disregarded and the values handled as whole numbers, with the resulting greater convenience. Equations (C) or (C') in practice may be solved for an element in a few minutes and interpreted as follows, provided there is not a consistent pattern to the element variation. (However, in all cases, at least ten readings should be taken as a minimum sample.)

1. *5 per cent criterion [Equation* (C)]. If N' is equal to or less than the number of readings recorded, then the average for that element is probably (95 chances out of 100) within ± 5 per cent of the correct representative average. If N' is greater than the number of readings taken, then the study does not meet our criterion of reliability, and a new study with N' or more readings of this element should be taken and rechecked.

2. 10 *per cent criterion [Equation* (C′)]. The same as above, but replace "5 per cent" with "10 per cent."

The two illustrations that follow show how the measure and criteria developed would be applied. For example, let us say our element readings were 6, 7, 6, 8, 7, 5, 6, 8, 7, 6, 7, 6, 6, and 7 (all in 0.01 minute). $\Sigma X^2 = 614$ and $\Sigma X = 92$; consequently $N' = 24.9$. Thus, with the real N of 14 and 25 values required to give an average with a probability of 95 chances out of 100 of being within ± 5 per cent of the correct average, we must conclude that the readings for the element are inadequate. Hence, a new study with at least 25 readings should be taken and rechecked.

For another example, let us say our element readings on another element were 10, 11, 10, 12, 11, 10, 12, 13, 10, 12, 10, 11, 11, 12, 11 (all in 0.01 minute). $\Sigma X^2 = 1850$ and $\Sigma X = 166$; consequently $N' = 11$. Thus the 15 readings that were obtained give an average that has a probability of 95 out of 100, or better, of being within ± 5 per cent of the correct average; hence, the average for the element is acceptable as representing the performance observed and a rating may be applied.

A Procedure for Developing Skill at Time Study Rating

Research involving an analysis of the performance of trained time study observers using conventional rating procedures shows that they may perform these judgments with surprising results. A study by A. J. Keim[51] showed that a trained group of time study engineers (approximately 50) rating films[52] of 57 performances at different paces, using the conventional subjective approach

[51] M. E. Mundel and A. J. Keim, Proceedings of Second Annual Purdue Motion and Time Study Work Session, *Misc. Bul. of Div. of Tech. Ext.*, Purdue University, April 1945.

[52] M. E. Mundel, and L. Margolin, Report of the 4th Annual Purdue Motion and Time Study Work Session, *Misc. Bul. of Div. of Tech. Ext.*, Purdue Univ., 1948. This study showed that with trained time study observers, "Ratings are more consistent . . . and . . . more accurate when made from motion pictures than when made from the actual performance of the operator . . .," p. 5. Consequently, these data presented here are from a situation where at least a reasonably fair situation was used. However, it should be noted that in both Keim's experiment and Lehrer's experiment (quoted later), the raters were

rated 46 per cent of the performances with less than ± 10 per cent error and 54 per cent with more than ± 10 per cent error.[53] The correct values were obtained by using the group average, corrected for concept of standard,[54] and adjusting for known relationships between certain of the 57 performances shown. (The 57 performances were really pace variants of only ten jobs.) Further experiments by Lehrer, with more carefully constructed films in which practically no method variation appeared from pace to pace and with extremely careful adjustment of the data to a comparable base, gave similar results inasmuch as they indicated that with 31 time study engineers observing various paces of four jobs, 19 per cent of their ratings, made in this conventional fashion, were within ± 5 per cent error, 42 per cent within ± 10 per cent error, and 58 per cent exceeded ± 10 per cent error.[55]

On the other hand, R. G. Carson reports (with respect to ratings made by six time study men on 63 films, over a six year period), "The standard deviation of independent ratings made by men trained together on operations with which they are familiar will be approximately 6.67 per cent. Differences between the standard deviations of different men are so small they can be attributed to sampling errors."[56]

Carson attributes this greater accuracy to the uniform, planned, periodic training given his group. Also, the men were all employed in one plant and were rating films of jobs in that plant. These conditions were not characteristic of the other studies. Carson's group placed 56 per cent of their ratings within ± 5 per cent error, 74 per cent within ± 7.5 per cent error, and 87 per cent within ± 10 per cent error.[57] However, information was not given concerning the range of performances presented to the group. A reduced range would reduce the apparent error or variability, particularly if the time study

---

not too familiar with the jobs being rated. Be that as it may, evidence will be presented in Appendix C to show that even under such circumstances other procedures may be used to reduce vastly the errors of judgment.

[53] A 10 per cent error was defined as a rating in error by 10 per cent of the value that should have been assigned. A pace of 75 (100 being standard) could thus be rated within ± 7.5 scale points and a pace of 140 within ± 14 scale points without exceeding the ± 10 per cent error as defined.

[54] Standard, as defined, may vary from plant to plant. Depending on both the definition and the scale, the typical operator with typical performance was variously defined as 75 (60 base) or 120, 125, 130, or 150, and so forth (100 base). The values actually assigned by the time study observers were corrected to the numerical value they would have assigned had they all defined typical maximum performance of the typical operator as 130, so as to make all data comparable. In this manner, erroneous conclusions arising from the use of different units were avoided. However, real differences in the concept of what could physically be expected from an incentive operator may have made the performance of these raters appear somewhat less accurate than it may, in reality, have been.

[55] R. N. Lehrer, "Development and Evaluation of a Pace Scale for Time Study Rating," *Doctoral dissertation*, Purdue University, June 1949.

[56] R. G. Carson, Jr., "Consistency in Speed Rating," *J. of Indusl. Engr.*, Vol. V, No. 1, January 1954, p. 17.

[57] *Ibid.*, p. 16.

men being tested had some knowledge of the approximate range covered.

While this accuracy is surprising, considering the difficulty of the judgment involved, such results can easily give rise in practice to extremely difficult situations and have led to such remarks as the following, which can hardly be disregarded.

> Obviously, if after months of negotiations and possibly strikes at great financial sacrifice to both sides, a settlement has been reached involving a ten per cent change in the basic rates, neither management nor labor is prepared to sacrifice its respective rights to the blind operations of a technique of questionable accuracy.
>
> The use of a time study technique to set production standards whose demonstrated inaccuracy may exceed this percentage can become the source of much controversy. Naturally the demand by either side to monopolize the function arouses the suspicion of the other. Thus the solution to the basic problem of the validity of existing time study practice lies at the very heart of satisfactory industrial relations.[58]

Suspicion arises because of the ease with which the entire scale may be shifted in the course of step 1. In management's hands this would possibly offset on all new jobs any wage increase gained, and, in labor's hands, produce opposite results. Even if this suspicion does not arise, the variation in the relative ease or difficulty of the standards possible with such procedures creates other problems. True, if the variation is random, the labor force as a group stands to gain as much as it loses, but the individual "inequities" create new pressures in the shop. It must be realized that the successful labor leader is committed to the removal of these in-group inequities almost as firmly as to the removal of what the group as a whole may feel are group "inequities."

In unorganized shops the situation is not greatly different, although grievances may not lead as rapidly to formal expressions of dissatisfaction.

We may easily see that the typical time study rating procedure, wherein the difficulty of the job under study is first judged in order to obtain a concept of adequate performance against which the second judgment, an appraisal of the observed performance is made, (regardless of the details of the actual procedure), may permit considerable error. This error may at times exceed the maximum amount permissible in the measurement if the measurement is to satisfy fully the requirements of most of the uses to which it may be put.

Error arises, it would appear, from two sources:

1. The inherent difficulty of embodying the base concept of standard performance in objective form, since it is different for each job.

2. The difficulty of making consistent appraisals with a multiplicity of mental standards of reference.

[58] W. Gomberg, *A Trade Union Analysis of Time Study*, 2nd Ed. Englewood Cliffs, N.J.: Prentice-Hall, Inc., 1955, p. 36.

The difficulty of obtaining similar results from different analysts in such a situation should be apparent, as well as the practical difficulties in obtaining uniformity of concepts and appraisals and, hence, full cooperation, among those who may be involved in an actual time study (that is, the time study man, the supervisors, the workers, and the union representatives). However, such procedures are in wide use, and in many cases appear to function satisfactorily. It should be understood that if management is to control, some attempt must be made to perform the function of work measurement.

Further, no matter which rating procedure is used, some attempt should be made to evaluate periodically the accuracy or quality of the ratings made by the time study group.

The discussion which follows has a two-fold purpose: first to describe a practical method for periodically evaluating the quality of the ratings made by a group of time study men and, second, to demonstrate the results of the "game" referred to earlier in the body of the chapter.

The data were obtained from ten time study men within a single plant. The working group had been complaining that the standards were inconsistent.[59] As a first step, 50 time studies were taken at random from the files. Of these 50 studies, 48 had ratings ranging between 95 to 105, with 100 = normal. The other two studies had ratings of 88 and 110, respectively. Management was aware that its time study group avoided studying performances which would be rated under 80 or over 120,[60] but wondered whether shop performances were actually as stable as this sample of studies indicated. Consequently, they had a 16-mm film constructed, showing ten paces of performing an actual job. The method used for all paces was identical. These paces were arranged in random order for presentation to the time study group. To make certain that the films were projected at the same speed at which they were taken, and thus keep random variations from being introduced by changes in projector speed, the projector shown in Figure 18.19 was equipped with a stroboscopic disc illuminated by a small neon lamp. The ratings were entered on forms by the ten men. One such form with the data for one man is shown in Figure 18.20.

The ratings for the ten men were collected and tabulated on the form shown in Figure 18.21. The sum and then the average of the ratings were computed for each film. Then an arbitrary set of ratings (column A) was entered on the sheet. This arbitrary set was computed from the film frame count per cycle for the ten films, each of which showed a different pace.

The first pace (or film) was arbitrarily assigned a rating of 100. The prod-

---

[59] It is worth noting that they called management's attention to standards which were tight, that is to say, did not allow enough time. They said nothing about standards that were loose.

[60] This is not an uncommon practice, but it still requires the time study man to identify performances outside of these limits so that he may avoid them.

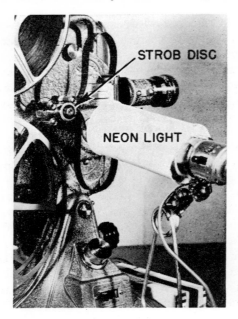

STROB DISC

NEON LIGHT

Fig. 18.19—Stroboscopic disc on projector illuminated by small neon light to permit exact control of speed of projection.

uct of the time per cycle at this pace, and a rating of 100, was computed. The ratings for the other paces were then assigned such that the cycle time for each pace multiplied by the assigned rating equaled the product obtained with the first film. These calculations produced a set of ratings correctly proportioned to the differences in paces but not representing any particular concept of standard. Hence, this series of ratings had subsequently to be multiplied by some constant, K, so that it would reflect the concept of normal held by the group.

This constant, K, was defined as the constant such that if the $\bar{X}$ values of ratings (group averages) were plotted against the KA values, the sum of the squares of the deviations about a 45° line would be at a minimum. Thus, the KA values would provide an ideal abscissa for graphic analysis of the ratings on forms such as Figure 18.20. Also, the KA values would represent a series of ratings, in correct proportion to the relative speeds of performance on the various films but representing the concept of normal held by the group. We might call the KA values, "the best approximation of the correct ratings."

The derivation of this K is as follows:

With 10 points, such as shown in Figure 18.22, the sum of the squares of the deviations, Σd^2, is

$$\Sigma d^2 = d_1{}^2 + d_2{}^2 \cdots d_{10}{}^2$$

or

$$\Sigma d^2 = (\bar{X}_1 - KA_1)^2 + (\bar{X}_2 - KA_2)^2 \cdots (\bar{X}_{10} - KA_{10})^2$$

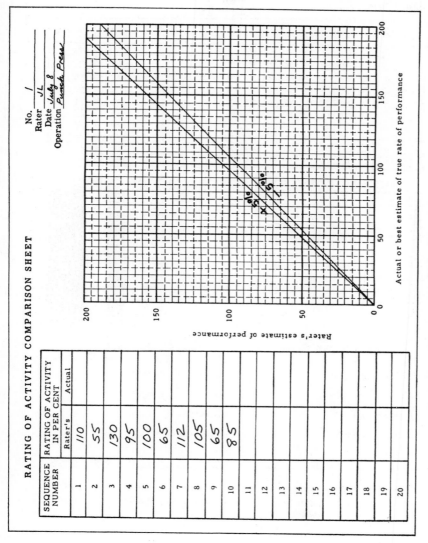

RATING OF ACTIVITY COMPARISON SHEET

No. _1_
Rater _JL_
Date _July 8_
Operation _Punch Press_

SEQUENCE NUMBER	RATING OF ACTIVITY IN PER CENT	
	Rater's	Actual
1	110	
2	55	
3	130	
4	95	
5	100	
6	65	
7	112	
8	105	
9	65	
10	85	
11		
12		
13		
14		
15		
16		
17		
18		
19		
20		

Rater's estimate of performance

Actual or best estimate of true rate of performance

Fig. 18.20 — Individual rating sheet with ratings of ten films.

377

RATING ANALYSIS CALCULATION

Organization ——— Co.
Operation PUNCH PRESS
Notes REGULAR TIME STUDY GROUP
Date JULY 19

$K = \frac{\Sigma \bar{X} A}{\Sigma A^2} = \text{———} =$

RATINGS

Film	JL	PG	MB	LM	KK	AD	AG	SM	PK	SS						Sum	$\bar{X}$	A	KA
1	110	105	110	121	115	100	105	110	115	115						1106	111	100	
2	55	50	60	70	80	50	70	40	80	60						615	62	37	
3	130	125	115	126	130	130	115	125	110	120						1226	123	109	
4	95	90	70	94	90	80	90	105	100	85						899	90	63	
5	100	100	90	107	100	105	95	105	95	95						992	99	74	
6	65	50	45	64	75	60	60	45	75	80						619	62	33	
7	112	115	105	121	97	120	105	120	114	115						1124	112	89	
8	105	105	100	114	96	105	100	115	102	100						1042	104	78	
9	65	80	65	64	83	75	85	55	85	95						752	75	43	
10	85	85	70	90	80	85	90	80	83	95						843	84	48	

RATINGS CONVERTED TO PER CENT OF CORRECT

																			R
1																			
2																			
3																			
4																			
5																			
6																			
7																			
8																			
9																			
10																			
$\bar{X}$																	$=\bar{\bar{X}}f$	$\bar{R}f=$	
R																$=\bar{R}m$			

ANALYSIS BY MEN

$\bar{R}m =$ $\bar{\bar{X}}m =$

$UCL\bar{X}_m = \bar{\bar{X}}_m + A_2\bar{R}m =$

$LCL\bar{X}m = \bar{\bar{X}}m - A_2\bar{R}m =$

$UCLRm = D_4\bar{R}m =$

$LCLRm = D_3\bar{R}m =$

ANALYSIS BY PACE

$\bar{R}f =$ $\bar{\bar{X}}f =$ $SD = \frac{\bar{R}f}{d_2} = \text{———} =$

$UCL\bar{X}_f = \bar{\bar{X}}_f + A_2\bar{R}f =$

$LCL\bar{X}f = \bar{\bar{X}}f - A_2\bar{R}f =$

$UCLRf = D_4\bar{R}f =$

$LCLRf = D_3\bar{R}f =$

M. E. Mundel 570115-5

Fig. 18.21—Ratings for ten men entered on analysis sheet with sums and averages computed and "arbitrary" ratings added.

and

$$\Sigma d^2 = \bar{X}_1{}^2 - 2\bar{X}_1KA_1 + K^2A_1{}^2 + \bar{X}_2{}^2 - 2\bar{X}_2KA_2 + K^2A_2{}^2 \cdots + \bar{X}_{10}{}^2 - 2\bar{X}_{10}KA_{10} + K^2A_{10}{}^2$$

and setting the first derivative with respect to K equal to 0,

$$0 = -2\bar{X}_1A_1 + 2KA_1{}^2 - 2\bar{X}_2A_2 + 2KA_2{}^2 \cdots -2\bar{X}_{10}A_{10} + 2KA_{10}{}^2$$

and solving for K,

$$K = \frac{\bar{X}_1 A_1 + \bar{X}_2 A_2 \cdots \bar{X}_{10} A_{10}}{A_1{}^2 + A_2{}^2 \cdots A_{10}{}^2}$$

or we may write

$$K = \frac{\Sigma \bar{X} A}{\Sigma A^2} \tag{A}$$

Equation (A) appears at the top of the sheet in Figure 18.21. The value of K is shown in the upper right-hand corner of Figure 18.23, and this K was used to compute the KA column shown in Figure 18.23. This column represents a set of ratings, properly proportioned to the true differences between the paces and such as to reflect the concept of normal held by the group.

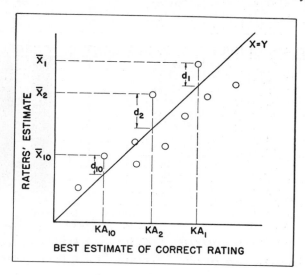

Fig. 18.22—*Plot of hypothetical ratings showing deviations used to derive K.*

It is worth noting that if the A values had been the KA values from another group of time study men, K would indicate the relationship between the two concepts of normal. Further, if the A column had been the KA values from an earlier set of ratings by the same group whose ratings are on the sheet, the K value would critique the stability of the concept of normal (provided, of course, enough time had elapsed so that the correct ratings were forgotten). Films with known values which can be used as a real basis of comparison are available from a variety of sources.

As the next step in the analysis, the ratings made by each man, at each pace, and the group average for each film, were converted to "per cent of correct

RATING ANALYSIS CALCULATION

Organization _____ Co.
Operation _PUNCH PRESS_
Notes _REGULAR TIME STUDY GROUP_
Date _JULY 19_

$$K = \frac{\Sigma \bar{X}A}{\Sigma A^2} = \frac{67180}{51942} = 1.29$$

RATINGS

MEN

Film	JL	PG	MB	LM	KK	AD	AG	SM	PK	SS	Sum	$\bar{X}$	A	KA
1	110	105	110	121	115	100	105	110	115	115	1106	111	100	129
2	55	50	60	70	80	50	70	40	80	60	615	62	37	48
3	130	125	115	126	130	130	115	125	110	120	1226	123	109	141
4	95	90	70	94	90	80	90	105	100	85	899	90	63	82
5	100	100	90	107	100	105	95	105	95	95	992	99	74	96
6	65	50	45	64	75	60	60	45	75	80	619	62	33	43
7	112	115	105	121	97	120	105	120	114	115	1124	112	89	115
8	105	105	100	114	96	105	100	115	102	100	1042	104	78	101
9	65	80	65	64	83	75	85	55	85	95	752	75	43	55
10	85	85	70	90	80	85	90	80	83	95	843	84	48	62

RATINGS CONVERTED TO PER CENT OF CORRECT | R

Film	JL	PG	MB	LM	KK	AD	AG	SM	PK	SS		R
1	85	81	85	94	89	77	81	85	89	89	(86)	17
2	115	104	125	146	167	104	146	83	167	125	(127)	(84)
3	92	89	82	89	92	92	82	89	78	85	(87)	14
4	116	110	85	115	110	98	110	128	122	104	110	43
5	104	104	94	111	104	109	99	109	99	99	103	17
6	151	117	105	149	175	140	140	105	175	186	(144)	(81)
7	97	100	91	105	84	104	91	104	99	100	97	21
8	104	104	99	113	95	104	99	114	101	99	103	19
9	118	145	118	116	151	136	154	100	154	173	(136)	(73)
10	137	137	113	145	129	137	145	129	134	153	(135)	40
$\bar{X}$	112	109	100	118	(120)	110	115	105	(122)	(121)	113 =$\bar{X}$f	Rf= 41
R	52	64	43	60	86	63	73	45	(97)	(103)	69 =$\bar{R}$m	

ANALYSIS BY MEN

$\bar{R}m = 69$ $\bar{\bar{X}}m = 113$

$UCL\,\bar{X}m = \bar{X}m + A_2\bar{R}m = 113 + .308 \times 69 = 134$

$LCL\,\bar{X}m = \bar{X}m - A_2\bar{R}m = 113 - .308 \times 69 = 92$

$UCLRm = D_4\bar{R}m = 1.777 \times 69 = 122$

$LCLRm = D_3\bar{R}m = .223 \times 69 = 15$

ANALYSIS BY PACE

$\bar{R}f = 41$ $\bar{\bar{X}}f = 113$ $SD = \dfrac{Rf}{d_2} = \dfrac{41}{3.078} = 13.3$

$UCL\,\bar{X}f = \bar{X}f + A_2\bar{R}f = 113 + .308 \times 41 = 126$

$LCL\,\bar{X}f = \bar{X}f - A_2\bar{R}f = 113 - .308 \times 41 = 100$

$UCLRf = D_4\bar{R}f = 1.777 \times 41 = 72$

$LCLRf = D_3\bar{R}f = .223 \times 41 = 9$

M. E. Mundel 570115-5

Fig. 18.23 — Rating analysis sheet, of Figure 18.21, completed.

(KA) rating" so as to obtain a common statistic and these are shown in the bottom table of Figure 18.23. These values were treated by standard statistical quality control techniques as shown at the bottom of Figure 21.5.[61] In this analysis UCL represents "upper control limit" and LCL represents "lower

[61] The constants A_2, d_2, D_4, D_3, are a function of sample size and may be found in any book on statistical quality control. In the case given here, the sample sizes by men and by films were the same size. This is not a necessity in making this analysis.

control limit." These are the maximum and minimum values reasonably expectable by chance alone,[62] considering the variability of the data. Values outside of these limits suggest the existence of some assignable cause other than chance. Hence, a slow pace, rated higher on the average than the *UCL* for averages, suggests that the slow pace affected the rating error, and so forth.

The subscripts in the formulas are m for men and f for film; $\bar{x}$ for control limits of averages and R for control limits for ranges, hence:

$UCL_{\bar{x}m}$ = upper control limit for men's averages.
$LCL_{\bar{x}m}$ = lower control limit for men's averages.
UCL_{Rm} = upper control limit for men's ranges.
LCL_{Rm} = lower control limit for men's ranges.
$UCL_{\bar{x}f}$ = upper control limit for group's average on a film.
$LCL_{\bar{x}f}$ = lower control limit for group's average on a film.
UCL_{Rf} = upper control limit for group's range on a film.
LCL_{Rf} = lower control limit for group's range on a film.
SD = standard deviation or limits such that:

$\bar{X} \pm SD$ probably includes 68 per cent of all expectable ratings.
$\bar{X} \pm 2SD$ probably includes 95 per cent of all expectable ratings.
$\bar{X} \pm 3SD$ probably includes 99.7 per cent of all expectable ratings.

"Out of control" and "probably out of control" values are marked with solid and broken circles, respectively. Examination of these out of control points in Figure 18.23 will reveal the following:

1. Different paces received a rating varying from the correct value by more than was ascribable to chance alone.
2. Slow paces resulted in loose standards.
3. Fast paces resulted in tight standards.
4. The time study men tended to see all performances as too much alike.
5. Paces below 80 would frequently have been accepted but misrated.
6. Paces above 120 would frequently have been accepted but misrated.
7. The time study men agree with each other better than they agree with the facts.
8. The time study men vary in their concept of normal.
9. There is reason to suspect that some time study men are more variable than others.

The individual rating form shown partially filled out in Figure 18.20 is shown completed in Figure 18.24. The 80 and 120 per cent rating points have been marked on the ordinate to highlight the ranges of actual paces

---

[62] The control limits are such that they should include approximately 99.7 per cent of all chance values.

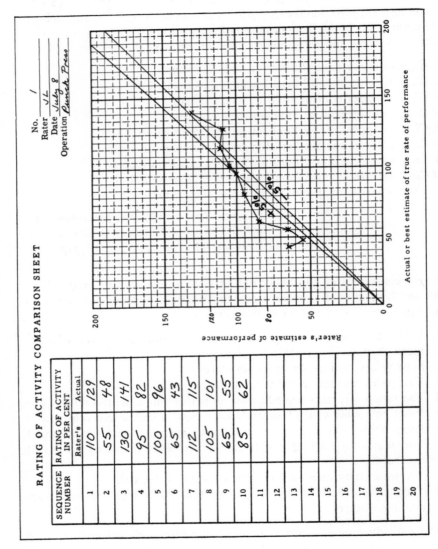

RATING OF ACTIVITY COMPARISON SHEET

No. _1_
Rater _JL_
Date _July 8_
Operation _Punch Press_

SEQUENCE NUMBER	RATING OF ACTIVITY IN PER CENT	
	Rater's	Actual
1	110	129
2	55	48
3	130	141
4	95	82
5	100	96
6	65	43
7	112	115
8	105	101
9	65	55
10	85	62
11		
12		
13		
14		
15		
16		
17		
18		
19		
20		

Rater's estimate of performance

Actual or best estimate of true rate of performance

Fig. 18.24 — Individual rating sheet with KA values and plot of ratings.

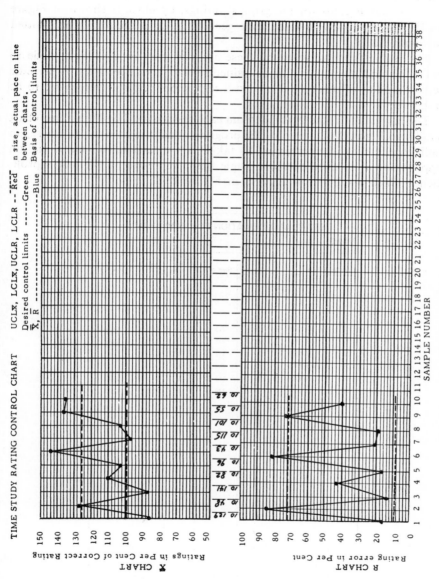

Fig. 18.25—Group $\bar{X}$ and R Charts of ratings, from Figure 18.23.

383

accepted as being within these limits. The time study man was still "playing the game" but the paces on the films did not obey the "rules."

An $\bar{X}$ and R chart for the groups' ratings, by films, is shown in Figure 18.25. The group displays the same general faults as the individual plotted in Figure 18.24.

The rating faults revealed by these analyses may be used as a guide to assist the time study group to be trained to rate more effectively. A periodic testing session of this type is almost a requisite if realistic ratings are to be obtained.

The individual $\bar{X}$ and R values from each session can be plotted on a chart similar to Figure 18.25 to show the progress of each individual. Likewise, an individual SD can be computed by taking a five-session, moving $\bar{R}$ and an appropriate d_2 so as to obtain a single figure representing the man's proficiency. Such a tabulation appears in Figure 18.26.

STANDARD DEVIATION FOR INDIVIDUALS

NAME J. Jones

Film No.	Date	Range	Sum of R's	Number of R's in sum	$\bar{R}$	S.D.
8	16 Dec 1958	36				
9	18 Dec 1958	45				
10	22 Dec 1958	59				
11	29 Dec 1958	40				
12	31 Dec 1958	33	213	5	42.6	13.8
13	5 Jan 1959	35	212	5	42.4	13.6
14	7 Jan 1959	Absent	167	4	41.8	13.6
15	9 Jan 1959	34	142	4	35.5	11.7
16	12 Jan 1959	41	143	4	35.8	11.7
17	14 Jan 1959	28	138	4	34.5	11.4

Fig. 18.26 — *Record of standard deviations of ratings, for an individual, from successive sessions.* (Adapted from U.S. Navy, Bureau of Ships, NAVSHIPS 250–746, supplement).

Many plants maintain data of this type as a means of assisting their time study group.

Allowances for Machine Time

In the body of the chapter it was suggested that the three basic solutions to the problem of machine time allowances were:

1. Make no adjustment.
2. Adjust the standards so that the probable production increment over standard is related to the per cent of manual work in the cycle.
3. Adjust the standard so that the expectable production increment over standard is the same for all jobs.

Before discussing the advantages and disadvantages of each of these three basic types of solutions (and variations thereof) some additional information should be examined.

An experimental investigation[63] of the phenomenon of increased pace on cycles containing rest gave the results shown in Figure 18.27. These data were obtained from work done by college students. They performed a job consisting of jabbing a stylus into four holes at the corners of a four-inch square, moving around and around as rapidly as possible for various predetermined periods, then stopping and resting for predetermined periods, and so forth (to imitate tasks on which the operator worked and then rested while he waited for the machine to perform its part of the cycle). Various predetermined arrangements were tested with a series of work spells. Due to the other obligations of the experimental operators used, the work spells were hardly extensive enough to allow the full effect of the intermittent rests to be evaluated. In other words, the full cumulative effect of the higher per cent operator paced work was not reached. Also, the operators were not sufficiently trained to permit them to utilize the effect of the rest pauses; their skill rather than their physical capacity limited their production at the arrangements that permitted higher paces. The low skill is also suggested by the drop in production during the cycles with a small per cent hand time, which indicates an unreasonably long warm-up period for such a simple task. However, the so-called law of diminishing returns undoubtedly had some effect also. Albeit, these data do verify that there is a pace increase possible when each cycle contains rest, as was originally suggested by shop data given to the laboratory for study.

The data obtained from earning curves at a plant where this factor was not taken into account indicate that the actual paces we may expect are as shown in Figure 18.28.[64]

[63] R. W. Llewellyn, "An Investigation of the Effects of Machine Time on Operator Pace," *M. S. thesis*, Purdue University, 1948.

[64] For obvious reasons this plant requested that its name not be disclosed.

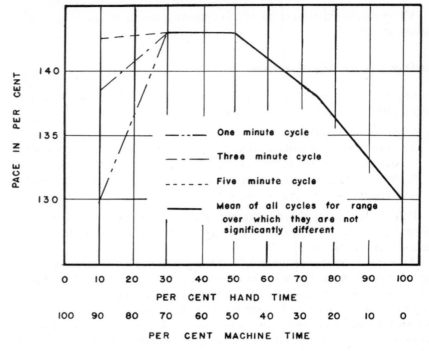

Fig. 18.27—Pace and per cent of cycle that is hand time, using college students. (From Llewellyn, R., op. cit.)

It is to be noted that the intersection of this curve with the ordinate has no real significance and, also, that its actual shape as it approaches the ordinate is in doubt because the so-called law of diminishing returns must certainly take effect some place in this region, particularly with short cycles. However, any error in this range is probably negligible because the portion of the cycle controlled by the operator, which the error would apply to, becomes exceedingly small in this region. Indeed, it would take a 100 per cent error in the curve of pace at 10 per cent hand time to affect the expected cycle performance time by as much as 5 per cent, and it is not anticipated that the errors on the curve even approach such a figure. Below 10 per cent hand time they are of even less consequence. It should also be noted that if the definition of standard is such that the typically expected production increment above standard is defined as other than 30 per cent, the ordinate values of Figure 18.28 will require change so that they express the expectable pace as properly related to the particular numerical designation assigned to the maximum pace typically expectable at 100 per cent hand time. For any ordinate value Y on Figure 18.28, the new Y', with the maximum pace on a 100 per cent hand job identified as X, would be:

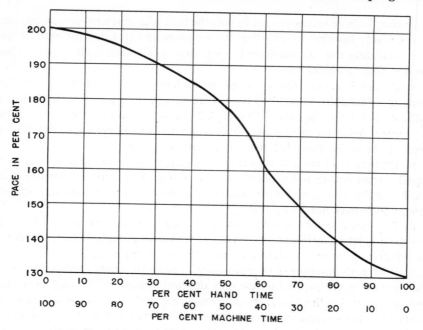

Fig. 18.28—*Pace and per cent of cycle that is hand time, from shop data. Per cent is based on base time.*

$$Y' = Y \frac{X}{130}$$

Now to return to the problem of allowances for machine time; let us examine the alternatives, one by one.

1. *Make no adjustment.* In cases where no incentives are in use, production over standard is seldom expected or realized. The production one can expect from manual, partly manual, and fully machine-controlled tasks is alike for all practical purposes, if no allowance for machine time is made. Such standards will be appropriate for all uses of standard times as given in Chapter 17. This will be true regardless of the amount of internal work, as long as the standard time for internal work does not exceed the machine-controlled time. While the manual or primarily manual job will provide the worker with greater flexibility in the use of his time in that he may voluntarily slow down and later speed up to achieve standard for the day, the machine worker may frequently have considerable rest inherent in his cycle. However, when internal work becomes extensive, such jobs require a continual, steady pace to achieve standard. Such conditions may give rise to some problem jobs in the shop. If such jobs are long running, worker rotation, special wage rates, or special allowances may be introduced.

In shops where incentives are in use, the lack of a machine-time allowance is frequently justified by pointing to incentives as extra pay for extra work and indicating that the machine job just does not permit such activity. This creates four problem areas:

a. Production expectancy varies on different jobs, depending on the amount of machine-controlled time, making scheduling and so forth more difficult. However, the data of Figure 18.28 indicate that this does not become a problem until the machine-controlled portion of the cycle exceeds 45 per cent of the cycle, provided there is no internal work.

b. Earnings will vary, as concerns the incentive, from job to job, even with equal worker ability and application. This may seriously upset the established job hierarchy. It may make the manual jobs more attractive than the machine jobs, which may not be desirable.

c. The machine jobs which, because of high overhead rates, may be well worth stimulating by incentives, may yield such poor potential that the workers do not attempt to earn such incentives. This may produce higher costs.

d. With high amounts of internal work, calling for steady application from the machine operator, real unrest may develop because of the lack of incentive potential. Further, workers may resist methods improvements on such machines. (Improvements to such tasks often involve making a maximum of the work internal.) Workers may also strenuously resist multiple machine assignments which cut into their rest time and do not increase the potential incentive.

2. *Adjust the standards so that the potential incentive increment over standard is related to the per cent of manual work in the cycle.* One common procedure for making such an adjustment is as follows:

$$\text{Allowance} = \frac{\text{rated internal manual time}}{\text{rated external manual time} + \text{machine controlled time}} \times \frac{\text{per cent expected}}{\text{average incentive}}$$

Such an allowance is applied to the whole cycle. It is to be noted that it more or less guarantees the average incentive attainment for the internal work, even if the internal work is done at standard. Such an allowance provides a considerable incentive for multiple machine assignments and increased internal work. It also tends to make the earning potential on machine-controlled operations with considerable internal work more like that of fully manual jobs. On the other hand, with cycles almost fully machine-controlled and with large amounts (but less than the machine cycle) of internal work, it tends to produce incentive pay for work at standard, creating the reverse problem of that listed as the fourth problem area under alternative 1.

It should be noted that the simple allowance calculation just given neglects to take into account the effect of the increased pace possible with the rest periods inherent in the cycle. To examine how this factor may be included let us examine a one-minute cycle as follows:

0.3 min; 30 per cent external manual time (rated and adjusted)
0.7 min; 70 per cent machine-controlled time
0.2 min; 20 per cent internal manual time (rated and adjusted)

If we consider 130 per cent the definition of expectable incentive pace, then Figure 18.28 may be read directly. With the operator working 50 per cent of the cycle, we may expect a pace of 177 per cent for the external manual work, hence a performance time of approximately 0.170 minutes. Now, following the policy of alternative 2, this job should have potential incentive earnings of:

$$\frac{.30 + .20}{1.00} \times 30 \text{ per cent} = 15 \text{ per cent}$$

Actually, taking into account the effect of the rest, the operator can be expected, without allowance for machine time, to perform the task in 0.170 + 0.700 min. = 0.870 min. The incentive increment attained will be (1.000 − .870)/1.000 = 13 per cent. Hence, some additional allowance X will be required to achieve the policy objectives, as follows:

$$\frac{1.00 \left(\frac{100 + X}{100} \right) - .870}{1.00 \left(\frac{100 + X}{100} \right)} = .15$$

and $X = 2.35$ per cent. With this machine time allowance, the incentive earnings will be:

$$\frac{1.0235 - .870}{1.0235} = .15 \text{ or } 15 \text{ per cent}$$

A table computed in such a manner from the data of Figure 18.28 but based on a definition of incentive performance as 120 per cent, is given in Table 15. This is used by the Mirro Aluminum Co. This table has been effective in increasing the equity on machine tasks and increasing the acceptability of multiple machine assignments.

3. *Adjust the standard so that the expectable production increment over standard is the same for all jobs.* While this policy makes the standards alike for scheduling, pricing, and so forth, it tends to produce incentive earnings on machine jobs without incentive effort. However, it maintains, even with incentives, the exact hierarchy of the wage scales from job to job, and may reflect the workers' concept of equity. In such cases, the introduction of multiple machine assignments and additional internal work may be resisted by the working group as "more work without more pay." On the other hand management may feel that they have been leaning over backwards to equalize

TABLE 15

Machine Allowance Chart
Standards Department, Mirro Aluminum Company[1]

Per Cent of Machine Time in Total Cycle	Per Cent of Internal Time in Total Cycle																			
	0-5 (1)	6-10 (2)	11-15 (3)	16-20 (4)	21-25 (5)	26-30 (6)	31-35 (7)	36-40 (8)	41-45 (9)	46-50 (10)	51-55 (11)	56-60 (12)	61-65 (13)	66-70 (14)	71-75 (15)	76-80 (16)	81-85 (17)	86-90 (18)	91-95 (19)	96-100 (20)
96-100	1	2	3	4	5	6	7	8	9	10	11	12	13	14	15	16	17	18	19	20
91-95			.9	1.9	3.0	4.1	5.1	6.2	7.4	8.5	9.7	10.9	12.1	13.2	14.5	15.6	16.8	17.8	19.0	
86-90					1.2	2.3	3.5	4.7	5.9	7.4	8.8	10.1	11.5	13.0	14.2	15.6	16.8	18.0		
81-85						.6	1.9	3.4	5.1	6.8	8.2	9.8	11.1	12.9	14.3	15.7	17.0			
76-80							.9	2.7	4.6	6.3	8.0	9.7	11.4	13.0	14.6	16.0				
71-75							.3	2.3	4.3	6.2	8.2	10.0	11.8	13.5	15.0					
66-70								2.2	4.3	6.4	8.5	10.4	12.3	14.0						
61-65								2.4	4.8	7.0	9.2	11.3	13.0							
56-60							.4	2.9	5.5	7.8	10.0	12.0								
51-55							1.2	3.7	6.5	8.9	11.0									
46-50							2.1	5.0	7.6	10.0										
41-45						.3	3.6	6.4	9.0											
36-40						1.9	5.2	8.0												
31-35					.2	3.8	7.0													
26-30					2.3	6.0														
21-25				.7	5.0															
16-20				4.0																
11-15			3.0																	
6-10		2.0																		
0-5	1.0																			

(Apply Allowances to Total Cycle)

[1] Courtesy J. Ruedebusch, Director of Industrial Relations.

incentive opportunity until such multiple machine assignments or better methods could be devised. Certainly it is a policy whose ultimate effects depend upon the relationship between management and the working group and the understanding of the full implications of subsequent changes. This may be too much to expect from some working groups.

Following this policy, and assuming the percentages of Figure 18.28 to be correct, a suitable allowance may be computed for jobs rated on a basis that did not take this phenomenon into account, so that the possible production expectancy on all jobs will be 130 per cent of standard,[65] as follows:

C = per cent of base time of cycle controlled by the machine, during which the operator rests.

H = per cent of base time of cycle controlled by the operator.

P = possible pace for job as indicated in Fig. 18.28 expressed as a fraction of 100 per cent pace.

A = per cent allowance required to bring production possibility up to 130 per cent of standard.

H/P = actual per cent of original base time of cycle that the hand time will actually take when performed at the pace made possible by the intermittent rest.

Then

$$\frac{C + H + A}{C + H/P} = 1.3$$

and

$$A = 1.3\,(C + H/P) - (C + H)$$

or

$$A = 1.3\,(C + H/P) - 100$$

Hence for 10 per cent machine time we get:

$$A = 1.3\,(10 + 90/1.34) - 100$$
$$A = 1.3\,(77) - 100$$
$$A = 100 - 100 = 0$$

For 65 per cent machine time we get:

$$A = 1.3\,(65 + 35/1.88) - 100$$
$$A = 1.3\,(65 + 18.6) - 100$$
$$A = 109 - 100 = 9 \text{ per cent}$$

An allowance table computed in this fashion is given in Table 16.

There is still another group of tasks that presents a problem requiring further manipulation of these data. Let us assume we have a task of which 60

---

[65] If the definition of standard involves an increment other than 30 per cent, the calculations will change accordingly, and will require first an adjustment of the ordinate in Figure 18.28.

TABLE 16

Machine Time Allowance[1] for 30 Per Cent Production Increment

Per Cent of Cycle Controlled by Machine	Per Cent
100	30
95	27
90	24
85	20
80	17
75	14
70	11
65	9
60	6
55	4
50	3
45 or less	00

[1] For a reference letter use V followed by the per cent of the cycle that is machine controlled, computed on the base times.

per cent is controlled by the machine. However, the operator prepares a load during part of this time and actually works 70 per cent of the cycle. From the table given previously, an operator with a cycle 70 per cent hand time would receive a 0 allowance; the inference is that he could go fast enough during the 70 per cent to exceed the standard by 30 per cent without an allowance. However, in this case, his excess productivity during 40 per cent of the cycle would show up; how fast he went during the remainder of the hand time would be of no value, since in this example the machine controls the production after the 40 per cent for hand time is completed. Consequently, a new allowance A' would have to be computed, as follows:

$$\frac{C + H + A'}{H/P' + C} = 1.30$$

where

A' = allowance with internal work, in per cent
P' = possible pace for all manual work as indicated in Figure 18.28 expressed as a fraction of 100 per cent pace

and

$$A' = 1.30 \, (H/P' + C) - (C + H)$$

and for the job being discussed

$$A' = 1.30\ (40/1.50 + 60) - 100$$
$$= 113 - 100$$
$$= 13 \text{ per cent}$$

Note that this is larger than the allowance which would accompany a job with 60 per cent machine time and no internal work. Other situations may be evaluated in a similar manner.[66]

---

[66] If a different definition of standard is in use, Figure 18.28 must be recalculated before this type of adjustment can be computed.

CHAPTER 19

Predetermined
Time Systems

Predetermined time systems employ first-order work-unit performance time data which have been obtained from a careful analysis of human performances. These data may be resynthesized into a standard time for a job, even when the job is entirely different from those previously studied. The presently available data may not permit this synthesis to be performed with absolute accuracy in terms of a fully consistent concept of standard. However, they produce a reasonable approximation which has considerable utility, if used with discretion.[1] The application of predetermined time data to a task results in a "predetermined time standard." The approach with such data primarily offers the opportunity to estimate the time for the performance of a task before it is performed; it also does away with the need for rating with each individual study. The technique, in its basic form, is primarily applicable to repetitive work. It is an alternative approach to setting standard times for the same type of operations for which direct time study-intensive sampling is

[1] It should be noted that most engineering techniques exhibit similar aspects. Building, bridge, road, and machine design usually employ "factors of safety," inasmuch as in the synthesis of the design, one assumes certain ideal materials or conditions and thus obtains answers somewhat less than accurate. However, if these answers are used intelligently they are of great utility. We have only to look around us to see the results. However, when time standards are used as a basis for cost determination or wage payments the tolerances to which one must work are considerably smaller than in most other design activity. Consequently, one must use even greater discretion with data such as are described in this chapter.

used. Of course, if part of a cycle is controlled by the use of a machine, data other than human performance time data will also be needed to complete the computation of the standard time.

As will be seen in the next chapter, the data from either the application of direct time study-intensive sampling or predetermined time systems may be used to build a higher order of predetermined times. This higher order, when the values are assembled for second-order work-units is called "standard elemental data." However, the data may also be assembled to produce a system of predetermined times for third-order work units. This chapter, however, will cover only the use of first-order work-unit predetermined time system data to obtain second- and third-order work-unit standard times.

As an alternative definition of predetermined time systems, in the terms used in the basic equation, given in Chapter 17, for a standard time:

1. W/C. A count of one is used. The cycle of work is set up before the work, or modeled. It is described in terms of first-order work-units. Some considerable judgment is needed to make certain that all the required motions are included in the model.
2. W/T. The time for each first-order work-unit is obtained from predetermined tables. Whatever the system of data employed, some judgment is necessary in selecting the appropriate time from the tables; the amount of judgment varies from system to system. Machine time is taken from similar tables for machines.
3. M. If the concept of normal implicit in the tables of predetermined times is different from that in use in the plant, a modifier is applied to all values. In the development of this modifier, ratings may be needed. Once this modifier has been determined, no subsequent individual judgments or ratings are needed.
4. A. An allowance is developed and applied in the same manner as with direct time study-intensive sampling.

Using tables of predetermined times one may:

1. Compare the time for alternative, proposed methods in order to permit an examination of the economics of the proposals prior to building the equipment or prior to production runs.
2. Use the time values to construct any of the time-scale, methods analysis charts as part of the previously described methods improvement procedures.[2]
3. Compute, with repetitive work, an estimate of manpower, equipment,

---

[2] See "Predetermined Time Standards," *Factory Management and Maintenance*, Vol. 111, No. 9, September 1953, pp. 134–139. From very early in the use of predetermined time data, the use of such data seems to have encouraged the making of such time charts and methods improvements.

and space requirements prior to production or prior to setting up the facilities.

4. Develop tentative layouts for assembly lines prior to their construction to minimize the amount of subsequent rearrangement and rebalancing.
5. Construct higher order work-unit predetermined time tables.
6. Determine job time standards.

In all of the above uses, the motion study techniques described in previous chapters may appropriately be employed to assist in constructing the method with the predetermined time data providing the time dimensions.

In addition to these uses, the data may provide an independent basis for checking direct time study standards. While there may at times be considerable disagreement between a direct time study standard and a standard based on predetermined times, a study of the differences may serve to increase understanding of the task and assist in determining the correct standard time. Eventually, basic data may serve in the development of standard times for all the uses of such values, as given in Chapter 17. However, as will be indicated later, it is doubtful whether some of the presently available data permit this to be performed within the permissible tolerances for all of the uses. Also, as will be seen, some types of work preclude the use of this approach.

To be applicable to a wide variety of jobs the data must be developed in terms of very small units of work such as therbligs. This introduces a new complication.

The time for a therblig has been shown to be a function of:

a. Distance.
b. Complexity of action.
c. Amount of body involved.
d. Bimanualness involved.
e. Whether the use of the feet accompanies the action.
f. The eye-hand coordination required.
g. The sensory requirements.
h. The weight or resistance involved and the per cent of time involved.
i. The preceding and following therbligs as well as the context and pattern of the task.[3]
j. The direction of the movement
k. The place of the therblig in the motion pattern.

---

[3] M. E. Mundel (with R. M. Barnes), "Studies of Hand Motions and Rhythm in Factory Work," *University of Iowa Studies in Engineering*, Bul. 12, 1938; a study of the time to carry, position, and place short cylinders in holes surrounded by varying degrees bevel showed that not only did the positioning time vary with the bevel, as one might expect, but the transport loaded time also varied despite the fact that the workplace dimensions, and hence the path of transport, remained constant. This and other similar experiments indicated that the time for a therblig is affected by what precedes and follows it and is not a constant.

l. The number of therbligs in the pattern and the length of time the pattern will be performed.[4]

m. The possible interactions of two variables.

n. Several other variables as yet unidentified, inasmuch as even when the effects of variables *a* through *l* are extracted, considerable variation in observed data still exists.

There are many systems of predetermined time data in current use.[5] These systems differ from each other in the following respects:

1. The number of variables from the preceding list which are taken into account.
2. The manner of adjusting for these variables.
3. The assumptions concerning the independence of individual motion times.
4. The level of performance on which the time values are based, viz., normal or incentive performance (as well as the range described in Figure 17.4).
5. The manner of classifying motions, i.e., therbligs (or modifications thereof),[6] groups of therbligs,[7] or body movements.[8]

Each of these systems of data consists of:

1. A system of notation for describing the job being studied.
2. A set of tables of time values organized in a manner determined by the categories of the system of notation used.

[4] This is particularly noticeable in short cycle jobs performed for long periods. For instance, a job may originally consist of four therbligs, *a*, *b*, *c*, and *d*. The original time may be the time for *a*, plus the time for *b*, plus the time for *c*, plus the time for *d*. As the job progresses and the operator develops familiarity with the task, part of *b* may be performed during *a* and part of *d* during *c*, thus reducing the cycle time. After a considerable number of performances, practically all of *b* may be performed during *a* and practically all of *d* during *c*, making the cycle time the time for *a* plus *c*. This phenomenon has not been well studied. Consequently, it is frequently difficult to determine beforehand where, between the two limiting conditions, the expectable method for a job will be.

[5] See H. B. Maynard (Ed.), *Industrial Engineering Handbook.* New York, N.Y.: McGraw-Hill Book Co., 1956, pp. 4–3 through 4–117.

[6] H. B. Maynard, G. J. Stegemerten, and J. L. Schwab, *Methods-Time-Measurement.* New York, N.Y.: McGraw-Hill Book Co., Inc., 1948; also M. E. Mundel and Irwin P. Lazarus, "Predetermined Time Standards in the Ordnance Corps," *The Journal of Industrial Engineering*, Nov. 1954, pp. 13–20 (based on I. P. Lazarus, "A System of Predetermined Human Work Times," *Ph.D. thesis*, Purdue University, 1952; and M. E. Mundel, *Motion and Time Study*, 1st Ed. Englewood Cliffs, N. J.: Prentice-Hall, Inc., 1950).

[7] R. M. Barnes, *Motion and Time Study*, 4th Ed. New York, N.Y.: John Wiley & Sons, 1958, pp. 462–471.

[8] J. H. Quick, J. H. Duncan, and J. A. Malcolm, Jr., "The Work Factor System," in Maynard, *The Industrial Engineering Handbook*, pp. 4–40 through 4–90; also G. B. Bailey and Ralph Presgrave, *Basic Motion Timestudy.* New York, N.Y.: McGraw-Hill Book Co., 1957.

3. A set of rules or conventions for using these tables in a consistent fashion. This aspect commonly amounts to a rather good sized book for each system.

It should be noted that an effective use of any system of these data depends upon a faithful following of the detailed conventions of application. Hence, the short treatment given here of the systems described in full in other original texts, devoted solely to a single system, is intended primarily as an appreciation of these systems rather than a complete treatment. A full study of a data system should be made before applying it.

Representative of the systems which give the time for therbligs and which consider these as essentially independent values, is *methods-time-measurement*.

Methods-time-measurement is a procedure which analyzes any manual operation or method into the basic motions required to perform it and assigns to each motion a predetermined time standard which is determined by the nature of the motion and the conditions under which it is performed.[9]

The classification of motions used in methods-time-measurement (MTM) can be seen from the tables I through X on pp. 399–401. The system of notation used to describe any motion consists of a compound alpha-numeric code consisting of a letter (or letters) to describe the motion group, followed by a number to describe the physical dimension of the motion (if applicable), followed by the "case" designator. For instance *M10A* is a *Move, 10 inches long*, of a type classified as *Case A*; *G4A* is a *Grasp, Case 4A*. The time values in Tables I through X are TMU's where a TMU = 0.00001 hour. These times are normal performance times without any allowance for personal needs, fatigue, or delays.[10] They were developed from motion picture time studies of a large number of operations.

The time values from Tables I through X are used in the same fashion as one uses observed values, to build numerically, rather than graphically, a simochart of an operation. Allowances are added to complete the standard time.

Work Factor,[11] another system, pioneered by J. H. Quick and W. J. Shea, considers motions as affected by the context of the motion sequence in which they lie. Five time values are given for each motion. The time values given in *work factor* (WF) tables are in 0.0001 minutes and are for incentive performance but do not include allowances for delays, fatigue, or personal time. The five values given for each motion consist of a basic value for a

---

[9] By permission from Maynard, Stegemerten, and Schwab, *Methods-Time-Measurement*, p. 12, Copyright 1948, McGraw-Hill Book Company, New York, N.Y.

[10] Maynard, *Industrial Engineering Handbook*, p. 4–17.

[11] "Work Factor" is the service mark (trade-mark) of The Work Factor Company and identifies their services, and their predetermined time system including the values and techniques of use. For a more detailed description see Maynard, *op. cit.*, pp. 4–40 through 4–90.

TABLE I—REACH—R

Distance Moved Inches	Time TMU A	B	C or D	E	Hand In Motion A	B	CASE AND DESCRIPTION
¾ or less	2.0	2.0	2.0	2.0	1.6	1.6	**A** Reach to object in fixed location, or to object in other hand or on which other hand rests.
1	2.5	2.5	3.6	2.4	2.3	2.3	
2	4.0	4.0	5.9	3.8	3.5	2.7	
3	5.3	5.3	7.3	5.3	4.5	3.6	
4	6.1	6.4	8.4	6.8	4.9	4.3	**B** Reach to single object in location which may vary slightly from cycle to cycle.
5	6.5	7.8	9.4	7.4	5.3	5.0	
6	7.0	8.6	10.1	8.0	5.7	5.7	
7	7.4	9.3	10.8	8.7	6.1	6.5	
8	7.9	10.1	11.5	9.3	6.5	7.2	**C** Reach to object jumbled with other objects in a group so that search and select occur.
9	8.3	10.8	12.2	9.9	6.9	7.9	
10	8.7	11.5	12.9	10.5	7.3	8.6	
12	9.6	12.9	14.2	11.8	8.1	10.1	
14	10.5	14.4	15.6	13.0	8.9	11.5	**D** Reach to a very small object or where accurate grasp is required.
16	11.4	15.8	17.0	14.2	9.7	12.9	
18	12.3	17.2	18.4	15.5	10.5	14.4	
20	13.1	18.6	19.8	16.7	11.3	15.8	
22	14.0	20.1	21.2	18.0	12.1	17.3	**E** Reach to indefinite location to get hand in position for body balance or next motion or out of way.
24	14.9	21.5	22.5	19.2	12.9	18.8	
26	15.8	22.9	23.9	20.4	13.7	20.2	
28	16.7	24.4	25.3	21.7	14.5	21.7	
30	17.5	25.8	26.7	22.9	15.3	23.2	

TABLE II—MOVE—M

Distance Moved Inches	Time TMU A	B	C	Hand in Motion B	Wt. Allowance Wt.(lb.) Up to	Factor	Constant TMU	CASE AND DESCRIPTION
¾ or less	2.0	2.0	2.0	1.7	2.5	0	0	
1	2.5	2.9	3.4	2.3				
2	3.6	4.6	5.2	2.9	7.5	1.06	2.2	**A** Move object to other hand or against stop.
3	4.9	5.7	6.7	3.6				
4	6.1	6.9	8.0	4.3	12.5	1.11	3.9	
5	7.3	8.0	9.2	5.0				
6	8.1	8.9	10.3	5.7	17.5	1.17	5.6	
7	8.9	9.7	11.1	6.5				
8	9.7	10.6	11.8	7.2	22.5	1.22	7.4	**B** Move object to approximate or indefinite location.
9	10.5	11.5	12.7	7.9				
10	11.3	12.2	13.5	8.6				
12	12.9	13.4	15.2	10.0	27.5	1.28	9.1	
14	14.4	14.6	16.9	11.4				
16	16.0	15.8	18.7	12.8	32.5	1.33	10.8	
18	17.6	17.0	20.4	14.2				
20	19.2	18.2	22.1	15.6				
22	20.8	19.4	23.8	17.0	37.5	1.39	12.5	
24	22.4	20.6	25.5	18.4				**C** Move object to exact location.
26	24.0	21.8	27.3	19.8	42.5	1.44	14.3	
28	25.5	23.1	29.0	21.2				
30	27.1	24.3	30.7	22.7	47.5	1.50	16.0	

TABLE III—TURN AND APPLY PRESSURE—T AND AP

Weight	Time TMU for Degrees Turned 30°	45°	60°	75°	90°	105°	120°	135°	150°	165°	180°
Small— 0 to 2 Pounds	2.8	3.5	4.1	4.8	5.4	6.1	6.8	7.4	8.1	8.7	9.4
Medium—2.1 to 10 Pounds	4.4	5.5	6.5	7.5	8.5	9.6	10.6	11.6	12.7	13.7	14.8
Large— 10.1 to 35 Pounds	8.4	10.5	12.3	14.4	16.2	18.3	20.4	22.2	24.3	26.1	28.2

APPLY PRESSURE CASE 1—16.2 TMU.   APPLY PRESSURE CASE 2—10.6 TMU

TABLE IV—GRASP—G

Case	Time TMU	DESCRIPTION
1A	2.0	Pick Up Grasp—Small, medium or large object by itself, easily grasped.
1B	3.5	Very small object or object lying close against a flat surface.
1C1	7.3	Interference with grasp on bottom and one side of nearly cylindrical object. Diameter larger than ½".
1C2	8.7	Interference with grasp on bottom and one side of nearly cylindrical object. Diameter ¼" to ½".
1C3	10.8	Interference with grasp on bottom and one side of nearly cylindrical object. Diameter less than ¼".
2	5.6	Regrasp.
3	5.6	Transfer Grasp.
4A	7.3	Object jumbled with other objects so search and select occur. Larger than 1" x 1" x 1".
4B	9.1	Object jumbled with other objects so search and select occur. ¼" x ¼" x ⅛" to 1" x 1" x 1".
4C	12.9	Object jumbled with other objects so search and select occur. Smaller than ¼" x ¼" x ⅛".
5	0	Contact, sliding or hook grasp.

TABLE V—POSITION*—P

CLASS OF FIT		Symmetry	Easy To Handle	Difficult To Handle
1—Loose	No pressure required	S	5.6	11.2
		SS	9.1	14.7
		NS	10.4	16.0
2—Close	Light pressure required	S	16.2	21.8
		SS	19.7	25.3
		NS	21.0	26.6
3—Exact	Heavy pressure required.	S	43.0	48.6
		SS	46.5	52.1
		NS	47.8	53.4

*Distance moved to engage—1" or less.

TABLE VI—RELEASE—RL

Case	Time TMU	DESCRIPTION
1	2.0	Normal release performed by opening fingers as independent motion.
2	0	Contact Release.

TABLE VII—DISENGAGE—D

CLASS OF FIT	Easy to Handle	Difficult to Handle
1—Loose—Very slight effort, blends with subsequent move.	4.0	5.7
2—Close — Normal effort, slight recoil.	7.5	11.8
3—Tight — Considerable effort, hand recoils markedly.	22.9	34.7

TABLE VIII—EYE TRAVEL TIME AND EYE FOCUS—ET AND EF

Eye Travel Time $= 15.2 \times \frac{T}{D}$ TMU, with a maximum value of 20 TMU.

where T = the distance between points from and to which the eye travels.
D = the perpendicular distance from the eye to the line of travel T.

Eye Focus Time = 7.3 TMU.

TABLE IX—BODY, LEG AND FOOT MOTIONS

DESCRIPTION	SYMBOL	DISTANCE	TIME TMU
Foot Motion—Hinged at Ankle.	FM	Up to 4″	8.5
With heavy pressure.	FMP		19.1
Leg or Foreleg Motion.	LM —	Up to 6″	7.1
		Each add'l. inch	1.2
Sidestep—Case 1—Complete when leading leg contacts floor.	SS-C1	Less than 12″	Use REACH or MOVE Time
		12″	17.0
		Each add'l. inch	.6
Case 2—Lagging leg must contact floor before next motion can be made.	SS-C2	12″	34.1
		Each add'l. inch	1.1
Bend, Stoop, or Kneel on One Knee.	B,S,KOK		29.0
Arise.	AB,AS,AKOK		31.9
Kneel on Floor—Both Knees.	KBK		69.4
Arise.	AKBK		76.7
Sit.	SIT		34.7
Stand from Sitting Position.	STD		43.4
Turn Body 45 to 90 degrees—			
Case 1—Complete when leading leg contacts floor.	TBC1		18.6
Case 2—Lagging leg must contact floor before next motion can be made.	TBC2		37.2
Walk.	W-FT.	Per Foot	5.3
Walk.	W-P	Per Pace	15.0

TABLE X—SIMULTANEOUS MOTIONS

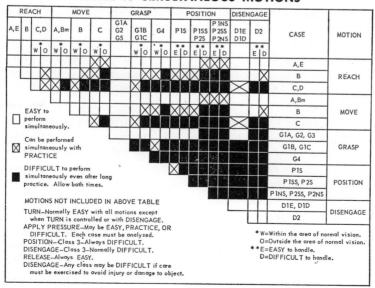

simple mimimal difficulty occurrence of a motion and four additional values for the time for the motion with 1 to 4 *work factors* of difficulty.

A "work factor of difficulty" is the presence of a manual control factor such as directional control (steer), care (precaution), change direction or definite stop. Weights or resistances above a given level are counted as one or more work factors, depending on the motion and the sex of the operator. The steps or levels for weight appear in the *work factor* tables. The *work factors* are considered equal in their effect upon motion times and the entry into the *work factor* tables is made dependent upon only the number of *work factors* present.

Human Performance Times,[12] a system of data developed by Dr. I. Lazarus and the author, is based primarily on therbligs but considers the time value for each motion to be affected by the full nature of the motion complex in which it occurs. The time values are given for therbligs, in 0.00001 minutes, as a function of the physical dimensions of the motions. These time values are subsequently grouped into time study elements and adjusted by means of the difficulty adjustments given in Table C.10 of Appendix C. thus giving an almost infinite number of values for each therblig. These data and their method of use, given in this chapter, take into account, to a degree, variables *a* through *i* of the list on pages 396–397. Variables *j* through *n*, if they enter into the problem being worked on, may still be sources of error. Moreover, errors may also be introduced by improper descriptions of tasks, wrong classifications of therbligs, poor element grouping, wrong uses of the difficulty adjustments, and incorrect allowances. In short, these data do not offer an absolute solution to the problem of work measurement, but if used intelligently they may help to provide a working solution to many problems.

In the development of these data, Dr. Lazarus collected a considerable series of time studies of industrial operations using a motion picture camera to make the complete time study record. All of the operators were experienced industrial operators. All of the dimensions and features of their jobs were recorded at the time the pictures were taken. The motion pictures were taken at 1,000 frames per minute to permit later rating against a multi-image loop (See Appendix C) by a group of experienced raters. The reliability of the samples of times for each therblig was checked using a statistical technique. The rated therblig times were subjected to a careful statistical analysis to determine the factors which affected the required time.

The final data obtained were tested, first by reconstituting the original jobs, and second, by synthesizing a second group of industrial tasks and comparing the standards thus developed against standards set independently by stop-watch time study and objective rating. The differences between the second set of pairs of values were in the order of the usual discrepancies

[12] Referred to in the Second Edition of this book as "Predetermined Approximate Performance Times." The name used here may be abbreviated HPT.

between pairs of independently set direct time studies-intensive sampling.[13]

The statistical analysis of the therblig time data revealed the following facts:[14]

TE and *TL* (*transport empty and transport loaded*)—The time for these therbligs was an exponential continuous function of distance.

G (*grasp*)—The time for grasp was a discrete function of the type of grasp. Four types of grasp were isolated:

1. Contact. Control gained by mere contact.
2. Contact pinch. Control gained by contact with one or more fingers sliding the object into a position so that the thumb could oppose them on the object.
3. Pinch. Control gained by maneuvering the hand so that the thumb and one or more fingers come into opposition on the object.
4. Wrap. Control gained by fingers and palm coming into opposition on the object.

P (*position*)—The time for position was found to be a function of the number of degrees of positioning required. A degree was defined as a restriction in a dimension or orientation which had to be provided by the operator. There are six possible sources of restriction but no more than five were found occurring at one time. The six sources are shown in Figure 19.1.

A (*assemble*)—The time for assemble was found to be a function of the distance of the restricted movement.

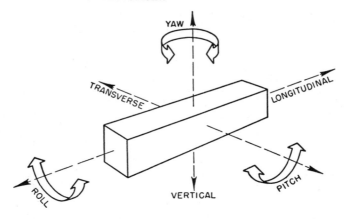

Fig. 19.1—*The six possible sources of restriction of position.* (From Lazarus, op. cit.)

[13] Standard deviation equals about 5 per cent.

[14] It should be noted that the data had been rated *objectively*; the effect of the six factors compensated for by the difficulty adjustments was therefore removed; the statistical analysis referred to above was to find the factors causing the residual differences in time values.

DA and *RL* (*disassemble and release load*)—The time for these therbligs appeared to be constant.

The manner of use of the data presented later involves grouping the therbligs into elements and applying to the elements the difficulty adjustments described in Appendix C. Thus, the method takes into account the variables that have just been listed for each therblig, those covered by the difficulty adjustments, and the effect of the context of the element the therbligs occur in, so as to produce standards fully compatible with standards set by direct time study-intensive sampling with objective rating.

The data developed by Dr. Lazarus were originally rated against an early multi-image loop which is not readily available. This loop was subsequently rated in comparison with the widely circulated bench-mark film shown in Figure C.5, Appendix C. The original values were then multiplied by a constant to convert them to the 100 per cent pace of the loop in Figure C.5, so that any plant could, if necessary, subsequently convert the values of the table to their concept of normal. These data are given in Table 17. The conventions for using these data are given at the bottom of the table.

TABLE 17

Human Performance Times (HPT) in 1/100,000 min. (0.00001 min.)[1]
(basic values subject to difficulty adjustment when assembled into elements)

TRANSPORT LOADED, TRANSPORT EMPTY OR FOR STEPS IN WALKING OR LEG MOVEMENTS

Distance (inches)	Time	Distance (inches)	Time	Distance (inches)	Time	Distance (inches)	Time
1	137	13	495	25	686	37	835
2	194	14	514	26	700	38	846
3	237	15	532	27	714	39	857
4	274	16	549	28	726	40	868
5	307	17	566	29	739	41	879
6	336	18	582	30	752	42	890
7	362	19	598	31	764	43	900
8	388	20	614	32	777	44	910
9	412	21	629	33	789	45	921
10	434	22	644	34	801	46	931
11	455	23	658	35	812	47	941
12	475	24	673	36	823	48	951

[1] Adapted from I. P. Lazarus, "Predetermined Human Performance Time," Ph.D. thesis, Purdue University, 1952, but adjusted to Hog Casing Loop concept of normal.

TABLE 17 (Continued)

GRASP

Condition	Time
Contact	139
Contact-pinch	222
Pinch	286
Wrap	453

POSITION

Condition	Time
1 degree	160
2 degrees	178
3 degrees	249
4 degrees	330
5 degrees	445

DISASSEMBLE

Condition	Time
All	381

RELEASE LOAD

Condition	Time
All	151

NON THERBLIGS

Sit	1560
Arise	1904
Eye Focus	416

ASSEMBLE

Distance (inches)	Time	Distance (inches)	Time	Distance (inches)	Time
$\frac{1}{4}$	0^2	$1\frac{1}{4}$	383	$2\frac{1}{4}$	800
$\frac{3}{8}$	19	$1\frac{3}{8}$	435	$2\frac{3}{8}$	852
$\frac{1}{2}$	71	$1\frac{1}{2}$	487	$2\frac{1}{2}$	904
$\frac{5}{8}$	123	$1\frac{5}{8}$	539	$2\frac{5}{8}$	956
$\frac{3}{4}$	175	$1\frac{3}{4}$	592	$2\frac{3}{4}$	1008
$\frac{7}{8}$	227	$1\frac{7}{8}$	644	$2\frac{7}{8}$	1060
1	279	2	696	3	1113
$1\frac{1}{8}$	331	$2\frac{1}{8}$	748		

[2] $\frac{1}{4}$ inch or less of assemble is contained in position.

Conventions:
1. Measure motion paths as straight line distances between terminal points, following location on body member that actually performs the therblig, *i.e.*, finger tip for pinch grasp.
2. For walking, divide into 27″ movements (steps), and use 27″ *TE* line.
3. For twisting or cranking movements, divide peripheral distance into N motions of radius of motion length and use N times such motions for time value.
4. For a *select and grasp*, approximate by using twice grasp time.
5. Use *RL* time even when letting go after contact grasp.
6. On foot pedals with fulcrum under foot measure distance at ball of foot.
7. For elements that involve overcoming weight or resistance, include the motions to the lever, weight, or piece in the element.
8. Eye focus time occurs (a) when the motion cannot be completed until the eyes have assisted in performing another task which would be concurrent if the eyes were not needed; (b) when the motion cannot be initiated until the eyes have made an observation they were not free to make during the preceding movement.

The procedure for using these data is given in the following case example. (The basic steps are italicized so that the reader may trace their use.)

1. *The actual or contemplated workplace or work area should be measured and a dimensioned sketch prepared. A summary should be prepared of what is accomplished by the operation.*

Figure 19.2 is a plan view of the workplace showing the drill fixture and the piece to be drilled. (The drill and controls have been left out to simplify the illustration.) Figure 19.3 is a drawing of the fixture and part concerned. In the part of the operation treated in this illustration, the operator must *get, place, and lock the piece in the fixture.*

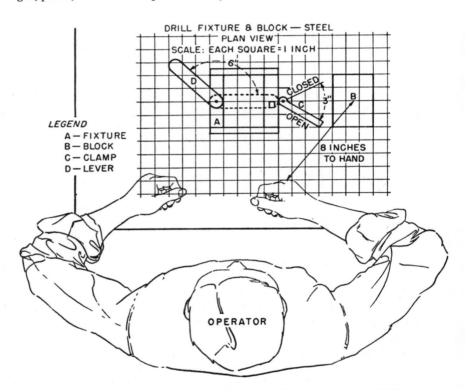

Fig. 19.2—Plan view of workplace of drill press operator. (Drill and controls left out to simplify illustration.)

2. *The elements of the work should be detailed in terms of constituent therbligs.*

A form, such as shown in Figure 19.4 may be used to list the therbligs in groups similar to typical time study elements following the criteria for

DRILL FIXTURE & BLOCK
ISOMETRIC VIEW

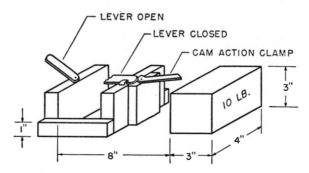

Figure 19.3 — Details of drill fixture and work-piece.

elements given in Chapter 18. The conditions surrounding the performance of each therblig should be evaluated carefully and noted in the proper column in terms of the variables previously given as controlling the time for each therblig. The conventions given at the bottom of Table 17 should be followed closely in establishing these conditions.

From these data, a simo-chart or man and machine chart may be constructed to aid in examining and improving the method. The manner of working with such a chart is the same as when such charts are constructed from observed data.

3. *The individual therblig times, from Table 17, should be entered next to each therblig.*

This has been done in Figure 19.4 in the columns headed Time Value. Unavoidable delays, holds, and so forth take their values from the controlling hand. The control during an element may shift from hand to hand.

4. *The total time for each element should be computed and transferred to a summary sheet.* The recapitulation section of the rear of an objective time study form is an ideal form in that it:

    a. Contains room for all the necessary computations.

    b. Permits assembling the data in the exact same manner as with observed data.

    c. Permits the front of the sheet to become a method record so that method and standard are preserved together as with regular, direct time studies-intensive sampling. In this manner any subsequent processing of these data does not require a separate procedure.

In computing the element time, care should be exercised to add all controlling time values. The total time obtained should be the same as the time represented by the longest column of a simo-chart drawn from the data. Note

MANUAL TIME DATA FOR _SUPPORT BLOCK #23_

OPERATION _DRILL MAIN HOLE_
MACHINE _DELTA 3_
FIXTURE _1622_
NOTES _10# BLOCK_

LAYOUT INFORMATION _SEE SKETCH_

HPT ELEMENT WORK SHEET

Page _1_ of _3_

Elem. No.	LEFT HAND				RIGHT HAND			
	Description	Ther.	Cond	Time	Time	Cond.	Ther.	Description
1	From free position to fixture	TE	8"	388	388	8"	TE	From free position to block
	Fixture	G	P	286	286	P	G	Block
		H	—	—	388	8"	TL	To fixture with block
		RL			445	5°	P	Block to fixture
					279	1"	A	Into bottom of fixture
				OK	151	—	RL	Block in fixture
	TOTAL				1937			
2	From fixture to lever	TE	4"	274	274	4"	TE	From block to clamp
	Lever D	G	C	139	453	W	G	Clamp
	Lever to closed position	TL	6"	336	173	—	(H)	To balance
	Lever	RL	—	151				
	While RH locks clamp	UD	—	—	237	3"	TL	Clamp to lock lever
					151	—	RL	Clamp
	TOTAL				1288			

Note: Only two elements are shown to shorten the illustration.

Fig. 19.4 — First step in use of "Human Performance Times" for determining standard time for "place and lock piece in fixture." (Only two elements are shown.)

in Figure 19.4, element 2, the left hand controls the element time for part of the element.

5. *The elemental times should be processed subsequently, as if they were rated, observed values from direct time studies.*

Difficulty adjustments from Table C.5, and allowances from Table 14, page 366, should be used. This has been done for the two illustrative elements, in Figure 19.5.

12													
13													
14													
15													

RECAPITULATION

ELEMENTS	1	2	3	4	5	6	7	8	9	10
Amount of body	C-2	C-2								
Foot pedals	F-0	F-0								
Bimanualness	H-0	H-0								
Eye-hand coordination	J-2	J-0								
Handling requirements	P-2	0-1								
Weight or resistance	10-11	4-3								
TOTAL TIME IN *MIN*										
NUMBER OF OBS.										
PRO-RATE DIVISOR										
AVERAGE PER CYCLE										
RATING										
RATED TIME	01937	01288								
PER CENT OF CYCLE	—	—								
I + ADJUSTMENTS	1.17	1.06								
BASE TIME	.0227	.0136								
I + ALLOWANCES	1.05	1.05								
ALLOWED TIME	.0238	.0143								

Fig. 19.5 — *Use of recapitulation section of objective time study sheet to complete determination of standard time for elements shown in Figure 19.4.*

It should be noted that this manner of adjusting the therblig values has the same effect as having an infinite number of values in Table 17. The difficulty adjustment allows not only for all sorts of conditions of work, but inasmuch as elements rather than therbligs are adjusted it also compensates for the context in which the therblig occurs.

6. *The method should be described in the usual manner on the front of the time study sheet and the final allowed times transferred to the front so as to complete the standard.*

The net result of this step will produce a sheet exactly like that of Figure 18.18b of page 369.

The standard time is now complete and in the same final form as when obtained with a direct time study-intensive sampling.

Supplemental Material

Predetermined motion time data has been in existence since the 1920's. However, the early developers of these data did not disclose either the method of developing the data or the data itself; it was closely held for proprietary use. The first general disclosure of such data occurred with the publication of *Methods-Time-Measurement*, by H. B. Maynard, G. J. Stegemerten, and J. L. Schwab, (McGraw-Hill, 1948). Subsequently, other sets of data were released. New systems were developed with the aim of overcoming what the authors felt were limitations or defects in existing systems. Some new systems were developed to produce freely available data so as to overcome restrictions placed on some of the data systems by the originators. Some systems were, without doubt, produced to "author a system." The number of such systems has lead some critics to refer to these as ". . . the alphabet soup of predetermined motion time systems; BMT, DMT, ISM, MTA, MTS, RMD, etc."[15] The HPT data presented in this book were developed to provide data which could be used in conjunction with the difficulty adjustments of objective rating. The effects of the factors for which difficulty adjustments are made are inextricably built into all of the other available data tables. Since the release of the HPT data in 1952, the data have been given extensive use in a variety of industrial plants and government installations. When the time study men are familiar with objective rating, these HPT data may be used with a minimum of additional training. Carefully applied, the standards produced appear to have an inherent variability of about the same order of magnitude as direct time study-intensive sampling with objective rating. Occasionally, unpredicted and sizeable discrepancies do occur. See footnote 4, page 397, in the body of the chapter.

Without doubt, the real utility of some of the data systems has been adversely affected by the unfortunately extravagant claims made by some of the early proponents of such data; claims with respect to both the accuracy and applicability of such data. The claims with respect to accuracy later became obviously extravagant when revisions and changes to the original data tables were published. Such changes would hardly have been needed had the original data possessed the properties claimed for them. Further, most of the systems do not produce fully compatible standards. Some of the difference can be correctly attributed to the different concept of normal built into the different tables; other discrepancies are difficult to explain unless one accepts the conclusion that they cannot be as accurate as many of them claim to be.

Some of the claims for accuracy have been accompanied by the attitude

---

[15] B. Gottlieb, "A Critical Analysis of Predetermined Motion Time Systems," *Proceedings, Sixteenth Annual Conference and Convention*, American Institute of Industrial Engineers, 1965, pp. 75–84.

that with such accuracy no labor group has any grounds for or right to object to the results obtained with such data. It is extremely doubtful whether any group of organized labor would accept such a view. The right to "grieve" over a particular time standard is a right commonly sought and held by such groups; a view to which this author is sympathetic. Further, it seems possible to hold such views without being partisan; the data associated with any of the time study or work measurement procedures, including predetermined time systems, is such that it seems relatively impossible to logically defend any other point of view.

The argument over these data, begun with their introduction, continues, and will probably continue. For those who wish to follow the argument in detail, the following reading list is suggested as representative:

Gerald B. Bailey, "Comments on 'An Experimental Evaluation of the Validity of Predetermined Elemental Time Systems'," *The Journal of Industrial Engineering*, Vol. XII, No. 5, September–October 1961.

Thomas R. Gockel, International Harvester Tested Formula—IHTF—Predetermined Time System at International Harvester Company, *Proceedings, Sixteenth Annual Conference and Convention*, American Institute of Industrial Engineers, 1965.

Bertram Gottlieb, "A Critical Analysis of Predetermined Motion Time Systems," *Proceedings, Sixteenth Annual Conference and Convention*, American Institute of Industrial Engineers, 1965. (Essentially the same talk was presented at the 32nd Annual Management Clinic of the Industrial Management Society, Chicago, 1968.)

John M. Honeycutt, Jr., "Comments on 'An Experimental Evaluation of the Validity of Predetermined Elemental Time Systems'," *The Journal of Industrial Engineering*, Vol. XIII, No. 3, May–June 1962.

Clifford Sellie, "Time Standards and Union Attitudes; The Positive Side of the Debate on Predetermined Times," *Proceedings, Sixteenth Annual Conference and Convention*, American Institute of Industrial Engineers, 1965.

J. B. Taggart, "Comments on 'An Experimental Evaluation of the Validity of Predetermined Elemental Time Systems'," *The Journal of Industrial Engineering*, Vol. XII, No. 6, November–December 1961.

J. Varkevisser, "The Relation Between Motion Patterns on Performance Time of Therbligs," *Journal of Methods-Time Measurement*, Vol. V, No. 6, March–April 1958.

CHAPTER 20

Standard Data Systems

Standard data systems is a term used to refer to predetermined time systems when the data is accumulated at the second-order work-unit level (or higher level), as compared with the first-order work-unit data more commonly associated with the term, predetermined time systems. *Standard data* (as the accumulated information is commonly called) may be accumulated at the second-, third- or fourth-order work-unit level. When the standard data is accumulated at the second-order work-unit level, it is often called *standard elemental data*; data associated with third- or fourth-order work-unit information is usually called *standard data*. The term, *universal standard data*, is sometimes employed when referring to data relating to third- or fourth-order work-unit times. This seems somewhat grandiose. In the remainder of this chapter the term *standard data* will be used to refer to all predetermined time data associated with second-order or higher order work-unit time systems. The term *standard elemental data* will be used to refer to data limited to second-order work-unit time values.

The data employed in standard data systems may be obtained from direct time study-intensive sampling, predetermined time systems, or any other applicable work measurement approach. Standard data systems, as one might expect, facilitate the setting of standard times prior to the inception of work. The standard time for a task, instead of requiring direct observation of the work, may be built up, or synthesized, from the existing data. In that second-order (or higher order) work-units are much larger than first-order work-units, the work of synthesizing a standard time with such data is less laborious and less time-consuming than with first-order work-unit predeter-

412

mined time systems. The synthesis, in most cases, is also easier than the making of a direct time study-intensive sampling; this cannot usually be said about the use of first-order work-unit data approaches. As with any standard time values, the standard data must be accompanied by an adequate written standard practice and understood as representing the time expected to be taken with some specified definition of standard time.

Standard data, in terms of the four factors associated with the equation describing a standard time, employs:

1. W/C. A count of one is used; one occurrence of the work-unit for which a time is being set is *modeled* or synthesized.
2. W/T. Taken from tables; the data reflects the characteristics of the procedures employed in developing such data.
3. M. Implicit in the data tables; a rating is not required (except perhaps to develop the tabulated data).
4. A. Applied to standard elemental data in the same manner as with direct time study—intensive sampling. In data tables for work-units larger than second-order, the incremental time for A may be included in the tabulated values.

Synthesized time standards from standard data do not completely replace other work measurement techniques, since they are usually developed from a systematic accumulation of data obtained by the use of other techniques. They do, however, reduce the number of individual studies that must be made, while at the same time increasing the consistency with which the values represent a fixed concept of standard. The final accuracy of time standards set from standard data, however, is still a function of the accuracy of the compiled data, although their consistency may be (and generally is) better inasmuch as random errors tend to be eliminated. Synthesized standard times from elemental data may be of sufficient accuracy to allow the determination of incentive rates prior to the inception of production.

Synthesized standards from standard data have four general advantages over individual time studies:

1. They are usually based on more data than an individual time standard and thus have more reliability provided the errors in the supporting data were random rather than biased.
2. They often eliminate the need for a great many studies. However, they involve considerable work and, where only a few jobs are involved, single studies are often simpler, unless the added consistency is worth the added effort.
3. They aid in estimating rates of production for price quotations on new products and in setting schedules.

4. They aid in setting up assembly or progressive work lines with a minimum of original unbalance.

Standard Elemental Data

To develop standard elemental data, it is necessary to have a series of time standards for a series of similar jobs. The time standards may be developed by direct time study-intensive sampling (Chapter 18), predetermined time systems (Chapter 19), or by means of one of the techniques discussed in chapters following this one. The time standards used to construct standard elemental data must have the following seven characteristics:

1. Adequate written standard practice with well-defined element end points.
2. Broken down into similar elements.
3. Similar methods used.
4. Similar equipment used.
5. Well chosen elements (see criteria given in Chapter 18, pages 319–321).
6. Rated to a uniform rate of activity.
7. Comparable allowances used.

In developing elemental data for a group of jobs, the following types of elements may be encountered:

1. Constant elements, identical from job to job.
2. Variable elements, similar in motion pattern from job to job but varying in difficulty (and in time required to perform) with the size, shape, and so forth, of the work. These may involve handwork or work with a machine if the machine work is operator paced.
3. Machine elements, mechanically controlled by the feed, speed, length of cut, and so forth, or welding current, thickness of material, and so forth.

These three types of elements may exhibit any of the following three characteristics of occurrence:

a. Repeated the same number of times in each job.
b. Repeated a different number of times in each job.
c. Appear in some jobs and not in others.

The building of data is not dependent upon any one method of obtaining time values. However, in some jobs, in order to meet the criteria for well chosen elements, it is frequently necessary to use rather short elements and both the time study machine, the memomotion procedure for direct time study-intensive sampling, or predetermined time systems, lend themselves to this more readily than do stop-watches. The full memomotion procedure and predetermined time systems also permit changing the elements if this is later found desirable. With any other procedure the data would then have to be regathered, which would be both time-consuming and expensive.

The development of standard elemental data requires an analysis of the available data in order to determine the variables or factors that must be taken into account when applying the data subsequently to other work. The general procedure may be summarized as consisting of the following seven steps:

1. Obtain time standards for as wide a range of jobs as possible within a given group of similar jobs.
2. Summarize the data on a spread sheet. The typical spread sheet contains columns for each element as well as columns for the values associated with the possible variables; the lines are for individual time standards. The elemental data and the data concerning the variables are "spread" across the line.
3. Be sure the data meet the criteria for such data, given earlier in this chapter.
4. Ascertain which elements are constant and which are variable.
5. For the constant elements, determine the average standard time.
6. For the variable elements:
   a. Determine, on a logical basis, which job characteristic or characteristics they are a function of.
   b. Plot, on a graph, the time for the element against the variable or variables. (*Note:* The variables may act in simple combination or they may interact.)
   c. Fit a smooth curve or curves to the points plotted. (Various mathematical techniques may be used to check the validity of the relationship shown, or to assist in fitting a smooth curve.)
   d. If the variable is discrete, that is, has only definite steps between the two limits, prepare a table for the range of jobs covered. If the variable is continuous, that is, has an infinite number of possible values between two limits, prepare a graph. The graph may be converted later to a table by grouping values within limits suitable for the purpose for which the standards are going to be used.
7. Prepare a form to facilitate the use of the standard elemental data for developing standard times on new tasks.

The application of the above procedure will be explained with data from a relatively simple case. Data from other more complex cases and related materials appear in the supplemental material appended at the end of the chapter.

ASSEMBLY OF RADIO-TUBE MOUNTS (THE STEPS
OF THE GENERAL PROCEDURE FOR DEVELOPING
ELEMENTAL TIMES ARE ITALICIZED SO THAT THE
READER MAY TRACE THEIR USE.)

1. *Obtain the time studies for as wide a range of jobs as possible, within a given group of similar jobs.*

Figure 20.1 is the face of the completed time study for one operation in the assembly of a radio-tube mount,[1] of which an exploded and assembly view is shown in Figure 20.2. This was one of a large group of time studies taken on assembly operations of radio-tube mounts.

2. *Be sure the time studies meet the criteria previously given.*

Additional studies similar to the one shown in Figure 20.1, for the other operations on this mount and the other tube types, were gathered. The studies were checked on the basis of the criteria listed as necessary attributes of time studies used in the preparation of standard elemental data. (In many cases, previously taken studies may fail to meet these requirements and have to be retaken.) It is worth noting that looking ahead to standard data may well influence the selection of elements.

3. *Summarize the data on a spread sheet.*

In the example being used to illustrate the steps given, the data were transferred to a form such as the one shown in Figure 20.3. Only a section of the summary is shown, since it would normally be quite lengthy, and a complete display of it would add only bulk to this first case. Note that the columns represent the elements and the variables; the lines represent the different tubes.

4. *Ascertain which elements are constant and which are variable.*

For instance, a study of the column for the element *assemble and weld getter* together with the method information from the time studies, and design information from the tube drawings, indicated that:

a. The same getter was used in all the tubes.
b. The time value did not vary greatly from tube type to tube type.
c. The method was identical in all cases.
d. The design of the tubes was such that practically no difference was involved from tube to tube in the element *assemble and weld getter.*

Hence this element is probably constant, and the variation from study to study is attributable to time study error (probably in rating).

In contrast, a study of the column *assemble top mica* showed that the time varied greatly from tube type to tube type. The tube details indicated that the number of holes in the top mica also varied from tube type to tube type.

---

[1] This is the inner works of the tube mounted on a glass base before enclosure in the glass envelope.

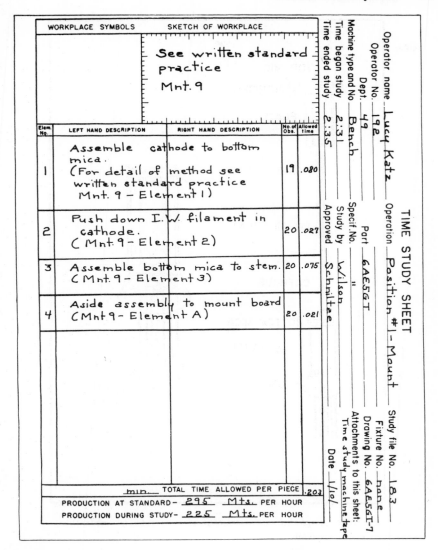

WORKPLACE SYMBOLS	SKETCH OF WORKPLACE			
	See written standard practice Mnt. 9			

Elem. No.	LEFT HAND DESCRIPTION	RIGHT HAND DESCRIPTION	No. of Obs.	Allowed time
1	Assemble cathode to bottom mica. (For detail of method see written standard practice Mnt. 9 – Element 1)		19	.080
2	Push down I.W. filament in cathode. (Mnt. 9 – Element 2)		20	.027
3	Assemble bottom mica to stem. (Mnt. 9 – Element 3)		20	.075
4	Aside assembly to mount board (Mnt 9 – Element A)		20	.021

min. TOTAL TIME ALLOWED PER PIECE .203

PRODUCTION AT STANDARD– 295 Mts. PER HOUR

PRODUCTION DURING STUDY– 225 Mts. PER HOUR

Operator name Lucy Katz

Operator No. 192

Dept. 49

Machine type and No. Bench

Time began study 2:31

Time ended study 2:35

Specif. No.

Study by Wilson

Approved Schnitzer

Part 6AE5GT

Operation Position #1 – Mount

TIME STUDY SHEET

Study file No. 183

Fixture No. none

Drawing No. 6AE5GT-7

Attachments to this sheet:

Time study machine tape

Date 1/10/

Fig. 20.1 — Front of time study sheet for first position in assembly line for 6AE5GT radio tube.

(The top mica is fitted over parts fitting into these holes.) Hence it is reasonable to assume that the time for *assemble top mica* is a variable.

All the elements were scrutinized and classified in a similar manner.

5. *For the constant elements, determine the average standard time.*

For the element *assemble and weld getter*, the average time for the few types shown on the partial summary sheet in Figure 20.3 is 0.0854 minute.

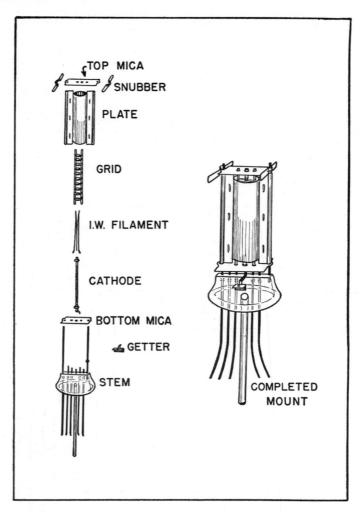

Fig. 20.2—Exploded and assembled view of 6AE5GT radio-tube mount.

(Of course, this average, in actual practice, was computed on the basis of all types shown on the whole summary sheet and not on just part of the sheet as shown in the illustration.) Instead of 15 readings or so and one rating, as with a single study, the average standard time for *assemble and weld getter* would, when computed in this new fashion, represent as many times this number of both readings and ratings as there are time studies. It should be much more reliable. At least the time standards for jobs for which this average value is used will be much more consistent in respect to ease or difficulty of

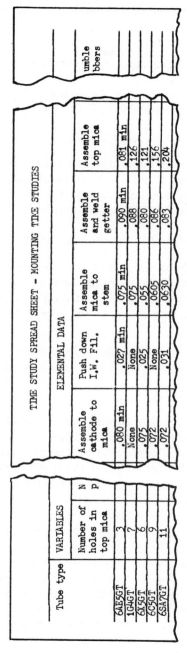

TIME STUDY SPREAD SHEET – MOUNTING TIME STUDIES

Tube type	VARIABLES		ELEMENTAL DATA					umble bbers
	Number of holes in top mica	N p	Assemble cathode to mica	Push down I.W. Fil.	Assemble mica to stem	Assemble and weld getter	Assemble top mica	
6AE5GT	3		.080 min	.027 min	.075 min	.090 min	.081 min	
1G4GT	7		None	None	.075	.088	.126	
6X5GT	6		.075	.025	.055	.080	.121	
6C5GT	9		.072	None	.0605	.086	.156	
6SA7GT	11		.072	.031	.0630	.083	.204	

Fig. 20.3— Section of time study summary sheet for mounting (assembly) operations on radio tubes.

419

attainment, as long as the timing and rating errors are random rather than biased.

6. *For the variable elements:*

    a. *Determine, on a logical basis, which job characteristic or characteristics they are a function of.*

    b. *Plot, on a graph, the time for the element against the variable or variables.* (*Note:* The variables may act in simple combination or they may interact.)

    c. *Fit a smooth curve or curves to the points plotted.*

This curve (or curves) will either pass close to the points or it will not. If two variables control the values, a series of parallel curves or a curve based on a compound variable may be necessary. For example if the time T is a function of variables A and B, the abscissa may be

$$A + B, \quad A \times B, \quad \frac{A}{B}, \quad A^n B^n$$

and so forth. A considerable amount of analysis may be necessary to determine the nature of the causal relationship. Semi-log and log-log graph paper are sometimes of great assistance in evaluating various hypotheses. If the curve does not fit the points reasonably well, any of the following faults may be the case:

1. The time studies were incorrectly or inconsistently rated.
2. Other variables as well as those plotted also affected the time.
3. The method varied.
4. An incorrect variable was used.

Each possibility should be investigated and evaluated. The validity of the curve should be checked by statistical methods. Note that even if the values fall along a smooth curve it is still possible that two types of errors occurred that compensate for each other, although this is not likely. The variables used should be reasonable. It is recommended that in those cases where a reasonable fit with a smooth curve cannot be obtained, or the reason for lack of fit explained with certainty, the investigations and study continue until they can be. Haphazard standard elemental times are never justifiable. A good criterion is, "Could this be explained logically?" The careful worker may well fit his curves mathematically, but they should still be explainable on a logical basis. It is worth noting that in many cases only a straight line is justifiable and that this straight line is often fitted by the method of least squares.[2] This procedure, however, is designed to determine the straight line with the best fit and not to justify the line. The fit should appear sufficiently reasonable to permit explanation to most working groups.

[2] See Supplemental Material for details of this method.

d. *If the variable is discrete, that is, has only definite steps between two limits, prepare a table for the range of jobs covered. If the variable is continuous, that is, has an infinite number of possibilities between two limits, prepare a graph.*

For the apparently variable element *assemble top mica* an inspection of the tube specifications revealed that the number of projections of the parts over which the top mica had to be fitted varied from tube type to tube type. This appeared to be a reasonable cause for the variation of time, so a tentative graph was drawn of standard time vs. number of insertions, as shown in Figure 20.4. (Since time values from many more types than those shown on

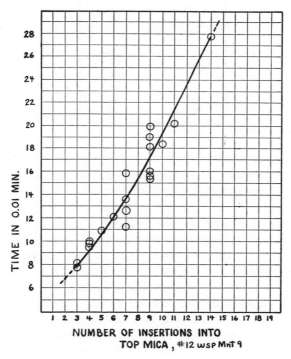

Fig. 20.4—Graph of time values for element assemble top mica in radio-tube mounting plotted against number of insertions into top mica.

the part of the summary sheet, used for illustration, were actually available, all of the available values are plotted. A considerable number of values are often necessary to obtain a reasonable curve.) Since the curve as shown was a reasonably good fit and the variable was logical and discrete, the table shown in Figure 20.5 was next constructed.

TIME   FOR
Assemble top mica
WRITTEN STANDARD PRACTICE
Mnt. 9
VARIABLE Number of insertions into top mica

Number of insertions into top mica	TIME IN MINUTES
3	.080
4	.092
5	.106
6	.120
7	.136
8	.154
9	.172
10	.194
11	.214
12	.236
13	.256
14	.276

Fig. 20.5—Table of basic time values for element assemble top mica read from graph in Figure 20.4.

If the variable is continuous, the problem is somewhat different. Some workers in this field prepare a formula for the continuous function, but if the formula is at all complex,[3] this is often considered merely an intermediate step before computing a table with sufficient values to permit close approximation of any value of the controlling variable or variables.

Care should be taken so that the use of the formula does not lead to extrapolation of the standard data beyond the range that the data covers and thus lead to serious errors. Some variables create discontinuous functions. For instance, the time to place 2 × 4 timbers on the bed of a cut-off saw will be a smooth function of their length until a length is reached such that the operator must change his method. The curve will then break and start off on a new line not connecting with the first line or curve.

In the course of the foregoing discussion, an example of how to handle each of two basic types of elements has been given. The method of handling machine-controlled times, when they occur (they do not in the group of jobs that were followed above), should be self-evident. The variables are

[3] For the typical person this is often the case. It certainly includes functions with fractional exponents.

much more obvious, and the time values should show much less random variation because they are not rated.

To complete the job of determining the elemental times for all of the elements in the tube assembly, each element would be treated as was the element *assemble and weld getter or assemble top mica*, depending on whether the element is apparently a constant or a variable. When a new tube is contemplated, by use of the design data and this group of elemental standard data, an accurate measurement of the time to assemble the tube mount may be synthesized. If it is desirable to use an assembly-line technique instead of a single assembler (and this is true of any line), it will be necessary to attempt to break up the job into the proper number of steps, using one of the several possible orders of assembly, and adding a handling element to each step. It will thus be possible to balance the line, as well as can be done,

```
                    ASSEMBLY LINE POSITION DESCRIPTION
    1. Tube type ................    6A8GT
    2. Date this standard set ....    10/12
    3. Station number ............      1
    4. Number of stations ........      7
    5. Elements.....                         Method No.       Time in Min.

          Assemble mica to stem       #3 Mnt.9         0.0720
          Assemble cathode to mica    #1 Mnt.9         0.0740
          Assemble and weld getter    #4 Mnt.9         0.0854

          Handling                                     0.0250


    6. Total time, this station, without balancing delay time ..........  0.2564
    7. Total line work time, without balancing delay time ..............  1.7234
    8. Ideal station time ..............................................  0.2462
    9. This station time in percent of ideal ..........................    104
   10. Amount of time this station time is over or under the ideal ......  +.0102
   11. Total allowed time, all stations ...............................   1.8900
   12. Line efficiency; total ideal divided by total allowed ...........   91.5 %
   13. Allowed time, this station .....................................    0.2700


    (Personal allowance to be provided by breaks and relief operators)
```

Fig. 20.6—Standard work sheet for assembly line position description.

prior to the inception of production. Perfect balance, which is seldom obtained, occurs when the total assembly time, divided by the number of stations, equals the individual station times. Since this seldom is achieved, the analyst usually uses his elemental times to find the longest operation in the line. This operation will determine the rate of production of the line. It is evidently desirable to expend some effort in devising better ways of performing the work done at this station. Considerable knowledge of product construction and possible juggling of operations is required in setting up effective assembly lines.

7. *Prepare a form to facilitate the use of the standard elemental for developing standard times on new jobs.*

Figure 20.6 is a standard work sheet for using the standard elemental data when developing a standard time for one position of an assembly line for the assembly of tube mounts. Note that lines are provided for showing how effectively the work has been divided among the positions on the line; this is a critique of the assembly line design.

The same procedure as has been outlined with respect to the foregoing case (steps 1 through 7) is applicable to the determination of standard elemental data for any group of jobs.

Standard Data

With maintenance work, or other similar activities, the tasks are usually numerous and the repetition relatively low. Standard data at the third-order work-unit or fourth-order work-unit level is of great assistance in achieving managerial control. The work of setting standard times from such data is relatively small.

The third- or fourth-order work-unit data may be obtained in any of the three following ways:

1. Built from standard elemental data.
2. Accumulated by appropriate work measurement techniques.
3. Acquired from outside sources.

The first method, building from standard elemental data, is the most laborious, particularly if the standard elemental data is to be synthesized from predetermined time systems. However, as will be seen later, other time study techniques may be employed to gather the necessary data much more rapidly and economically. The third approach offers only speed of acquisition as its main advantage. In most cases the hypothetical methods used to synthesize such data will differ from the particular methods in use so much that the validity of the use of such data is dubious. In most cases they are applied with so-called "craft allowances" ranging from 30 to 100 per cent in order to allow for these unevaluated, unknown differences.

Whatever approach is chosen, the most basic problem is to organize the data for ease of access into what is called a *work dictionary*. For instance, the third-order work-units for aircraft maintenance could be indexed under a five-part, compound index as:

1. Model number.
2. Major category.
3. Item number.
4. Part number.
5. Action code, e.g., inspect; remove, inspect and replace; remove and replace; remove, repair and replace.

Note, the first four items are similar to the use of a noun and a number of adjectives to fully identify an object. The fifth part provides the verb.

In a similar fashion, plant maintenance work could be indexed as:

1. Plant component: structure; production equipment; service equipment; and so forth.
2. Specific type: wall; floor; window; lathe; shafting; truck; and so forth.
3. Model number.
4. Type.
5. Part.
6. Action code.

In any case, as a first step in constructing standard data, the manner of intended use should be fully investigated so that the work dictionary can be compiled and used as a guide for the development of the actual time data.

Supplemental Material

Four types of supplemental material are included. The four types are:

1. Fitting straight lines by least squares.
2. Reducing continuously variable data to reasonable sized tables.
3. Standard elemental data for operations with machine elements.
4. Standard elemental data with families of curves.

Fitting Straight Lines by Least Squares

The method of least squares is used to find the line $Y = a + bX$ such that the sum of the squares of the deviations of the data points about the line are at a minimum. The two equations

$$Na + b\sum X = \sum Y \text{ and } a\sum X + b\sum X^2 = \sum XY$$

are solved simultaneously to obtain a and b. Y is the time and X is the variable affecting the element; hence, a value for each of these is available for each of the N sets of data used for the determination of standard elemental times. The values

$$\sum X, \ \sum Y, \ \sum X^2, \ \sum Y^2, \ \text{and} \ \sum XY$$

($\sum Y^2$ is not needed but accompanies the calculating procedure) may be obtained simultaneously on modern calculators; hence, the work is by no means as complicated as it appears. Only the straight-line fitting procedure is given here because it is the most commonly used. Various curves may be fitted in a similar manner. Reference should be made to a good statistics text.

If much work of the above type is to be done, a computer program may be prepared and used to produce the values a and b directly from a raw data input.

Reducing Continuously Variable Data to Reasonable Sized Tables

Figure 20.7 is part of one of a series of tables of standard elemental data for the operation of a board scoring machine. If such tables become unwieldy in size, they may readily be shortened by the following procedure:

1. Group the values of the variable such that each group covers a 5 per cent range of the time values.
2. Place the midpoint of the time range as the tabular value for this range of the variable.

For example, the first value in the first time column of Figure 20.7 is 0.00315 min. per sheet; 0.00315 × 1.05 = 0.00331. This range from 0.00315

SCORING STANDARD DATA

TABLE # 2 — Time for element 4

NUMBER PER TRAY	396	372	312	288
CALIPER	.028	.030	.035	.038
PERIMETER — INCHES				
60.26 to 60.75	.00315	.00335	.00400	.00433
60.76 to 61.25	.00317	.00335	.00402	.00436
61.26 to 61.75	.00319	.00340	.00405	.00439
61.76 to 62.25	.00322	.00343	.00408	.00442
62.26 to 62.75	.00324	.00345	.00411	.00445
62.76 to 63.25	.00326	.00347	.00414	.00449
63.26 to 63.75	.00329	.00350	.00417	.00452
63.76 to 64.25	.00331	.00352	.00420	.00455
64.26 to 64.75	.00333	.00355	.00423	.00458
64.76 to 65.25	.00336	.00357	.00426	.00462
66	.00340	.00362	.00432	.00468
67	.00345	.00367	.00438	.00474
68	.00350	.00372	.00444	.00481
69	.00354	.00377	.00450	.00487
70	.00359	.00382	.00456	.00494
71	.00364	.00387	.00461	.00500

Fig. 20.7 — *Part of a table of standard elemental data for one element of operating a board scoring machine. (Courtesy G. Kaplan, Western Printing and Lithographing Co.)*

to 0.00331 covers sheets from 60.26 inches perimeter to 64.25 inches. The first eight lines of Figure 20.7 (considering only the first column) could be replaced with one line reading:

60.26–64.25	.00323	

Standard Elemental Data
for Operations with Machine Elements

Figure 20.8 is a picture of the operation of keyway milling on a Kent-Owens milling machine. The HPT data synthesis for the manual part of the

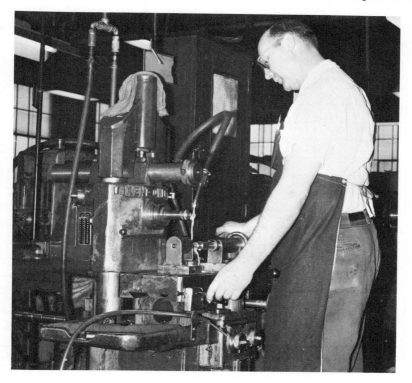

Fig. 20.8 — Milling keyway on Kent-Owens mill.

job is shown in Figure 20.9 and the computation of the allowed time is shown in Figure 20.10. Data such as these were used to construct the standard time computation sheet shown in Figure 20.11 for all keyway milling. The shop in which these data were developed and used was a job shop. They did custom

| | MANUAL TIME DATA FOR | _Keyway Cutting_ | | | | | | HPT ELEMENT WORK SHEET |

MANUAL TIME DATA FOR _Keyway Cutting_

OPERATION _7_
MACHINE _124 - K-O Mill_
FIXTURE _Tailstocks with 4" handwheel_
NOTES _Piece from rack to table and table to rack during machine cycle_
LAYOUT INFORMATION _Largest piece that fits on table — 14.5#_
See photo # M293

HPT ELEMENT WORK SHEET

Page _1_ of _1_

Elem. No.	Description (LEFT HAND)	Ther.	Cond	Time	Time	Cond.	Ther.	Description (RIGHT HAND)
1 (Unload)	Hit hand wheel	G	C	139	475	12"	TE	To part in tailstocks
	Release; 3 turns	TL	2"x19	3686	453	W	G	Shaft
					2897	see LH	H	During loosening
	For RH	UD	—		381	—	DA	From centers
					475	12"	TL	To table
					151	=	RL	Piece on mach. table
					04832			
2 (Load)	For RH	UD			307	5"	TE	To new shaft
					453	W	G	Shaft
					362	7"	TL	To centers
					330	4°	P	To right center
					71	1/2"	A	To right center
					137	1"	TL	Shaft to left center and throw stop
					249	3°	P	On left center and throw stop
	Tighten 3 turns	TL	2"x19	3686	3686	see LH	H	For clamping
	Crank handle	RL	—	151		—" 12"	RL TE	Away from shaft
	To feed	TE	10°	434				
	Feed lever	G	C	139				
	Engage	TL	2"	194				
				06513				
3 (Mach)	Stock up on table, aside finished piece and TE to Tailstock crank during machine cycle of cut and table return of .08							

Fig. 20.9 — First step in use of HPT data for determining standard time for manual elements for job shown in Figure 20.8.

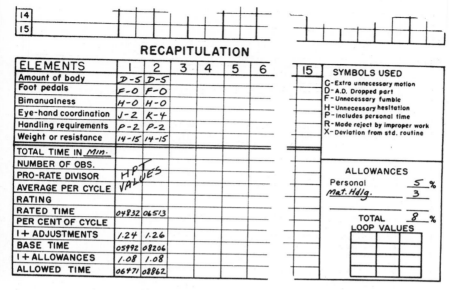

Fig. 20.10—Use of recapitulation section of objective time study sheet to complete determination of standard time for manual elements of job shown in Figure 20.9.

work for other manufacturers. Runs were usually short. Each lot of product was different. Direct time study-intensive sampling or building standards for each job directly from predetermined times would have taken too long and been too expensive. Using forms such as shown in Figure 20.11, the standard time for each job was set before the work began. Using these data to schedule men and machines, a 25 per cent cost reduction was achieved.

Standard Elemental Data with Families of Curves

Polishing and buffing are two jobs for which it is extremely difficult to set accurate and consistent standards. On such jobs it is extremely desirable to develop standard elemental data so as to achieve uniformity of standards. The parts studied in this case and their identification numbers are shown in Figure 20.12. Drawings of some of the parts appear in Figure 20.13. The standard workplace is shown in Figure 20.14. The full memomotion time study technique was used to obtain data to study thoroughly. If in the subsequent calculations various points appeared out of line, even the ratings could therefore be reviewed or the method used on the particular job could be reexamined in detail. Only about 15 rolls of film were used since the one per second timing allowed extensive recording with only a small amount of film.

KEYWAY CUTTING CALCULATION SHEET

Date _____   Type of keyway _____
Customer _____   Dimensions _____
Part No. _____   Name _____   Cutter diameter _____ inches
Material _____
Machine _____
Fixture _____
Weight of part _____ lbs. at operation   Weight Adjustment from Table I _._ = W

NOTE: Center alignment inspection by foreman, go - no-go during machine cycle.

1. LOAD FROM TABLE TOP (USE APPROPRIATE LINE AND MARK THIS LINE)   TIME IN MINUTES
   A. Kent-Owens,middleclamp,3" handle diameter   .0701 + .0632W
   B. Kent-Owens,tailstock,4" handle diameter   .0627 + .0565W
   C.
   D. K & T.,tailstock,5" handle diameter   .0903 + .0813W
   E.
   F. Cinn., tailstock,3½" handle diameter   .0631 + .0568W
   G. Cinn., middle clamp,3½" handle diameter   .0756 + .0681W
   H.   [   ]

2. CUT KEYWAY, USE TABLE II FOR CORRECT MACHINE
   Cutter size _____ , Feed _____ Speed _____   [   ]

3. UNLOAD TO TABLE TOP (USE APPROPRIATE LINE AND MARK THIS LINE)
   A. Kent-Owens,middleclamp,3" handle diameter   .0684 + .0639W
   B. Kent-Owens,tailstock,4" handle diameter   .0517 + .0483W
   C.
   D. K & T.,tailstock,5" handle diameter   .0704 + .0640W
   E.
   F. Cinn., tailstock,3½" handle diameter   .0476 + .0445W
   G. Cinn., middleclamp,3½" handle diameter   .0631 + .0590W   [   ]

4. HANDLING TO AND FROM RACKS (Calculate appropriate line)
   A. Kent-Owens (Extend when piece is more than 14.5#)
                        .0329 + .0289W   _____
   B. Cinn. (Extend when piece is more than 25#)
                        .0296 + .0260W   _____
   C. K & T. (No extension to total in this line)
                        .0332 + .0291W   _____   [   ]

5. CYCLE TIME CORRECTION (Disregard this item if an extension to total
                          cycle time was made in item 4)
         Time for A,B or C of item 4   _____
         Subtract machine time,item 2 -   _____
   If difference is positive, extend
   to total cycle time column   _____   [   ]

   ┌─────────────────────────────────┐
   │ Calculations by _____   │   TOTAL BASE TIME,MINUTES   _____
   │ Checked by   _____   │
   └─────────────────────────────────┘

                    ALLOWANCES   5% Pers.,   3% M.H.   _____

              TOTAL STANDARD TIME IN MINUTES PER UNIT   ═══════════

              STANDARD TIME IN HOURS PER 100 UNITS   ═══════════

                 PRODUCTION PER HOUR AT STANDARD   ═══════════

Fig. 20.11 — Calculation sheet for computing standard time from standard elemental data for cutting keyways on milling machines.

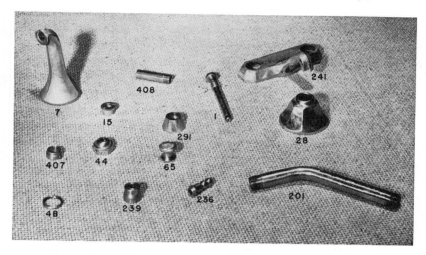

Fig. 20.12—Plumbing fixture parts studied.

After examining the film, 25 standard elements were set up. Subsequently, all the films were analyzed onto time study sheets. The physical dimensions of the parts and the final allowed times per element were summarized onto the time study spread sheet shown in Figure 20.15.

These data were treated exactly as were the tube data described in the body of the chapter.

Element 22 is selected for examination in this supplemental material because it shows the method of handling an element with two variables, which is not an uncommon occurrence. In this particular case, data, which at first appeared to have excessive and unreasonable scatter, were successfully explained and shown to be quite justifiable, as indicated in Figure 20.16.

It is worth noting that time standards set from these data produced the most consistent standards this plant had ever had, as verified by production records as men shifted from job to job. This appraisal was concurred in also by the workers and foremen, whose comments in this plant were freely made and honestly conceived.

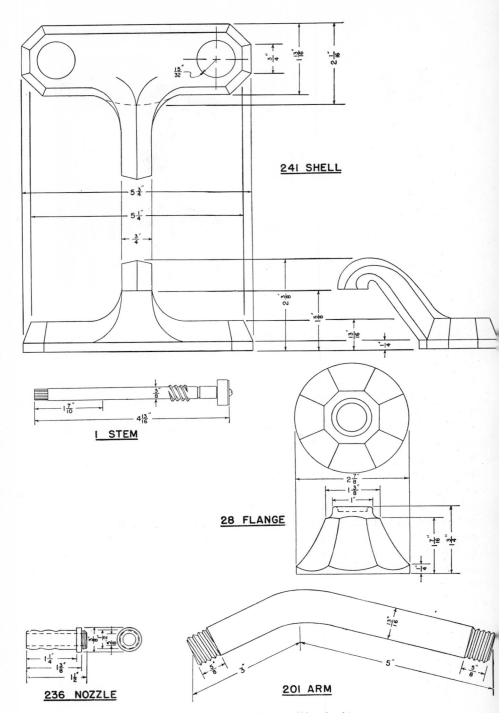

Fig. 20.13 — *Drawings of some of the plumbing parts.*

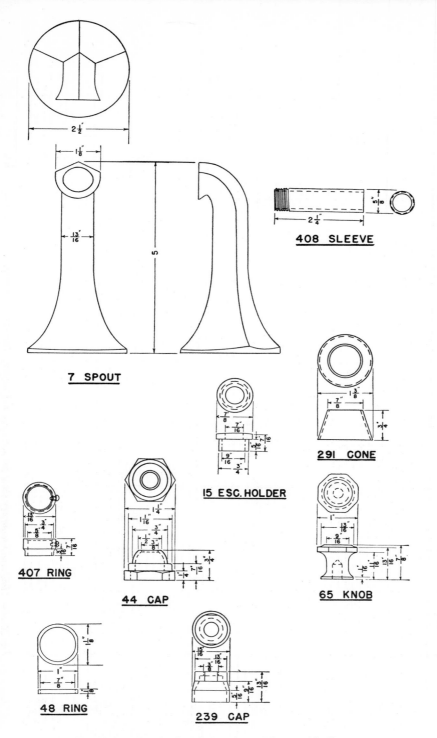

408 SLEEVE

7 SPOUT

291 CONE

15 ESC. HOLDER

407 RING

44 CAP

65 KNOB

48 RING

239 CAP

Fig. 20.14—Standard workplace for polishing and buffing.

Part	Weight oz.	Area sq. in. Type	Number	1	2	3	4	5	6	7	8	9	10	20	21	22	30	31	40	41	50A	50B	51	52	53	54	55	56
1 STEM	2 1/2	2 R	9			.094		.027	.033	.056				.065		.035												
7 SPOUT	10 1/2	7	1						.034													.110	.474					
7 SPOUT		13	1				.042															.127		.688				
7 SPOUT		2	1				.040		.036													.113			.127			
7 SPOUT		20	1				.040		.037													.129					.306	
7 SPOUT		20	1				.049		.032												1.132							.438
7 SPOUT		20 IR	1				.048		.033					.063		.993												
7 SPOUT		20 C	1							.055							.073	.180										
7 SPOUT		20	1							.052									.038	.229								
15 ESC. HOLDER	1/2	1 1/2 C	9			.083		.026	.035	.053								.022										
15 ESC. HOLDER		1 1/2 R	5 1/2			.061		.023	.035	.048				.066		.064												
28 FLANGE	1 1/2	2 1/4 IR	1										.217			.184												
28 FLANGE		10 R	1											.059		.267												
28 FLANGE		10 F	1									.075						.021										
28 FLANGE		22 1/2 F	10						.031	.050							.068	.050										
31 O. H. SCREW	—	—	53	1.073	.033						.062			.067	.449													
44 CAP	1	50 R	20								.323	1.302		.063		1.560												
44 CAP		2 1/2 IS	3 1/2			.045		.023	.033								.063	.039										
44 CAP		2 1/2	4			.055			.030	.046									.038	.067								
48 RING	—	—	30								.037	.431			.307													
65 KNOB	1 1/2	3 1/3 VIR	1								.065	.101				.439												
65 KNOB		3 1/3 IS	4			.031		.023	.032	.048							.064	.057										
201 ARM	6 1/2	10 8/10 R	1				.048							.058		.258												
201 ARM		10 2/10 R	1						.036							.207												
201 ARM		20 C	1				.049		.033									.240										
236 NOZZLE	1	2 IR	1							.054				.064		.144												
236 NOZZLE		2 IS	3			.033		.023		.055							.071	.031										
239 CAP	1/2	2 1/2 C	4					.023	.036	.055							.064	.020										
241 SHELL	11 1/2	15 7/10	1				.047		.031													.119			1.166			
241 SHELL		9 1/10	1				.042		.036													.134		.680				
241 SHELL		24 8/10	1				.041		.033												1.090							.857
241 SHELL		9 1/10 IR	1				.040		.035					.054		.636												
241 SHELL		15 7/10 OVR	1				.050		.037					.057		1.169												
241 SHELL		24 8/10 IS	1							.048							.062	.516										
291 CONE	1	3 R	1							.055						.107												
291 CONE		3 C	5			.040			.037	.049							.063	.031										
407 RING	1/2	1 IR	7			.066		.034		.048				.058		.113												
407 RING		1 IS	3			.037		.028	.031	.046							.067	.029										
408 SLEEVE	1	4 1/2 R	5			.073		.027		.048				.065		.130												
408 SLEEVE		4 1/2 C	6			.073		.028	.032								.065	.032										
408 SLEEVE		4 1/2 C	10			.171		.024	.033	.055									.038	.047								

Fig. 20.15—Time study summary sheet for polishing and buffing, giving part numbers, physical characteristics, and allowed times for each element.

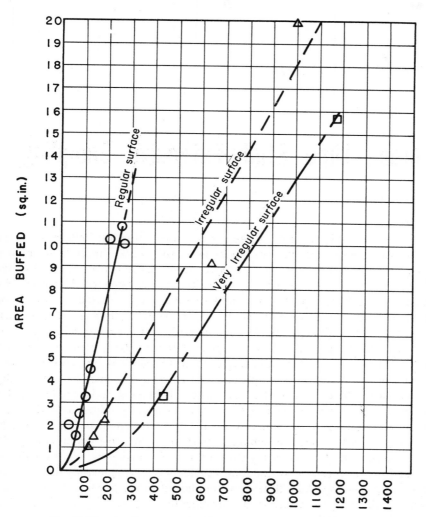

Fig. 20.16—Graph for Element No. 22, Buff, in polishing and buffing plumbing fixtures.

CHAPTER 21

Direct Time Study-Extensive Sampling

Direct time study-extensive sampling is a procedure for setting standard times wherein the observations are made, as with work sampling, at random intervals (rather than continuously) over an extensive period. Each observation, as with work sampling, is classified into a category. However, the categories, other than idle, rest, and so forth, are the second-, third- or fourth-order work-units associated with the activity observed. Idle or rest categories are kept separate. The per cent of total observations represented by any one category is taken as representative of the percent of the total time attributable to that category. Because the work is not observed continuously, a work count to apply against the work time must be acquired by some means other than direct observation. Ratings may be applied to the observations of active categories. Allowances may be added as with direct time study-intensive sampling. While the technique may be used to study the same type of jobs for which direct time study-intensive sampling is used,[1] its greatest field of use is for the study of non-repetitive jobs, or jobs with too much internal variation, or too long a cycle for convenient study by means of intensive sampling. As will be seen, standard data for third- or fourth-order work-units may be determined conveniently and directly with extensive sampling. The method record, when the study is used to determine third- or fourth-order work-unit standard times, is usually not as fully described as with direct time study-intensive sampling.

The technique is particularly useful for setting standard times for work such as non-repetitive office activities, the activities in analytical laboratories,

---

[1] This approach permits a time study to be made without the use of a stop-watch; some regard this as an advantage.

436

maintenance, custom manufacturing and custom assembling, and so forth. Shipbuilding, electric switchgear assembly, heavy engine assembly, custom assembly of motors with generators and pump accessories, aircraft overhaul, flight line maintenance, and plant maintenance are also typical of the variety of work for which the technique has proved useful for setting standard times to assist in maintaining managerial control.

As an alternative definition, in terms of the factors of the basic equation for a standard time:

1. W/C—Obtained from production records covering the period during which the observations are made.
2. W/T—Observations are made of employees at random intervals. The per cent of the total observations represented by any one category is taken as representing the per cent of the total time spent at that category. The validity of this may be tested by statistical means; it is a function of the per cent of total time represented by the category and the total number of observations.
3. M—A rating may be made by any one of the standard methods and applied to active categories. Because each observation of an active category is rated, there is a tendency for random errors to be removed; bias type errors, if present, remain.
4. A—As with direct time study-intensive sampling a percentage, determined by policy, is added; the extensive sampling study may also provide some additional information relating to A.

The first step in making a direct time study-extensive sampling is to arrange for the obtaining of the two data items, the *work-unit count* and the *work-time data*. The work-unit count is the number of times the work-units being studied are produced during the extensive period studied. The work-time data refers to the number of hours worked by the employees who are producing the work-units. These new items will be used in the calculations. It is vital to arrange for a source for these at the beginning of the study.

The categories selected for recording the observations are identified as "p's" or fractions of the total work time, and, in addition, delay elements should also be categorized in advance. As a general principle, excess categories can be combined with other categories after the study is completed but categories not separated in the study cannot later be isolated. Hence, if a category appears somewhat useful, it should be separated when the study begins.

The first basic difference between the technique being described and direct time study-intensive sampling is in the manner of making observations. Instead of continuously observing the task and recording the time at the end of each separated category, the task is observed at random intervals, as with work sampling. However, instead of merely noting the category of work being performed, as with work sampling, the performance is rated (objectively or subjectively) and a rating entered on the record instead of merely a check mark, except in the case of personal time or non-operator controlled delay elements. The sampling times may be established by any of the methods described in Chapter 9. It is worth noting that a whole series of jobs may be observed in sequence, and a whole group of standards worked on simultaneously. Separate category lists would be used for each group of jobs.

In making the observations, the observer proceeds as with work sampling, identifying the category, but the observation time is slightly longer so that the observer may rate the performance.[2] Only delays are recorded in the same manner as normal work sampling; the reason for not rating these should be obvious. However, each irregular element, whose time depends upon worker diligence, should be listed as a separate p and observations of this activity should be rated.

Various statistical controls may be used to check on:

1. The acceptability of each day's sample.
2. The reliability of the average $\bar{p}$ or per cent of time spent on each category as indicated by all the samples available at any particular point in the study.

The details of applying these statistical controls are presented in the supplemental material appended at the end of this chapter.

If the categories of a direct time study-extensive sampling are second-order work-units and objective rating is used, the difficulty adjustments are computed for each category in the same manner as with direct time study-intensive sampling. If the categories are third- or fourth-order work-units and objective rating is used, the difficulty adjustments are computed for the average or typical conditions accompanying the work, except for the adjustment for weight. For weight adjustments, only the 5 per cent or basic values are used, with the weight being taken as the average of weights lifted. If there is great variation with respect to weight or force overcome during the category, the average may be obtained by recording the necessary information during the sampling period. (Information concerning unusual difficulty adjustments may be obtained in the same way.) Hence, under some circumstances each observation may lead to a recording of the category, the rating, and the information relating to the difficulty adjustments.

At the conclusion of the study, the values for each $\sum n$ (the number of a particular category of observation) and the $\sum N$ (the total number of all observations) are tabulated. (If other data related to the difficulty adjustments have been recorded, they also must be tabulated separately for each

---

[2] Objective rating is particularly helpful here in that only one concept of normal speed need be used and the rater does not need to "reset his sights" for each observation; the observation time per observation may be held to a short interval.

category.) The ratings for each category are tabulated separately. The average rating, $\bar{R}$, for each category may be computed as:

$$\bar{R}_i = \frac{\sum R_i}{\sum n_i} = \frac{\text{sum of all ratings of category } i}{\text{total number of observations of category } i}$$

The standard time for each category is computed by means of the following formula:

$$ST_i = \frac{(T \times 60 \times \bar{p}_i) \times [\bar{R}_i \times (1 + \text{Adj.}_i)] \times (1 + \text{All.}_i)}{WC}$$

where

ST_i = Standard time for category i, in minutes.

T = work time, in hours, covered by the study, usually from time cards or job cards.

60 = conversion of T to minutes.[3]

$\bar{p}_i$ = per cent of time spent at category i.

$\bar{R}_i$ = average rating for category.

$(1 + \text{Adj.}_i)$ = 1 + difficulty adjustments for category i. (If ratings are subjective, this term will disappear.)

$(1 + \text{All.}_i)$ = 1 + allowances for category i.

WC = Work count; number of times the work-unit was performed. (A source for this, to match the period of the study, must be arranged for prior to starting the study.)

The basis for the formula is simple:

$T \times 60 \times \bar{p}_i$ = time attributable to work-unit i, in minutes.

$\bar{R}_i \times (1 + \text{Adj.}_i)$ = correction for diligence of worker and difficulty of task using objective rating. [With subjective rating, this term is $(\bar{R}_i)$.]

$(1 + \text{All.}_i)$ = Allowances for the category.

The product of all of the above terms is the standard time for all the performances of work-unit i, in minutes; dividing by the work count puts this on a one performance basis, giving a standard time per work-unit, in minutes, as with direct time study-intensive sampling.

The preceding discussion gives basic theory involved. The two cases which follow relate to non-repetitive work, an area of activity wherein the technique is of great utility. The first case is from the metal-clad cabinet assembly department of the S & C Electric Co. of Chicago, Ill.; the second case is from a large office of the Army Materiel Command. Non-repetitive activities, such as are represented by these two illustrations, frequently are large labor-consuming areas in a plant or government activity. If work measurement is vital to effective management, these areas likewise must be measured and

---

[3] If the standard time is to be expressed in decimal hours, this factor is omitted.

brought under control. Gross statistical (in the sense of historical) procedures have been employed in the past for such work. Such measures often leave much to be desired. In contrast, the procedures described in this chapter have many advantages.

CASE I THE METAL-CLAD ASSEMBLY DEPARTMENT
OF THE S & C ELECTRIC CO., CHICAGO, ILL.[4]

The S & C Electric Company manufactures large, heavy-duty electrical switchgear. The typical unit consists of one or more bays (cabinets), each bay being about $3 \times 3 \times 9$ feet, although these dimensions vary from unit to unit. A typical bay is shown in Figure 21.1 and a series of bays composing

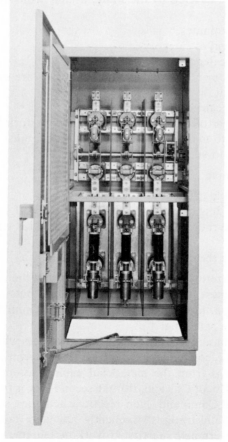

Fig. 21.1 — Sample bay from assembly department of S & C Electric Co., Chicago, Ill. Each bay made is custom built and different from all other bays. (Courtesy S & C Electric Co.)

[4] This case was worked on by R. Amstutz, A. J. Mandele, and M. A. Ottow of the Industrial Engineering Division of the S & C Electric Co., and the author. The data are reproduced with the kind permission of the S & C Electric Co.

a complete unit are shown in Figure 21.2. The final assembly department has several unique aspects that differentiate it from the normal type of activity for which time standards are commonly engineered. These differences are:

1. The work is not repetitive and the summing up of the "units of output" (fifth-order work-units) is not a simple counting of the finished pieces. The units are individually designed to meet customer requirements.
2. The details of the work methods used by the employees, on each different task, are not economical to describe; hence there is difficulty in defining the "standard man-hours of work input" wherein both the method and the degree of diligence of the employee is fully defined.
3. The employees work as a group on a considerable number of units simultaneously, shifting back and forth and helping each other as needed. It is difficult to get accurate time-keeping charges against each unit.

It would appear that the only repetitive aspects of the work situation are the specific fourth-order work-units, such as *door installed, panel installed, screen installed, PCS switch installed, MAG switch installed, fuse mounting in-*

Fig. 21.2—A complete unit from assembly department. (Courtesy S & C Electric Co.)

stalled, (*x*) *feet of bus-duct installed,* and so forth. These work-units meet the three criteria given in Chapter 17:

1. They fit into a clear hierarchy of countable, convertible units of quantification from objective to workload.
2. They permit a meaningful forecast of the workload to be made in terms related to the required manpower.
3. A firm relationship of the work-unit to the required manpower resources can be established.

It should be noted that if a set of work-units is devised which meets the first two criteria, but none of the work measurement techniques currently in use is applicable, then either a modification of existing techniques or a new technique is needed. The work-units "speak for the situation"; the work measurement technique selection or design is the problem of the analyst. (Notes on the use of a modified version of direct time study-extensive sampling, designed to meet the requirements of a situation somewhat different from switchgear assembly, appear in the Supplemental Material of this chapter.) Various amounts[5] or quantities of these components (fourth-order work-units) appear in each assembly. However, for any component, the work of installation (and consequently, the time required at a given level of effort) varies from assembly to assembly. The work may vary even for like components on the same assembly. To make a sufficient number of direct time studies so as to permit the making of tables of time values, for the installation of each component, with the time required being given as a function of all the factors affecting the difficulty of installation, would be an extremely lengthy and uneconomical task, to say nothing of the labor to apply such data. Similar difficulties would beset an attempt to create performance standards for unit *acts* and apply these to set standard times.

The solution to the problem lies in considering the time *for a component installed* as being best represented by the rated average of a sizeable sample of such component installations. If the sample is a sufficiently random mix of installations, it may be used to predict realistically and accurately the time for subsequent *groups* of installations of the subject component. In short, an extensive sampling time study is suggested, with each *p* representing all the time for *a type of component installed* (fourth-order work-unit), together with a suitable method for determining a *work count* (*WC*) for each such work-unit. Such a study may be performed in the manner described in this chapter.

To relate this time study method to the work done in the final assembly department of the S & C Electric Company:

1. A complete list of bay components (as assembled in the final assembly

---

[5] In some cases, with some bays, the amount is 0.

department) was prepared. This list contained every *thing* that might cause work on a bay in the final assembly department. This is the list of p's for the sampling study by tasks. A section of this list is shown in Figure 21.3.

Component	Work unit	Initial work count	Work units done prior	Work units added	Work units left	Net Work Count
			BAY COMPONENTS – METAL CLAD ASSEMBLY DEPARTMENT			
Doors	Door	16	8	60	11	57
Panels	Panel	28	27	74	10	65
Indoor roofs	Roof	18	8	59	7	62
Screens	Screen	12	6	43	9	40
Front handle	Handle	16	5	55	14	52
Gasketing, rubber	Foot	336	120	1766	224	1758
OBS switches	Pole	24	21	120	17	106
Potheads	Pothead	11	9	47	16	33
Lights	Light	9	7	39	11	30
Line bus	Foot	192	64	1387	119	1396
Install and wire interlock	Interlock	8	6	49	11	40

Fig. 21.3—*Part of the task list, by components, for assembly of bays.* (Courtesy Industrial Engineering Dept., S & C Electric Co.)

2. A specific work-unit was devised for each component or p so as to provide a basis for counting. These work-units also are shown in Figure 21.3. These work-units were chosen so their count indicated the relative amount of work and also so that they could be counted from the design drawings.

   (*Note:* In the case being discussed here, the selection of the method of counting was a relatively simple problem. This is not always so. In many applications of the technique of direct time study-extensive sampling the success or failure of the work-measurement effort hinges on the design of a satisfactory way of performing this step. Reference should be made to the three criteria of satisfactory work-units given in Chapter 17.)

3. A set of drawings was obtained for all bays which were in the assembly department and a work count made for all work-units of all bays on the assembly floor (see Figure 21.3).

4. Just prior to beginning the study, an inventory was made of all work-units completed on all bays in the assembly department. When this inventory was deducted from the count obtained in step 3, above, the remainder represented the workload (work count by fourth-order work-units) remaining on bays already on the floor.

5. Arrangements were made to obtain the work-unit count of all bays released to the assembly department during the study period, to add these to the work count from step 4 (see Figure 21.3).

6. An observer was assigned to each of the two shifts. The random pattern of observations employed was to make sampling rounds as frequently as possible with random breaks for the observers.

7. A five-week sampling period was employed. Taking into account the desired accuracy, the scheduled mix, and the number of observations anticipated per day (500 to 700 = workers × sampling rounds), the five-week period was selected.[6] Part of the several-page, daily, sampling sheet is shown in Figure 21.4. Note, some observations show more than one rating in an observation space. This could refer to either two or more men on a task on one bay or several men doing the same thing on different bays. These were not differentiated.

8. Control charts were maintained for each category. While they occasionally showed "out of control" conditions, these were, in all cases, traceable to the flow of work and hence were not excluded from the sample. The cause of the variation was non-random, as far as days went, but the day was a valid sample. A control chart for the *p*, *assemble doors*, is shown in this chapter's Supplemental Material.

9. At the conclusion of the five-week sampling period an inventory was taken of the bays on the assembly floor to determine the work count of tasks not completed at this cut-off point in the study. This was deducted from the work count obtained from step 5 to give a network count for work performed during the study period.

10. The standard time for each work-unit was computed by means of the formula given previously, except that they were expressed in man-hours instead of man-minutes. The T used was the total of all direct labor, man-hours of work expended in the department during the five-week, two-shift, study period. Figure 21.5 shows sections of the two-page, standard time application sheet for applying the standards. This sheet may be used as follows:

   a. To determine the assembly time when bidding, so as to estimate an assembly cost.

   b. To "load" or schedule work into the assembly department.

   c. To credit work done in assembly, in standard man-hours, to compare to actual man-hours, so as to measure operating effectiveness and so forth.

Inasmuch as the work units are not credited as "performed" until a unit

---

[6] Actually a one-week practice period for the observers preceded the five weeks of the study. This "dry run" served to familiarize both observers and workers with the procedure and permitted a last check on the work-unit list, the forms, and so forth.

PERFORMANCE SAMPLING DAILY DATA SHEET   ASSEMBLY DEPT.

Observer _A. Mandel_   Number of employees ___27___

DATE _4/24/_

Sheet _1_ of _4_

Time of observation

Task	7:32	7:59	8.23	9.08	9:40	10:11	10.33	10.50	11:17	11:29	11:41	1.08	1.22
Doors	80 85	80	80 80 75	80	80 90	80					80 70	80 80	
Panels	90	90	90		90								
Indoor roofs									70	75		70	65
Screens		90		75	75	75							
Front handle	75						80	80					
Gasketing,rubber	80	80						80					
GBS switches	70 75 70										80 70	80	
Potheads		80	75	70	70						70		
Lights													
Line bus					80		80 90	90 85	85 85	08	80 70		
Read plans	✓	✓						✓	✓			✓	
Personal	✓✓		✓✓			✓			✓				

Fig. 21.4—Part of daily sampling sheet for sampling time study by tasks, assembly department, S & C Electric Co.
(Courtesy Industrial Engineering Dept., S & C Electric Co.)

STANDARD TIME APPLICATION SHEET - METAL CLAD ASSEMBLY

CDA _____   CUSTOMER _____   SO _____   DATE _____

ITEM	UNIT OF MEASURE	QUANTITY	STD. HOURS*	STD. HRS ALLOWED
Move to assembly area	Bay	_____	.4002	_____
Doors	Door	_____	1.0820	_____
Indoor roofs	Roof	_____	.3358	_____
Gasketing, rubber	Foot	_____	.0266	_____
PCS switch fused	Switch	_____	.6416	_____
Line bus	Foot	_____	.0659	_____
Flexible connectors	Foot	_____	.0122	_____
			SUB-TOTAL *	
* Includes 10% allowance				
Stock up tools, sharpen, study prints			4.8%	_____
			TOTAL ALLOWED HOURS	_____

Fig. 21.5—Sections from the standard time application sheet for assembly of electric switchgear units. (Courtesy Industrial Engineering Dept., S & C Electric Co.)

is completed and moved from the department, a four-week, moving average is used to measure effectiveness and smooth out the fluctuations. It should be noted also that the use of a four-week, moving average:

1. Increases the size of the mix used to measure performance.
2. Gives a weekly measure of performance.

By doing this, the reliability of the measure is enhanced and yet values of performance are obtained at suitable intervals.

The data were economical to develop and economical to use, and brought reasonable control to a non-repetitive situation. Greater productivity and better scheduling, pricing, and use of floor space resulted from the application of these standards. It is to be noted, however, that the methods are not described in detail. When a considerable number of component design changes or mounting methods changes take place, either a complete new study will need to be made or a series of direct time studies-intensive sampling of the new components or mounting methods will be needed. The standards described are not fully "engineered," but may be used for almost all uses of time standards, including wage incentives, if a proper plan is used.[7]

The observations made in this study were rated subjectively by the procedure described in Appendix B. Had they been rated objectively, the difficulty adjustment would have been based on whatever condition was deemed typical of each task. (The adjustment could also have been determined from a short sampling study.)

CASE II Application of Direct Time Study-Extensive Sampling by Tasks to an Army Materiel Command Office[8]

The basic procedure employed in this study was identical to the one employed at the S & C Electric Company. Of particular interest, however, is the selection of the work-units. The main purpose of the study was to permit manning in terms of the work-load and to measure effectiveness. Hence the categories were third-order work-units. These tasks were selected so that a work count could be:

1. Anticipated.
2. Readily ascertained when completed.

This concept is the same as that employed in the previous illustration.

A partial list of tasks and the standard times obtained follows. (Note the different work units.)

Work-Unit	Oper. No.	Std.Hrs/WC	Work Units/Std. Hr.	How Work Unit is Counted
Initial editing	010	.1988	5.03	Document edited
Editing listings	011	.0132	75.76	Line item listed
Document review	020	.0703	14.22	Line item reviewed
Prepare action copy	030	.1174	8.52	Document action copy made
Incoming property information posted	060	.048	20.8	Line item posted
Property disposal information posted	190	2.06	.485	Line item posted

It should be noted that this procedure identifies work in sufficient detail such as to permit realistic use of the standard for the purposes listed in Chapter 17.

[7] This takes us beyond the range of this text and will not be discussed here.

[8] Courtesy Army Management Engineering Training Agency, Rock Island, Ill.

In any application of this technique, the work-unit list should be carefully planned so that normal work planning sources may be used to obtain the work count and so that the standards are readily applicable for the purposes intended. Considerable use is being made of this technique as work measurement is extended to non-repetitive work areas in industrial, sales, office, and government activities.

Supplemental Material

The supplemental material of this chapter is divided into two sections:

1. Statistical controls which may be applied to examine the characteristics of the observations made by direct time study-extensive sampling.
2. The use of direct time study-extensive sampling in situations where "multi-factor" work-units are encountered.

Statistical Controls for Direct Time Study-Extensive Sampling

In the body of the chapter it was noted that various statistical controls may be used to check on:

1. The acceptability of each day's sample.
2. The reliability of the average $\bar{p}$, or per cent of time spent on each category, as indicated by all the samples available at any particular point in the study.

The manner of employing these statistical controls is as follows:

Let us assume that our p_1 from the first day was 24 or 24 per cent or 0.24 of the total time. Let us further assume that during the second to fifth day p_1 was .26, .24, .22, and .26, respectively. The cumulative average $\bar{p}$ can be found by averaging these, provided the total number of observations each day was identical. If this condition is not met, then $\bar{p}$ may be found by:

$$\bar{p} = \frac{\sum n}{\sum N}$$

where

$\sum n$ = sum of the number of observations of p on all days through the date for the calculation.

$\sum N$ = sum of the number of all observations through the date for the calculation.

In the case being discussed:

$$\bar{p}_1 = \frac{.24 + .26 + .24 + .22 + .25}{5}$$

A control chart for p may also be plotted, as with normal work sampling observations, to check on the possible occurrence of non-random, assignable causes which may affect the validity of a day's sample or for trends or changes in the total situation. Likewise, the reliability of $\bar{p}$ may be checked to determine when the study has reached the desired level of accuracy.

The limits for the daily control chart for p may be plotted around the first $\bar{p}$ computed from the first five values of p. Subsequent calculations will give the reliability of $\bar{p}$.

The upper and lower control limits for p are based on $\bar{p} \pm 2\sigma_p$ where $\sigma_p = \sqrt{\bar{p}(1 - \bar{p})/N}$ and N equals the number of observations made per day. The reliability of $\bar{p}$ is based on $\bar{p} \pm 2\sigma_{\bar{p}}$ where $\sigma_{\bar{p}} = \sqrt{\bar{p}(1 - p)/\sum N}$ and $\sum N$ is the grand total number of all observations. The 2σ limits were chosen to maintain the same reliabilities as with readings for direct time study-intensive sampling.

Figure 21.6 is a control chart from the S & C study (Case I of this chapter) for the work-unit, *door installed*. It will be noted that the daily value is frequently *out of control*. Each *out of control* point has two possible causes:

1. The sample was biased by poor methods of observation.
2. The work-unit occurred an unusual number of times.

Each out of control point on Figure 21.6 was separately investigated. Each out of control point was traced to a fluctuation in the number of doors installed that day. However, the time standard sought was for *door installed*, rather than *average doors per day installed*. Hence the data did not need to be rejected as would have been done had the cause been the first type indicated above.

Direct Time Study-Extensive Sampling, with Multi-factor Work-units

With indirect work, situations are frequently encountered where the statistical interface (see Supplemental Material, Chapter 17) between the fourth-order work-units and the fifth-order work-units is either so complex, or the relationship between the two orders of work-units is so tenuous, that the necessary information cannot be obtained from the study of a single man's work. The work-units produced have a multi-factor relationship with the time required. Hence the term, multi-factor work-units. A modification of direct time study-extensive sampling has been found to be fully applicable for developing time standards in such situations. The modification consists of a hybrid approach using both the extensive sampling technique and mathematical analysis.

With the hybrid approach, the observations are made in the same manner as with direct time study-extensive sampling. The categories are work-unit

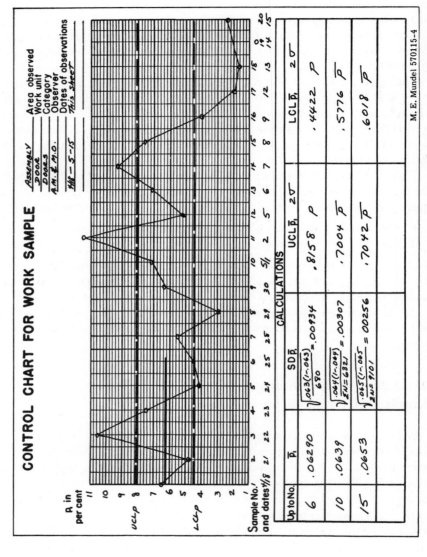

Fig. 21.6—*Control chart for daily p_1 assemble doors.* (Courtesy Industrial Engineering Dept., S & C Electric Co.)

oriented. The information concerning the work-count is obtained from other data sources. However, in contrast with the more normal work situation, the correct way to count the work-units is not usually known. The proper way of counting the work-units is determined by a mathematical analysis of the time information and all of the possible work-count information. The mathematical techniques used range from linear programming to curve fitting "by eye."

A technique of this type is needed with work-units such as "Sausage manufacturing in-plant inspection service provided," a work-unit described in Chapter 17 as being produced by the Meat Inspection Activity of the Consumer and Marketing Service of the U.S. Department of Agriculture. This work-unit presents a work measurement problem quite different from the work-units described in previous chapters. However, the Meat Inspection Activity has 16 such work-units produced in over 1000 locations. Many other government regulatory agencies have similar work. The work of roving, in-plant inspectors in private industry, salesmen, and similar jobs have many aspects in common with the work of the government regulatory inspectors. There is much need for an adequate technique for determining required manpower resources for, and allocating to, such activities. The tasks performed by the sausage (or other process plant) inspector are neither cyclic nor repetitive. The inspector of the process-type plant travels in a random fashion throughout the plant, responding only at times to specific work-generating systems such as the before start-up sanitation check, checking incoming shipments of raw materials, or placing government seals on products moving under Federal control. Most of the time is spent maintaining surveillance, random spot-checking of meat ingredients, spices, labels, net weights, continuing plant sanitation, employee hygiene, and so forth. A motion picture record of such an activity would be difficult to make although it could be made. However, how one would analyze it leaves much open to question. The predetermined time system approach is clearly inappropriate. Certainly some other technique needs to be employed.

It must be remembered, in the situation being discussed, we are not seeking a work measurement coefficient that will tell us only how much inspection capability is required for the situation which is the subject of the work measurement study, although this is the usual condition for work measurement. Rather we are seeking to relate various dimensions (a multiplicity of factors) which might characterize any establishment, to the need for inspection capability. To restate this, rather than a work measurement coefficient for a *specific* plant inspected we are seeking the standard data coefficients for converting *any* plant of the general type serviced to a statement of the required inspection capability resource. We are seeking a coefficient for converting a quantity of workload (the pertinent dimension of each and all of the plants of the type under consideration) to a quantitative expression of required resources (inspection capability). This type of work measurement problem is akin to many other diverse government activities.

Let us examine various aspects of the modified direct time study-extensive sampling technique in terms of its use for setting time standards for the jobs of maintaining process-type plant inspection surveillance.

It was found that it was not possible to record, by manual means or even by voice tape, a running account of what any inspector did, together with the time for each part of his activity. The work pattern was so varied that while one set of acts was being recorded (together with their time and appraisal of pace) another set of events had occurred and was missed in the recording. Further, the quantity of records made from the observation of one inspector would have been enormous; from the requisite group, the quantity preposterous. However, inasmuch as the inspectors worked by themselves, or completely independently from all of the other inspectors in a multi-inspector establishment, it seemed that random trips to observe the inspector would either be a hopeless task or produce bias in the data. The observer needed to stay with the inspector. If the observer was with the inspector at all times, a stratified or periodic type of observation would make better use of the observer's time. In most cases to date such a sampling pattern has been used. The observer also, as with the normal time study method, could evaluate the pace whenever the activity which was being performed at the time an observation was made was of such a nature as to permit this to be done. Hence, bias by the inspector's work pace could be removed.

However, when the matter of a work-count is considered, a new problem arises. In contrast with most situations subjected to work measurement, the variables which affect the requisite capability of process inspection in a plant have a more tenuous effect. Also, they could not be ascertained *a priori* with any certainty. This is another way of saying that the proper method of counting the work-units could not be determined before the studies were completed. Hence, data concerning all possible ways of counting the work-units was collected. A number of sets of complete observed data, together with data relating to the possible work-counts, had to be obtained in different plants so as to permit examination by mathematical techniques to determine which, if any, ways of counting had any real relationship and, if so, in what manner.

In actual practice, four veterinarians were trained to carry on the work measurement study. Three particular features are worth noting. First, the four veterinarians trained (and assigned for six months to this activity) were normally supervisors of processed meat inspectors. They had also done the work themselves. They also had considerable professional pride in seeing a job done correctly and had great insight into the work. Second, Dr. Donald Houston, the veterinarian who trained them, fully understood the objectives, the work-unit structure of the agency and "stayed with" the work measurement activity to assist in any difficulties encountered. Thus the work was a regular managerial activity rather than a nuisance project. Third, the group, as a group, made several practice studies to detect any defects in the procedure and to see if all eventualities had been anticipated. Subsequently, the procedure was reduced to its final form. These "dry-runs" eliminated much potential backtracking after the study started and should be considered as an almost absolute necessity when this or any sampling technique is used.

The actual routine of the study was relatively simple. For six months, each of the four observers went each week to a different meat processing plant. The plants were selected so as to give a wide variety of types and combinations of processing, and so as to cover all sections of the country. Travel and initial observations of how effectively the inspector to be observed maintained the plant in conformance with Federal standards occupied each Monday. On Tuesday the observer followed the inspector all day so as to habituate the inspector to being observed. Also, values of some of the work-units were collected and arrangements made to obtain the work-counts for the days during which actual sampling observations were to be made. On Wednesday and Thursday the actual sampling studies were made and values of the work counts appropriate to those days were collected. Friday was devoted to reducing the obtained data to summary form for submission to the central office and for return travel to the observer's home station.

In the above fashion 96 sets of sampling observations and related values of work-counts were collected. Each set consisted of the data concerning the work-counts and summarized data concerning the performance, together with a narrative description of the plant and its management so as to provide a basis for further analyzing the data in case they did not yield to routine approaches.

The following data concerning the work-counts was collected separately for each fourth-order work-unit; that is, for each type of meat processing over which surveillance was maintained, e.g., sausage manufacture, meat smoking, meat curing, edible oil rendering, and so forth. (The listing also contains the instructions given the observers in order to make sure that the work-counts were collected in a consistent fashion.) It will be noted that the items appear as variables unless one realizes that had they been phrased fully, the items would have appeared as: *square feet maintained under surveillance, number of rooms maintained under surveillance,* and so forth.

a. *Square Feet.* Review blueprints or step-off area when small enough. Include only the area used for the major categories to be studied, e.g., sausage, curing, etc.

b. *Number of Rooms.* A room is a walled-off enclosure. If the room is used for more than one major category, count under each category.

c. *Pieces of Equipment.* Use the special form prepared for this purpose.

Pieces of equipment, if used for more than one major category, should be counted under each category of use. Do not include small pieces of equipment such as smoke trees.

d. *Floors.* This refers to multi-level operation. Count only the number of floors used for the major category.

e. *Positions.* Count the number of house employees working in each major category. If the employee works in more than one major category, count in each category.

f. *Base Items.* A major processed item such as fully cooked ham, sweet pickle ham, all-meat bologna, belly bacon, jowl bacon, etc.

g. *Products.* The number of separately labeled outputs made during the observation period, for example $\frac{1}{2}$-lb. bacon, 1-lb. bacon, hotel-pack bacon, etc., Cryovac ham, boneless ham, sliced ham.

h. *Batches.* In sausage, count the number of chopper loads; in curing, count lots pumped; in smoking, count smoke-house loads. If possible, estimate the size of the batches.

i. *Lines.* The number of automated, mechanized, or manual coordinated packaging lines set up. For example, if six employees are packaging bacon from one slicer, count as one line.

j. *Pounds.* Total pounds of product processed or held under the supervision of the meat inspector being logged exclusive of pounds sliced or packaged. Product held includes ham in cure, sausage in dry room or cooler, dry salt products in storage, etc.

k. *Pounds Sliced.* Number of pounds of products sliced under the major category.

l. *Pounds Packaged.* Number of pounds, under the major category, packaged into self-service packs, for example, 8-oz. franks, 1-lb. franks, etc.

m. *Samples Taken.* Samples taken for submission to government laboratory.

n. *Required Samples per Week.* Number of samples that must be taken per week for submission to the government laboratory to conform to required inspection procedures. This may vary, depending upon station policy.

o. *Seals.* Number of government seals placed.

p. *Shipments.* Number of incoming government-sealed shipments accepted.

q. *Export Certificates.* Number of export certificates issued.

r. *Work Spell.* Length of work spell of the inspector.

The data on performance were recorded over a two-day period during which each observation made was classified both as to major category (or fourth-order work-unit), such as "smoked product inspection provided" or "cured product inspection provided," and so forth, as well as by sub-category, or purpose, such as with respect to sanitation, ingredients, spices, net weight of packages, labeling, laboratory sampling or temperature check, as appropriate. (Not all subcategories were pertinent to all fourth-order work-units.) Further, each observation was evaluated as to necessity and pace. If the observer noted that the inspection activity was not necessary it was categorized as "excess." If the observation was recognized as being of a necessary activity and was manual, it was rated. If not manual but cognitive, it was accepted at face value; that is, given a 100 per cent rating. This part of the procedure was akin to the handling of observations with normal direct time study-extensive sampling.

To continue, in addition to the categories described, the observer also had spaces on his recording form for indicating observations of the following categories:

1. Idle or personal time.
2. Travel inside the plant when such travel could not be ascribed to a fourth-order work-unit (the usual case as reflection will confirm).
3. Travel external to the plants, when an inspector had a multi-plant assignment.
4. Operational supervision; the inspector was obtaining conformance to Federal standards by his visible presence although he was not physically active.[9]

The recorded performance observation data were summarized for each fourth-order work-unit (and its subcategories) as well as for the additional categories. A time attributable to each separate category was computed by the following formula which is the mathematical statement of the sampling theorem stated earlier in this chapter:

$$T_a = T_T \times \frac{n}{N} \times \bar{R}(1 + \text{Adj.}) \times (1 + A)$$

where

T_a = time attributable to a proper performance of the work-unit.
T_T = total time covered by the observations.
n = the number of observations of the particular category.
N = the total number of observations of all categories.
$\bar{R}$ = the average rating of all of the observations of the category.
$(1 + \text{Adj.})$ = a factor to include the difficulty adjustments (objective rating was used).
$(1 + A)$ = an additive to provide a predetermined amount of personal

---

[9] Real insight into the activity is necessary to separate this from "idle"; a further reason for the selection of the type of observer used. The observational procedure was designed to remove any bias caused by inspector method.

time wherein A is a decimal expression of the portion of time so allotted by policy.

When all of the sets of data had been collected, the analysts further adjusted the performance data so as to make all of the data comparable. To achieve this adjustment the time per category was converted to the per cent of the day taken by the category. Inasmuch as each inspector had only one day of capability available per day, this percentage is a measure of the per cent of the inspector's capability required to produce the work-unit. If the work-unit is further recognized as requiring the provision of the capability daily for a year, the per cent thus computed for a data set may be thought of as the per cent MY (man-year) required under the configuration of work-units associated with the particular data set.

Thus, the analysts had for each different fourth-order work-unit, and for each establishment, a number of sets of data which gave the per cent MY capability and the values for all work-counts which constituted the dimensions describing the establishment. By various mathematical techniques[10] the pertinent work-counts were determined and evaluated.

Evaluation, however, also included an examination of the credibility of the results. For instance, the required MY capability for "Sausage manufacturing in-plant inspection service provided for one year" was finally determined to be a function of:

$$E + P + W(10)$$

where (with respect to sausage manufacture):

E = number of pieces of major equipment.

P = number of plant direct-labor employees.

W = average hourly weight of product in thousands of pounds.

There is no aspect of the above equation which strained the credulity of the loggers (who had experience at this work). It seemed reasonable that the number of pieces of major equipment (a measure of the sanitation problem including area), the number of employees (a measure of the number of places violations could occur), and the production (a measure of the batches which had to be observed), all affected the required capability. Further, the plotting of the values represented by the equation $E + P + W(10)$ against the MY of required capability for each data set indicated a good fit; there were no data points which suggested the existence of sizeable unexplained variation. The plot of the data sets for the sausage inspection activity appears in Figure 21.7.

In a similar fashion other fourth-order work-units were found to be determinable as follows. (The values relate to equipment, personnel, and so forth, in the plant, assigned to the specific product group.)

[10] Correlation, multiple regression and linear programming, as well as curve fitting were used.

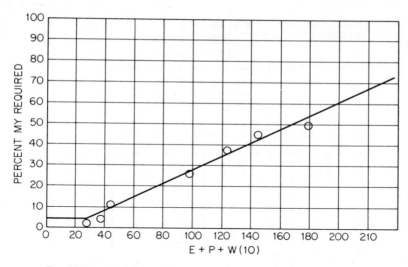

Fig. 21.7 — *Weighted values of work counts plotted against MY of required inspection capability for "Sausage manufacture in-plant inspection service provided."*

Product Group	Factors and Relationship with MY
Canning	$MY = f(BI + PR + 3W)$
Smoked product	$MY = f(0.5E + P + W)$
Curing	$MY = f(A + E + 2P + 5R)$

and so forth, where:

f = function of
BI = number of base items
PR = number of products made during average day
W = average hourly weight of product in thousands of pounds
E = number of pieces of major equipment
P = number of direct-labor personnel in plant
R = number of rooms

The final form of the data for "Inspection required for sausage manufacturing plant provided for one year" is shown in Figure 21.8. Similar tables were developed for all fourth-order work-units related to processed product.

Internal travel was found to be a function of the area of the plant devoted to each different type of fourth-order work-unit, e.g., a sausage plant generated an internal travel workload of 0.12 per cent of a man-year per 1000 square feet, canning 0.04, smoking 0.18, and so forth.

The data described to this point cover all activities performed within

```
PROCESSED MEAT INSPECTION DIVISION
NON-REPETITIVE ASSIGNMENT STANDARD : #1

                    ACTIVITY : Sausage
Variables included: (1) Equipment (E) per standard list
                    (2) Plant employees (P)
                    (3) Average hourly production (W)
                    (4)
                    (5)
Equation:  Base computed value (BVC) = E + P + W(10)
```

BVC	Basic % M.Y.	BVC	Basic % M.Y.	BVC	Basic % M.Y.	BVC	Basic % M.Y.
22	1	97	26	172	51	247	76
25	2	100	27	175	52	250	77
28	3	103	28	178	53	253	78
31	4	106	29	181	54	256	79
34	5	109	30	184	55	259	80
37	6	112	31	187	56	262	81
40	7	115	32	190	57	265	82
43	8	118	33	193	58	268	83
46	9	121	34	196	59	271	84
49	10	124	35	199	60	274	85
52	11	127	36	202	61	277	86
55	12	130	37	205	62	280	87
58	13	133	38	208	63	283	88
61	14	136	39	211	64	286	89
64	15	139	40	214	65	289	90
67	16	142	41	217	66	292	91
70	17	145	42	220	67	295	92
73	18	148	43	223	68	298	93
76	19	151	44	226	69	301	94
79	20	154	45	229	70	304	95
82	21	157	46	232	71	307	96
85	22	160	47	235	72	310	97
88	23	163	48	238	73	313	98
91	24	166	49	241	74	316	99
94	25	169	50	244	75	319	100

Fig. 21.8 — Standard data for "In-plant sausage manufacture surveillance maintained."

federally inspected processing establishment.[11] These standard data permit the dimensions of each establishment served (the quantity of workload) to be converted to a statement of the quantity of manpower resources required for each establishment. Previous manpower allocations were made on the basis of pure judgment. Work measurement was used to introduce a rationale, consistency, and an equitable distribution of work to individuals.

---

[11] There are some other minor activities which are performed and for which work measurement coefficients have been developed but which have not been discussed. The discussion of these would add only length to this presentation.

CHAPTER 22

The Fractioned Professional Estimate

In the setting of a standard time by means of a *fractioned professional estimate* (FPE), one or more individuals, knowledgeable in the subject matter of the work-unit (or work-units), lists the components of the work-unit as a first step. The listing must be in discrete, homogeneous steps (lower-order work-units), sufficiently small so that an estimate of the time required to perform each separate step may be made with reasonable accuracy. The key word is *reasonable*. In this case reasonable means sufficiently close to expectable fact so that the corrective action (of the subsequent steps of managerial control) is minor. However, it is worth noting that even gross errors of estimate can later be detected and can be corrected after a small lapse of time. Of course, to make a fractioned professional estimate (FPE), experience in actually performing either the work-unit or work-units like it, is desirable in addition to knowledge in the subject-matter area.

The making of an FPE includes the making of visible, documented assumptions concerning all of the steps in the work-unit, as well as all of the factors affecting the workload. This listing facilitates the employment of the details of experience for the conversion of these steps to a quantitative statement of the resources required. Further, the FPE constitutes a recording of the "know-how;" it also pinpoints steps where technological change would be particularly effective.

The FPE is the principal technique used in setting standard times for activities such as those analyzed with the network diagrams explained in Chapter 7. It also is an ideal technique for setting standard times for workers in research and development laboratories, or foremen and other supervisors. It can also be used for salesmen. It is applicable to many government field workers, such as the Field Veterinarians of the Animal Health Service of the U.S. Department of Agriculture, Mine Inspectors of the U.S. Department of the Interior, Soil Conservation Field Men of the U.S. Department of Agriculture, Auditors of the U.S. Department of Defense, and so forth. It can also be applied to product design engineers, industrial engineers, management analysts, tool designers, and so forth.

In the areas of activity which have been enumerated, time standards are set presently, for the most part, by a judgmental process[1] partially similar to the FPE but differing in one vital way: the components of the work-unit assigned as a task are not separated. Hence, these details are not recorded. The FPE introduces the following advantages:

1. The basis of the estimate, the lower-order work-units, can be examined and discussed.
2. The accuracy of the estimate can be checked, part by part.
3. The subsequent correction of the estimate may be performed with respect to either the anticipated lower-order work-units or the anticipated time required for their performance.
4. The details of the "know-how" are recorded.
5. The effect of technological change can be pinpointed.
6. The need for technological change can be pinpointed.
7. Participation in making the estimate can be obtained on a meaningful basis.
8. The estimates permit more effective control because of their more adequate size.

For the above reasons, the use of FPE's is an important way of providing standard times for facilitating managerial control in areas of activity long considered as not readily amenable to real managerial control.

The FPE also replaces, to a large extent, the concept of the *manning pattern*. A manning pattern results when gross historical data are used to determine how many of one type of employee (such as personnel interviewer) are needed per other type of employee (such as employee hired), or when the number of designers is computed on the basis of the number or value of designs, and so forth.

An FPE, in terms of the four factors associated with a standard time, has the following characteristics:

1. W/C. A count of one is used; a model of the work-unit is constructed in terms of separable, smaller work-units.
2. W/T. An estimate is made of the time required for each of the smaller work-units by people knowledgeable in the subject-matter area; experience with the work-unit or similar work-units is highly desirable.
3. M. Implicit in the estimates.
4. A. May either be implicit in the estimates or an allowance may be added after the estimates are completed.

Two cases dealing with the use of an FPE will be presented in the body of

[1] If they are set at all.

this chapter. A third, and somewhat more complex case, appears in the Supplemental Material.

CASE I   THE USE OF THE FPE FOR A PROJECT-TYPE WORK-UNIT

"The word *project* is used to describe all of the activity associated with the attainment of a goal when the activity necessitates some extensive, unique responses, different, in many details, from the previous performance of tasks employing the same area of knowledge or different in that considerable ingenuity may be required in devising or developing an answer.

"A project exists when the goal is to produce an advance in the state of an art, to develop a design with unique features, to select a preferable course of action from among many alternatives, and so forth.

"The meaning of the word *project* will include the performance of the design activities within an industrial enterprise, such as physical plant design; product-process design (including research and development); man-job design (including the relationships between man-jobs); control-system design; or the design of a method of employing a specific technology to handle a problem within a control system, e.g., the design of a mathematical model and the development of the method of solving such a model. A pure research activity would also be described as a project or a series of projects, depending upon the singularity or multiplicity of the separable goals, as well as upon the level of control being examined. A project, therefore, may be considered as a unique fifth-order work-unit, a one-of-a-kind output, containing highly individualized problems."[2]

A project, in some cases, may be represented by a network diagram, as in Figure 7.1, or each step of such a network may be considered a project, depending upon the level of control being examined. Whichever is the case, the FPE used to develop the time values shown in Figure 7.2 would be made separately for each activity in the network.

Each activity in such a network, or any separable project which is not part of a network, should have a *project plan*, whether an FPE is to be made or not. A project plan is merely a listing of the separable, discrete, homogeneous steps contemplated as necessary to achieve the goal. The conversion of a project plan to an FPE requires only the use of experience to estimate the time for each step. Part of a project plan converted to an FPE is shown in Figure 22.1. Note that each separated step begins with an action verb. Such a format assists in keeping the steps homogeneous. However, it does not seem appropriate to make this too rigid a rule. Too many small steps make a project plan confusing; steps which are too large for estimates defeat the purpose.

[2] M. E. Mundel, *A Conceptual Framework for the Management Sciences.* New York, N.Y.: McGraw-Hill Book Company, 1967, pp. 243–244.

TECHNICAL PLAN _ LIVESTOCK SLAUGHTER INSPECTION STAFF PROJECT 67-3

Project Description and Objective:

To investigate present meat industry handling practices and methods,
prior to and after freezing, of meat byproducts (offal) and to determine and recommend, if needed, adequate handling practices, freezing
methods and controls to assure wholesomeness of meat byproducts
intended for both domestic and export markets. This project will consist of three (3) subprojects.

Subproject 1

This subproject will consist of a study of current industry offal handling
practices and freezing methods. This study will be limited to livers,
kidneys, hearts, and tongues. This subproject will consist of four (4)
phases.

PHASE I

Review literature and consult scientific experts in government, industry,
and trade associations to determine recommended chilling, freezing, and
holding temperatures for meat byproducts.

Man Hours	Step	
40	A.	Search published scientific sources for chilling and freezing standards and time-temperature relationships for meat byproducts.
25	B.	Search published trade association (American Society of Heating, Refrigeration & Airconditioning Engineers, etc.) sources for recommended product freezer and freezing standards.
25	C.	Consult with USDA scientific experts (microbiologists, food technologists, etc.) for unpublished scientific opinions and recommendations for freezing of meat byproducts.
20	D.	Search for and solicit industry opinions on sound industry procedures for packaging and freezing meat byproducts.

PHASE II

This phase will consist of a study design.

Man Hours	Step	
6	A.	Consult with statistical staff to design statistically sound survey plan of industry meat byproduct handling practices and freezing methods.
12	B.	Determine type of temperature measuring devices needed to con- duct survey.

Fig. 22.1—Part of a project plan converted to an FPE.

Common sense must be employed. However, in most cases, literature search,
work performed on travel status, experimental setup design, experimentation, computation, consultation, and so forth, usually should be recognized
as separate steps.

The making of a project plan has several advantages. First, it provides
a basis for a discussion between the person undertaking the project and his
supervisor concerning the feasibility of the contemplated sequence. Second,

a file of such project plans (after their completion) provides a record of the "know-how" for performing such work. This record is invaluable in orienting new members of a project group in the manner in which work is done. Third, it facilitates the project workers proceeding in an orderly fashion. When the FPE's are added, the value of the project plan is enhanced. These FPE's provide a basis of agreement between the person undertaking the project and his supervisor concerning the depth to which the project is to be undertaken. Second, the "know-how," when the project is completed, includes the knowledge of the amount of manpower associated with steps of such projects. Third, it also orients the new employee with respect to the depth to which the typical project is pursued.

The project plan with its FPE's has still additional values related to managerial control. When the time dimensions of each project are known, the person undertaking the project can examine his current calendar of work and determine when he can complete each step, phase, or total project. The apparently feasible schedule may be determined. If such a schedule is satisfactory, the subsequent performance may be monitored by the person on the project and assistance sought when schedule nonconformance appears likely, as well as when subject-matter assistance is needed. A better managerial climate with less "expediting" can be obtained. If, on the other hand, the feasible schedule is not suitable, the FPE's of the project as well as other work on the calendar will be examined. The alternatives of changing project schedules, dropping projects, altering the various FPE's to change the depths to which various steps of various projects are to be pursued, and so forth, will be examined. Such a procedure makes it much more likely that the most suitable alternative will be selected than in a situation where neither project plans nor FPE's exist and chance determines the alternative which occurs.

Simple reporting systems comparing the FPE's to actual times are frequently used in order to assist each person on project work to aid in maintaining managerial control; guidance is sought when nonconformance to schedules appears in the offing.

It can be seen that if the FPE's are unrealistic, much corrective action will take place, although attention will be focused on the cause. However, managerial action to minimize the effect of schedule failure can be taken. Also, subsequent FPE's will reflect the details of experience more accurately and will more closely approach reality.

CASE II   THE USE OF THE FPE TO SET
SUPERVISORY STANDARDS

The application of the technique to supervisory activities has other benefits besides the determination of how much supervisory work can be given to a supervisor. The development of an FPE for a work-unit consisting of supervision is, in most cases, also the first detailing of how the task of supervision is to be performed, although certainly such detail would seem to be a prerequisite for obtaining a known quality of supervision. Of course, if how supervision is to be performed has already been documented, the development of the FPE is much easier; unfortunately, this is seldom the case. Further, the FPE represents, to a large extent, an agreement between the upper manager and the supervisor concerning how time will be spent; hence much less time is needed for what is otherwise normal routine discussion concerning who should do what. In addition, if effective supervision is not obtained under the pattern of the FPE, then alternative strategies can be evolved and tried.

An examination of the method of using an FPE with supervisory work seems a particularly useful example in that such activity is found in all organizations, both industrial and governmental. For instance, in the meat inspection activity described in Chapter 17 there is a fourth-order work-unit, "Supervision of inspectors provided." The illustration which follows consists of the data developed by means of the FPE approach, by line managers, staff, and experienced circuit supervisors for the assignment of "Officer in Charge" (OIC). The OIC is the supervisor of a group of plants and inspectors in an assigned area in the meat inspection activity. Although this supervisory task is performed by a government employee, the procedure with an industrial job would be exactly the same. The details, of course, will vary with every supervisory position. It was anticipated that the data from the FPE would be used in the following manner:

1. The existing OIC assignments would be measured to determine the equity of the assignments.[3]
2. The assignments would be adjusted to provide the proper workload.[4]
3. The forecasts of new plants by size (number of inspectors) and type for future time periods would be used to determine the increment to the workload of the OIC's and to assist in determining when changes in manpower resources would be needed.[5]

The group[6] decided that the work of an OIC could be meaningfully divided into major subgroups:

[3] If this was not an on-going activity, these assignments could have been synthesized. The procedure would work in the same manner except for this difference.

[4] If adequate manpower is not available, the FPE provides the basis for the OIC and his boss agreeing on what corrective action, e.g., extra time or some work slighted, is most appropriate.

[5] With an industrial supervisor the items used to structure the FPE would probably be products, lots, machines, workers, and so forth, rather than plants and inspectors. This difference would affect only the details of making and using the FPE. The general procedures of developing and using the FPE would not change.

[6] This is from the meat inspection activity of the Consumer and Marketing Service and represents the results of the coordinating efforts of Dr. Donald Houston, a veterinarian

1. Office activities.
2. District meetings.
3. Administrative travel.
4. Travel between plants.
5. Review and evaluation of program and personnel.

Each of these subgroups was individually examined and work-units and substeps identified. An FPE was made for each substep. The individual FPE's were added for each work-unit and, with a man-year taken as 2080 hours of work, the hour values were converted to man-years (MY) to facilitate use. For instance, office duties were listed and the FPE's made as follows:

1. *Office Duties.*   *Hours/month*
   a. Assignment lists.   1
   b. Daily assignment adjustments.   1
   c. Review periodic reports.   10
   d. Counsel on construction.   6
   e. Correspondence and reports to District Director's Office.   20
   f. Telephone contacts (all).   8
   g. Arrange and promote training programs.   4
   h. Appeals (Packer).   4
   i. Study memos, letter, regulations, etc. to keep current.   10
   j. Public relations (meetings, etc.).   2
   k. Investigate and report on employee actions.   1
   l. Evaluation and promotion.   2
   m. Contacts within other state and Federal agencies.   2
   n. Industrial relations.   2
   o. Union relations (AFGE).   1
   p. Special projects and visitors.   12
   q. Interview new employees.   2
   Total = 88 hours/month = 1056 hours/year . . . . 51.00% MY

The details of the other work-units and their FPE's were:[7]

2. *District OIC Meetings.*
   One meeting per month, all day
   8 hours/month = 96 hours/year . . . . 4.60% MY

3. *Administrative Travel.*
   Two five-hour trips per month
   10 hours/month = 120 hours/year . . . . 5.70% MY

---

assigned to lead the work measurement activity, with a group following only the general procedure set forth by the author; the actual work is by Dr. Houston and his group, although I have taken certain liberties to shorten the example.

[7] The list given here is somewhat shorter than the actual list, so as to shorten the presentation. The part shown has been chosen so as to show all the kinds of work-units encountered and how they were used to set standards.

4. *Between Plant Travel Time.* (Based on dispersion of plants in the circuit.)
   a. *All plants in circuit in one metropolitan area.*
      1. For plants reporting directly to the OIC
         One trip per month; one hour per trip
         1 hour/plant/month = 12 hours/year/plant . . . . . 0.57% MY/plant
      2. For plants reporting to a subordinate supervisor
         One trip per three months; one hour per trip
         $\frac{1}{3}$ hour/plant/month = 4 hours/plant/year . . . . . 0.20% MY/plant
   b. *Plants scattered in one metropolitan area and in surrounding territory.*
      1. For plants reporting directly to the OIC.
         One trip per month, two hours per trip
         2 hours/plant/month = 24 hours/plant/year . . . . 1.14% MY/plant
      2. For plants reporting to a subordinate supervisor.
         One trip per three months; two hours per trip
         $\frac{2}{3}$ hour/plant/month = 8 hours/year . . . . 0.39% MY/plant
   c. *Plants scattered all over the territory with no cluster in any metropolitan area.*
      1. For plants reporting directly to the OIC.
         One trip per month at three hours per trip
         3 hours/plant/month = 36 hours/plant/year . . . . 1.71% MY/plant
      2. For plants reporting to a subordinate supervisor.
         One trip per three months; three hours per trip
         1 hour/plant/month = 12 hours/plant/year. . . . . 0.57% MY/plant

5. *Review and Evaluation of Program and Personnel.*
   a. *Standard for VS Review.*[8]

	Total time per month (average in minutes)
Review use of procedures	
Ante-mortem and humane slaughter	60 min.
Post-mortem	50
Carcass dispositions	30
Product review	
Offal: coolers, condemned inedible control	60
Departmental review	
Sanitation, facilities, general operation	60
Administrative review	60
Direct supervision, training, planning	90
Habituation and internal plant travel	30
Total = 82 hours/year = ...	3.84% MY/inspector

   b. *Standard for VI Review.*

Review use of procedures	
Ante-mortem and humane slaughter	30 min.
Post-mortem	60

[8] A category of inspector who is also a subordinate supervisor. In the review of a VS the work accomplished by his subordinates is also reviewed. This is why the VS review time is somewhat greater than the VI review time shown later.

Carcass dispositions	30
Product review	
Offal, cooler, condemned inedible control	30
Departmental review	
Sanitation, facilities, general operations	45
Administrative review	15
Direct supervision; training, planning	120
Habituation, internal plant travel	15

Total = 69 hours/year = ... 3.31 % MY/inspector

The following formula was used, together with the FPE data, to compute the supervisory workload associated with any circuit:

$$SWL = 61.00 + T_1 N_1 + T_2 N_2 + VS \times 3.84 + VI \times 3.31$$

where

SWL = supervisory workload in percent of man-years/year.
61.00 = the percent of man-years for the constant part of the work:
      1. Office duties.
      2. District OIC meetings.
      3. Administrative travel.
T_1 = a travel time based on how the plants are dispersed.
N_1 = number of plants reporting directly to an OIC.
T_2 = a travel time based on how the plants are dispersed.
N_2 = number of plants reporting to a subordinate supervisor.
VS = number of subordinate supervisors reporting to OIC.
VI = number of inspectors reporting directly to the OIC.

Using the PFE's and the above formula, the Consumer Protection Activity determines its supervisory manpower needs. The same data is used to assign work to individuals, constantly appraise the changes in workload, and redistribute the work as feasible. Further, the standards constitute a plan for supervision; if difficulties are encountered the strategy may be changed in a known fashion.

Supplemental Material

CASE III   THE USE OF THE FPE TO ASSIST MANAGERIAL
CONTROL IN THE ANIMAL HEALTH DIVISION,
AGRICULTURAL RESEARCH SERVICE, U.S. DEPARTMENT OF AGRICULTURE

The Animal Health Division (AHD) represents a particularly complicated problem for managerial control, as control was defined in Chapters 1 and 17. The resources for the AHD are appropriated by the Congress as 14 separate funds. The use of each fund is restricted (with some small exceptions) to the work of controlling, eliminating, or preventing either a specific disease or specific group of diseases of animals, or for the maintenance of humane methods of handling animals. The work, however, is carried out under fifty State-Federal agreements, or agreements covering an area. The total territory covered consists of the fifty States, Puerto Rico and the Virgin Islands. The work necessary to achieve the program goals is shared between Federal and State employees in a different manner in each area covered by an agreement. Hence, although managerial control must begin with the usual identification of the hierarchy of work-units, the conversion of these work-units to a statement of required resources must be performed on an area-to-area basis before being aggregated into a national budget.

The work-units, at the measurable level, consist of services rendered by veterinarians, epidemiologists, diagnosticians, livestock inspectors, and various support personnel, in assisting in diagnosing animal diseases of economic importance, in making trace-backs to determine and eliminate the source of the disease, in maintaining a monitoring service to make certain that a disease which has been eliminated in an area is not reintroduced, and so forth. The list of work-units is far too extensive to reproduce in its entirety in this book. This illustration will therefore be limited to an example selected to demonstrate the method of making and using an FPE.

For instance, one of the fifth-order work-units produced in most of the areas served is: *A healthier animal population maintained by attention to direct control and elimination of hog cholera in swine.* Typical of the fourth-order work-units produced in the field as component parts of this fifth-order work-unit are:[9]

10901. *Diagnostic referral completely processed*
10902. *Epidemiological study completed*
10903. *Garbage feed premise maintained under inspection*

Managerial control requires (among other things) that:

1. A forecasting system be developed to project the number of each work-unit that will be required in an area.
2. A coefficient be developed to permit each individual work-unit (or any number of it) to be converted to a statement of the amount of resources required.
3. The forecasting system be checked by a comparison of the actual events to the anticipated events and the actual use of resources be compared to the planned use of resources.

Normal biometrical methods make item 1 (above) feasible; these same

---

[9] I have retained the numbering system of the AHD. The list has been greatly foreshortened.

approaches facilitate the performance of part of item 3. Various information flow systems are required, of course, but these only require the application of well-known data-collection technology. However, to achieve the remainder of the items, some type of standard time is necessary. It is conceivable that the necessary data could be collected by a self-reporting system. However, such systems require an enormous effort on the part of all men in the system, an enormous data reduction procedure, and still fail to give results which have the advantages of the FPE (as those were listed at the beginning of this chapter). It should also be obvious that other work measurement methods listed in preceding chapters are not applicable here.

A project team for the initial effort consisted of an industrial engineer, a thoroughly knowledgeable veterinarian from the central staff, an administrative clerk, and the Federal-Veterinarian-in-Charge from the "pilot" state. It was anticipated that if a standard time for all work-units could be completed for a pilot state, the task of replicating the effort in other states would be greatly reduced; the methods, the procedures, and even the format of the FPE's would be available to them. The additional states would need merely to adapt them to the peculiarities of their territories.[10]

As a first step, the project group developed the details of the hierarchy of work-units referred to earlier. Subsequently, they developed an FPE for each fourth-order work-unit in terms of third-order work-units. Part of such an FPE for work-unit 10901, *Diagnostic referral completely processed*, is shown in Figure 22.2. Where the word "standard" appears in the columns "Factors affecting time," the task was repeated in so many FPE's that a standard time was agreed upon for use in all FPE's. The FPE shown in Figure 22.2 shows only 10 of the 21 steps associated with the total FPE for the work-unit.

All of the FPE's for all of the fourth-order work-units were assembled by fifth-order work-units for convenience of use. Subsequently, a work-unit forecasting system was devised for each fourth-order work-unit and the standard time used to convert this to a statement of the amount of manpower needed to produce the required number of work-units during the year for which a budget was being estimated. This is called "the budget year" or BY. A tabulation of the standard times for the fourth-order work-units comprising the fifth-order work-unit, *A healthier animal population maintained by attention to direct control and elimination of hog cholera in swine*, is shown in Figure 22.3. A form showing the use of the standard time and the forecast of the anticipated number of the fourth-order work-unit 10901, *Diagnostic referral completely processed*, is shown in Figure 22.4. Note the accounting for the split of work between Federal and State employees for this State.

---

[10] This is true in general. However, a few states have required outputs not found elsewhere; in such cases they would need to originate an FPE for these exceptions.

BASIC TIME ESTIMATE DATA FROM PROFESSIONAL EXPERIENCE

STATE: Maryland DATE: Current year

5TH ORDER WORK UNIT CODE	5TH ORDER WORK-UNIT DESCRIPTION
109	Healthier swine with respect to HOG CHOLERA

4TH ORDER WORK UNIT CODE	4TH ORDER WORK-UNIT DESCRIPTION
1091	Diganostic referral completely processed

ACTION	MODIFIER	SUBJECT	SPECIAL FACTORS AFFECTING TIME	TIME PER OCCURANCE IF PRORATA	CATEGORY OF PERSONNEL DIRECTLY INVOLVED			
					HOURS Fed. Diag.	HOURS St. Diag.	HOURS Fed. Vet.	HOURS St. Vet.
01. Receive phone call	from office	a suspected case of hog cholera	STANDARD		.17	x*	N/A	
02. Make arrangements by phone	with vet., diagnostician or state employee	to accompany to premises	Average 3 calls		.50	x	.17	x
03. Drive car		to farm	Average trip (outgoing)		1.50	x	.75	x
04. Discuss herd history	at farm with farmer		Average		.50	x	.50	x
05. Change clothing	at farm	to work clothes	STANDARD		.17	x	.17	x
06. Inspect and observe	ante-mortem at farm	swine herd	Average herd size		.42	x	.42	x
07. Take temperatures and collect blood samples	at farm with help	swine	10-20% of average herd; 5-6 blood samples		1.00	x	1.00	x
08. Make post-mortem and collect tissue	at farm, with help	swine, complete necropsy	2 carcasses		1.00	x	1.00	x
09. Fill out form	at farm	ANH 13-7	Added time during post-mortem; STANDARD		.17	x	.17	x
10. Follow-up disposition of carcasses	at farm	carcasses	By owner		.75	x	.75	x

*Indicates same time if done by alternative employee

Fig. 22.2—Part of the FPE for 4th-order work-unit, "Diagnostic referral completely processed."

STANDARD TIME DATA SHEET FOR BUDGETING AND REPORTING

5TH-ORDER WORK UNIT CODE	5TH-ORDER WORK UNIT DESCRIPTION	STATE	DATE LAST UPDATED
109	A healthier animal population maintained by attention to direct control and elimination of HOG CHOLERA in swine (Fund 400)	Maryland	Current fiscal year

4TH-ORDER WORK UNITS (COMPONENTS OF OUTPUTS)	WORK COUNTS FOR REPORTING AND ESTIMATING	MAN-HOURS BY CATEGORIES OF PERSONNEL						REPORTING TIME VALUES
		Fed. Diag.	St. Diag.	Fed. Vet.	St. Vet.	Fed. Insp.	St. Insp.	
01. Diagnostic referral completely processed	Referrals completely processed	11.43	x	8.35	x			19.78
02. Epidemiological study completed	Studies completed including all premises	49.22	x					49.22
03. Garbage feed premise maintained under inspection	(1)Per premise visit (2)Per district mon't./mo (3)Wash.gbge.ctr./week					1.78 8.00 28.00	x x	1.78 8.00 28.00
04. Quarantined herd administered because of garbage feed lot problem	Quarantine completed and removed					9.11	x	9.11
05. Quarantined herd administered other than garbage feed premise problem	N/A in Maryland							
06. Herd depopulated to remove focus of infection	Herd depop'ed. appraised Premise cleaned and disin. Quarantine released			18.25 1.50	18.17 x	10.75 7.00		29.00 7.00 1.50
07. Survey activity performed	N/A in Maryland							
08. Concentration point and interstate movement monitored	21-day quarantine released					2.17		2.17
09. Minute-man activities completed	Per presumptive or infected premise; Per man of 2-man team					15.60		15.60

x = Alternative person who may perform work; use same time as counterpart

Fig. 22.3—Standard times for all field produced 4th-order work-units comprising 5th-order work-unit, "A healthier animal population maintained by attention to direct control and elimination of HOG CHOLERA in swine."

REQUIRED RESOURCES COMPUTATION SHEET

STATE	DATE
Maryland	Budget year

5TH ORDER WORK UNIT CODE 109
5TH ORDER WORK-UNIT DESCRIPTION Healthier swine with respect to HOG CHOLERA

4TH ORDER WORK UNIT CODE 1091
4TH ORDER WORK-UNIT DESCRIPTION Diagnostic referral completely processed

WORKLOAD GENERATING SOURCE
Private practice vets., owners, state inspectors, etc., requesting diagnostic assistance

PERSONS DIRECTLY INVOLVED Fed. Diagnostician, State Diagnostician, Fed. & State Vet.

PERSONS PROVIDING SUPPORT

HOW DIRECT WORK IS DIVIDED	WORKLOAD SPLIT	Fed. Diagnostician – 67%; State Diagnostician – 33%
	INTERNAL SPLIT	Fed. Vet and State Vet assist the diagnosticians 80% of time; 50% split each

OTHER DATA AFFECTING PRORATA DISTRIBUTION OF TIME VALUES

NUMBER OCCURRANCES IN YEAR	DESCRIPTION	Diagnostic referr.				Positive case			
		BY	+1	+2	+3	BY	+1	+2	+3
	FISCAL YEAR	24							
	WORK COUNT					1			

NUMBER OF SIGNIFICANCE TO FEDERAL EMPLOYEES BY CATEGORIES

NUMBER OF SIGNIFICANCE TO STATE EMPLOYEES BY CATEGORIES

FEDERAL REQUIRED RESOURCES COMPUTATIONS:

10901 Time = No. of D.R. x hrs/D.R. x Fed share
Diagnostician
$\quad$ 24 $\quad$ x $\quad$ 11.43 $\quad$ x $\quad$ .67 $\quad$ = 184 hrs

10901 Time = No. of D.R. x hrs/D.R. x Fed share split x Fed share assist
$\quad$ 24 $\quad$ x $\quad$ 8.35 $\quad$ x $\quad$ .50 $\quad$ x $\quad$ .80 $\quad$ = $\quad$ 80 hrs

STATE REQUIRED RESOURCES COMPUTATIONS:

10901 Time = No. of D.R. x hrs/D.R. x State share
Diagnostician
$\quad$ 24 $\quad$ x $\quad$ 11.43 $\quad$ x $\quad$ .33 $\quad$ = 91 hrs

10901 Time = No. of D.R. x hrs/D.R. x State share split x State share assist
State Vet
$\quad$ 24 $\quad$ x $\quad$ 8.35 $\quad$ x $\quad$ .50 $\quad$ x $\quad$ .80 $\quad$ = $\quad$ 80

VETERINARIAN 80
LIVESTOCK INSP.
EPID. OR DIAG. 184
PORT INSPECTOR
INVESTIGATOR
VETERINARIAN 80
LIVESTOCK INSP.
EPID. OR DIAG. 91
INVESTIGATOR

Fig. 22.4—Forecast of work-units and required resources for 4th-order work-unit, "Diagnostic referral completely processed."

Using such procedures, as well as other work measurement methods for other parts of the AHD, it is possible to greatly reduce the speculative elements in the budget and greatly increase the effectiveness of managerial control. The use of the FPE makes possible the economical application of work measurement to areas of activity usually thought of as not only uneconomical to measure but also outside of the range of feasibility.

CHAPTER 23

Time Standards by Fiat

A time standard by fiat is one which is implicit in the design criteria used to design the work-unit or output. (The word *fiat* is used to indicate that the standard is by decree rather than by measurement.) This is the simplest type of work measurement. Of course, it is not always applicable. However, there are many areas where a failure to recognize the existence of this type of standard has caused the expending of much fruitless effort on the wrong aspects of managerial problems. For a simple example, let us take the case of an in-plant seminar with ten days of all-day meetings. The standard time for the seminar leader, *for leading this seminar*, is ten man-days. (This example is so simple that it may sound inane. However, it will be shown that the same simple concept has great applicability to problems which appear to be hopelessly complex if viewed from a wrong aspect.) Of course, the ten man-days does not include the time to plan the seminar; the planning time might well be the subject of an FPE, as those were described in the preceding chapter. However, in the case being discussed, if one wishes to change the manpower resource required to lead the seminar, the problem to tackle is the design of the larger work-unit, *seminar completed*. The problem is one of changing the design of the output rather than one of complex work measurement.

The concept of a standard by fiat is a necessity if we are to think of the cycle of managerial control as being applicable to all of the manpower resources of an organization. It also is useful in directing our attention to the areas where change is feasible rather than expending fruitless efforts on work measurement.

Let us take a somewhat more complex example than the one given previously. Let us assume that we are attempting to determine the total number of men required for the Secret Service of the United States. If we were to make a complete work-unit analysis of the hierarchy of work-units of this organization[1] one of the sub-fifth-order outputs would be: *A guarded White House*. Within this sub-fifth-order output one of the fourth-order outputs would be: *A guard post maintained 24 hours a day all year*. The determination of the number of such guard posts needed is a design problem; it is a function of the design criteria of a guard post. It is not a work measurement problem. The work measurement problem concerns only how many man-years are needed per year to maintain each such post.

For instance, the design criteria for such posts may be: "All avenues of approach to the White House are to be under the simultaneous observation of at least two posts at all times; each post must be under the simultaneous observation of at least two other posts; the posts must be unobtrusive."[2]

Some may question the validity of using design criteria of the type given. However, this use would appear to be no more arbitrary than putting one spare tire in an automobile, two ice-cube trays in a refrigerator, and so on. One may object and say these substantive design criteria are based on market surveys, consumer-use reports, and so on. However, surely one should anticipate that the Chief of the Secret Service uses a parallel experience-study procedure for developing his design criteria. The similarity should be obvious. Note also, the selection of two ice-cube trays per refrigerator affects the amount of manpower resources needed to make refrigerators, although additional work measurement studies are needed to determine the effect. In the case of the White House guards the effect is merely more immediately discernable and less subject to modification once the design criteria have been fixed.

With respect to the White House guard posts, the work measurement problem concerns only the determination of the amount of manpower resources required to produce a unit of output, *One guard post maintained 24 hours a day, all year*. Predetermined time systems cannot be used. Extensive or intensive sampling studies would shed no light on the problem. The appropriate approach is much simpler.

Let us examine the actual work measurement problem. Each fourth-order work-unit requires 365 (days) $\times$ 24 (hours/day) = 8760 hours of direct "on-post" time each year. A guard works eight hours per day, five days a week, $52\frac{1}{4}$ weeks per year, or 2090 hours per year. However, as in most such cases, one cannot expect all of these hours to be available for the direct production of "on-post time": the fourth-order work-unit has associated

[1] Such an analysis has been made and is used for budgeting. For obvious reasons it cannot be given here.

[2] For obvious reasons the statement is hypothetical, resembling only in general nature the actual criteria. For a similar reason, the data given later are fictitious substitutes for the real data.

with it other tasks besides being "on-post." For instance, experience may indicate that 14 per cent or 293 hours[3] per year will be lost because of sick and annual leave. This must be taken into account when computing the manpower resources needed per fourth-order work-unit produced. There are additional losses created by additional design criteria associated with the fourth-order work-unit. For instance, it may have been decided that it is desirable for the guards to maintain proficiency in the use of small arms and that two hours per month (another design criterion with a fiat-type, but verifiable, effect) should be devoted to this. There will be other similar factors. A table may be constructed as:

Payroll time	*hrs*	*2090 hours/year*
Less:		
Sick and annual leave at 14 per cent	(293)	
Small arms proficiency training		
2 hours/month × 12 months	(24)	
Physical fitness		
1 hours/day × 261 working days	(261)	
First-aid refresher courses		
8 hours/course × 1/year	(8)	
Lectures on handling the public		
8 hours/lecture × 2/year	(16)	
Total deductions from available time	(602)	
Time available for actual guard post work		1488 hours/year

Hence, work measurement coefficient equals:

$$\frac{8760 \text{ hours/post/year}}{1488 \text{ hours on-post time/man/year}} = 5.89 \text{ man-years/post}$$

The manpower required in man-years (MY) for all the guard posts would be the number of such posts multiplied by 5.89. Essentially, the standard is by fiat, being computable from the design criteria. It is to be noted that this situation, properly analyzed, is one of relative simplicity.

It should further be noted that the sub-fifth-order work-unit, *A guarded White House,* will contain other fourth-order work-units. If these are to be aggregated, each fourth-order work-unit must be subjected to an adequate time study or work measurement procedure, as the terms are used in this book. Each fourth-order work-unit may need a different procedure, but each must be subjected to work measurement before being aggregated to determine the total manpower resources needed for the fifth-order work-unit. Unfortunately, all are not as simple as the one given. However, the one given would not be simple if the concept of design criteria and a standard by fiat were not separated and identified.

---

[3] The use of fictitious numbers does not affect the validity of the example.

Supplemental Material

Let us examine some additional examples. An organization may wish to divide a country into territories or regions to facilitate administrative activities. It may wish to have a regional director (of sales, service, and so forth). It may also want an assistant regional director in order to make certain that there is always someone readily available in the region to perform the assigned functions. It is important to recognize that the first and most important problem is the selection of the basis for dividing the country into regions. What basis is to be used? What are the design criteria? Subsequent to this, an FPE approach may be used in order to determine whether a regional director can do all of the things he is expected to do. Perhaps the use of the FPE will show that the work of two regions could be combined under one regional director. However, this combining would result in a change in the design criteria for a region, and in a change in the design criteria for a regional director. These are not work measurement problems.

In a chemical plant it may be desirable to have an individual to watch certain gages and controls *in case something happens*; then he is there to react. The placing of a man at such a post is the result of design criteria; it is not a simple work measurement problem. The design criteria may not, of course, be correct. However, the recognition of the area of examination, is a first step toward the development of a solution. Perhaps the real risk of something happening should be evaluated. Perhaps the "watcher's" span of attention (the number of gages watched) can be increased without increasing the risk; perhaps the possibility of simultaneous emergencies is too high to do this. These are not work measurement problems as we have defined them. They concern the design of the output; that which has been called design criteria. Management technologies other than those described in this book must be used. Methods studies involving mathematical models may be undertaken to improve the design of the output. The subsequent standard time will be essentially by fiat, as the term has been used.

CHAPTER 24

Time Standards
by Mathematical Analysis

In most cases, data obtained over a period of time concerning the production of outputs and the use of manpower resources may be subjected to mathematical analysis to determine the relationship between required manpower resources and outputs. The result is a *standard time derived by mathematical analysis*. The available mathematical techniques are numerous; additional judgment may be introduced to alter or modify the data so that values approaching real standard times may be obtained. The mathematical techniques usually enable one to determine time standards faster than with any other type of approach. In some cases they are the only readily feasible methods. The use of such techniques does not, of course, preclude possible subsequent refinement with other more detailed techniques. As with direct time study-extensive sampling, the most difficult problems encountered in the use of the mathematical techniques usually concern the determination of the work-units and how to count them.

In terms of the factors constituting the equation of a standard time, time standards by mathematical analysis employ the following:

1. W/C. The number of work-units produced may be taken from historical records; as an alternative, a data gathering system may be introduced to obtain these data over a selected period of time. The period of time needed depends upon the mix contained in the work-unit work count.
2. W/T. The work time may be taken from past payroll or attendance

records or gathered in connection with the data gathering system related to the work-units or outputs.

Note: With some mathematical techniques the simple division of the work time by the work count (as with other work measurement techniques) may appear to be replaced with a much more complex mathematical analysis, depending on the relationship between the units used to count the work and the work time. This comes about because, in some cases, the work time associated with a variety of work counts may be aggregated. The mathematical techniques are employed to determine how much of the total time to divide by each separable work count; the basic equation still holds.

3. *M.* Depending on the mathematical technique chosen, the value of *M* may be taken as 1 (past performance is assumed to be satisfactory) or judgment may be used in a systematic fashion so as to introduce an *M* greater or less than unity.
4. *A.* If historical data is used, the value of *A* is usually implicit in the data; if a special data gathering technique is employed, the data may be adjusted to correct the actual *A* to some desired value.

In much of the literature the types of standards discussed in this chapter are referred to as statistical standards. In that the word, statistical, is commonly associated with the theory of probability, and in that probability is not necessarily computed with so-called statistical standards, the titles, mathematical time standards, or time standards derived mathematically seem more appropriate ways of referring to these types of standard times.

The primary advantage of standards derived by mathematical procedures is the rapidity with which they can be determined for most situations. Therefore the development of such standards often precedes the employment of other techniques. The mathematical standard serves as a stop-gap standard, until accurate measurements may be developed. However, there are situations wherein the mathematical techniques seem to offer the only feasible approach.

The usual form of a mathematically derived standard time is a standard expressed in *man-hours per work-unit*, as with standard times developed with other procedures, but the work-unit, instead of being a second- or third-order work-unit is frequently a work-unit encompassing all of the activity required to produce a fourth-order work-unit, or the entire processing of a product, or a large phase of the processing, or the processing of a variety of products with some similarity. However, this is not an inherent limitation in the techniques available. Standards for smaller work-units may be derived by mathematical procedures. In some cases the mathematical approach may be the most suitable of all of the work measurement methods.

An examination of the basic steps in mathematically deriving a standard, as compared with the steps of other work measurement techniques, will reveal the reasons for the rapid computation of the statistical standard as well as its inherent deficiencies. However, if these deficiencies are understood, the standards may have considerable utility. The comparison is as follows:

Steps in Other Techniques	Steps in Computation of Mathematical Standard
1. Define standard of measurement.	Past practice (or some gross modification of it) accepted as typical performance.
2. Describe product, equipment, and record method for detailed operation. (Not fully implemented with some techniques.)	No method record made. Only a rough description of the work-unit is made, and a variety of similar work-units may be lumped together.
3. Observe time taken by an actual operator, or postulate such time values.	Production and work time records used.
4. Rate or relate observed performance to definition of standard, or select a suitable estimate.	An arbitrary mathematical basis is used to determine the relationship between production and man-hours.
5. Apply allowances of a known amount.	Usually assumed to be included in gross production and work time records.

As indicated, the means of determining a mathematical standard is relatively simple. A mathematical relationship is determined between man-hours expended and the work-units produced. Often, the records necessary for the computation of such a standard are already available as part of the organization's normal production and payroll records. However, this is seldom true of indirect work or service activities. These are seldom counted in a manner appropriate for even mathematical techniques. If service activities are represented by a suitable hierarchy of work-units, the mathematical techniques may be highly effective procedures.

Note also that the application of a mathematical standard may require the assumption that past practice was not unusual in any respect and that the performance indicated may be expected in the future. As an alternative, gross assumptions as to the quality of the total of past performance may be made and used to modify the results. Whichever assumption is made, deviations from some mathematical standards are often hard to interpret. There is often no way of separating the amount of deviation ascribable to factors subject to the control of the working group whose performance is measured by the standard, and the amount ascribable to factors outside their control. In such cases, even when the performance meets the mathematical standard, the significance is not always clear. Inasmuch as mathematical standards lack most of the basic controls of the other work measurement approach, we have no way of knowing whether changes both in the factors controlled by the group and in factors outside of their control counterbalanced each other. This defect is primarily associated with the simpler techniques.

For instance, in a foundry the simple mathematical standard may be computed for the number of man-hours per ton of castings produced. A change in the number of man-hours per ton may be due to a different work pace, to more or less difficult castings, to a change in the size of castings requiring more or less castings per ton, to a change in the amount of delays caused by the equipment, to more or fewer new and less skilled additions to the work force, to more or less supervision, to changes in the efficiency of scheduling, or to unbalanced changes in different directions in several of these factors. In addition, the factors cited are by no means a complete list. Consequently, if performance deviates from the simple mathematical standard, remedial measures are not specifically indicated and additional data must be obtained in order to determine the necessary action. This is in comparison with performance measured against standards where the method and the work-unit are more specific and most of the effect of factors outside of the control of the group being measured are removed from the measure of performance of the group. However, the simple mathematical standard does measure the over-all effect of all of the factors affecting the work force and thus has considerable management utility if used with a great deal of discretion. In particular, all deviations should not immediately be ascribed to poor performance from the work force.

Mathematical standards derived by more complex methods have been used with considerable success for some but not all of the common uses of work measurement.[1] They are frequently basic measures that may be supplemented eventually with standards for smaller work-units. However, it should be pointed out that there are situations, particularly where the final work-unit has almost infinite variety, in which the mathematical standards are the only standards feasible on an economic basis, and their wise use is often of tremendous assistance to management. Particularly with certain types of service work-units, the use of mathematical techniques appears to be the only feasible method for work measurement. However, these techniques are not the simple ones. Also, the use of newer work measurement techniques, such as those described in Chapters 20 through 23, permits many applications of more detailed work measurement to be made in situations previously deemed uneconomical to measure except with gross mathematical standards.

In summary, mathematical standards, correctly derived, may be used for

---

[1] Such standards came into wide use in government operations between the years 1917 and 1949 because of the Congressional prohibition, during this period, of direct time study.

almost all of the uses of standard times. In some cases they are fully comparable to standard times derived by other methods. Of course, in some cases, the details of the manner of use need to be altered. For instance, if the mathematical standard for a foundry is man-hours per ton of castings,[2] it would probably not be proper to compute an individual's pay on this basis. However, a whole plant's productivity wage increment may be based on a measure of this general type, if the product mix is stable. However, in most cases, a simple measure of this type is seldom feasible; a better system of work-units is needed.

Most work with mathematically derived standards has suffered from either the use of an inadequate system of work-units for describing the outputs, or from the use of unreasonable assumptions in manipulating the data. In many cases both types of errors have been made. With an adequate system of work-units and with adequate mathematical procedures excellent results can be obtained; situations which defy the setting of standards by other methods may be handled, in some cases, quickly and with ease. Some procedures may involve much detail but they enormously extend the range of work to which work measurement may be applied to usefully serve management control systems.

Supplemental Material

The supplemental material of this chapter increases in mathematical complexity in each of the four sections. However, nothing other than high-school algebra is needed for a study of these materials. The details of the techniques are described and examples are given. Four approaches are examined. They are:

1. The simple computation of a gross mathematical standard.
2. The computation of a gross mathematical standard by curve fitting or simple regression.
3. The use of specialized data collection methods and mathematical techniques for deriving standards more detailed than gross standards.
4. The use of linear programming and multiple regression for deriving standards more detailed than gross standards.

The Simple Computation
of a Gross Mathematical Standard

A gross mathematical standard is one wherein the work count of a single work-unit is used to quantify the output. It gives an over-all measure reflect-

---

[2] If the mix of the size of castings is not a stable statistic, this will not be a good work-unit.

ing the results of all the factors affecting the work situation. This procedure is the least applicable, of all of the procedures given in this book (with due allowance for the range of application of each), for the derivation of work measurement values for all of the uses of managerial control. The error is usually in the assumption that the single work count is an effective indicator of the required manpower resources.

For an example of the procedures, prior to a discussion, suppose the production and payroll records of a foundry gave the following data (the numbers have been rounded for convenience):

Month	Man-Hours of Direct Labor	Tons of Castings Produced
Jan.	4,800	550
Feb.	3,300	480
Mar.	3,900	350
Apr.	3,000	240
May	1,000	150
June	1,200	350
July	3,200	390
Aug.	4,500	490
Sept.	4,000	590
Oct.	6,200	840
Nov.	4,600	700
Dec.	6,300	640

Three methods of computing gross mathematical standards are in common use. They are:

1. *The standard based on the weighted average.* From the data given, the total man-hours for the twelve months were 46,000; the total tons of castings produced, 5,770. For the period, 7.96 man-hours were expended per ton of castings produced. This standard reflects not only the monthly figures but gives more weight to the months with more tons or more man-hours.

2. *The standard based on the unweighted average.* If we compute the man-hours per ton for each month and average these figures, we obtain a standard of 8.11 man-hours per ton. This standard gives each month an equal weight, regardless of tons produced or man-hours consumed.

3. *The standard based on a fixed measure other than the average.* Taking the hypothesis that work previously performed without a standard time to work against is performed in an inferior fashion, as far as diligence of work and supervision are concerned, some applications of gross mathematical standards employ measures such as the third quartile as the basis of the standard. To

determine such a measure for the data previously given, it is necessary to compute the man-hours per ton for each month and then place these in an array as follows:

Man-Hours Per Ton	Month
3.42	June
6.57	November
6.66	May
6.78	September
6.88	February
7.38	October
8.20	July
8.73	January
9.18	August
9.84	December
11.13	March
12.50	April

The third quartile is defined as a value below which are three-quarters of the values. In this case the third quartile would be between 6.78 and 6.66, or 6.72 man-hours per ton. In an isolated application such a procedure may be justifiable, but when several such standards are in use in different parts of one plant such a procedure introduces new, questionable features. It has already been noted that the mathematical standard confuses factors under the control of the group (whose performance is measured against the standard) with factors outside of their control. If the data for one standard have more dispersion than the data for a second standard, we have no way of knowing whether the difference in variation is attributable to the first work group or not, or what factor caused the additional variation. The use of the third quartile, or any similar measure, to set the standard will result in a standard furthest from the average for the group of data with the most dispersion. Consequently, it may be more difficult to attain this standard than another standard for another task whose data showed less dispersion. It will also be more difficult to administer such a set of standards in a uniform fashion and their already limited utility will be further reduced.

The value of a standard computed by one of the gross computational methods lies in the simplicity of the calculation; this may be a small value if the results are not valid. Reasons for suspecting the validity are often numerous. First, if the data given, such as were used in the preceding examples, are the only data, nothing is known about the quality of performance implicit in the data and in the resultant standards. This certainly detracts from their usefulness. Second, if nothing is known concerning the manner in which manpower was allocated during the data base period, we may have even less use for the resultant standard. If monthly manpower was allocated on the basis of gross outputs scheduled, or if the gross outputs were scheduled on the basis of the monthly man-hours available, the computed standard may be merely a recomputation of the a priori assumption; this would hardly appear useful. It is not uncommon to find either such a circular computation or computations approaching such nonsense.

Third, and most important, the gross computational methods assume that gross outputs, in the manner used to count them, are directly related to man-hours required. As noted in Chapter 17, when discussing hierarchies of work-units, and as noted earlier in this chapter, this is not usually a valid assumption. Further, using the gross computational techniques, particularly methods 1 and 2, how well the computed standard really fits the data is not known.

As will be seen later, almost any other method of computing a mathematical standard, other than the three described here, appear more useful. Certainly, more information than mere gross data seems necessary if the standard is to have any credibility. However, the methods described are employed and their defects must be understood if one is going to suggest alternative procedures.

A type of gross unweighted mathematical standard is often hidden under the names *manning ratio* or *staffing pattern*. Staffing patterns were mentioned in Chapter 22; it was further indicated that in many cases an FPE could be developed more usefully to set a standard for many situations currently covered by staffing patterns. A staffing pattern was defined as follows: "Ratios of one type of employee to another type are used to set a 'standard' for manning." For example, a plant may have seven tool designers and 300 direct machine operators. The staffing pattern for tool designers is 1 per 42.9 workers. These gross measures are often used as rules of thumb to compare various periods of activity or different plants. There are great dangers in their use. The danger increases as the relationship between the two groups used in the ratio becomes more tenuous. For instance, it would seem more reasonable to accept a ratio of chair-assistants per dentist, or tool-crib attendants per machine operator, than the example given previously of tool designers per machine operator. In either case, however, the use of an FPE approach seems more realistic unless a quick temporary rule of thumb is desired. Using such ratios to compare from plant to plant is even more dangerous. The assumptions concerning the similarity of the factors affecting the ratio are too large for ready acceptance. At the very most, such ratios may have some value in assisting in evaluating a change from period to period within a plant, or the difference between plants. If, in such cases, an investigation is made concerning the reason for the change in values within the plant, or the reasons for the differences between plants, some additional useful information may result.

The Computation of a Gross Mathematical
Standard by Curve Fitting or Simple Regression

Curve fitting is the development of a curve for the plot of a number of data sets when each data set represents a work count and a work time value.

Simple regression is the development of a statement describing a straight line relationship among data sets, such as described above, by the method of least squares. (See Supplemental Material, Chapter 20, item 1.)

For an example let us use the same data as was used with the discussion of the simple computation of a gross mathematical standard.

Figure 24.1 is the graph of the data previously given, with a trend line drawn. The trend line would be taken as a standard. In this case the standard would be variable and would be a function of the tons of castings scheduled.

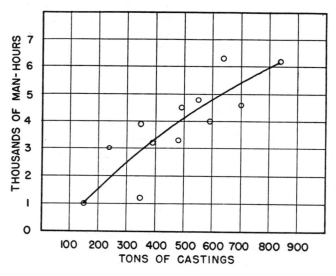

Fig. 24.1 — *Man-hours of direct labor expended per month in a foundry vs. tons of castings produced per month. A trend line has been drawn.*

To fit a trend line some assumption must be made concerning the probable nature of the relationship, i.e., straight line, hyperbola, and so forth. Just what relationship is shown in Figure 24.1 is not easily determined. In some cases, plotting the data on log or semi-log graph paper assists in formulating some hypothesis concerning the nature of the relationship. Whatever relationship is finally assumed, the reliability of the relationship should be evaluated by statistical means in order to avoid making the standard reflect a chance or spurious relationship. (The subject of statistical reliability of relationships is beyond the scope of this book and reference should be made to adequate material on this subject before endeavoring to apply this procedure. Particular reference should be made to "curve fitting," "goodness-of-fit," and "correlation.")

As an alternative to mathematical analysis and curve fitting, a visual method may be employed to fit a credible curve to the data points. The criteria would be credibility and a sufficiently good fit such that all data points are either within ± 5 per cent of their equivalent value on the curve or a valid reason for the lack of fit, which does not conflict with the theory of the curve, has been ascertained. Such an approach may require the introduction of additional work-units; if this increases validity, it seems appropriate.

As an alternative to fitting a curve, as in Figure 24.1, a straight line may be fitted to the data by the method of least squares. The use of this approach involves two assumptions which are not always valid:

1. A straight line is the best explanation of the relationship between the two variables.
2. Large deviations from the line (the distance from a data point to the fitted line) should be given greater weight in locating the line than small deviations.

In either case, curve or straight line, the plot of Figure 24.1 reveals two facts not revealed by any of the gross computational procedures. It reveals that the fitted curve and the actual data have many discrepancies; some of these discrepancies are sizeable. For instance, at 640 tons of castings per month the actual man-hours used exceeded the amount explained by the standard by approximately 1,300 man-hours or 26 per cent. Also, at 350 tons per month, one data set exceeded the amount explained by the standard by approximately 900 man-hours or 30 per cent; with another data set for the same tonnage the man-hours used were below the amount suggested by the trend line by 1,800 hours or 60 per cent.

It would appear most reasonable to assume that there are additional sources of variation or additional variables that have not been accounted for; that the trend line shown has severely limited utility. If additional data is not available, it does not appear that such a trend line could serve well the purposes of managerial control.

However, let us assume that more than a trend line of a gross mathematical standard of low utility is desired and that additional data is available or can be collected. Further, let us assume that we wish to apply curve fitting in a useful fashion. Our first change must be to discard the concept of a single work count and find a series of work-units which are more appropriate.

Let us assume that an analysis of the outputs or shipments of castings reveals that when the castings are separated by factors affecting the amount of time required per casting weight, there appear to be at least three different kinds of castings:

1. Castings ranging from 1 to 10 pounds, without cores.
2. Castings ranging from 1 to 10 pounds, with cores.
3. Castings ranging from 11 to 50 pounds, without cores.

A new table may be constructed as:

Month	Man-hours of Direct Labor	Tons of Castings		
		Type 1	Type 2	Type 3
January	4,800	400	30	120
February	3,300	80	95	305
March	3,900	200	89	61
April	3,000	100	95	45
May	1,000	50	16	84
June	1,200	0	28	322
July	3,200	250	23	117
August	4,500	250	85	155
September	4,000	300	23	267
October	6,200	450	51	339
November	4,600	300	45	355
December	6,300	450	79	111

Even a cursory analysis of the data indicates that the mix of kinds of castings is fluctuating; that the single work count was not a reliable statistic. Let us array the table by man-hours to obtain:

Month	Man-hours of Direct Labor	Tons of Castings		
		Type 1	Type 2	Type 3
December	6,300	450	79	111
October	6,200	450	51	339
January	4,800	400	30	120
November	4,600	300	45	355
August	4,500	250	85	155
September	4,000	300	23	267
March	3,900	200	89	61
February	3,300	80	95	305
July	3,200	250	23	117
April	3,000	100	95	45
June	1,200	0	28	322
May	1,000	50	16	84

As a side note, the above data reveal the incorrectness of the third quartile method for the gross standard; the mix at the third quartile level is not a representative mix; a standard set on this mix will not predict manpower requirements.

A straight line may be fitted to the above detailed data by simple means. Equations may be written for the first three months, as follows:

$$6,300 \text{ hrs.} = 450X_1 + 79X_2 + 111X_3$$
$$6,200 \text{ hrs.} = 450X_1 + 51X_2 + 339X_3$$
$$4,800 \text{ hrs.} = 400X_1 + 30X_2 + 120X_3$$

where

X_1 = the standard time per ton for castings of Type 1 (unknown).
X_2 = the standard time per ton for castings of Type 2 (unknown).
X_3 = the standard time per ton for castings of Type 3 (unknown).

Values for X_1, X_2, and X_3 may be computed from these simultaneous equations by the simple algebraic procedure of determinants.

A weighted value of the outputs may now be computed for each month by multiplying the outputs by their respective computed times. A new graph may be drawn of the computed man-hours versus the actual hours. If a good fit is not obtained, a new computation should be made, or in that three adjoining points were used, a curve may be detected and fitted by visual or mathematical means. If the curve is poorly defined, three close data points (in this case, January, November, and August; or February, July, and April) may be used to get time values to assist in plotting the points in a manner better defining the curve.

However, if the function still appears to be a straight line, but the points do not fit the line well, three new data sets should be selected. If the relationship is found to be a straight line, but the computations from the first three points do not give a good fit, the months selected for the new computation require that some additional assumptions be made. For instance, if it does not seem reasonable to assume that the pace of work ever exceeded a reasonable pace, the data from the three lowest points (with respect to the first line) would be used to set up new equations. As an alternative, if it can be assumed that the pace, from month to month, varied from above normal to below normal, the data from points which tended to place the line so that an equal number of points were above and below it would be used for the three new equations. In some cases facts such as the knowledge of much idle time during a particular month may be ascertained and such points allowed to fall well off the curve. (Such points would, of course, not be used to compute the values of standard times.) If a good fit on a believable basis cannot be obtained, the investigation must continue until explanations of the data points seriously off the line (more than say ± 5 per cent) can be made, or the system of work-units expanded to enable the close fitting of a line or curve. In this respect the work resembles that used with direct time study-extensive sampling with multi-factor work-units, as described in the Supplemental Material of Chapter 22, item 2.

The curve fitting methods which have been described have much utility. However, in many cases, when the work-unit system is expanded to its true size so that the categories are relatively homogeneous, the number of work-units may exceed the number of data sets which can be obtained. In such cases, the mathematical technique described is not applicable; more complex mathematical approaches must be used; such techniques are described in the next two sections.

The Use of Specialized Data Collection Methods and Mathematical Techniques for Deriving Standards More Detailed than Gross Standards

In the cases of mathematically derived standards which were discussed to this point, when there were deficiencies in the standards, the usual cause was the inadequacy of the work-counting system. Other defects were in some cases indicated but the foregoing was basic. As noted in Chapter 17 the problems of "what to count" and "how to count" must be solved before one can select and apply a work measurement technique.

In addition to the types of work situations described to this point, situations will also be encountered in which the work-unit list is large, the work is performed in scattered locations, and observations may not be feasible. Such characteristics often accompany service-type work-units. However, work measurement data is needed to effect managerial control; some special techniques must be developed and applied.

In such cases it is not likely that historical data containing work counts of a suitable list of work-units is available, although such data is occasionally found. In most cases, some sort of data collection system must be designed and put to use. In such cases a self-reporting system may often be used in which the people doing the work report their use of time and the work completed. These data are then used to determine a standard time for each work-unit identified. Obviously, a consistent set of work-units must be used. Obviously, there are risks concerning the accuracy of reporting and of errors in the tabulation of such data. Experience suggests that the reporting of the use of time and the completion of work-units usually should be restricted to a base period used to establish the time standards. The base period should be as short as possible, yet extensive enough to provide a sample of the mix of work. Subsequent reporting may be confined to reporting the work-units produced. Attempts to maintain a continuous reporting of both time use and work performed frequently deteriorate in accuracy unless the reporting group fully believes in the need for such data on a continuous basis. In all cases, the need to demonstrate to those reporting the necessity for the data collection is a prime requisite. The more professional the group, the more the demonstration of need is feasible; the more true participation for the necessary duration can be obtained.

One of the typical places where such an approach is one of the few feasible approaches is with so-called undercover work. To attempt to observe such work would obviously be impossible. Also, maintenance work, sales work, purchasing offices, and so forth, may at times be advantageously studied with this technique. The technique can be substituted for the use of the FPE approach when some real amount of repetition of the work-units can be expected, or when the number of work-units is extremely large. Various data gathering and data reduction techniques may be employed to reduce the cost of and the time required for setting such standards.

The Office of the Solicitor, U.S. Department of the Interior, presented a complex work measurement problem for which the self-reporting approach was appropriate. The discussion which follows will present the analysis of the problem situation which led to the selection of the technique. This will be followed by a short discussion of the actual methods used, the standard times obtained, and the use made of these data.

The work-unit structure of the Office of the Solicitor was discussed in Chapter 17, pages 299 through 301. It will be recalled that there were 29 locations, 36 program branches and bureaus served, and 59 fifth-order work-units. The fifth-order work-units were types of *matters*. A matter was defined as a document or inquiry requiring a formal professional response.[3]

From the above brief material let us define the basic workload forecasting and work measurement problems before examining further details. First, no data existed which would permit a forecast of the workload; it had never been counted or quantified as matters in the fashion proposed. Second, the associated activities were performed in 30 locations (29 subarea offices and Washington). Third, with 36 sixth-order work-units (Offices and Bureaus served) and 59 fifth-order work-units (types of matters), there are potentially 2,124 separate third-order work-units, if a third-order work-unit is "All of the tasks associated with the production of one matter (fourth-order output) of one kind of a fifth-order output for each sixth-order work-unit." Hence, if the time associated with a performance of a particular third-order work-unit is affected by the location in which it is performed, then there are potentially $2,124 \times 30 = 63,720$ work-units to forecast and for which work measurement coefficients must be developed.

For the above reasons a self-reporting type approach was selected. Such an approach could be carried on over an extensive period so as to cover a

---

[3] This is a brief description; the work-unit, in actual practice, was defined much more fully to assure uniform counting of outputs produced.

representative sample of the mix of outputs; it would not require the addition of a large number of analysts; it would not require observers who would need to be able to tell what an attorney was working on by observation (if this is at all possible); such an approach would allow both a work-count (as a basis for future forecasting) and an attributable time for each third-order work-unit in each separate office to be accumulated simultaneously. Of course, such an approach would not permit purification of the time data by extracting any unreported idle time from the reported data, or by judging pace; reported data would have to be accepted at face value. Values could not be generated for M and A in the basic equation of a standard time. An assumption would have to be made that adequate values were included in the self-reported data and that these values were not excessive. Obviously, the quality of the data would reflect the attitude and ability of those being measured. Hence, adequate steps were taken to assure effective participation of all professional staff. The need for the study was demonstrated; the backing of the study by the Chief Solicitor was made clear.

To facilitate the reporting of the work-count for each work-unit, a coding system was devised. Although a six-digit code was used, the last two digits were for the collection of information not directly related to the work measurement study. Hence, they will not be discussed here.

The first two digits were used to identify the *program served*; the second two digits indicated the *subject-matter nature* of the "matter."

The codes were:

CATEGORY I CLASSIFICATION BY PROGRAM AREA (FIRST TWO DIGITS)[4]

When the activity or matter concerns serveral Bureaus or Offices an appropriate summary number is to be used, e.g., if the problem concerns 51 and 53, use 50; if the problem concerns 19 and 43, use 10; if 25 and 61, use 10.

10—. Office of the Secretary
    18—. Ofc. of Water Resources Research
    19—. Job Corps

20—. Ofc./Asst. Secy. for FW&P
    22—. Bu. of Com. Fisheries
    25—. Bu. of Spt. Fish. & W.
    28—. National Park Service

30—. Ofc./Asst. Secy. Mineral Resources
    31—. Geological Survey
    32—. Bureau of Mines
    34—. Office of Geography
    35—. Office of Coal Research
    36—. Of./Minerals & Solid Fuels
    37—. Oil Import Administration
    38—. Office of Oil & Gas

[4] From "Workload Analysis Reporting System," Office of the Solicitor, U.S. Department of the Interior, November 1967.

40—. Ofc./Asst. Secy. Pub. Land Mgmt.
  41—. Bu. of Indian Affairs
  42—. Office of Territories
  43—. Bu. of Land Management
  48—. Bu. of Outdoor Recreation

50—. Ofc. Asst. Secy. W&PD
  51—. Bonneville Power Admin.
  53—. Bureau of Reclamation
  56—. Southeastern Power Admin.
  57—. Southwestern Power Admin.
  58—. Alaska Power Admin.

60—. Asst. Secy. Water Pollution Control
  61—. Federal Water Polln. Control Admin
  65—. Ofc. of Saline Water

80—. Asst. Secy./Administration

90—. Asst. Secy./Administration
  91—. Ofc. of Mgmt. Oper.
  92—. Ofc. of Survey Review
  93—. Ofc. of Budget
  94—. Ofc. of Mgmt. Research
  95—. Ofc. of Personnel Mgmt.

CATEGORY II   CLASSIFICATION BY TYPE OF WORK (SECOND TWO DIGITS)

These classifications are grouped by kinds of matters having some general relationship to assist in locating them and are not necessarily strict subdivisions of the general group heading.

INTERNAL, Office of the Solicitor
—00. Personnel actions, including supervision, work assignment, work organization, improvement study, etc., internal to the operation of the Office

PERSONNEL, other than Office of the Solicitor
—10. Organization and individual duties
—11. Safety problems or reports
—12. Speeches or publications by employees
—13. Employee claims for loss, damage or injury
—14. Coordination between bureaus or offices
—15. Conflict of interest issues or opinions.
—16. Other employee problems or matters, other than classified above, including internal regulations
—17. Internal reports, other than safety
—18. Reports of the Department or Branches or Offices
—19. Improvement studies

CONTRACTS-RATES, including documents, letters, discussion advice, formats, opinions, negotiation, litigation, etc., excluding patents and copyrights
—20. Power development
—21. Power other than above
—22. Water user, irrigation
—23. Water user, other than irrigation
—24. Construction, other than power
—25. For research and development, other than mgmt.
—26. For goods or services other than above
—27. Rate and Fee Development

LEASES, including claims, permits, licenses but excluding patents and copyrights
—30. Lease, oil and gas
—31. Lease, other minerals
—32. Lease, other than above
—33. Permits, all
—34. Licenses, all

PATENTS AND COPYRIGHTS
—40. Applications
—41. Acquisitions

—42. Licenses
—43. Search
—44. Not otherwise classified

LAND-Ownership, mining claims, grants, entries, etc.
—50. Acquisition by exchanges
—51. Acquisition by gift or donation
—52. Acquisition by eminent domain
—53. Acquisition by purchase
—54. Grants or patents
—55. Entries, all aspects
—56. Transfer
—57. Mining claims
—59. All other

LEGISLATION-POLICY, including Congressional, State, Proclamations, Policy Statements and Departmental Regulations for external application
—60. Congressional legislation
—61. State legislation and regulations
—62. Proclamation
—63. Departmental Policy, not concerning personnel
—64. Departmental Regulations for external application

TORTS; CLAIMS (other than land and not related to contracts)
—70. Tort, trespass
—71. Tort, all other
—72. Discretionary irrigation
—73. For loss or damage, other than employee

INDIANS
—80. Probate
—81. Tribal laws and customs
—82. Jurisdiction over, other than tribal
—83. Rights, privileges and responsibilities other than above
—84. All other

MISCELLANEOUS
—90. Rights and privileges, other than Indian and not classifiable into any previous category
—91. General Correspondence, not classifiable into previous categories
—92. Grants and loans
—93. Mixed batch of various letters or documents
—94. Water pollution abatement
—95. Water quality standards
—99. Not otherwise classifiable

In addition to the coding details already given, each attorney and all clerks who were assigned the task of collecting the data were given a uniform set of instructions and a uniform set of forms. The form for the collection of work-count information (by location) is shown in Figure 24.2. The form for reporting the use of time (by individual attorney) is shown in Figure 24.3. This last form, used daily by the attorneys, produced a considerable amount of data. Hence, the format was designed to be "machine readable"; the data could be converted directly to punch card or magnetic tape record.

The data were collected for a six-month period so as to provide data from a representative mix of work. The data were processed in the following manner:

The data contained in the Work Log and Document Count forms were converted to punched cards. The combined inputs of matters processed and related work times were matched and merged onto a tape. The tape was processed to produce printed summary data, and data sorted by divisions and by field offices. These data provided, for each location, the average time

```
Document  Count          United States Department of the Interior
                                        Office of the Solicitor
SOLICITOR'S     WORKLOAD       ANALYSIS      PROJECT

Office: _____        Week ending: _____
```

WORKUNIT CODE	Initial Pending	Received Tally	Count	Disposed Tally	Count	Final Pending

Fig. 24.2 — Form for use in Office of Solicitor for collection of work count of work-units completed in a location.

standards[5] for the various matter codes processed. In addition, time standards were established for matters regardless of which Bureau or Office created the workload. Each location was given a complete set of time standards. The complete list consisted of a mixture of the following three kinds of standard times:

1. A time standard for each *kind of matter* (category II of the classification) was developed without regard as to which Bureau or Office it concerned.
2. A time standard for each *kind of matter by program area* (categories I and II of the classification) was developed where there were ten or more occurrences of the matter within the Office of the Solicitor.
3. A time standard for each *kind of matter by program area by Division or Office of the Office of the Solicitor* was developed where that Division or Office had five or more occurrences of that kind of matter.

Each Division and Office was given the time standards meeting criterion 3 above that it generated during the study. Where there were less than five occurrences, the time value used was determined by criterion 2 above. If no value existed in the 2 accumulation, the weight value of criterion 1 above was used. In this way every Division and Office had the best available time standards for any type of work that might occur. It is to be noted that the time standards derived from those matters occurring frequently in a Division or Office will constitute the great bulk of its work; that the infrequent use of the balance of the time standards will have only a minor effect in its periodic reports.

Three exceptions to this method in selecting time values were made. Basic time values meeting criterion 1 were used for code 91, General Correspond-

[5] These were called "weights" in the actual study.

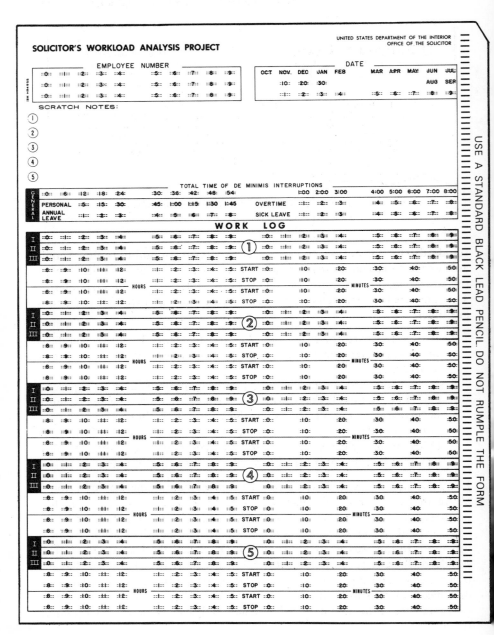

Fig. 24.3 — Form for use by attorneys in Office of Solicitor for reporting use of time during data collection period.

ence; code 93, Mixed Batch of Documents; and code 99, Not Otherwise Classifiable.

A non-matter factor was developed which reflected time expended that was not picked up in the standard times; e.g., time expended but no matter recorded, and other similar recording errors. Since no one office differed from another in this respect by more than one or two per cent and since these differences did not appear to be statistically reliable, a common non-matter factor was applied to all divisions and offices as part of an allowance. (This is related to A in the basic equation for a standard time.)

In this manner a work measurement coefficient was developed, for each fourth-order work-unit for each office, for use with a forecasting system related to the need for assistance generated by each type of work in each Office or Bureau served. A sample of the work measurement data is shown in Figure 24.4.

WEIGHTS FOR MATTERS
OFFICE OF THE SOLICITOR
U.S. DEPARTMENT OF THE INTERIOR

PROGRAM AREA CODE - 43 - Bur. of Land Mgmt.

FOR USE IN OFFICE 06 - PUBLIC LANDS

EDITION 1

Matter code	Weight	Matter code	Weight	Matter code	Weight	Matter code	Weight
4300.	10.30	4326.	5.17	4350.	5.10	4380.	1.51
4310.	4.39	4327.	2.43	4351.	3.68	4381.	3.72
4311.	1.88	4330.	5.97	4352.	2.88	4382.	2.91
4312.	16.50	4331.	8.10	5353.	4.32	4383.	8.14
4313.	2.57	4332.	0.74	4354.	6.31	4384.	3.00
4314.	3.72	4333.	3.55	4355.	17.54	4390.	2.79
4315.	2.57	4334.	12.76	4356.	1.37	4391.	1.64
4316.	10.23	4340.	5.56	4357.	14.93	4392.	3.24
4317.	0.40	4341.	1.00	4358.	4.71	4393.	4.63
4318.	1.25	4342.	1.48	4360.	2.16	4394.	4.78
4319.	54.58	4343.	0.34	4361.	2.75	4395.	7.25
4320.	5.32	4344.	8.91	4362.	5.14	4399	3.03
4321.	0.50			4363.	2.32		
4322.	2.36			4364.	13.66		
4323.	4.09			4370.	2.13		
4324.	1.51			4371.	10.74		
4325.	2.33			4372.	2.51		
				4373.	5.02		

Fig. 24.4—Time standards for matters for one Program Branch served by one location of the Office of the Solicitor, U.S. Department of the Interior.

Subsequently, a forecasting system and a work-performed and backlog reporting system (by work-units) were developed and put in use. These systems, together with the work measurement data make it possible for the Solicitor to:

1. Objectively estimate the professional manpower required for future periods of time.
2. Allocate professional manpower to locations.
3. Temporarily redeploy manpower to locations where undesirable backlogs occur.

4. Evaluate the degree to which productivity is maintained or improved.

5. Evaluate the timeliness of service rendered (backlog analysis).

These, as have been frequently noted, are the managerial uses of work measurement data. For situations, such as the Office of the Solicitor, the self-reporting approach appears to be almost the only feasible approach. The data are being used successfully.

In other situations, difficulties have been encountered in the use of such self-reporting work measurement techniques. These difficulties are usually attributable to three types of causes. First, the system of work-units may have been inadequately developed; the work-units did not meet the critieria for well-chosen work-units. The usual defects are that they are usually not mutually exclusive nor all-inclusive; they do not relate to the objectives of the organization. Second, the purpose of the self-reporting may not have been made clear. Indeed, in many cases a system for use of the data may not have been contemplated or designed. It is hard to get effective cooperation in reporting under such circumstances. Third, inadequate time may have been spent in training the people to properly and accurately self-report. Such systems are frequently referred to as "garbage-in" systems. If these deficiencies and their causes are understood and avoided, much effective use may be made of procedures such as described in this section.

The Use of Linear Programming and Multiple Regression for Deriving Standards More Detailed Than Gross Standards

In the section dealing with curve fitting it was indicated that situations might be encountered where the use of appropriate work-units causes the number of kinds of work-units to exceed the number of data sets. A data set, it may be recalled, consisted of information concerning a number of work-counts of a variety of work-units, together with the aggregated work time for the total outputs in the data set. In such cases the normal use of simple simultaneous equations is not feasible. Also, curves cannot be fitted until each work-unit is given a weight. Such a problem did not arise in the use of self-reporting for the work measurement study in the Office of the Solicitor (preceding section) because the data were collected so that an aggregated work time was found separately for the work count of each work-unit. It is worth noting, however, that the number of work-units was very large. If the total work time in each location had not been so separated, it is doubtful whether even a mathematical "unscrambling" or attributing of the work time to each separate work-count would have been feasible.

This section will examine two techniques for setting standard times in situations wherein four conditions exist:

1. The output data and the associated time data is available only as a series of data sets with each data set containing work counts of more than one work-unit.
2. The work count of each work-unit in each data set is separated from the work counts of other work-units.
3. The time for each kind of work-unit is not separated in each data set; the work time is available only as an aggregate for each data set.
4. The number of different work-units for which work counts are available exceeds the number of data sets available; the reverse may also be true.

Such a set of conditions are encountered frequently when using historical production and work time data. The reason for the conditions existing is simple. The data are taken from past records. At the time the events occurred the work-unit structure was not defined. Hence, no division was made of the total time for the data set. For instance, the data available may concern the installation of ship boilers. The total time attributable to each boiler installation may be a matter of record. So are the drawings of each boiler, but each drawing was not described as a series of work-counts of the variety of fourth-order work-units which comprise the fifth-order work-unit, *the particular boiler installed*. Hence, time was not allocated by the fourth-order work-units. The fourth-order work-units and their associated work count may be such as given in the partial list which follows:

(square feet of)	boiler foundation installed
(number of)	boiler tubes installed
(volume of)	header installed
(weight of)	header installed
(number of)	large valves installed

As an additional example, the data may relate to a foundry making very large castings such as steel rolling mill frames, or main ship engines. The historical data may be identical in nature to the data for the installation of boilers. The nature of the available data is different from that associated with Case 1 of Chapter 21, the metal-clad assembly department of the S & C Electric Company. In that case it was noted that: "The employees work as a group on a considerable number of units simultaneously, shifting back and forth and helping each other as needed. It is difficult to get accurate time-keeping charges against each unit."

The four conditions describing a situation, for which the techniques to be described will be applicable, will also be found when the relationship between the third-order work-units and the fourth-order work-units is complex and hard to define. Reference should be made to the section on *direct time study-extensive sampling, with multi-factor work-units*, Chapter 21, where such a situation was described.

A similar problem will also be encountered when making a work measurement study of some industrial sales forces, public relations groups, press services, or Market News Services or Crop Reporting Services of the U.S. Government. It is worth noting that in these situations the development of standard times by means of other work measurement approaches may appear to be (and may actually be) a hopeless task. However, with the techniques which will be described in this section, the development of standard times is a relatively simple task, even in such situations.

In all of the preceding situations (with the exception of the S & C Electric Company) the N number of data sets may be represented by a series of N equations, one for each data set, constituting a partial mathematical model of the situation, as follows:

$$BV + WC_1 1 \times ST_1 + WC_2 1 \times ST_2 \cdots + WC_i 1 \times ST_i + S_1$$
$$= \text{Sum } MH_1$$

$$BV + WC_1 2 \times ST_1 + WC_2 2 \times ST_2 \cdots + WC_i 2 \times ST_i + S_2$$
$$= \text{Sum } MH_2$$

$$BV + WC_1 N \times ST_1 + WC_2 N \times ST_2 \cdots + WC_i N \times ST_i + S_N$$
$$= \text{Sum } MH_N$$

where:

$BV =$ A basic value associated with any level of operation (unknown)

$WC_1 1 =$ The work count of work-unit 1 in data set 1 (known)

$WC_2 1 =$ The work count of work-unit 2 in data set 1 (known)

$WC_i 1 =$ The work count of work-unit i in data set 1 (known)

$ST_1 =$ The standard time for work-unit 1 (unknown)

$ST_2 =$ The standard time for work-unit 2 (unknown)

$ST_i =$ The standard time for work unit i (unknown)

$S_1 =$ Some amount of time (called slack time), contained in data set 1, which cannot be explained by the indicated relationships (unknown).

Sum $MH_1 =$ The sum of the man-hours of work time associated with data set 1 (known). (In some cases it may be more convenient to use man-weeks, man-months, or man-years. Whichever unit of time is used, the standards derived by mathematical methods will have the same dimensions as used in the sum.)

$WC_1 2 =$ The work count of work-unit 1 in data set 2, and so forth, down to data set N.

Linear programming and *multiple regression* are the names associated with two mathematical routines for finding values for the unknown in such systems of equations.

The use of linear programming provides a solution wherein:

(A) $S_1 + S_2 \cdots + S_N = $ A minimum value; referred to as *residual slack*
(B) $BV, S_1, S_2, \ldots, S_N \geqq 0$
(C) $ST_1, ST_2, \ldots, ST_i \geqq 0$
(D) It is not necessary that all work-units be assigned a standard time other than 0.
(E) Further, it is assumed that any work count multiplied by the appropriate standard time is part of a linear function; e.g., a work count of 30 of work-unit 1 takes three times as long as a work count of 10 of work-unit 1, one-half the time of a work count of 60, and so forth.

The use of multiple regression provides a solution wherein:

(A) $S_1{}^2 + S_2{}^2 \cdots + S_N{}^2 = $ A minimum value; referred to as *residual variance.*
(B) $BV, S_1, S_2, \ldots, S_N \gtreqqless 0$
(C) $ST_1, ST_2, \ldots, ST_i \gtreqqless 0$
(D) It is not necessary that all work-units be assigned a standard time other than 0.
(E) Further, as with LP, it is also assumed that any work count multiplied by the appropriate standard time is part of a linear function.

An examination of the conditions under which a solution is obtained by either method will indicate that the techniques must not be employed blindly. The solutions reached must be carefully examined and the validity checked with other criteria. For instance, Figure 24.5 shows the plot of a series of data sets and the solutions arrived at by linear programming (LP) and multiple regression (MR).

The solutions for $ST_1, ST_2, \ldots, ST_i$ are obviously different for the LP and MR solutions.

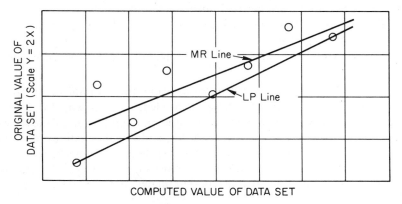

COMPUTED VALUE OF DATA SET

Fig. 24.5 — Lines fitted to data sets by LP and MR.

The use of LP to obtain a solution assumed that:

1. The average difficulty of the work-units contained within any one work count does not vary significantly from data set to data set.
2. The best performance was reasonable; the other data sets represent siutuations where more work could be done, or unique unmeasured conditions exist.
3. The work counts are parts of linear functions.
4. The relative values assigned to ST_1, ST_2, ..., ST_i are reasonable.
5. The work-units assigned a standard time of 0 are not related to the use of time.

Note all of these assumptions are acceptable unless more facts are obtained. The partial mathematical model of the situation wherein only N equations are used is not a complete model. Note also, assumptions 1 and 2 above may be somewhat difficult to verify without a trial application of the answers derived by the use of LP. Assumptions 3, 4, and 5 are different in that they may be avoided by adding supplementary equations to the system of N equations or by converting work-counts which are part of non-linear functions to become parts of linear functions. (This conversion is discussed in Case II later in this section.)

The use of MR to obtain a solution assumed that:

1. The average difficulty of the work-units contained within any one work-count could vary significantly from data set to data set.
2. The data sets represent performances of unknown quality; only the average has any significance; it is a performance which, it is reasonable to expect, will be repeated in the future. (This statement can be altered if use is made of an M arrived at by judgment and which is used to modify ST_1, ST_2, ..., ST_i. In such cases, additional information is needed to develop a value for M.)
3. The work-counts are parts of linear functions.
4. The relative values assigned ST_1, ST_2, ..., ST_i are reasonable even if they are negative.
5. The work-units assigned a standard time of 0 are not related to the use of time.

As with LP solutions, not all of these assumptions would be acceptable without more facts. More information is needed. Also, as with LP, assumptions 1 and 2 are difficult to verify without a trial application of the answers derived by the use of MR. Also, as with LP, additional equations or conversions of work-counts may be added to the system of N equations to avoid assumptions 3, 4, and 5. Obviously, the possibility of a negative standard time (part of assumption 4) must be eliminated if the answers are to be believable.[6]

---

[6] In general, a negative standard time indicates some deficiency in the system of work-units used in the N equations, or some wrong method of counting.

From the foregoing comparison, we may see that assumptions 1 and 2 should be used as criteria for choosing one or the other of the two techniques. Obviously each situation must be examined carefully to see which assumptions are most appropriate. Therefore, the general guides which follow, resulting from a variety of applications, are not to be taken as inflexible criteria.

LP appears more appropriate when the work situation has either of the following two sets of characteristics (in addition to the four general conditions given at the start of this chapter):

1. The relationship between the third- and fourth-order work-units is not direct, e.g., the "sausage manufacture surveillance provided" described in Chapter 21, or in Market News Services, sales offices, and so forth. (An example will be given later.)
2. The relationship between the third- and fourth-order work-units is direct and the work-count of each kind of work-unit in each data set is so high that a different mix of difficulty from data set to data set is not a tenable assumption.

MR appears more appropriate when the work situation contains one of the following three sets of characteristics (in addition to the four general conditions given at the start of this chapter):

1. The relationship between the third- and fourth-order work-units is direct, as with ship boiler erection or with the making of large castings, and when, in addition, the work-count of the work-units is so low that a different mix of difficulty from data set to data set is a tenable assumption.
2. The relationship between the third- and fourth-order work-units is direct and the work-count from data set to data set is high but there is reason to believe that the work-units are not really the same from data set to data set for reasons beyond the control of the producing group.
3. The relationship between the third- and fourth-order work-units is direct and the work-count from data set to data set is high but there is reason to believe that there are random errors in most of the work counts.

When work situations not clearly meeting any of the five types given above for LP and MR are encountered, the only reasonable approach seems to be to try both and examine the answers and the situation before making a choice.[7]

---

[7] In addition to the criteria affecting the choice of LP or MR a few additional criteria have been suggested at various times. These additional criteria are of a somewhat different nature. For instance, LP has been suggested as preferable because it is easier to explain to a group. This may be so, but an explanation of either technique assumes a considerable educational level. If a group can understand one technique they should be able to understand the other. Further, the time to run an MR type solution on a computer has been shown to be less than the time to run an LP solution. However, this seems a frivolous

With either MR or LP, hand computations with problems containing many work-units and many data sets can be long and arduous. Some short-cut methods are available for both LP and MR. For large problems, access to a computer and appropriate programs is highly desirable. However, even large computers have limitations concerning problem size. Common limits range from 20 data sets of 30 work-counts each (medium computers) to 50 data sets with 200 work-counts (large computers). Problems whose size is in excess of these limits are conceivable but not common.[8]

Four cases will be discussed. The first will be examined fully. With the remaining three examples, only those features which differ from the first example will be discussed.

CASE I Work Measurement Standards for the U.S. Livestock Market News Service

As an illustration, let us examine an application of LP to a service-type activity. This illustration represents type 1 of those situations listed as appropriate to handle by LP. The particular illustration has been chosen for a variety of reasons. First, it represents a type of work for which work measurement has often been thought of as infeasible. Second, the application to a problem of this type requires that many additional types of facts, not contained in the N basic equations, be brought into the problem. Thus, the solution of this problem facilitates the demonstration of many things that could not be demonstrated with a simpler example. The illustration concerns the development and use of time standards for assisting managerial control in the Livestock Market News Service of the Consumer and Marketing Service, U.S. Department of Agriculture.

The objective of the Livestock Market News Service is to facilitate the maintenance of an orderly market by gathering, collating, and distributing timely information concerning the supply and movement of market cattle, swine, sheep, and wool to buyers and sellers. To this end they gather information concerning daily transactions with respect to quantity and price, evaluate the reliability of the information, observe incoming shipments with regard

---

criterion; a problem with eight data sets and ten different work-units per data set may take 12 seconds to run by MR, 24 seconds by LP. In addition, it has been shown that if data is generated at random to produce data sets meeting exactly condition 1 of the conditions for which MR is suggested as a technique, MR predicts the place such future data sets would fall on a plot of actual versus computed work time better than LP. This should surprise no one. Figure 24.5 demonstrates that this is the nature of the techniques. Finally, it has been suggested that if a computer is available and only an MR or LP program is available, that the available program should be used. As an expedient, this may be so, but if the other program would fit the situation better, it would seem advisable to obtain a program; they are available. The criteria given in the text are suggested as more appropriate than these peripheral considerations.

[8] However, I have not yet encountered problems larger than this. M.E.M.

to quantity and quality, distribute information concerning volume, quality, and price to their local area and to a central location for nationwide distribution.

It would not appear that any of the work measurement procedures discussed to this point would be feasible in such a situation; the work is non-routine. Even an FPE would be difficult except on a day-to-day basis; this does not appear as a reasonable solution. Hence some new approach is needed.

The Livestock Market News Service maintains offices in 42 cities in the United States. These are cities in which there is an important market in cattle, swine, sheep, or wool. It is important to be able to determine the amount of manpower needed to man each existing office and to periodically evaluate the changes in markets so as to reallocate manpower. Also, when a new market develops, work measurement data of the standard data type is needed to determine the required manpower. What is needed is standard data for all fourth-order work-units associated with any fifth-order work-unit, *A (specific) market reported.*

People knowledgeable in Market News work were asked to assist in preparing a list of potential fourth-order work-units. (These are the types of "components". from which "a market reported" can be said to be "assembled.")

The fourth-order work-units listed contained the following:

1. Classes of animals reported.
2. Number of terminal market days reported.
3. Number of buyers and sellers associated with the market reported.
4. Auction market days reported by federal personnel.
5. Carload lots of cattle reported at terminal markets (by 1000's).
6. Carload lots of cattle reported at auction markets (by 1000's).
7. Carload lots of cattle sold direct reported (by 1000's).
8. Carload lots of swine reported at terminal markets (by 1000's).
9. Carload lots of swine reported at auction markets (by 1000's).
10. Carload lots of swine sold direct reported (by 1000's).
11. Carload lots of sheep reported at terminal markets (by 1000's).
12. Carload lots of sheep reported at auction markets (by 1000's).
13. Carload lots of sheep sold direct reported (by 1000's).
14. Carload lots of wool reported (by 1000's).
15. Auction market days reported by state personnel supervised.
16. Number of state reporters supervised.
17. Number of miles to make market rounds per week driven.

It should be noted that, as is appropriate to fourth-order work-units of a service activity, the outputs have been described with a past tense verb in order to reduce confusion with activities. Also, all of the figures are "dimensions" of the market reported; they are not changeable by choice. Further, the tasks associated with something "reported" are not pinned down; the relationship between the third- and fourth-order work-units is not clear. The situation is clearly identifiable as the first type given as appropriate for LP.[9]

As a next step in the problem situation being examined, the people familiar with the Livestock Market News Service were asked to pick 12 offices meeting certain criteria. The reasons for this selection of 12 from the 42 offices were as follows:

1. As will be noted when the criteria are given, this increased the knowledge concerning that which the data represented.
2. It set aside 30 other data sets to test the credibility of the data obtained.
3. This would reduce the size of the problem to fit the available computer.

The 12 offices were selected to meet the following criteria:

1. The 12 included various sizes of offices ranging from the smallest to the largest.
2. Only offices were selected that were known to require good reporters and where the workload was felt to be such that the reporters were kept relatively busy at all times. Hence, the N equations would be realistic if the work-units had been chosen well.
3. Only offices were selected that were considered to be doing an effective job of reporting. There seemed to be no point in developing standards for work improperly done.
4. The mix of offices selected included offices such that each work-unit appeared in one or more of the N (12) equations. In this way all work-units would be considered.

Subsequently, the work-count for each of the fourth-order work-units was obtained for each of the 42 offices. The work time for each office was determined from payroll records. The 12 (N) equations were constructed where the WC_1 through WC_{17} represented the work-counts of the 17 different work-units; S_1 through S_{12} represented the 12 unexplained times; the Sum MH_1 through Sum MH_{12} represented the payroll time in the 12 offices; ST_1 through ST_{17} represented the 17 potential standard data values sought. The data were fed to a computer under control of an LP program. Answers were returned after approximately two minutes of computer main-frame time.[10]

The answers were examined by the Market News people for credibility. For instance, the free operation of the computer produced a value for work-

[9] There are also market reporting groups for poultry and dairy products, cotton, grain, vegetables, and so forth. The approach described here can be used with all of these and similar information-gathering groups. A press service seems no different.

[10] A terminal having access to a time-shared computer was used.

unit No. 15, *Auction market days reported by State personnel supervised,* but a 0.0 value for No. 16, *Number of State reporters supervised.* Discussion among the Market News group led to the conclusion that this was an error; market days reported by State personnel could increase without adding to the workload of Federal personnel, but increasing the number of State reporters would increase the workload. Hence, fourth-order work-unit No. 15 was removed from the equations.

A new solution was obtained and work-unit No. 16 then had a value. However, other difficulties remained. *Terminal swine reported* (work-unit No. 8) had a value, but *Auction swine reported* (No. 9) and *Direct swine reported* (No. 10) did not; the computer gave the standard time for No. 9 and No. 10 as 0.0. That No. 9 was 0.0 was believable; the State reporters covered the swine auction markets. A 0.0 standard time for *Direct swine reported* was not acceptable.

The concensus of the Market News people was that the work associated with an increment to a market of *1000 carload lots of direct swine reported* was less than that associated with *1000 carload lots of terminal swine reported,* but more than that associated with an increment of *one buyer or seller associated with the market reported.* Hence, two new equations were written:

$$T_{10} \leqq T_8$$
$$T_{10} \geqq T_3$$

In a similar fashion many additional equations (called restrictions) were added. However, one work-unit which was considered important either failed to enter the solution, or when driven in by restrictions, produced intolerably large slack values in offices which were considered to be efficient. The work-unit was No. 17, *Number of miles to make market rounds per week driven.* Examination of this variable showed that high values were associated with offices still being shown as having excessive slack, but all offices whose slack had approached a 0.0 value showed about 300 miles for a work-count for this work-unit. To remove this non-linear effect, work-unit No. 17 was altered to *Number of miles in excess of 300 per week to make market rounds driven.* The subsequent solution had the following properties:

1. It fitted all N equations.
2. It fitted all restricting equations.
3. It produced values for all of the variables people knowledgeable in the work felt were important. (The list was somewhat shorter than the original list.)
4. The relative values of the time standards for the different work-units, and so forth, seemed appropriate to those who knew the work.
5. It left only a small amount of residual slack at locations where its existence seemed readily explainable as extra capability. The people who

had worked in those offices felt more work could be done if necessary. (However, typical was an office with five people and 4.80 man-years of workload, and so forth.)

Subsequently, the standard data derived from the computer were applied to the other 30 offices to compare the evaluation of the manning thus obtained with all other information available concerning each office. The data were used to determine the man-years of effort per year that appeared necessary to man each office; this was compared to current manning.

The data indicated slightly more than one extra man-year at one office (slack = 1.1 man-years); this turned out to be the home office of the "relief" man who substituted for other personnel when they were on vacation. The data also indicated an office where 2 man-years were assigned but only 0.75 man-years of work appeared. This was found to be the office used for training new men; the 0.75 man-years of workload enabled an experienced man to report the market and still have time for training; the additional man-year was the trainee. Several offices were found with excessive manpower; later site visits confirmed this and the men were transferred to other types of work in the Department. In no case did there appear any conflict between the workload as measured by the standard data and all available facts. The data are currently used to determine annual budgets, and to periodically assess the change in markets and the advisability of reallocating personnel. The data can be used to determine the resources required when a new market reporting office is considered.

It is worth noting that the largest amount of time spent by those engaged on the project was in determining the list of potential fourth-order work-units. Work on this was carried on sporadically over a three-month period. The work-counts were determined by each office in about one week. Four hours at the computer terminal were used during the actual development of the standard times.

CASE II   Work Measurement Standards When Linear Programming or Multiple Regression Are Used and the Work-Counts Display Non-linearity

In some cases, using either LP or MR, the plot of the man-hour data originally associated with the data sets versus the man-hour values for the data sets computed from the derived weights may resemble Figure 24.6.

Obviously, the linear answer is wrong; a curve must be fitted to the data points as shown in Figure 24.6. (*Note:* The curve was the last item drawn in Figure 24.6; it was added after the non-linearity was detected.) If the shape of the curve is credible and the fit reasonable, the curve may now be used to construct a table of standard times which does not assume linearity of the

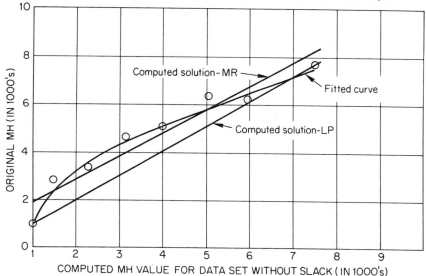

Fig. 24.6—Curve fitted to data-set points after inspection revealed non-linearity.

work-counts. For each computed value of the abscissa, a man-hour time may be determined. For instance, in Figure 24.6, for a weighted value of the work counts of 4,000, a man-hour time of 5,100 is indicated. A table may be constructed for all possible values of the sum of the weighted work-counts to produce a standard data table.

CASE III   WORK MEASUREMENT STANDARDS BY LINEAR PROGRAMMING OR MULTIPLE REGRESSION WHEN SOME OF THE WORK-COUNTS ARE KNOWN TO COME FROM NON-LINEAR FUNCTIONS

When determining the work-units to use in LP or MR computations, information may be available which indicates that the work-counts of one or more of the variables will not be part of a linear system. For instance, the time spent pouring molten steel into a large casting will not be a function of the amount of steel. The time for the work-unit, *steel poured*, will consist of a constant time for the tasks of set-up and prepare, plus a variable depending upon the amount of steel poured. In a similar fashion, the work-count of almost any work-unit produced in different amounts at different times may belong to a non-linear function. The work-counts associated with the data sets need conversion to a linear function before the LP or MR solution is attempted. Figure 24.7 is the conversion graph for such a work-unit. If the actual work-count is used to enter the abscissa, the "converted work-count"

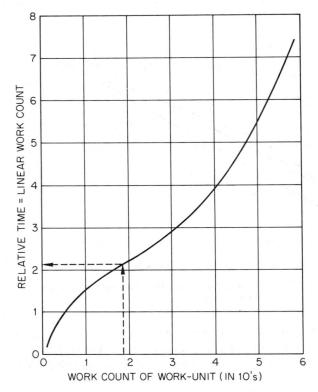

Fig. 24.7—Graph for converting work count of work-unit which is part of a non-linear function to a linear work-count.

which is part of a linear system may be read off the ordinate. The lines added to the curve indicate how an original work-count of 19 is altered to a "converted work-count" of 22 which is then part of a linear function.

CASE IV   REDUCING THE POSSIBILITY THAT "RATIONALIZATION" IS USED TO EXPLAIN RESIDUAL SLACKS IN AN LP OR RESIDUAL VARIANCE IN AN MR PROBLEM

In Case I the slacks obtained in the original solution were carefully examined for credibility after the solution had been obtained. Some may feel that this offers too much opportunity to "bend" the facts to fit the solution. In some applications, the anticipated slacks are removed from the Sum *MH* terms before the solution is attempted in order to reduce the chance of biasing the analysis of the results. Instead of using actual payroll man-hours for each data set, an estimate of the required man-hours is used. If the estimates are correct and rational, the residual slacks in the solution will approach 0.0. This presumes, if the answers are credible, that the basis of the estimates was good. However, the use of the mathematical procedure reduces the basis of these estimates to a quantitative statement of the weights for each component part. These quantitative statements make possible the subsequent computation of work standards without the use of the skill previously employed in making the estimate. Like the FPE, the technique makes it possible to change from a "visceral standard" to documented repeatable information.

CHAPTER 25

Applying Motion and Time Study

Motion and time study activities are only of value to an organization when they are carried on in a manner designed to serve the organization's objectives. The objectives of an organization are established by top management.

"It is worth noting that the performance of this step of setting objectives is the primary differentiating characteristic between the top management of an industrial enterprise operating in a free economy and either an industrial enterprise operating in a state economy or the top management of a government organization. The top management of an enterprise in a free economy has economic objectives; there is considerable freedom of choice in developing substantive programs to achieve these objectives. An enterprise in a state-owned economy usually has substantively stated goals assigned to it. It may have some freedom of choice with respect to the economic aspects of achieving them, but in stringent economies, such as represented by communist or fascist states, these economic choices may be either severely delimited or nonexistent.

"A governmental organization, even in a free economy, usually has substantively stated goals, which are either assigned or derived from more general statements of the nature of desired achievements; in addition, there are usually numerous economic restrictions concerning the allowable nature of programs to be followed in achieving the goals."[1]

---

[1] M. E. Mundel, *A Conceptual Framework for the Management Sciences*. New York, N.Y.: McGraw-Hill Book Company, 1967, p. 274. (A few phrases have been deleted.)

The usual measure of the effectiveness of the management of an industrial enterprise is the amount of profit that it makes. Indeed, the need for profit is overwhelming; without a profit the organization cannot endure. The usual measure of the effectiveness of either an industrial enterprise operating in a state economy or a government organization is whether (or to what extent) it achieves its substantive goals. Indeed, the need for some reasonable achievement is overwhelming; the manager of a government organization who cannot "deliver" usually will be replaced. Hence, it is easy to see why industrial enterprises are money motivated; why government enterprises or organizations are program motivated.

The difference is most evident with a military base. The commander may consider using time study but the objective is to determine the amount of resources that he needs to meet the maximum workload that may be imposed upon the base during an emergency; the use of motion study would be to increase the capability to take on more workload during an emergency. There will not necessarily be any savings, in the same sense as in the industrial enterprise.

However, none of the foregoing alters the essential nature of the manner in which the techniques of motion and time study may be employed to serve the managerial needs of an organization.

The techniques of motion study (and other appropriate technologies) are employed in the cycle of managerial control in designing or selecting outputs, in planning ways of producing them, and in determining the workload required to produce the desired quantity of outputs.

The techniques of time study are employed in the cycle of managerial control in developing numerical coefficients for converting quantities of workload to quantities of required manpower resources required. When the quantity of required manpower resources makes the outputs of the industrial enterprise unprofitable, the techniques of motion study (and other technologies) are employed to find cheaper (manpower or other resource-wise) ways of producing the outputs, or alternative outputs. When the quantity of required manpower resources makes the outputs of a government organization excessively expensive (manpower-wise) such that a reasonable achievement of the goals cannot be attained, the techniques of motion study (and other appropriate technologies) are employed to find more effective ways of producing the required outputs.

In any organization, when a production plan has been established, whether the outputs are substantive or service-type outputs, some means is needed to constrain the activity. Information flow systems must be designed to compare events to plans. Work measurement data will be the basis of manpower-use plans. The same data will be involved in the subsequent comparison of events with plans. Methods study (the procedure analysis aspects) will be basic to the design of such management information systems.

Motion and time study, as has been shown, may be used in any cycle of managerial control; the priorities will differ when the motivations of the organizations differ. Failure to understand these differences can cause much frustration and failure. The industrial organization usually needs to employ time study to determine costs and motion study to reduce them. The government organization usually wishes to determine costs only so that the economic limitations set for its objectives are reasonable; it wants to use motion study to assist in making the achievements of objectives feasible or in increasing the substantive achievements.

The Executive Office of the President of the United States, Bureau of the Budget, has attempted to increase the economic motivation of agencies through changes in the budget process. For instance, in Bureau of the Budget, Circular A-11, "Preparation and submission of annual budget estimates," we find the following:

"Work measurement, unit cost and productivity indexes should be used to the maximum extent practicable in justification of estimates for staffing requirements for measurable workload. The agency should be prepared, upon request, to submit detailed analyses of workload, manpower and productivity trends in support of budget estimates.

"Properly developed work measurement procedures should be used to produce estimates of the man-hours per unit of workload, such as man-hours per claim adjudicated, man-hours per man maintained in the field, man-hours per infested acre of pest control, etc., depending on the agency. These estimates should represent an acceptable level of performance based on current realistic time standards. If the agency does not have a work measurement-system that provides this type of information, the use of statistical techniques based on historical manpower input and work output may be used."[2]

Hence, in both industrial enterprises and in government organizations we find pressure for the effective use of techniques and procedures as presented in this book. Private industry has economic pressure; government agencies have pressure from their Chief Executive through the budget process.

The effective use of techniques, such as presented in this book, is limited only by the imagination and ability of the analyst who uses them. The ability must include not only the ability to use the techniques to obtain answers to problems but the ability to persuade people to use these answers. It would seem reasonable to suggest that basic to success in "selling" ideas is the need to carry on the work with openness, pleasantness, honesty, working systematically and scientifically.

Further, the work of a group, such as a motion and time study group, is usually aided when they have (1) policies and procedures for routine activities,

[2] *Op. cit.*, Sec. 24.3, Revision of 25 July 1968.

(2) an adequate reporting system to higher levels of management, and (3) when they assist others in the organization by giving formal and informal training in their field of work. While these general aspects are equally applicable to both private industrial and governmental organizations, the details will differ greatly. As has been noted, most private industry has a substantive product which serves as a natural framework, not only for the managerial control cycle, but for the whole of the industrial activity. General suggestions for items (1), (2), and (3) may be made with reference to the industrial scene. These are contained in the Supplemental Material attached to this chapter. General suggestions for similar parallel activities in government service-output organizations would be lengthy and diverse; a natural framework for them and a general organizational rationale have not been sufficiently developed to permit a short presentation within the limits of this book. However, one general suggestion can be made. Most government organizations do not have hierarchy of work-units around which to structure not only their motion and time study activity but also their basic managerial controls. A vital first step toward successful use of motion and time study in a government organization would be the development of such a hierarchy. A sample hierarchy of workunits is included in this book as Appendix A.

Supplemental Material

The supplemental material of this chapter is primarily directed at the private industrial organization. Some of the material, however, will be equally applicable to government or service-type organizations. The supplemental material is divided into three parts:

1. Policies and procedures.
2. Reports.
3. Training in motion and time study.

Policies and Procedures

In the widespread use of motion and time study in an organization, there are certain relatively routine activities that must be performed. The means of carrying on these routine activities should be definitely stated. A group of policies is necessary to achieve consistency of actions. Formal procedures are necessary to routinize the carrying out of the policies.

Policies are statements of the aims to be sought in handling recurring types of situations. They are the rules by which the organization functions and are vital in all phases of plant activity. Procedures are the details of the methods to be employed to achieve these aims.

In this discussion, each policy, and its accompanying procedure, required for the carrying on of these routine motion and time study activities will be discussed. An actual example will be given where it is deemed desirable. It should be noted that as the size of the organization decreases, more and more of the functions involved in carrying on these routine motion and time study activities will devolve on one individual. On the other hand, in a large organization many details will be delegated to specialists. However, these functions should be performed in all organizations if maximum value is to be obtained from the motion and time study work.

For the routine motion and time study work to be effective, the policies and procedures should cover at least the following six items:

1. Who shall determine the standard method?
2. How will the standard method be made regular practice?
3. What does standard time represent?
4. Who shall determine the standard time and how will it be determined?
5. Under what conditions may a standard time be changed?
6. How will production be reported? If incentive wages or cost accounting is involved, a means of reporting individual or group performance, as related to standard, is required. (However, procedures for this phase are usually intimately connected with production and inventory control and payroll functions and vary with the nature of the shop, with the production (job or continuous), as well as with other factors. Therefore, a discussion of this item is out of the question in this book.)

1. *Who shall determine the standard method?* In some plants the work of developing standards is divided between two groups: one, a methods group for developing standard methods and, two, a time study group for developing standard times. In simple assembly industries, these two functions are likely to be grouped together. As the nature of the product and the production sequence increase in technical complexity, these functions will be spread among more and more groups. In industries involving a great deal of machining, a group called "tool engineers" may take over many of the methods functions. In organizations with service outputs the motion and time study activities may be carried on by line people aided by staff. (Motion and time study procedure are for the use of such groups, no matter what they choose to call themselves.) Regardless of whether there is one group, two, or more, or what they are called or choose to call themselves, the final responsibility for determining methods must be placed somewhere in the organization in such a way that standard times will accompany only the methods they were designed for, so that there will be a constant striving for better methods, and also so that the two will complement one another.

Sample. The standard process sequence as well as the standard practice for each job in the sequence shall be specified by the chief manufacturing engineer, who shall consult with foremen, department superintendents, quality department, design engineers, tool engineers, plant engineers, and time and motion study engineers, but shall retain final responsibility for the selection of the methods. (Naturally, in a large plant, more and more subordinates will do the actual work.)

In many plants, the jurisdiction of the chief manufacturing engineer may be different from that suggested here, depending on the individual, the size of the plant, product, process, and plant custom. In some cases the chief manufacturing engineer will be called the plant superintendent, and so forth. Titles vary widely. Suggestions for changes in methods may develop in many places in the management of an organization. Motion and time study workers may suggest tool or design changes, design engineers may suggest process changes, or quality control workers may suggest new motion patterns. It is important that an individual or group making such suggestions report to some central source in order to:[3]

1. Request permission to proceed with an innovation.
2. Provide a record of what is changed.
3. Provide material to guide other groups in achieving similar results. (The larger the plant, the more important this last item becomes.)

In the interest of saving the time of the executive who reads it, as well as adequately presenting the material, the report may well be constructed around a suggested outline.

Sample. (For procedure relating to suggestions for changing methods.) The following outline is to be used as a guide in reporting suggested changes to the chief manufacturing engineer. It is suggested that as far as possible a proposal for change be built around a letter having four sections as follows:

A. Identification (use interoffice form).
   i. Date
   ii. From
   iii. To
   iv. Subject
B. Advantages and disadvantages.

Under this head the reporting person should summarize what would be accomplished by the change, the estimated saving in money, scrap, or increase in output or quality, as appropriate; the cost of the change, and any training problems involved, and so forth.

C. Exhibits.

Supporting data that are attached to substantiate the claims under item *B* should be listed here and indexed, but appended after item *D*. In as far as possible, standard charts should be used to increase intelligibility.

---

[3] This is separate and distinct from employee suggestion plans. See also the section on reports beginning on page 535.

D. Specific proposal.

All that has to be done to put the proposal into effect should be listed here, so that if permission is granted not only does the executive know exactly what he is agreeing to, but also, so that if the proposal is accepted it may be achieved rapidly. In the case of a change already made, all that has been done should be summarized here.

2. *How will the standard method be made regular practice?* As was established in the chapters on time study, the determination of standard time is preceded, usually, by the determination and recording of a standard practice. For adequate performance to be obtained in a production shop, regardless of the purpose of the time study, the standard method, in the form of a Written Standard Practice (WSP),[4] as well as the standard time, must be supplied in some manner to the operator. Methods which have been carefully developed must be used if their value is to be obtained. The WSP giving the method to be followed on a job should be designed, as was noted earlier, for use in connection with time study. The instructional material for use by the operator or for use by a group leader, foreman, or special instructor may well be an adaptation of this. The more continuous the production, the more likely that these two versions of the WSP will exist. The economic reasons for this should be obvious. In a jobbing shop, with extremely short runs, the economical WSP for operator use may be merely a copy of the written standard practice from the time study. It is often merely a list of steps, a blueprint, and a list of tools, but this is inadequate. In jobbing shops, it is frequently desirable to design general routines for each type of job and merely add specific details to them to adapt them to a particular job. WSP and supervision are a good means of consistently obtaining effective, low-cost methods. Where large numbers of people perform the same operation, a very detailed instruction sheet may be prepared. Figure 25.1 is a reproduction (greatly reduced) of part of the leaflet printed for the tomato peeling operation described in Chapter 14. This leaflet was printed and distributed to all peelers who participated in this program. Over 10,000 copies were used.

Modified versions of this at some plants use small 35-mm pictures or Polaroid pictures[5] to show the steps described on the instruction sheet. Actual photographic prints are pasted on the instructions to save printing costs. If much detail is required, pictures are cheaper and more effective than lengthy descriptions.

This critical aspect of methods and standards work is worthy of considerable discussion. In all too many plants, carefully developed standards

---

[4] Also referred to as Standard Operating Procedure (SOP), or Instruction Sheet.

[5] A regular 35-mm still camera takes about 20 to 36 pictures on a roll, so these illustrations are not excessively expensive. The quality of Polaroid pictures has so improved and they are so simple to take that this appears to be an ideal method.

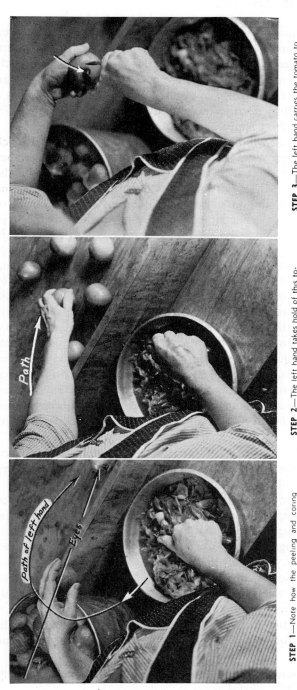

STEP 1—Note how the peeling and coring knife is held. The finished tomato is in the left hand. While the right hand shakes off the last peeling on the knife, the eyes are picking out the next tomato to be peeled. The left hand, at the same time, deposits the finished tomato in the bucket without looking at the bucket, and then moves to the tomato the eyes have picked out.

STEP 2—The left hand takes hold of this tomato in the position in which it will hold the tomato for coring, to avoid the waste of effort and time that is often used in shifting the tomato around after it is picked up.

STEP 3—The left hand carries the tomato to the worker while the right hand advances the knife to meet the tomato so that as soon as the tomato is in coring position, the coring can begin. Note that the left wrist is slightly twisted and that the knife is inserted at the edge of the core nearest the worker so that a single twist of both the left and right hand will enable the knife to go completely around the core in a single stroke without shifting the left hand's hold on the tomato.

Fig. 25.1—Tomato peeling instruction sequence. Reproduced from Purdue Agri. Est. Bul., Misc. Pub. 23 (Rev.), July 1944.

are poorly applied because of the inadequateness of the method information accompanying them, which is supplied to the shop. When the standard practice is not transmitted to the workers, deviations in methods commonly ensue. Also, when methods and standards are changed, the failure to detail the methods often allows the change in standards to be misinterpreted as a "speed-up" and poor labor relations may needlessly result. Part of a fully detailed job instruction sheet appears in Figure 25.2a and b.

The instruction sheet used to accompany each standard issued at Patrick Cudahy, Inc. of Cudahy, Wis., has been instrumental in reducing labor disputes. This instruction sheet is reviewed by the time study man and the departmental union steward. The steward signs the original copy indicating that he has read and understood the sheet. (He does not have the choice of approval or disapproval but is encouraged to indicate whether any job steps have been neglected.) A sample of such an instruction sheet is shown in Figure 25.3.

A similar instruction sheet in use at a printing and children's game plant is given in Figure 25.4. At this plant, many of the games are assembled by sequential crews (line work) and the individual standards are summarized in a crew or process standard as shown in Figure 25.5. Note that delays caused by unbalance in the line are indicated at each appropriate position. Transmitting information concerning these delays to the shop is excellent preparation for future changes when work may be added to these stations *without increasing the time allowed.* The workers occupying positions containing delays are given to understand that at some time in the future when better methods are devised, this delay time may be assigned to productive work. Discussing this, when the standard is issued, greatly facilitates future understanding.

The policy for WSP should place responsibility for their creation, state the requirements for them, their authority, and when they are to be available with respect to the inception of production.

Sample. The chief manufacturing engineer shall develop the WSP, when possible, prior to the inception of production.[6] If this is not possible, a tentative method will be arranged in consultation with the departmental foremen, time study man, tool engineer (these two men may be one and the same), and others, as necessary. The WSP shall be followed except where obvious errors exist, in which case the chief manufacturing engineer shall be notified immediately. The chief manufacturing engineer shall develop and apply improved methods whenever economically feasible.

The WSP shall be of two forms: one form for the process sequence, the other form for giving, for each step in the sequence, the list of tools and

---

[6] This is frequently delegated to the time and motion study group who must usually obtain the participation of other affected parties in the development of the WSP.

SECOND INSPECTION

No. SI 14
Issue 2
Sheet 1 of 3
3-6-

OPERATION: Gap Gage Earthworm Tractor 5 3/4" Rings

EQUIPMENT

1 Sizer Ring Gage	1 V Trough
1 Set Feeler Gages	1 V Trough (non-sectioned)

REQUIREMENTS

Operator will wear gloves when handling rings.

All pans of rings will be lifted by service men.

Pan ticket will remain in pocket on side of pan, except when being read by operator.

Operation will be performed by checker.

Ring gages will be checked at the beginning of each shift by a checker.

A ticket showing ring gage size, variation number, feeler gage number, operator's clock number and date will be filled out when ring gage is checked and will be kept with gage while it is in use.

Feeler gages will be kept at the Foreman's desk and will be returned to desk at end of working period.

SPECIFICATIONS

Gage Size: 5.747   Gap Clearance: .011 - .021

Rings will be gaged on a percentage basis. Operator will gage every 8th ring, beginning with bottom ring and ending with top.

If any ring is found out of limits, operator will check 8 rings above and 8 rings below place from which reject was removed until all rings not within limits have been rejected.

SECURE RINGS

1. HAVE SERVICE MAN PLACE ENTIRE TEST of rings at back of bench in a horizontal position.

CHECK SET-UP

2. CHECK PAN TICKET to see that previous operation has been completed. Check number of rings in pan against count shown on ticket. (Count remnant row and add to number in full rows). If counts do not agree, have floor clerk make necessary corrections.

Fig. 25.2a—Written standard practice for operation. Reproduced by courtesy of D.C. Parsons, Methods and Standards Supt., Perfect Circle Co. (*continued*).

SECOND INSPECTION   WRITTEN STANDARD PRACTICE   No. SI 14
                        The Perfect Circle Co.   Issue 2
                                                  Sheet 2 of 3
OPERATION: Gap Gage Earthworm Tractor 5 3/4" Rings   3-6-

GAGE RINGS

3. REMOVE EVERY 8TH RING from first row of pan, beginning with bottom ring and ending with top.

4. PLACE RINGS ON BENCH in front of first row with gaps toward operator in the order removed from pan.

5. REMOVE SPECIFIED NUMBER OF RINGS from remaining two rows in the manner described in Steps #3 and #4.

6. MOVE GAGE to a position at left end of first pan.

7. PICK UP FEELERS AND HOLD them between thumb and index finger while gaging rings. (When placing ring in gage or removing ring from gage, hold feelers in palm of hand.)

8 PICK UP ONE RING from first stack on right approximately 1" on right of gap with thumb and index finger of right hand.

9. BRING RING TO A POSITION OVER GAGE.

10. GRASP RING on left of gap with left index finger and thumb, placing middle fingers on top of ring and thumbs on face and corners about ½" on either side of gap.

11. TILT RING SLIGHTLY AND SLIP BACK OF RING INTO GAGE.

12. INSERT REST OF RING INTO GAGE by squeezing thumbs together toward gap.

13. ROLL THUMBS OFF RING to release points slowly. Do not flip points into gage. Be sure back of rings is pressed firmly into gage.

14. TEST GAP by placing Go feeler between points, starting at inside diameter and bringing feeler toward operator through gap. Go feeler should pass between points freely. If feeler passes through gap with a slight drag, ring should be rejected.

15. PLACE NO GO FEELER BETWEEN POINTS, starting at inside diameter and bringing feeler toward operator through gap. The feeler should either refuse to pass or should fit very tightly. Do not force feeler between the points.

16. REMOVE RING FROM GAGE by closing gap with thumb and index fingers of each hand and lifting ring. Do not flip points out of gage.

17. PLACE IN NON-SECTIONED TROUGH ON LEFT OF GAGE AND AT SAME TIME REPEAT STEP #8, if ring is within limits.

    a. If ring is not within limits, place in sectioned trough on left of gage in section marked for that type reject.

Fig. 25.2b — Written standard practice for operation (concluded).

PRODUCTION STANDARD--JOB SUMMARY SHEET

PAGE NO. __1__ OF __3__ DEPT. __Process Ham__   STUDY DATE __2-16-__   STUDY NO. __3-6-111__

OPERATION __Bone 4½-5½ S.S. Picnics -Skin On__   JOB __Bone Picnics__

MACHINE __- - - - - - --__ MACHINE NO. __- - - - - --__AUX.EQUIP. __- - -__   Job Symbol __150-4__

NO.	DETAILED DESCRIPTION OF JOB ELEMENTS		STD.ALLOWED TIME/UNIT
	LEFT HAND	**RIGHT HAND**	
1.	Grasp picnic from conveyor or from pile at side of operator. Slide picnic on cutting board to position in front of operator - face side up.	Hold knife.	.0371
2.	Pick up steel from cutting board - Hold steel - aside steel to cutting board.	Slide knife blade across steel. (3 strokes)	.0408
3.	Smooth out skin around shank end - pull up on skin during cut - use skin as handle to roll picnic over so skin side is up. Roll picnic back so face side is up - aside skin to conveyor.	Slit skin on shank end - cut skin away from skin side of picnic complete skinning by cutting away skin from shank end on face side.	.2786
4.	Hold picnic down on cutting board.	Make horizontal cut at side of picnic length of the arm bone to the area in the center of the picnic near the bone.	.1390
5.	Hold picnic - grasp and hold bone at center area. Hold bone at blade end, until bone is free of picnic.	Guide knife along contour of arm bone, around center area of bone until entire center area is free of picnic. Cut away meat at blade end of arm bone. Cut away meat from shank end of arm bone until bone is completely free of picnic.	.5877
6.	Aside bone to top conveyor - hit counter on return motion to record number of picnics boned.	Aside picnic to bottom conveyor.	.0370

REMARKS				
	CONVERTED TO		Cwt.	STD.ALLOWED TIME MIN/UNIT	1.1762
	BASIS UNIT	Wt. Per Piece	4.83 Lbs	STD.HRS/ 100 UNITS	1.9603
	STD.ALLOWED TIME MIN/UNIT		.2435	UNIT HRS.	51.0
	STD.HRS./100 UNITS		.4058	OBSERVED BY	A.D.
	UNITS /HRS.		246.4	APPROVED BY	

Fig. 25.3—Job summary sheet from Patrick Cudahy, Inc., Cudahy, Wis. (Courtesy C. J. Allen, Chief Industrial Engineer.)

523

PRODUCTION STANDARD—OPERATION METHOD SUMMARY SHEET

Page No. 1 of 7

Department Box

Operation and No. Wrap box, bottom

Product Sewing card 4600

size 8½ x 8-1/8 x 1-1/16

Work Unit Game

Machine(s) and No. A-1

Study Date 12/8/

Study No. 551208-01

No.	Detailed Description of Operation Elements	Std. Allowed Time/Unit
1	Reach 18" to bottom wrap, grasp sheet, move 18" to and place on feeding table, help center box on bottom wrap, carry to machine plunger, fit on plunger and release. Reach 18" to supply of stayed bottoms, grasp one and carry to and center on positioned bottom wrap, pick up and carry to, fit on and release on machine plunger.	.0446
2	Reach to right and move stack of stayed boxes with both hands into position to feed single boxes to positioning area. NOTE: Supply girl puts boxes into original position from truck.	.0008
3	Delay element. Load glue pot, load wraps. Reduced to a per cent as it occurs 1 time per hour and added as an allowance - 2.5%	

REMARKS:

Std. Allowed Time Minutes/Unit	.0454
Standard Hours/ 100 Units	.0756
Units/Hour	1320
Observed by:	G. Kaplan
Approved by:	

Fig. 25.4—Operation standard sheet from printing plant. (Courtesy G. Kaplan, Western Printing and Lithographing Co., Racine, Wis.)

524

PRODUCTION STANDARD
JOB SUMMARY

Page No. 8 of 8

Department Box

Product and No. Sewing Cards, 4600

Operation(s) and No.(s) Complete assembly

Study Date 12/8/

Study No. 551208, 1-7

Work Unit Game (#4600)

Total Operations

Operation	Std. Hrs./ 100 Units	Units/Hr./ Operator	Crew	Hrs./ 100 Units Delay Time/ Operator
1. Wrap box bottom	.0756	1320	1	.0049
2. Assemble platform and tray	.0761	1315	1	.0044
3. Accordian fold six card insert and				
insert in game	.0712	1385	1	.0093
4. Select, fold and insert six strands	(.0932			
of yarn	(.0932	1070	2	.0678
5. Wrap box cover	.0805	1245	1	-------*
6. Close box and stack on table	.0438	2260	1	.0367
7. Supply two wraps, trays, cards; load				
skid with finished boxes	.0592	1790	1	.0213
*Pacing Operation .0805	Totals .5928		8	.1444

		REMARKS:
Crew Efficiency	92 %	
Std. Hrs./ 100 Units/Crew	.6440	
Crew	8	
Std. Hrs./ 100 Units/Oper.	.0805	
Units/Hr./ Crew	1245	

Daily std. 7.5hrs x 1245 = 9320

TS2

Fig. 25.5 — *Crew summary of standard operation sheets.* (Courtesy
G. Kaplan, Western Printing and Lithographing Co.,
Racine, Wis.)

WRITTEN STANDARD PRACTICE

PROCESS EARTHWORM TRACTOR PISTON RINGS

STEP NO.	NO. DEPT.	MACHINE	OPERATION	METHOD STD.	STD. TIME
1	9 Foundry	Class L	Mold	FM-7	.28 minute per unit of 4
2	9 Foundry	On Conveyor C-1	Pour mold	FM-8	.10 minute per tree of 40
3	9 Foundry	Bench and Hoist BH-3	Shake out	FM-9	.51 per tree of 40

Fig. 25.6 — Written standard practice for process, also called "master route sheet" or "routing."

equipment, the specifications for the job, and complete details for performance. (They should follow the sample WSP's given as examples in Figures 25.2 through 25.6.) It is to be noted that the process standard is usually done well in most plants, but that the operation standard is frequently skimped. Also, as an additional illustration, Figures 22.2 and 22.3 represent the equivalent of the industrial WSP for the very different output, *healthier swine.*

3. *What does standard time represent?* Since this is to be the unit of measurement, it must be defined and the definition generally known throughout the plant. Samples, as well as the reasoning behind the development of one definition of standard time, were given in the Supplemental Material of Chapter 17. Consideration should be given to union participation in its formulation, to help develop a socially acceptable definition. The definition may well be embodied in a multi-image, pace-film loop.

4. *Who shall determine the standard time and how will it be determined?* The time study, rating, and allowance procedures should be specified, with the deviations that will be allowed in unusual cases. This is the only way to obtain a uniform time study practice. This uniform practice may be changed from time to time, but a good uniform practice insures the use of the best knowledge obtainable at any time. The practices outlines in Chapters 18 through 24 may be followed. The procedure should indicate:

A. The assignment of responsibility for the supervision of the following:
B. The nature of the method record.
C. The manner of obtaining the work time and work count.

D. Number or basis of number of readings to be taken with direct time study.

E. Permissible use of standard data.

F. Manner of handling irregular elements.

G. Basis of rating and standard secondary adjustments.

H. Standard allowances.

I. The manner of reporting allowed times and standard methods as necessary to the payroll department, schedule department, shop supervision, and the like.

J. A method of handling grievances, related to standards.

Sample. This procedure, concerned primarily with direct time study-intensive sampling, is sufficiently important that an outline manual is reproduced here, almost in full. Various versions of this manual are in use by numerous companies. If other methods of work measurement are to be used, a similar manual should be developed. This illustration will then serve as a guide. In order to conserve space, where material normally included in the manual is reproduced elsewhere in this book, the location of the material will be cited instead.[7]

MANUAL OF TIME STUDY PROCEDURE

BASIC POLICY: The head of time study shall review all actual time studies and accept responsibility for their reliability. He shall be responsible for proposing changes in the time study procedure but must obtain the chief manufacturing engineer's consent to all major revisions of the procedure. The head of time study shall see that all time studies follow standard time study practice.

SUMMARY (For related details see detail sheets corresponding to step number.)

1. Notify operator and foreman that study is to be made and why.

2. The time study man is responsible for the standardization of the work-station, etc. Check method of performance with foreman. Do not issue orders directly to operator. Deal through the foreman unless he, in your presence, instructs the operator to do the job in the manner you request.

3. Identify the work-unit, the unit in which production is measured. Break the job into the smallest elements which are practical and possible to accurately time and which conform with standard elements. Write these elements in detail on the front of the time study sheet and number them. Abbreviate these descriptions on back of sheet for actual timing.

---

[7] The procedure items are numbered so as to facilitate reference to them. In some shops union participation is obtained by training union time study stewards in this procedure. In actual practice, each detail item appears on a separate sheet, so as to facilitate adding notes or issuing revised detail sheets one at a time as needed.

4. Fill in on time study sheet the department, the operation, operator's name and clock number, details of tools and such as make, model, and serial number of equipment or machines and all other applicable items. Make a written note of any condition of equipment or workplace affecting the operation.

5. Enter time of starting actual recordings, on back of time study sheet, and start stop-watch. Write the time that each element is completed in space provided at side of each element description.

6. Continue to leave watch running and repeatedly record time required to complete each element. Write down the watch reading and description for any foreign element (non-routine occurrence) that happens during the course of the study. Make notes concerning foreign elements in lower right of time study sheet. Use standard symbols where possible.

7. Before leaving the job, rate the speed of the operator and list the difficulties inherent in each element of the job.

8. The next step (done in office) is to subtract each element clock reading from the preceding reading to get the actual time required for that element.

9. Calculate the observed average time for each element. This is the sum of the individual time values divided by the number of values. If the element does not occur per each work unit, indicate the proper prorate divisor.

10. The average time for each element is then multiplied by the rating. The answer is the speed rated time for the element.

11. When weights or resistances over 20 lbs. are involved in the job, the per cent of cycle taken by each rated element time is computed. The difficulty adjustments are entered. The rated time for each element is multiplied by 1.00 plus the total difficulty correction for the element, expressed as a decimal. This product is the base time.

12. The allowances are added to give the total standard time per time study element.

13. The standard time per unit is in minutes. It is necessary to convert it into standard hours per 100 or per 1000 units. This is done by multiplying by 100 or 1000 and dividing by 60.

14. The production per hour or hourly requirements are found by dividing the standard hours per 100 units into 100 or per 1000 units into 1000.

15. The piece rate per 100 or per 1000 pieces is obtained by multiplying the hours per 100 or per 1000 pieces by the base rate applicable to the operations. The standard time for standard time plans is found by multiplying the unit time by appropriate values.

16. The time study must be approved by the Time Study Supervisor prior to issue.

17. The time study will be used to issue the:

   a. Instruction and layout (2 copies) [See Figure 25.2 through 25.5.]
   b. Notice of piecework rate (1 copy) [See Figure 25.7].

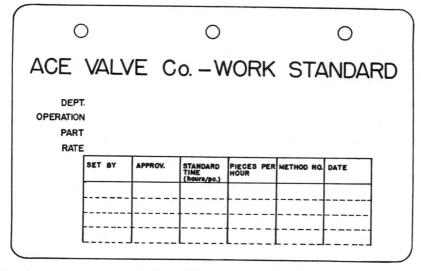

Fig. 25.7 — Sample time standard sheet for rate book.

18. In cases of failure to meet standard production:
    a. "Production Check Study" will be made and a report issued.
    b. A meeting may be held with the departmental foreman and steward to discuss the problem.

DETAIL SHEETS

2.10 Specific responsibility of time study section. Time study is a service activity. The time study man works primarily in an advisory capacity and should not tell production supervisors what to do. The time study man can and should advise supervisors whenever possible and work closely with them. The time study man may also make recommendations to the plant superintendent.

The time study man is responsible for establishing the method of operation for the job to be studied. The time study man together with the foreman will make the necessary adjustments and see that the operator is following the required method before beginning the study. The time study man is responsible for recording all of the conditions surrounding the job which he feels will help insure that the resulting production standard will be for a particular standardized operation.

The time study section is responsible for:

1. Establishing and issuing time standards, after management's approval, for production supervisors, payroll and production control. Unless the supervisor has a factual basis for rejection, these standards are valid.

2. In cooperation with production supervisors, for establishing and recording acceptable work methods on operations, including speeds, feeds, motions, and hand and crew balance, etc.
3. The acceptability of the operator available for the time study.
4. Notifying supervisors of changes and improvements that will facilitate production and reduce costs, and for reporting on such changes.
5. Notifying production supervision and timekeeping of changes in standards.
6. Keeping records of production standards up to date.
7. Assisting in determining causes of failures to achieve standard production.
8. Periodically auditing standards for correctness and applicability and taking the necessary steps to correct for any changes introduced since the setting of the standard.

2.20 Service operators. In order to study the required time, the time study man will (after obtaining the foreman's help or permission) instruct the service operators in following a prescribed routine designed to accomplish the necessary work with the least effort.

2.30 Specific responsibility of production supervisors. The production supervisor's duties include "properly understanding and using production standards." The production supervisor is responsible for:

1. Instructing employees in standard methods.
2. Cooperating with time study in the development of standard methods. The foreman must define the work assignment of the employees under study.
3. Assisting in the elimination of unnecessary walking, handling, motions, and delays.
4. Controlling delay time. For seeing that allowable delays are accurately reported.
5. Knowing what is included in the standard method when instructing a worker.
6. Reporting all changes in methods to the time study department.
7. Eliminating any work started to overcome a temporary difficulty.
8. Letting the operators know the piece price or standard time or standard production expected per hour.
9. Seeing that time, production, and delays are accurately reported.
10. Seeing that the proper management attitude is maintained during all discussions of time standards.

3.10 Description. The written description of the job, in the form of elemental descriptions, should be sufficiently complete with respect to motions, tools and equipment, workplace, workplace layout, flow of work, working conditions and material so that the job could be reproduced from this description in only one manner.

3.11 Elements. The job will be described in terms of elements chosen so as to meet the following criteria:

    a. Easily detected and definite end points.

    b. As small as is convenient to time.

    c. As unified as possible.

    d. Hand time separate from machine time.

    e. Constant elements separated from variable elements (as concerns a series of similar jobs).

    f. Regular elements separated from irregular elements.

    g. Internal hand time kept separate from external time.

3.20 Work-units. The work-unit or unit of production should be identified and defined.

3.31 Films. On jobs which are difficult or laborious to describe, a motion picture record of the method should be made.

3.32 Still pictures. Polaroid pictures of workplaces should be used instead of sketches in all possible cases. A boldly marked scale should be included in the picture to give dimensions. (Use sticks with alternate black and white bands 1″ in length.)

4.10 Materials handling. Indicate all pertinent information relative to delivery and disposal of direct and indirect materials.

4.20 Assistance given. Indicate all service performed by others for the operator and the relationship of these services to productivity.

6.10 Number of readings. An adequate sample of readings shall be taken so as to be reasonably representative of the performance observed. [See Table 12, page 338.]

7.10 Pace defined. The pace of the operator (or speed or rate of activity) is defined as the rate at which muscular force is applied to the body, arm, hand, or finger movements, disregarding the affect of job difficulty and hence, as the observed rate of acceleration of *the body member controlling the speed of doing the work*. [See Appendicies B and C.]

7.11 Pace scale. The 100 per cent pace and speeds above and below 100 per cent are specifically defined in the standard film loop when it is projected at the proper speed. [See Appendicies B and C.]

7.12 Assigning a rating. The time study man shall be familiar with the appearance of the standard scale of paces and shall appraise the job while he is studying it so that when he has completed his readings of the element times he is able to enter a pace rating for each element. This pace rating shall represent the average speed at which that element was performed as compared with the standard loop and no attention shall be paid to the difficulty of the element. Any numerical value which the time study man deems appropriate may be used although in most cases extreme performance should be scrutinized carefully. (It is to be noted that extremely difficult elements may be performed slowly, particularly where heavy weights are involved.)

7.13 Motion pictures. In cases where the time study man is not certain of the rating, a film record may be made. Use constant speed drive on camera and take pictures during time study.

7.20 Process controlled elements. The time for some elements is controlled by the requirements of what is being worked with rather than by the diligence of the operator. In such cases, no matter how hard the operator tried to do the task, he could not reduce the time. If the time observed is the time required by the material rather than the operator, a rating of—[the value representing the typical incentive pace] will be used without any adjustments for difficulty.

9.10 Prorating. Prorating is reducing the allowed time per time study element to a per work-unit value. For example, if the time study element was for "closing box of two engines," then only $\frac{1}{2}$ of the time study element is allowable per engine; hence divide by 2.

11.10 Difficulty adjustments. The difficulty on each element will be described in terms of the proper classification from each of the six categories of difficulty. The selected values will be added for each element, to obtain the total difficulty correction for the element. If an element has a weight adjustment, the per cent of the rated cycle time taken by that element will be computed, to determine the correct weight adjustment. [See Table C.10, Appendix C.]

11.20 Difficulty adjustment notes; general. The difficulty adjustment value for an element for any category will be the maximum applicable value for any reasonable portion of the element. (If weight or resistance to overcome is involved, the hand motions toward the weight should be in the same element as those with the weight.)

11.21 Difficulty adjustment notes; when pedals are held down during the job. The pedal correction is only for those elements in which the pedal is actually manipulated. Such elements, if similar to subsequent ones, except for this factor, may have to be prorated.

11.22 Difficulty adjustment notes; interpreting difficulty classifications. Elements corresponding to the various categories are listed next to them as a guide. [These notes should refer to elements, not jobs. A specially annotated table of difficulty adjustments should be prepared in each plant.]

12.10 Personal allowances. A personal allowance of 5 per cent will be added to the difficulty adjusted time to allow for personal needs.

12.20 Allowances, machine controlled operations. The standard time will be based on the standard time for manual work during the machine down time plus the allowance-adjusted time for the machine controlled part of the cycle. [See Supplemental Material, Chapter 18.]

17.10 General policy. In general, the standard will be developed for the smallest group practical; the individual standard will be given whenever economically and practically possible.

17.20 Crew standards, line activity. Where a crew works in sequence, the standard will be based on the longest operation in the line. The standard will also give the efficiency of the line set up so as to indicate the possibilities of future rate changes by a better distribution of work. The efficiency will be computed in the following manner:

$$\frac{\dfrac{\text{Total standard time of all operations}}{\text{Number of operators}}}{\text{Standard time of longest operation}} \times 100 = \text{efficiency in per cent}$$

When the individual instruction cards are issued, the per cent of full operation will be indicated for each position. Delay time will be shown and line balance noted as the cause when appropriate.

Although it is not practical to suggest a general method of handling grievances, this would appear to be an excellent place to summarize some facts bearing on the problem. Considerable administrative difficulty with time standards can be avoided if work with them is preceded by the realization that their application involves an extremely senstitive area of human relations, and, also, that time standard are far from *absolute* measures.

All methods of determining standards have at least several possible or probable sources of error. In using these methods one should attempt, insofar as possible, to control and reduce all controllable sources, while still recognizing that the values produced are only approximations of the concept of standard; one must set and apply policies concerning them with this in mind.

It should be obvious that, in most cases, various social controls, informal in nature, assist in maintaining the standards. Therefore, the grievance procedure should be developed with a full understanding of the total situation.

5. *Under what conditions may a standard time be changed?* Properly set standards may be guaranteed against revision except in specified cases, rather than whenever actual production becomes out of line with expected production. Poorly set standards require constant revision and lead to industrial chaos. An organization must realize that unusual workers will exceed standards by considerable amounts. Recognition of this fact is particularly important if incentive wages are used, such as piece rates or time standards with pay in terms of standard hours of work done. (The latter is the same as a piece rate except that it is more convenient, since it allows changing basic pay with automatic adjustment of the incentives, without complete retyping of the rate book.)

Maximum individual production tends to give lowest cost of manufacture. If rates are continually revised downward merely because unusual workers exceed them, a ceiling is in effect placed on earnings, and workers soon become aware of this. Of course, it is undesirable to have whole groups of workers making excessive earnings because of improperly set rates. They create friction with other groups. Such situations are best avoided by adequate time study procedures. When workers are aware of ceilings on earnings, they restrict production, which raises costs. If rates are to be effective, or if standards are to be used as real goals, they must be sufficiently reliable to be guaranteed, except for changes in the basic conditions.

Sample. The company will not change any regular production standard, regardless of how high earnings over day rate may be, unless there has been a significant change in method affecting the standard by 5 per cent or more or where an error has been made in arithmetic computation or in typing or posting of a production standard. A method change means a change in speeds, feeds, design, material, quality requirements, jigs, fixtures, dies, machinery, number on crew, or a different method or process of doing the work, including different hand and body motions or crew balance. This would naturally change the way of performing the work, requiring either more or less time, and would naturally require a different production standard. However, only that part of the production standard affected by the method change will be modified. The records in connection with any change, because of arithmetic, typing, or posting errors or method change are always available for review by an affected employee or his authorized representative.

Many minor improvements are made from time to time that individually would not increase or decrease the time required to any appreciable extent. However, over a period of time, several of these minor changes may accumulate and materially affect the time required. From time to time, standards will be reviewed and, on jobs where several of these changes combine to produce a 5 per cent or greater change in the time required, the time standard will be changed.[8]

6. *How will production be reported?* To control activities properly it is necessary to know how much of each individual's time is expended per unit on each operation (if the individual's work is separately identifiable), or how much group time is expended (if the production of the group is kept in a common pool). The production record is an aid in properly attributing cost and is a necessity if incentive wages are used. Methods of performing this function vary widely, depending on the industry. This variation is so wide that no single sample illustration can be offered as typical. The complete design of an integrated system is a considerable task, and process charts-combined analysis may well be used in its formulation.

---

[8] The extreme importance of an adequate WSP should be apparent here.

Reports

Reports from staff departments, such as an industrial engineering department, usually fall into two categories: (1) reports on specific proposals, and (2) reports on total accomplishment, usually on a periodic basis.

While in many cases these may be informal reports, varying in style from project to project and period to period, they are usually a recurring type of

```
METHOD PROPOSAL SUMMARY
 1.  _____ Date          1. Fewer people
                                    2. Fewer steps
 2.  _____ To        3. Less time on a step or steps
                                    4. Less time in production
 3.  _____ From       5. Less space
                                    6. Less time for critical skills
 4.  _____ Subject      7. Less time on critical equipment
                                    8. Increased quality
     _____            9. Less cost
                                   10. Less skill on step or steps
     _____           11. Better control
     Improvement will ( insert proper numbers or describe if not classifiable):
 5.  _____

 6.  If this proposal is approved, it will be necessary to ( summarize ):

     _____
     _____
     _____
     _____
     _____

ATTACHMENTS: (Insert number of sheets in boxes, follow with page numbers on lines.
 7.  [ ] _____ Cost of change estimate detail sheet
 8.  [ ] _____ Original charts
 9.  [ ] _____ Proposed charts, including summary and comparison
10.  [ ] _____ Proposed equipment list and details of placement
11.  [ ] _____ Jig, fixture, workplace or layout sketches or drawings
12.  [ ] _____ Job instruction sheets as required for proposal
13.  [ ] _____ Additional attachments list
14 . FINANCIAL ASPECTS OF CHANGE AND EVALUATION OF CHANGE ( summary)
     a. _____ (who) estimated the annual volume
     b. _____ (who) estimated the fixed cost of tools , etc.
     c. _____ Time new method would take to pay for itself out of savings.
     d. _____ Original labor cost and hours, annual
     e. _____ Proposed labor cost and hours, estimated annual
     f. _____ Cost of change
     g. _____ Net savings, annual ( estimated )
```

Fig. 25.8—Form for methods improvement proposal.

report. In such cases, considerable executive time may be saved by adopting a standard format. The use of a standard format becomes increasingly important as the organization becomes large, although, in the small organization, where each man may have a variety of duties, the time saving aspects of standard formats may well be worthwhile.

When the report concerns the subjects covered in this book, the individual report on a specific project normally forms the basis for acceptance or rejec-

---

PROCEDURE PROPOSAL SUMMARY

1. _____ Date   1. Fewer people
                                                2. Fewer steps
2. _____ To   3. Less time on a step or steps
                                                4. Less time to complete procedure
3. _____ From   5. Less space
                                                6. Less time for critical personnel
4. _____ Subject   7. Less time on critical equipment
                                                8. Increased accuracy
5. $ _____ Annual saving   9. Cheaper procedure
                                               10. Less skill on step or steps
6. ___ New Procedure   11. Better control

7. ___ Improved Procedure

8. ___ Improved Forms
9. Improvement will (insert proper numbers or describe if not classifiable):

10. If this proposal is approved it will be necessary to (summarize):
_____
_____
_____
_____
_____

11. Financial aspects of change and evaluation of change. (summary)
_____
_____
_____
_____
_____
_____

ATTACHMENTS (insert number of sheets before comma, follow with page numbers

12. ___ , _____ Original procedure chart

13. ___ , _____ Proposed procedure chart

14. ___ , _____ Proposed equipment list and details of placement

15. ___ , _____ Form designs and instructions for use, by forms

16. ___ , _____ Job instructions, by persons

17. ___ , _____ Additional attachments list

Fig. 25.9a—Form for procedures improvement proposal.

tion by operating management. If the individual reports are adequately formulated, the problem of submitting adequate periodic reports concerning total activity (in these areas) is greatly facilitated. The periodic report may be merely a summary of the individual reports.

A form suitable for summarizing the content of a method proposal is shown in Figure 25.8. A form for summarizing a procedure proposal is shown in Figure 25.9a. Inasmuch as it is difficult to summarize a process

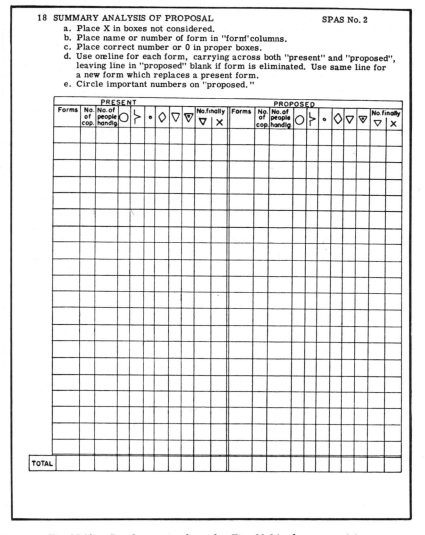

Fig. 25.9b—Supplementary form for Fig. 29.14a for summarizing and comparing two process charts-combined analysis.

chart-combined analysis directly on the chart, when the procedure proposal concerns two process charts-combined analysis, Figure 25.9a is often accompanied by a form such as shown in Figure 25.9b, which summarizes and contrasts the details of the two procedures involved—the original and the proposed. A form suitable for summarizing the content of a work measurement proposal is shown in Figure 25.10.

Periodic reports from staff departments serve several purposes. The first is to inform management concerning the results of the activity in order to

---

WORK MEASUREMENT PROPOSAL SUMMARY

REASONS FOR STDS.

1. _____ Date   LIST A

                                                   A. Correct clerical error

2. _____ To   B. Correct old standard

                                                C. Improve quality or yield

3. _____ From   D. Change in work unit

4. Subject   E. Other. Specify in item 7

    _____ Revised standard

                                                 LIST B

    _____ Reason for revision from list A   F. New product

                                                  G. New equipment

    _____ New standard   H. New method

                                                I. Other. Specify in item 7

    _____ Reason for setting from list B

5. _____ Check if method proposal gives details

6. Operation or operations and department or departments involved:

    _____

    _____

    _____

7. If this standard is installed, it will be necessary to (summarize, including any unusual features) :

    _____

    _____

    _____

    _____

8. _____ Job description sheets have been prepared.

9. ATTACHMENTS. Insert number of sheets before comma; give page numbers and, except for preprinted item, titles, after comma.

    _____ , Production standards notice

    _____ , _____

    _____ , _____

10. FINANCIAL ASPECTS OF CHANGE

    a. _____ (who) estimated annual volume

    b. _____ Current or original annual labor cost and hours

    c. _____ Proposed annual labor cost and hours

    d. _____ Net annual estimated cost reduction, dollars

Fig. 25.10—Form for work measurement proposal.

answer the ever-present question, "Is it worth continuing?" The second purpose is to create a record indicating rate of performance so as to assist in planning future activity or programming the workload of individuals responsible for the function reported on. The reports may also serve the industrial engineering administrator in operating his department, and in planning budgets.

METHODS IMPROVEMENT AUDIT

                                        INSTALLATION
                                        DEPARTMENT
                                        DATE ENDING, PERIOD COVERED

I   METHODS PROPOSALS
    a. _____ Total proposals of method changes made to date.
    b. _____ Cumulative changes proposed prior to period and awaiting action.
    c. _____ Number of method changes proposed in period.
    d. _____ Number of changes acted upon:
       _____   1. From prior periods.
                     2. From reporting period.
    e. _____ Number of changes awaiting action (b + c - d).
    f. _____ Number of changes approved and approval %; -- $\frac{\text{Approved}}{\text{Reviewed}}$ x 100.
       _____   1. For prior period
                     2. For reporting period.
    g. _____ 1. Total savings of accepted proposals from Method Proposal
                     Summary Sheets, cumulative for a year.
       _____ 2. Average increase in production for reporting period.
       _____ 3. List highest three.
       _____
       _____

II TALLY OF CATEGORIES OF SAVINGS ACCEPTED DURING PERIOD
    a. _____ Fewer people
    b. _____ Fewer steps.
    c. _____ Less time on a step or steps.
    d. _____ Less time in production.
    e. _____ Less space.
    f. _____ Less time for critical skills.
    g. _____ Less time on critical equipment.
    h. _____ Increased quality.
    i. _____ Less cost.
    j. _____ Less skill on step or steps.
    k. _____ Better control.
    l. _____ Miscellaneous.

III NUMBER OF SOP'S PREPARED FOR SHOP METHODS
    a. _____ Revised.
    b. _____ New.

IV SUGGESTION PROGRAM
    a. _____ Number of suggestions submitted for period and cumulative.
    b. _____ Percent of employees submitting suggestions.
    c. _____ Percent and number of ideas approved.
    d. _____ Number of suggestions held over one month.
    e. _____ Cost savings resulting from suggestion program:
                     From reporting period.
       _____   Cumulative yearly.
    f. _____ Cost of administering program.

V   TRAINING PROGRAMS
    a. _____ Number of supervisors trained in Methods Improvement:
                     1. In reporting period
       _____ 2. Total, to date.
    b. _____ Number of employees trained in Methods Improvement:
                     1. In reporting period
       _____ 2. Total, to date.

Fig. 25.11 — Form for periodic reporting or auditing of methods improvement activity. Developed by **Dr. I. Lazarus,** Army Ordnance Corps.

The periodic report or audit forms shown in Figures 25.11, 25.12, and 25.13 were originally created by the staff of the the Management Engineering Training Program of the Ordnance Corps of the U.S. Department of the Army. Figure 25.11, the methods activity audit, was designed by Dr. I. Lazarus; Figure 25.12, the procedure activity form, was designed by Mr.

```
        PROCEDURE  ANALYSIS  ACTIVITY  AUDIT  SHEET
        _____ INSTALLATION

        _____ DEPARTMENT

        _____ DATE ENDING, PERIOD COVERED

   I    ACTIVITY
        a. _____  Total number of man hours spent in procedure and forms
                          design studies during report period.
        b. _____  Reduction in man hours of work load per month as result of
                          procedure and forms design changes during report period.
        c. _____  Cumulative savings in man hours, 12 month running total.

   II   PROCEDURE STUDIES
        a. _____  Approximate number of procedures in installation.
        b. _____  Total number of procedures recorded graphically at end of
                          last report period.
        c. _____  Number of procedures recorded graphically during this report
                          period.
        d. _____  Total number of procedures recorded graphically at end of
                          this report period.
        e. _____  Number of procedures proposals submitted during report period.
        f. _____  Number of procedure proposals accepted during report period.

   III  FORMS DESIGN
        a. _____  Total number of forms in use at end of last report period.
        b. _____  New forms created not replacing old forms.
        c. _____  Number of forms combined.
        d. _____  Number of forms eliminated.
        e. _____  Net change in number of forms in use.
        f. _____  Total number of forms in use at end of present report period.
        g. _____  Number of forms simplified.
```

Fig. 25.12—Form for periodic reporting or auditing of procedure improvement activity. Developed by J. Moquin, Army Ordnance Corps.

J. Moquin; Figure 25.13, the work measurement activity form, by Mr. C. Schneider.

An alternative form of a methods improvement audit appears in Figure 25.14; an alternative form of a work measurement audit appears in Figure 25.15. By evaluating these activities in terms of the contribution to plant

---

WORK MEASUREMENT DEVELOPMENT AND APPLICATION AUDIT

_____ INSTALLATION

_____ DEPARTMENT

_____ DATE ENDING, PERIOD COVERED

I   LABOR STANDARD DEVELOPMENT
a. _____ Total number labor standards, present.
b. _____ Total number labor standards, last report.
c. _____ Number increase over last report.
d. _____ Total number labor standards revised; method change.
e. _____ Total number labor standards revised; other reasons.

II   STANDARD HOURS COVERAGE
a. _____ Total elapsed man hours during report period covered by standards.
b. _____ Total daywork man hours during report period.
c. _____ Total elapsed man hours during report period.
d. _____ Percentage of hours covered by labor standards.
e. _____ Total number of operations performed during report period covered by labor standards.
f. _____ Total number of operations performed during report period not covered by labor standards.
g. _____ Percentage of operations performed covered by labor standards.

III PRODUCTIVITY ANALYSIS
a. _____ Total standard man hours produced on work covered by standards.
b. _____ Total elapsed man hours on work covered by standards.
c. _____ Percentage productivity.

IV   DELAY HOURS ANALYSIS
a. _____ Total machine downtime delay man hours.
b. _____ Percentage of machine downtime to total elapsed man hours.
c. _____ Total set-up delay man hours.
d. _____ Percentage of set-up time to total elapsed man hours.
e. _____ Total miscellaneous delay man hours.
f. _____ Percentage of miscellaneous delay to total elapsed man hours.
g. _____ Total delay man hours.
h. _____ Percentage total delay to total elapsed man hours.

Fig. 25.13 — Form for periodic reporting or auditing of work measurement activity. Developed by C. S. Schneider, Army Ordnance Corps.

C.B.C.   CODE 1464 - B   DATE **March 30**

METHODS IMPROVEMENT AUDIT - PERIOD **Feb. 14**   TO **March 14**

1.   METHODS PROPOSALS

a.   **64**   Total Proposals of Method Changes made to date since Sept. 1, 1958.

b.   **11**   Number of method changes proposed in period.

c. $**110,247**   1.   Total savings of accepted proposals from Method Proposal summary sheet made to date since Sept. 1, 1958.

d. $ **22,703**   2.   Total savings of accepted proposals from Method Proposal summary sheet cumulative for period.
Less cost of Equipment if any and IE expense $1,900 per period.

$ **10,851**   List highest three.   Pickle Curing *

   7,088   Casing Shipping *

   4,772   Hog Kill *

2.   TALLY OF CATEGORIES OF SAVINGS ACCEPTED DURING PERIOD

a.   **6**   Fewer people

b.   **—**   Fewer steps

c.   **6**   Less time on a step or steps

d.   **—**   Less time in production

e.   **—**   Less space

f.   **2**   Less time for critical skills

g.   **—**   Less time on critical equipment

h.   **—**   Increased quality

i.   **6**   Less cost

j.   **—**   Less skill on step or steps

k.   **—**   Better control

l.   **—**   Miscellaneous

Submitted by _____

*   See attached sheet for details

Fig. 25.14—A plant methods improvement audit. (Courtesy C. J. Allen, Chief Industrial Engineer, Patrick Cudahy, Inc.)

profitability, the economics of the operation of the motion and time study activity are readily evaluated by line management. These periodic reports are readily assembled. Each motion and time study analyst, after completing a task, turns in two copies of a form similar to Figure 25.8 or 25.10, as appropriate. One copy is filed in a monthly folder from which the monthly

P.C. Inc 1463-B   DATE March 30

Mr. M. F. Cudahy:

WORK MEASUREMENT PROGRESS REPORT - PERIOD Feb. 14 _____ TO March 14

1. STANDARDS ESTABLISHMENT

    A. Number of Standards at beginning of period.   3,772

    B. Number of New Standards Established. ("Established" includes re-
        organizing job, writing-up method, reviewing method with
        supervision and steward).   11

    C. Total number of Standards at end of period.   3,783

2. STANDARDS REVISIONS

    A. Number of Standards indicated as needing revision during period.   131

    B. Number of Standards revised.   131

    C. Net result of those revised.

        A. Total estimated annual man hours of work affected.   313,477

        B. Total number of workers affected.   344

        C. Estimated reduction in annual earned direct labor hours.   9,722

        D. Estimated annual payroll savings for month. $ 26,220.00
    Includes cost of equipment, if any plus I E expense $4,212/period

        E. Estimated annual payroll savings. Sept. 1, 1958 to date * $133,350

RECAP		PLANT EVALUATIONS		
Total plant	1,372	Hog Kill - 1		
Total incentive paid workers	1,091	Hog Offal - 5		
Total production workers	1,222			
% Total production workers	90.1	RECAP		
% Total Plant	78.5	Standards	$	3,517.00
% Jobs on Standard	82.3	Methods	$	22,703.00
% Hours on Standard	73.7	Total	$	26,220.00

*   Total represents decreased labor minus increased costs due operations
    changed for quality or yield reasons.

cc: HH Holcomb, JK Stark, E Scheidenhelm, N Sherman, MS Hungness

                                Submitted by _____

Fig. 25.15—A plant work measurement audit. (Courtesy C. J.
    Allen, Chief Industrial Engineer, Patrick Cudahy,
    Inc.)

audit is compiled. The other copy is filed, by analyst, to facilitate periodic review of his activity by the Chief Industrial Engineer.

Training

Inasmuch as the procedures of motion and time study are not commonly understood, particularly in the newer areas of application, in-plant training courses or conference sessions for all groups affected are highly desirable. With motion and time study regarded today as a tool to be used by most of the divisions of an organization, means of distributing the knowledge is often required for its effective use. A staff specialist frequently assumes the responsibility for the educational training of the organization, although this is one of the most common instances of the utilization of outside help. Certainly, at the very least, the help of the most properly oriented and knowledgeable group should be sought.

Any training program for an organization should be designed specifically to meet its needs. It is not possible, therefore, to lay down a recommended educational program. In each case there will be differences in:

1. Typical problems created by outputs and processes.
2. Educational level of the trainees.
3. Objectives of the training.

However, the basic principles embodied in successful programs will be applicable. They are as follows:

1. *The course should be given on company time during regular working hours.* If the program is to be considered as dealing with material of direct interest to the organization and the individual, this is an absolute necessity.

2. *Sessions of three hours duration, with breaks on the hours, are about a maximum, if the purpose is merely to update the person's knowledge.* Two hours is about a minimum in such cases. However, the higher the educational level of the group, the longer the daily training session may be. One meeting a week is usually sufficient. This is not the case, though, when the individual is fully relieved of his duties during a training period and expected to fully use the materials discussed. In such cases the whole working day may be used.

3. *The activity should be varied.* Lecture, discussion, demonstration, and practical work should be interspersed.

4. *Extensive use should be made of visual aids and demonstrations.* During the early part of the course there is usually considerable advantage in obtaining visual aids from outside sources to increase the "psychological distance" and objectivity of the trainees. As the course progresses, the emphasis may swing to in-plant illustrations.

5. *Participational teaching should be used.* In general, this may be obtained

by having the group read the topic for a session prior to the meeting and attempt to apply the material discussed, after the meeting. Thus, after the first meeting, the conference leader may answer questions on the new topic, give a short lecture on additional aspects, show the application of the material, and have the group work a problem with it. Subsequent to this, the conference leader should have the group discuss their applications of the topic of the preceding session.

6. *The reading material should be geared to the educational level of the trainees.* Particular note should be taken that the educational level of the typical industrial employee is rapidly rising in the United States and the material should not be insultingly simple.

7. *The conference leader should be skilled at such activity and should have a first-hand knowledge of the material.* He should be in a position that will aid him in commanding the respect of the group.

8. Last, but not least important, *the training program must be given the effective and visible support of an executive sufficiently high in the organization so as to encourage fully effective participation in the training.*

Appendix A:
A Hierarchy of Work-units

The concept of a hierarchy of work-units was introduced in Chapter 17. The work-unit hierarchy (or the work-unit structure) was shown to have the same relationship to a service type output that an engineering drawing has to a hardware type product. The work-unit concept was also shown to be of great assistance in determining how to count work. Further, the concept of the different sizes of work-units was used in clarifying the differences and similarities of the various time study techniques.

Unfortunately the work-unit structure of an organization is as peculiar to that organization as an engineering drawing is to the hardware that it represents. Hence, an illustration can only be a guide, an example, a help in seeing the result of applying the work-unit analysis concept. However, anyone attempting to make such an analysis for his own organization ought to be able to look at a complete work-unit structure to see what a completed one looks like. The following pages present the complete work-unit structure of the Meat Inspection Activity of the Consumer and Marketing Service of the U.S. Department of Agriculture. All of the activities have been covered with time standards set at the fourth-order work-unit level. The particular technique used for each fourth-order work-unit is indicated on the figures describing the fourth-order work-units, Figures A6 and A7.

546

UNITED STATES DEPARTMENT OF AGRICULTURE

CONSUMER & MARKETING SERVICE

MEAT INSPECTION ACTIVITY

WORK-UNIT STRUCTURE

(This cover sheet shows the relationships among the work-units and provides an index to the detailed sheets which follow.)

8th-order work-unit		Figure A1		
7th-order work-units	7-1. Figure A2	7-2. Figure A2	7-3. Figure A2	7-4. Figure A2
6th-order work-units	From 1.6-1. to 1.6-15. Figure A3	From 2.6-1. to 2.6-12. Figure A4	3.6-1 Figure A4	From 4.6-1. to 4.6-50. Figure A4
5th-order work-units	Figure A5	Figure A5	Figure A5	Figure A5
4th order work-units	From 4-1. to 4-33. Figure A6	From 4-1. to 4-33. Figure A7	From 4-1. to 4-33. Figure A7	Figure A7

3rd-order
work-units

Third-order work-units for this agency are defined as all of
the tasks associated with the production of one unit of a
4th-order work-unit. Each 4th-order work-unit will have
a separate task list. The task lists were developed by an
on-site (or other appropriate method) study for each 4th-order
work-unit.

*Fig. A—Cover sheet for work-unit hierarchy for Meat Inspection
Activity.*

547

THE UNITED STATES DEPARTMENT OF AGRICULTURE

THE CONSUMER AND MARKETING SERVICE

CONSUMER PROTECTION WITH RESPECT TO MEAT AND MEAT PRODUCTS

STATEMENT OF OBJECTIVE

Type: Constructive service

Mission area: The protection of public health and economy of purchase[1] by assurance of a safe, wholesome and properly labeled supply of meat and meat products in the channels of commerce supplying the American and foreign buyer.

Purpose   a. Intent: Freedom from unhealthy, undersirable or improperly labeled meat and meat products in the channels of commerce.[2]

b. Dimension: The risk of economically undesirable products or products possessing a risk to human health entering the channels of domestic or foreign commerce.

Goal: Zero risk

Limitations: Surveillance and control are limited to meat and meat products produced for or in interstate or foreign commerce.[3]

Freedoms: Slaughter and meat processing plants may not engage in interstate commerce unless the meat and meat products are produced under the surveillance of Federal inspectors; the plants facilities must receive Federal approval prior to the granting of Federal inspection; meat may not move in interstate channels without Federal approval; only Federal inspectors may grant official certification of the wholesomeness, etc., of meat and meat products destined for export.

1. The exclusion of watery bacon or ham, underweight packages, cheaper ingredients than shown on the label, and so forth.
2. The meaning of safe, wholesome, and properly labelled shall be defined by the Secretary of Agriculture.
3. This limitation was reduced by the passage of the Wholesome Meat Act of 1967.

Fig. A.1 — The 8th-order work-unit of the Meat Inspection Activity.

7-1. Inspection services provided in official establishments for
domestically destined product. (An official establishment
is one which requires inspection because it is engaged in
interstate commerce and which has been approved for meat
inspection.)

7-2. Inspection service provided in nonofficial establishments for
domestically destined product, for which the service is reimbursed, and other reimbursed services other than export certification. (A nonofficial establishment is either one which does
not require inspection but wants to operate under it, or needs
some of the inspection service such as approval of part of the
facility so that the meat may be Federally graded, although the
grading is provided by a different Federal group.)

7-3. Inspection service provided for product destined for export.
(This would be part of the work otherwise done under the category of work-unit 7-1 unless separate records were kept. It
may also be caused by a separate work generating system; the
taking of meat and meat products out of cold storage for re-
inspection before exporting.

7-4. Inspection service provided for intrastate plants under the
provisions of the Wholesome Meat Act of 1967.

Fig. A.2—The 7th-order work-units of the Meat Inspection Activity.

(All of these work-units are prefixed with 1 to identify them with 7-1.)

1.6-1. Inspection service provided for a year for plants wherein the workload is less than enough to employ one inspector fully, but because of either the nature of the work or the isolated location of the plant, the plant requires one inspector; the work is slaughter inspection only.

1.6-2. Same as 6-1. but the work is with respect to processed meats or processing only.

1.6-3. Same as 6-1. but the work is with respect to both processing and slaughter.

1.6-4. Inspection services provided for a year for plants wherein the workload is less than enough to employ one inspector fully, but because of both the nature of the work and the location of the plant, the inspection work may be combined with the inspection work required to be performed at one or more additional plants; the work is slaughter only.

1.6-5. Same as 6-4. but the work is processing only.

1.6-6. Same as 6-4. but the work is with both processing and slaughter.

1.6-7. Inspection service provided for a year for plants wherein the workload is such as to require exactly one inspector; the work is slaughter inspection only.

1.6-8. Same as 6-7. but the work is processing only.

1.6-9. Same as 6-7. but the work is with both processing and slaughter.

1.6-10. Inspection service provided for a year for plants wherein the inspection workload requires more than one but less than six inspectors; the work is with slaughter only.

1.6-11. Same as 6-10. but the work is processing only.

1.6-12. Same as 6-10. but the work is with both processing and slaughter.

1.6-13. Inspection service provided for a year for plants wherein the workload is such as to require six or more inspectors; the work is with slaughter only.

1.6-14. Same as 6-13. but the work is processing only.

1.6-15. Same as 6-13. but the work is with both processing and slaughter.

Fig. A.3—The 6th-order work-units of work-unit 7–1. of the Meat Inspection Activity.

6th-ORDER WORK-UNITS FOR 7-2.

(All of these work-units are prefixed with 2 to identify them with 7-2.)

2.6-1.   I.D. houses inspected.

2.6-2.   Animal food establishments inspected.

2.6-3.   Food product establishments inspected.

2.6-4.   Public warehouses inspected.

2.6-5.   Non-federally inspected plants reviewed for suitability for meat
          grading.

2.6-6.   Inedible rendering plants surveyed.

2.6-7.   Specification service provided.

2.6-8.   Samples collected for the Public Health Service.

2.6-9.   Blood samples collected for the Animal Health Division.

2.6-10.   Other samples collected for other Agencies

2.6-11.   Back tags transferred in I.D. houses.

2.6-12.   Other miscellaneous reimbursable services performed.

6th-ORDER WORK-UNITS FOR 7-3.

(All of these work-units are prefixed with 3 to identify them with 7-3.)

3.6-1.   Export certifications provided.

6th-ORDER WORK-UNITS FOR 7-4.

(All of these work-units are prefixed with 4 to identify them with 7-4.)

4.6-1.   One for each State. Services provided in cooperation with the
          State under the provisions of the Wholesome Meat Act of 1967.
thru   The outputs may vary from State to State depending on the nature
4.6-50.   of the Federal-State arrangements.

*Fig. A.4 — The 6th-order work-units for 7th-order work-units 7–2.,
7–3., and 7–4., of the Meat Inspection Activity.*

551

```
        5th-ORDER WORK-UNITS FOR ALL 6th-ORDER WORK-UNITS

6th-order
work-unit                        5th-order work-units

1.6-1.    1. One such plant for which inspection service is provided.
1.6-2.    1. One such plant for which inspection service is provided.
1.6-3.    1. One such plant for which inspection service is provided.
1.6-4.    1. One such plant for which inspection service is provided.
1.6-5.    1. One such plant for which inspection service is provided.
1.6-6.    1. One such plant for which inspection service is provided.
1.6-7.    1. One such plant for which inspection service is provided.
1.6-8.    1. One such plant for which inspection service is provided.
1.6-9.    1. One such plant for which inspection service is provided.
1.6-10.   1. One such plant for which inspection service is provided.
1.6-11.   1. One such plant for which inspection service is provided.
1.6-12.   1. One such plant for which inspection service is provided.
1.6-13.   1. One such plant for which inspection service is provided.
1.6-14.   1. One such plant for which inspection service is provided.
1.6-15.   1. One such plant for which inspection service is provided.


2.6-1.    1. One such plant for which inspection service is provided.
2.6-2.    1. One such plant for which inspection service is provided.
2.6-3.    1. One such plant for which inspection service is provided.
2.6-4.    1. One such warehouse for which inspection service is provided.
2.6-5.    1. One such plant reviewed.
2.6-6.    1. One such plant surveyed.
2.6-7.    1. One equivalent man-hour of specification service provided.
2.6-8.    1. One such sample collected.
2.6-9.    1. One such sample collected.
2.6-10.   1. One such sample collected; additional numbers for each kind
             of sample.
2.6-11.   1. One back tag transferred.
2.6-12.   1. As needed.


3.6-1.    1. One export certification provided.


4.6-1.
thru      Currently being designed.
4.6-50.
```

*Fig. A.5—The 5th-order work-units for all 6th-order work-units of
the Meat Inspection Activity.*

552

(Each 5th-order work-unit contains a unique mix of these 4th-order work-units; the mix is determined by an on-site examination of each 5th-order work-unit. The data obtained during the on-size examination is recorded on form MI-462. These data are used for the selection of the correct standard times. The method used for developing the standard data is indicated to the right of the work-unit number. The meaning of the codes is at the bottom of this sheet.)

4-1.	DTS-IS	Calf slaughter in-plant inspection service provided.
4-2.	DTS-IS	Cattle slaughter in-plant inspection service provided.
4-3.	DTS-IS	Hog slaughter in-plant inspection service provided.
4-4.	DTS-IS	Sheep slaughter in-plant inspection service provided.
4-5.	DTS-IS	Goat slaughter in-plant inspection service provided.
4-6.	DTS-IS	Horse slaughter in-plant inspection service provided.
4-7.	DTS-ESMFWU	Sausage manufacture in-plant inspection service provided.
4-8.	DTS-ESMFWU	Canning in-plant inspection service provided.
4-9.	DTS-ESMFWU	Smoked product manufacture in-plant inspection service provided.
4-10.	DTS-ESMFWU	Curing in-plant inspection service provided.
4-11.	DTS-ESMFWU	Edible oil refining in-plant inspection service provided.
4-12.	DTS-ESMFWU	Pork cutting and trimming in-plant inspection service provided.
4-13.	DTS-ESMFWU	Beef cutting in-plant inspection service provided.
4-14.	DTS-ESMFWU	Inedible oil rendering in-plant inspection service provided.
4-15.	DTS-ESMFWU	Beef boning in-plant inspection service provided.
4-16.	DTS-ESMFWU	Pork boning in-plant inspection service provided.
4-17.	DTS-ESMFWU	Shipping and receiving under seal in-plant inspection service provided.
4-18.	DTS-ESMFWU	Frozen food manufacture in-plant inspection service provided.
4-19.	DTS-ESMFWU	Hotel-restaurant-institution portioning and packaging in-plant inspection service provided.
4-20.	DTS-ESMFWU	Offal in-plant inspection service provided.
4-21.	DTS-ESMFWU	Import reinspection in-plant service provided.
4-22.	FPE	Periodic appraisal of inspectors provided.
		a. Livestock slaughter inspectors
		b. Processed product inspectors
4-23.	FPE	Supervision of inspectors provided.
4-24.	SRMC	Payroll details and other servicing of inspectors provided.
4-25.	SRMC	Label review and approval services provided.
4-26.	SRMC	Facilities review and approval services provided.
4-27.	DTS-ES	Chemical analysis support provided.
4-28.	SRMC	Pathological tissue examination support provided.
4-29.	SRMC	Microbiological analysis support provided.
4-30.	FIAT	Relief capability for sick and annual leave provided.
4-31.	FPE	Training support provided.
4-32.	FPE	Standard procedures for inspection provided.
4-33.	FIAT	Agency administration provided.

DTS-IS	- Direct time study-intensive sampling
DTE-ESMFU	- Direct time study-extensive sampling with multi-factor work-units
FPE	- Fractioned professional estimates
SRMC	- Self-reporting followed by mathematical calculation
DTS-ES	- Direct time study-extensive sampling
FIAT	- Fiat

Fig. A.6 — The 4th-order work-units for 5th-order work-units 1.6–1.1. through 1.6–15.1. of the Meat Inspection Activity. The method used to set standard times is also shown.

4th-ORDER WORK-UNITS FOR 5th-ORDER WORK-UNITS 2.6-1, through 2.6-12,

(Each 5th-order work-unit contains a specific 4th-order work-unit, as shown, plus a mix from 4th-order work-units 4-13. through 4-32. The method used for developing the standard data is indicated to the right of the work-unit number. The meaning of the codes appears at the bottom of the preceding sheet.)

5th-order
work-unit

2.6-1.1.	4-1.	FPE	I.D. house in-plant inspection service provided.
2.6-2.1.	4-2.	FPE	Animal food plant in-plant inspection service provided.
2.6-3.1.	4-3.	FPE	Food product establishment in-plant inspection service provided.
2.6-4.1.	4-4.	FPE	Public warehouse on-site inspection service provided.
2.6-5.1.	4-5.	FPE	Non-federally inspected plant reviewed on-site for suitability for meat grading.
2.6-6.1.	4-6.	FPE	Inedible rendering plant on-site survey performed.
2.6-7.1.	4-7.	SRMC	Specification service in-plant provided.
2.6-8.1.	4-8.	FPE	Samples collected in-plant for Public Health Ser.
2.6-9.1.	4-9.	FPE	Blood samples collected in-plant for Animal Health Division.
2.6-10.1.	4-10.	FPE	Samples for other agencies collected in-plant.
2.6-11.1.	4-11.	FPE	Back tags transferred in-plant in I.D. houses.
2.6-12.1.	4-12.	FPE	Other in-plant services provided.
	4-13.	FPE	Appraisal of inspection service performed.
	4-14.	SRMC	Billing and collection performed.

4-23 through 4-33 are the same as with 5th-order work-units 1.6-1.1 through 1.6-1.15.1. See preceding sheet.

4th ORDER WORK-UNITS FOR 5th-ORDER WORK-UNIT 3.6-1,

4-1.	DTS-ESMFWU	Export certificate issued in-plant.
4-2.	SRMC	Export certificate central file maintained.
4-3.	SRMC	Export certification billing and collection performed.
4-4.	FPE	Appraisal of inspectors performed.

4-23. through 4-33. are the same as with the 5th-order work-units 1.6-1.1 through 1.6-1.15.1. See preceding sheet.

4th ORDER WORK-UNITS FOR 5th-ORDER WORK-UNITS 4.6-1, through 4.6-50,

This is a new program. The outputs and the work-units are being designed.

Fig. A.7 — The 4th-order work-units for 5th-order work-units 2.6-1. through 2.6-12. of the Meat Inspection Activity. The method used to set standard times is also shown.

Appendix B:
Effort Rating

This Appendix presents the practical details of a commonly employed procedure for rating the performance observed during the making of a time study, a procedure called "effort rating."[1]

In Chapter 18, rating was described as a two-step process:

1. The time study man must judge the difficulty of the job under observation and form a mental concept of what the performance of this job would look like if it met the requirements of standard performance as defined by the definition the observer is working with.
2. The time study man must appraise the actual performance under observation as compared with the concept formed in step 1 and place a numerical value on this appraisal.

In order to speak meaningfully about "what the performance of this job would look like," and so forth, one must identify an observable characteristic (or observable characteristics) on the basis of which one will render his judgments or form his concepts. "Effort," the characteristic used in "effort rat-

[1] The author wishes to point out that he makes no claim whatsoever to originality in this appendix. He has drawn on the works of Carroll and Presgrave, two of the best known advocates of this procedure, and is deeply in their debt for the concepts and procedures described herein. Phil Carroll, Jr., *Time Study for Cost Control*. New York, N.Y.: McGraw-Hill Book Co., Inc.; R. Presgrave, *Dynamics of Time Study*. New York, N.Y.: McGraw-Hill Book Co., Inc.

ing," is defined as *the apparent exertion and speed exhibited in doing the work.* Obviously, not too much attention should be given to the apparent exertion or it will also be necessary to appraise and take into account the type of operator; high exertion from an inferior operator would have to be discounted and low exertion from a superior operator would have to be taken at more than face value. If, as would appear proper, we are to take speed as the primary characteristic, then we need to have some concept of the proper speed (or rapidity of motion) for the job; in short, what speed we can typically expect from the typical operator.

Presgrave describes "normal effort" (or speed) as equivalent to either of the following two illustrations:

1. Dealing 52 playing cards into four piles in 0.50 minutes.

   The dealing of cards is done with the cards in the left hand, the thumb advancing the top card each time, the right hand grasping the pre-positioned corner of the top card between its thumb and first finger, carrying it to the proper pile before releasing it, and then reversing the motion back to the pack. Four piles are formed by the dealing, one in front of the dealer and the other three at the other three corners of a one-foot square.

2. Walking at 3 miles per hour, taking 27-inch steps.

   One should bear in mind that Presgrave's concept of normal is such that the average worker, with incentive, can exceed standard by 30 per cent. If one maintains the same physical concept of what can be expected from an incentive worker, but defines typical incentive performance as 125 per cent, then the speeds at normal become 0.50 min. × 125/130 or 0.48 min. for card dealing and 3 m.p.h. × 130/125 or 3.12 m.p.h. for walking.

The Society for Advancement of Management has prepared an extensive series of films and circulated them among an enormous number of time study men in order to obtain a general consensus on the effort or speed exhibited and has published these films and these values. (Professor T. U. Matthew, formerly of the University of Birmingham, England, has performed the same task, with these films, in the United Kingdom.) Such a group of films is designed to provide the time study man with a means of becoming familiar with the appearance of normal or standard speed for a variety of jobs.

In practice, the time study man is expected, while the time study is being made, to select from his concepts (gained by experience on similar jobs, knowledge of similar tasks, exposure to films available, and so forth) the concept that will serve for step 1 of the two steps previously given as necessary for rating. He can then perform step 2 and place a value on his time study sheet as shown in Figure B.1. This figure is used to multiply the average time

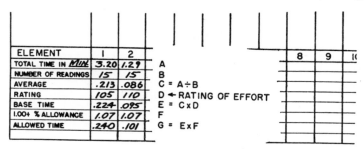

ELEMENT	1	2					8	9	l(
TOTAL TIME IN *Min*	3.20	1.29	A						
NUMBER OF READINGS	15	15	B						
AVERAGE	.213	.086	C = A ÷ B						
RATING	105	110	D ← RATING OF EFFORT						
BASE TIME	.224	.095	E = C x D						
1.00+ % ALLOWANCE	1.07	1.07	F						
ALLOWED TIME	.240	.101	G = E x F						

Fig. B.1—Section of time study sheet with effort rating and base time.

taken for the element and thus produce a *base time*, as described in Chapter 18. A machine controlled element would be assigned a rating of 100.[2]

The time study man may find it advantageous to rate individual element readings which he feels certain of and to use these to check his rating of the average of all readings. Exact agreement is unlikely (due to the sampling error of individual readings) but some check is considered possible.

It is to be noted that the type of rating which has been described is the type of rating used by the men reported on by Carson, quoted in Chapter 18, Supplemental Material, Part 2. Further, it is essentially simple in concept, although the crux of the problem appears to be the necessary exposure to performances of a variety of tasks, the ratings of which are known, in order to develop a broad enough basis for performing step 1 of the rating procedure. However, it should be obvious that the more similar the jobs in a shop are, the easier this procedure will be.

---

[2] The entire procedure may be based on 60 being defined as normal, in which case the numbers will be different, but the results will be the same.

Appendix C:
Objective Rating

In Chapter 18, objective rating was described as a rating procedure using anchored judgment. Two steps are involved, the two steps being in the reverse order of the two steps of conventional rating. The two steps are:

1. The rating of the observed pace against an objective pace-standard, which is the same for all jobs. In this rating, no attention whatsoever is paid to job difficulty and its limiting effect on possible pace; hence, a single pace-standard may be used instead of a multiplicity of mental concepts.
2. The use of a *difficulty adjustment*, consisting of a percentage increment, added after the application of the numerical appraisal from step 1 has been used to adjust the original observed data. This percentage increment is to be taken from experimentally determined tables of the effect of various observable factors that control the exertion required at a given pace.

The requirements for making possible the performance of step 1 of objective rating are met by the following procedure, which will be fully discussed prior to examining the requirements for performing step 2.

A. In actually taking direct time studies the first requirement is an objective such as the definition of standard time given in the Supplemental Material of Chapter 17, although any version may be used.

The one suggested was as follows:

DEFINITION—*The standard time for a job will be 130/100 of the amount of time that will be necessary to accomplish a unit of work:*

1. *using a given method and equipment,*
2. *under given conditions,*
3. *by a worker possessing sufficient skill to do the job properly,*
4. *as physically fit for the job, after adjustment to it, as the average person who can be expected to be put on the job,*
5. *and working at the maximum pace that can be maintained on such a job day after day without harmful effects.*

B. Next it is necessary to obtain some physical representation of this (or whatever version of this definition is chosen), on one very simple task. It is important to note that only one task is required. This may be done in any one of four ways.

1. The time study group may make a series of films of a worker at different paces on a simple job, and ask management to select one of these as representing their concept of standard pace. It is true that judgment must be exercised here and some original error is possible, but this is not of prime importance. At least a standard of unchanging pace is set up. Also, if management wants to assume this prerogative, it should be assumed at a high enough level. It is worth noting that the pace selected may also be jointly negotiated by labor and management, in which case the accuracy with which it represents the definition of standard is of less consequence, although this will be discovered later through experience with its use. At least it will be acceptable to both parties and without such mutual acceptance joint agreements concerning money per hour appear inadequate to say the least. However, care should be exercised that any existing, generally accepted pace is not unduly disturbed. A negotiation for pace should not be a subterfuge for a concealed negotiation for a wage increase.

Critics of time study will refer to the managerial decisions required, in selecting this film, as "value judgments" and charge that time study based on such a bench-mark concept is not measurement. It is true that the pace selection is a "value judgment," but so is the selection of any unit of measurement which meets sociological rather than physical criteria (see chapter 17). However, whether or not time study is measurement depends on how the standard is *applied* rather than how it is *selected*.

Figure C.1 shows the time study group at the Mirro Aluminum Co. taking films of a simple operation for development into this type of bench-mark. A close up of the operation being filmed, "Wrap Aluminum Measuring Cup for Bulk Shipment," is shown in Figure C.2.

When management rates the series of films made, under the procedure being described, there will inevitably be some inconsistencies in their ratings.

Fig. C.1 — Filming for the bench-mark films at the Mirro Aluminum Co. (Note the use of the synchronous motor-driven camera and the absence of special lighting.)

Fig. C.2 — The simple task being filmed in Figure C.1

Therefore, to interpret their ratings, *KA* values must be derived for each film as was discussed in the second part of the Supplemental Material of Chapter 18.

At the Mirro Aluminum Co., as in the numerous other organizations where this procedure has been used, the *KA* values were discussed with management and the films were viewed repeatedly before a final selection of the 100 per cent pace film was made.

Figure C.3 shows the small bench job, "Brush Valve Diaphragm" used by the Johnson Service Co. as a subject for its bench-mark film. Figure C.4 shows the "Measure Hog Casings" of Patrick Cudahy Co. In all of these illustrative cases the job referred to was the subject of the single film created to provide the pace-standard for step 1 of the objective rating procedure. Other organizations have used tasks of comparable simplicity drawn from their own work.

Fig. C.3—"Brush Valve Diaphram," a bench operation, is used for a bench-mark film at Johnson Service Co.

2. One may also accept proposals such as those of Ralph Presgrave, who, in his *Dynamics of Time Study*,[1] suggests a standard pace as that equal to dealing 52 playing cards into four piles in 0.50 minutes or walking at the rate

---

[1] It is worth noting that Presgrave offers these as examples of *standard effort* and suggests that with practice one can determine a mental concept of standard effort on other jobs. The pace, at standard effort with Presgrave's rating system, will naturally be different with each job, depending on the difficulty of the job. The use of Presgrave's card dealing pace proposed here is different from the *use* proposed by Presgrave.

Fig. C.4—"Measuring Hog Casings" (used for sausage casings) is the operation used as a bench-mark job at Patrick Cudahy Co.

of three miles per hour. These are usable when the definition of standard is the same as the one last given, since Presgrave's concept of standard is similar to the one previously stated. If the definition is changed, the pace on the examples must also be changed.

3. As another procedure, a simple job may be shown to large groups of industrial engineers and the values (corrected for different concepts of standard) averaged and used as a basis for the standard pace.[2]

However, there are some drawbacks to this alternative. There may be real differences in the concepts of normal within the group and these differences will be hidden by averaging. These differences may represent valid differences in the dynamics of the situation portrayed roughly in Figure 17.4 and the reduction of these differences may create inequities.

4. As another procedure, an organization may accept a bench-mark film made by another company. They may use either the values assigned by the orginating organization or assign a new set of *KA* values. This alternative has frequently been followed by small organizations as an economical procedure. There are psychological advantages in having a bench-mark pace

---

[2] Films of such standards are in existence.

standard made of a job in the plant, but any operation will meet the requirements of the technique of objective rating.

This second step in the procedure being outlined here, with any of the four alternative procedures, results in the formal selection of at least one film showing the standard rate of activity with any one job. This film represents the unit of measurement, or the rate of activity representing 100 per cent standard pace.[3] With a record of this type, the standard rate of activity may be actually included in the labor contract. At the very least, it is available for comparison and for use in the obtaining or the placing of discussions of ratings on an objective basis, such as can never be the case where the standard represents merely the time study man's unanchored, mental concept of proper performance. This is still, however, not enough for actual use. It is highly desirable to prepare films showing step-by-step deviations from standard pace on the one job (step films), so as to establish markings on the scale of pace and to facilitate the rating. The films may be in loop form; that is, the front end spliced to the back so as to permit continuous projection for any period of time. Also, such films are commonly made with the frames divided into different areas, each area showing a different pace, so that a group of steps may be projected simultaneously. Such films are called *multi-image films*. A short section of such a film presently in use in a variety of industrial plants (see alternative 4 of step B) is shown in Figure C.5 and the originating company's pace values for the twelve paces simultaneously presented are given in Figure C.6. Another company, in a different industry, which uses the same film as its bench-mark, uses the values given in Figure C.7. Note, however, that the values of Figures C.6 and C.7 have a constant ratio between them. It should be obvious that once a standard pace has been selected by any one of the procedures that were enumerated, the step or multi-image films can easily be prepared.[4] Experiments have shown[5] that probably about 6 per cent change in pace is the usual minimum detectable difference; hence, the steps on the film should, for ideal use, approximate this magnitude. However, while a considerable group of regular time study engineers was used to obtain these data relating to minimum detectable pace difference, it

[3] As will be shown after the discussion of difficulty adjustments, the 100 per cent selected subjectively by management needs some additional modification to create the *objective* 100 per cent standard.

[4] A considerable number of such films have been constructed and carefully evaluated since being proposed in the 1947 edition of *Systematic Motion and Time Study*, the predecessor of this book. Copies of a variety of multi-image films which are in use by a number of companies may be obtained from the author.

[5] M. E. Mundel and R. N. Lehrer, "An Evaluation of Performance Rating," *Proceedings National Time and Motion Study Clinic*. Chicago, Ill.: Industrial Management Society, 1948; also R. N. Lehrer, "Development and Evaluation of a Pace Scale for Time Study Rating," *Doctoral dissertation*, Purdue University, June 1949.

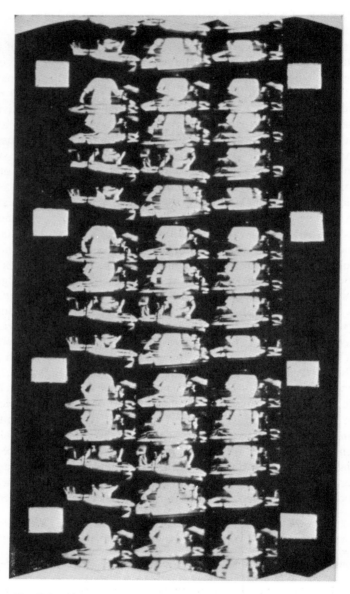

Fig. C.5 — *Short section of twelve-image multi-image loop used in one plant. Each of the pictures shows a different page. For a close-up of this task, see Figure C.4.*

141	132	120
100	93	82
74	67	53
44	40	36

Fig. C.6 — Rating values for multi-image loop of Figure C.5 when projected at 1000 frames per minute.

152	142	129
108	100	88
80	72	57
47	43	39

Fig. C.7 — Values given multi-image film of Figure C.6 for use in a different industry.

is possible that with training this may be subject to reduction; therefore, this percentage should not be considered as an absolute value. This completes the preliminary activity necessary to make possible the performance of step 1 of the objective rating procedure.

In practice the time study man, in performing step 1 of the objective rating procedure, may do one of the following:

1. Compare the observed job with his concept of the scale of standard pace as obtained by considerable exposure to the multi-image or step films. He should refresh his memory each day.

2. Compare a film of the observed pace (see previously detailed "full memomotion time study procedure" in Chapter 18) with the multi-image films with simultaneous projection by two projectors.

In either of the above cases the time study man must only judge whether the job being studied (actual performance or film of performance) is being performed at a pace (rate of activity) equal to any one of the steps on the multi-image step film (or single-image step films), or between any two of the steps, and then assign a rating as indicated by the predetermined values of the steps. He pays absolutely no attention to the limiting effect of job difficulty on the possible pace for the task. The subjective inference required in performing step 1 of conventional rating has been eliminated.

Experimentation has shown that the group of experienced time study men, using conventional methods (Appendix B), who were able to place only 19 per cent of their ratings within ±5 per cent of the correct value and 42 per cent within ±10 per cent, were able with objective rating to place 64 per cent within ±5 per cent of the correct value and 87 per cent within ±10 per cent, on the same tasks. Step films were used as a standard of reference.[6]

6 Lehrer, *op. cit.*

The jobs being rated were different, of course, from the task shown in the step films. These results are unusually significant when viewed with the realization that this group of time study men all had over a year's experience with conventional procedures yet increased their accuracy by this significant amount on the first series of trials with objective rating with step films. While it is true that the jobs used were simple, they were similar in both rating situations, and other variables such as familiarity with the tasks were equal.

In a second experiment involving 73 industrial engineers, the group rated three different paces for each of six different jobs, using: (1) their own method of rating; (2) a single-image film for a pace-rating aid, rating on an objective basis; (3) a 12-image multi-image film for a pace-rating aid, rating on an objective basis.[7] The ratings from method (1) were made comparable to each other to remove the effects of different concepts of standards or different numerical designations thereof; the ratings from (2) and (3) were comparable without any adjustment. Radkins found the ratings from all three phases similar in accuracy and consistency, despite the newness to the group of the rating method used in (2) and (3). However, the objective rating technique tended to eliminate the common fault of seeing different paces as alike. Figure C.8 shows the straight lines (fitted by the method of least squares) for the average ratings for the group for all three parts of the experiment. (A 45-degree line would be ideal.) The ratings made with the aid of the multi-image loop were statistically significantly different in this respect from the conventional ratings. Hence, it appears reasonable to suggest that objective rating with the use of the single-pace concept offers a more reasonable chance of obtaining the requisite accuracy in time study. The long history of actual industrial use further supports this view.

A word of caution—the observer must realize fully what is meant by *pace*. Experiments have shown (as perhaps one might expect) that rating films with a wrong concept of pace may lead to gross errors in rating.[8]

The concept of pace, as used, requires some understanding of the basic mechanics of human motion. It has been found that the hand or arm, when making a movement, accelerates for a relatively constant portion of the distance traveled, moves at constant velocity for another relatively constant portion, and decelerates for another relatively constant portion.[9] These proportions do not appear to be affected by the pace.[10] The percentage of time spent in acceleration, constant velocity, and deceleration with free movement

[7] A. P. Radkins, "Comparison and Evaluation of Three Time Study Rating Techniques," *M.S. thesis*, Purdue University, June 1950.

[8] H. Smalley, "An Evaluation of Two Methods of Measuring Motion Paths," *M.S. thesis*, Purdue University, August 1947.

[9] Wayne Deegan, "The Development and Use of a New Technique for Measurement in Time and Motion Study," *M.S. thesis*, University of Iowa, 1935.

[10] M. E. Mundel (with R. M. Barnes), "Studies of Hand Motion and Rhythm Appearing in Factory Work," *University of Iowa, Studies in Engr.*, Bul. 12, 1938, p. 10.

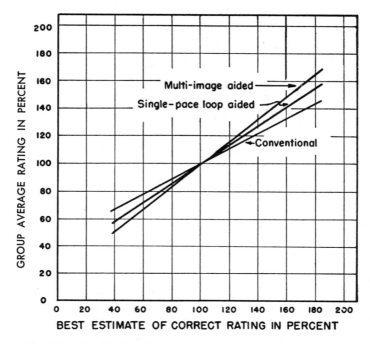

Fig. C.8 — *Straight lines fitted to average ratings assigned three pace variants of six jobs by 73 industrial engineers using three methods of rating.*

appears to be in the neighborhood of 40, 20, and 40 per cent respectively.[11] Now, one of the basic laws of physics is the equation: force = mass × acceleration. In respect to human motions, this may be interpreted as: the application of muscular force to a body member (or eye, and the like), with other variables constant, will produce an acceleration proportional to the force. It would therefore seem reasonable to define *pace* or *rate of activity* as *the rate at which muscular force is applied to the creation of body, arm, hand, or finger movements, disregarding the effect of job difficulty (mass constant)*, and, hence, as *the observed rate of acceleration of the body member doing the work*. The preceding information has been given to explain a reasonable, yet at first glance peculiar, phenomenon. If the time for a given distance of body member movement, such as a movement of the arm about the elbow, is determined, a good deal less than twice the time will be required for twice the distance of movement at the identical pace or rate of activity or required rate of application of muscular force, assuming unhindered movement, all three being synonymous. If equations for distances are set up as a function of time, it will be found that for a given rate of acceleration, a, the time will increase

[11] Wayne Deegan, *op. cit.* The discussion which follows holds true no matter what these percentages actually are.

as the square root of the ratio of distances with an increase of 100 per cent (double original) distance accompanied by approximately a 41 per cent increase in time.[12]

An indication of the validity of this reasoning is available. Hoover,[13] using ten male operators and a metabulator to measure their oxygen consumption, determined the energy required for 5-, 10-, and 15-inch movement of the full arm, at three different paces. At any one pace, the time allowed for a movement was based on an assumed fixed value of a, acceleration, and the previously referred to equations for distance as a function of time. Under these conditions Hoover found, ". . . the energy expenditure under equal pace was definitely not a function of length [of movement] but that pace exerted a significant effect upon this expenditure."

The distance-time diagram of Figure C.9 shows the effect of increased distance on the time for an arm movement with an assumed rate of activity. This is based on experimental data as previously indicated.

Consequently, it may be seen that the average velocity of a body member movement is not the correct guide to use to judge pace, but what must be judged is the rate of acceleration near the inception of the movement and the rate of deceleration near the conclusion of the movement. It is also worth noting that micromotion analyses usually reveal that most of the time, with an effective method (particularly on small jobs), is spent on the red-blue or terminal group of therbligs rather than on the green or movement group; therefore considerable attention should be paid to the rate of activity with which the small motions of these terminal therbligs are performed.

Throughout the entire preceding discussion no attention has been paid to job difficulty or pace hindrances such as weight moved, eye-hand coordination required, or any of the factors except apparent pace, although these other factors also control the amount of actual muscular force required. This was

---

[12] This statement is at variance with previously reported data in: W. Deegan, "The Development and Use of a New Technique for Measurement in Time and Motion Study," *M.S. thesis*, University of Iowa, 1935; and R. M. Barnes, "An Investigation of Some Hand Motions Used in Factory Work," *University of Iowa Studies in Engr.*, Bul. 6, 1936. In these studies, operators were asked to make 5-, 10-, and 15-inch movements not only for a short period, but at a pace they felt they could maintain all day. Although a mathematical analysis of the time required at a given pace would give time values of (with the 5-inch movement taken as 100 per cent) 141 per cent for the 10-inch, and 173 per cent for the 15-inch movement, only 110 and 115 per cent were obtained in the experiments referred to, probably due to the operators' unconscious imposition of a somewhat similar tempo on all three jobs. The validity of the subjectively selected tempos was not investigated. Actually, with a 10-inch movement being performed in only 10 per cent more time than a 5-inch, the rate of acceleration must be higher (although it probably will be applied for the same proportion of the movement), thus the rate of application of muscular force must be higher, and consequently the pace, as the term is used in this book, is higher.

[13] J. E. Hoover, "Analysis of Variation of Human Energy Consumption with Length of Movement under Equal Pace," *M.S. thesis*, Purdue University, August 1950.

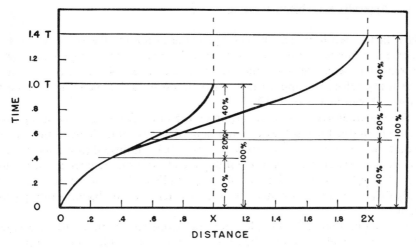

Fig. C.9 — *Distance vs. time curves for movements of X and 2X distance at a given pace.*

intentional inasmuch as no consideration can be given to these in the first judgment of pace, which is made in comparison with a single pace standard. Otherwise, a separate standard would have to be used for each job and the procedure would resemble the typical conventional method with most of its drawbacks.

To summarize the procedure being suggested for performing step 1 of the objective rating procedure:

The time study observer will relate the performance observed, when studying a job, to the standard pace by anchored judgment. Prior to taking any studies, the time study department in which the time study man works, or the time study man himself if he is the only one engaged in that activity, will have determined by experimentation or by an adaptation of available standards, a physical representation of the standard rate of activity or pace as called for by the definition of standard that management aided in formulating. As alternatives, management may aid in selecting a pace or a joint management-labor committee may select it. The time study man should have then become familiar with various possible paces, and their percentage of standard pace.

When the time study observer is taking a time study, he compares the observed pace of the operator on each element or observation, (depending on the technique being used), regardless of the difficulty of the element, to the standard pace or rate of activity or the calibrated steps thereof (two procedures were given). He expresses the relationship in per cent of standard: e g., 95, or 90 per cent, and so forth, if the actual performance resembles one of the slower, step films (the value actually used will not be limited to the actual values of the steps), or 105, or 110 per cent, and so forth, if it is more like a faster step film. This percentage is the rating for the element. Experiments have shown that this can be done with a reasonable degree of accuracy. On machine-paced elements, the rating is, of course, 100 per cent.[14] A rated time study before the application of the necessary adjustments for job difficulty is shown in Figure C.10.

The next required action for setting up the objective time study rating procedure in usable form is the determination of a table of difficulty adjustments so that the time obtained by time study, after being adjusted to standard pace, may be further adjusted to represent the rate of exertion included in the definition of standard for the actual job being studied. This will enable the time study observer to perform step 2 of the two steps of the objective rating procedure.

It is obvious that all jobs could not be performed at the standard pace, since practically all will be more difficult than the job with which standard pace is defined and further, some jobs will be more difficult than others. Some tasks, for instance, will involve heavier parts, closer visual work, and so forth. These job differences will place different limits on the pace possible on each job with a fixed rate of exertion relative to the maximum possible on the job, but they may be objectively evaluated. The method will consist of determining the various factors that make for difficulty in the job, evaluating their effect, and including a *difficulty adjustment*[15] in computing the standard for the job, so that all the standards will be consistent in regard to attainability. As will be shown, these difficulty adjustments may be set up in tabular form.

The work of developing these difficulty adjustments is probably not fully complete, but even at their present stage of development they offer a much more satisfactory and reliable procedure than leaving the adjustment to the mental evaluation of the time study man, as is inherent in conventional rating procedures. If inconsistencies appear in the results of the application of these difficulty adjustments, then the source may be traced and lasting corrections made, a course of action that is not possible with the conventional approach. The reduction of such difficulty adjustments to tabular form should remove from the time study procedure additional sources of subjectively caused variation and should thereby aid in meeting objections such as those raised by Gomberg ,Gottlieb, and other forward-looking analysts.

The work on difficulty adjustments necessary for performance of step 2 of the objective rating procedure was begun in 1940 by postulating the factors

---

[14] The use of different numerical scales would not affect this procedure, although different values would of course be used in such cases, in place of the numerical values given as illustrations in this paragraph.

[15] In the predecessor of this book these were called *allowances*. Because of its varied use in the field, the term *allowance* has been set aside to cover simpler and more empirical adjustments, such as personal time, and the corrections required by the use of a single standard pace rating system have been renamed *difficulty adjustments*.

ELEMENTS / CYCLES

No.	TERMINAL POINT	1 R	1 T	2 R	2 T	3 R	3 T	4 R	4 T	5 R	5 T	6 R	6 T	7 R	7 T	8 R	8 T	9 R	9 T	10 R	10 T	11 R	11 T	12 R	12 T	13 R	13 T	14 R	14 T	15 R	15 T
1	RL pen into rack	03		3 59		3 13		3 72		3 34		3 89		3 45		3 02		3 56		3 17		3 71		3 27		3 83		3 41		3 97		3
2	DA filling cap	21 18		78 19		33 20		89 17		53 19		07 18		64 19		20 18		76 20		34 17		90 19		46 19		03 20		59 18		16 19		
3	RL cap	41 20		96 18		52 19		10 21		72 19		27 20		84 20		39 19		98 21		55 21		10 20		66 20		22 19		79 20		37 21		
4	RL clip top	56 15		10 14		69 17		34 (20)		86 14		42 15		99 15		53 14		14 16		68 13		24 14		80 14		38 16		94 15		52 15		
5																															
6																															
7																															
8																															
9																															
10																															
11																															
12																															
13																															
14																															
15																															

RECAPITULATION

ELEMENTS	1	2	3	4	5	6	7	8	9	10	11	12	13	14	15
Amount of body															
Foot pedals															
Bimanualness															
Eye-hand coordination															
Handling requirements															
Weight or resistance															
TOTAL TIME IN Min.	.45	2.80	2.99	2.07											
NUMBER OF OBS.	15	15	15	14											
PRO-RATE DIVISOR	1	1	1	1											
AVERAGE PER CYCLE	.030	.187	.199	.148											
RATING	115	105	110	95											
RATED TIME	.035	.196	.219	.141											
PER CENT OF CYCLE															
1+ ADJUSTMENTS															
BASE TIME															
1+ ALLOWANCES															
ALLOWED TIME															

SYMBOLS USED

C - Extra unnecessary motion
D - A.D. Dropped part
F - Unnecessary fumble
H - Unnecessary hesitation
P - Includes personal time
R - Made reject by improper work
X - Deviation from std. routine

ALLOWANCES

Personal _____ %

TOTAL _____ %

LOOP VALUES

141	132	120
100	93	82
74	67	53
44	40	36

Fig. C.10— Rated time study for filling fountain pens for inspection previously shown in Figure 18.9.

that affected job pace as indicated by experimental or practical evidence.[16]
These were listed as:

1. Total amount of body involved in the element.[17]
2. Foot pedals used during the element.[18]
3. Bimanualness of the element.[19]
4. Eye-hand coordination required to perform the element.[20]
5. Handling or sensory requirement of the element.[21]
6. Resistance that must be overcome on the element—that is, thrust on levers or weight lifted.[22]

Percentage adjustments were then calculated from these data with the realization that most of them, particularly the Iowa experiments, were performed at maximum pace and it was anticipated that this, in some cases, possibly maximized the indicated percentage difference; some were accordingly scaled down. Also, some of the experiments emphasized the difficulty increment by increasing its importance in the cycle through a reduction of all other usual variables and sources of time consumption. These were also scaled down. Subsequently, on a rather informal basis, using the same operator and the same exertion, pairs of jobs as available[23] were compared in respect to the time taken on various elements. The only difference between any pair of jobs was in a single factor, such as amount of body used. These informal experiments in some cases gave figures somewhat different from those deduced from the data previously footnoted (as were then available), and thus many of the original reductions were checked or modified. Time standards were set using these preliminary percentage adjustments, and the results carefully observed. Minor adjustments were made in the percentages until the standards set in this manner predicted performance in an apparently consistent fashion. Such results were, of course, undoubtedly influenced by the

---

[16] Not all of these were at first identified but this is the list at present. The footnote on each item indicates the experimental evidence that pointed to the existence of the factor.

[17] M. E. Mundel (with R. M. Barnes and J. M. MacKenzie), "Studies of One- and Two-Handed Work," *University of Iowa Studies in Engr.*, Bul. No. 21, 1940.

[18] R. M. Barnes, H. Hardaway, and O. Podolsky, "Which Pedal Is Best?" *Factory*, Jan. 1942, pp. 98, 99; also Tung-Sol Lamp Works shop data, N.J., 1940.

[19] M.E. Mundel, et al., *op. cit.*, footnote 17, *passim*.

[20] M. E. Mundel (with R. M. Barnes), "Studies of Hand Motions and Rhythm Appearing in Factory Work," *University of Iowa Studies in Engineering*, Bul. 12, 1938, pp. 19–42; also M. E. Mundel, "A Study of Simultaneous Symmetrical Hand Motion," *Doctoral dissertation*, University of Iowa, 1939.

[21] M. E. Mundel (with R. M. Barnes), "A Study of Hand Motions Used in Small Assembly Work," *University of Iowa Studies in Engineering*, Bul. 16, 1939, pp. 20–27.

[22] J. Amar, *The Human Motor*. London: G. Routledge and Sons, 1920.

[23] Time study experimentation in industry is unfortunately often affected by expediency and the author must confess that this preliminary experimentation which was conducted on an industrial job during 1939 and 1940 suffered from this not unusual feature. However, some later experimental evidence can now be reported in lieu of these data.

tendency of the shop to "make the standards work," and by the small range of difficulty covered in the initial installation. Beginning in 1942, however, research activity has been directed at analyzing the characteristics of the objective rating procedure and the nature of the necessary difficulty adjustments. The results of the initial studies of pace appraisal were previously reported. Beginning in 1952, extensive industrial applications have been made; the industries have ranged from meat packing to shipbuilding. The procedure has become common-place.

The results of the studies into the difficulty adjustments form part of the material of this section of this appendix, although they are by no means as complete as one could desire. For instance, only certain points in some of the scales have been determined; the rest of the scales for these factors have been set in "apparent" correct proportion. At any rate, the final values given in this appendix are being used in numerous good-sized applications in many countries and appear[24] to function more smoothly than conventionally set standards.

The research is given in extremely brief form because including it in full would dwarf the rest of the text. It is to be noted that all the adjustments are indicated as positive increments of time above the time required at the standard pace (film loop or concept of rate of activity); hence, the film loop or concept should, at 100 per cent pace, represent the concept of standard time on an extremely simple operation as was suggested. Also, these adjustments may only be used when all jobs are first rated against a single standard pace that does not take job difficulty into account. Essentially the developed data are intended for use as follows:

A. Separate adjustments are to be made for each element.

This would appear reasonable if we stop to consider a task such that for 10 per cent of the time the operator pushes a lever with a 15-pound resistance. Let us further assume that the rest of the task involves almost no weight or resistance but only such as would occur loading extremely light parts into a fixture. One could hardly expect the element containing the heavy resistance to be performed at the same pace as the rest of the job, and vice versa. Consequently, each element will be adjusted separately.

B. The total difficulty adjustment for an element will be the simple sum of all the appropriate values from the scales for all of the factors.

C. The difficulty adjustments will be separate from the pace rating.

If the rating is 90 per cent and the total difficulty adjustment is 12 per cent,

---

[24] The difficulties of accurately determining this in the actual shop have been suggested several times. In addition, the variability of people, both in capacity and use of capacity, tends to confound the variables. The applications include an enormous variety of industrial and governmental activity. However, some of the installations have been large enough to indicate that it is unlikely that the standards set were artificially "made to work" by the working force.

the observed time for that element will be multiplied by 0.90 and then by 1.12. The 0.12 and 0.90 cannot be added, otherwise the actual increment would vary with the pace observed, which would not be correct. (If a different numerical scale or scale base is used, then the values used will change, but the essential procedure will not.)

D. The factors for which difficulty adjustments will be added are:

1. Amount of body used.
2. Foot pedals.
3. Bimanualness.
4. Eye-hand coordination.
5. Handling or sensory requirements.
6. Weight handled or resistance encountered.
7. Other special constraints on work speed.

This seventh factor, which did not appear in the original list, has been added as the result of various situations encountered during the initial fifteen years' experience with extensive and varied applications of objective rating.

A detailed discussion of each of these factors follows.

1. *Amount of body used.* Early research indicated that a 10-inch guided movement took more time when the movement was far enough away from the body to require a movement of the full arm about the shoulder than when sufficiently close to the body to permit movement primarily about the elbow.[25] The actual percentage difference in time obtained in these experiments could not be used due to certain features of the experiment.[26]

Subsequent research was set up to evaluate separately the two types of movements.[27] Finger-actuated switches were arranged so that a series of 10-inch movements of the forearm, without wrist action, could be contrasted with a series of 10-inch full arm movements, without wrist action. The finger switches were placed so as to prevent the operators from performing part of the movement with the wrist, inasmuch as this would reduce the amount of body used and eliminate part of the imposed differences. Actually, using a series of ten college students, the full arm motion (disregarding the time to actuate the switches) was found (with an accurate electrical kymograph for timing equipment) to take approximately 8 per cent longer than the forearm movement. However, it was suggested that the terminal therbligs,

[25] Mundel (with Barnes), "Studies of Hand Motions and Rhythm."

[26] The operators were requested to work at a pace they thought they could keep up all day, and the full arm movement and forearm movements were two of the four or more movements in the cycle. Besides having no check on the validity of the pace subjectively selected, there is no way of checking on the evenness or unevenness of beat possibly imposed by the subjects and thus reflected in the data in contrast to the imposed physical differences that were being evaluated.

[27] M. E. Mundel and A. P. Radkins, unpublished research, The Purdue Motion and Time Study Laboratory, 1949.

in practice, are usually a larger portion of the element than they were in this test situation; if they were taken as 50 per cent and assumed unchanged from forearm to forearm-upper arm movements, then the obtained difference would have been 4 per cent. Actually, in the experiment, the terminal therbligs were performed more rapidly after the slower full arm motion than after the forearm motion, possibly due to the greater overlap of finger reaction time with the arm movement. Increasing the actual terminal therblig values from the experimental data to a weight of approximately 50 per cent the cycle would leave only a 1 per cent differential between forearm and full arm movements.

While the results were statistically significant, there is no indication that they were accurate to within 1 per cent of the data from a larger sample; consequently, the 3 per cent, which was the differential originally contained in the semi-empirical table, has not been changed.

Sekerci,[28] experimenting with weight lifting, with two basic conditions, (1) lift with legs (as from floor) and, (2) lift with arms (as from bench), found:

The time for the leg-lift at low weights was 10 per cent greater than with the arm-lifts.

The various effects of weight are discussed later in this appendix and are reflected in the table of adjustments for weight. The 10 per cent basic differential is most properly handled in the factor being discussed here and is included in the difficulty adjustments suggested for factor 1 and given in Table C.1.[29]

2. *Foot pedals.* Since the use of different parts of the arm changes the cycle time, it is not unreasonable to assume that this should apply in general to the leg and foot as well. A study indicated that the operation of different foot pedals required different amounts of times ranging at maximum pace from approximately 0.005 to 0.007 minutes.[30] As the smallest time study element usually is 0.04 minute with stop-watches or 0.02 minute with memomotion time study, this indicates a maximum difference of 5 per cent (stop-watch) to 10 per cent (memomotion) in an element that could be attributed to the type of foot pedal. However, of the five types of pedals studied, four showed a maximum range of difference of 0.0005 minute, which is approximately 1 to 2 per cent of the smallest common time study element. Realizing that this is about half of the usual element, we may deduce that the better pedals

[28] O. F. Sekerci, "An Investigation of the Effect of Weight Lifted on Productivity," *M.S. thesis*, Purdue Univ., August 1953. Sekerci reached other conclusions as a result of a peculiarity of his curve fitting method. These other conclusions have no bearing here. The conclusion quoted was not affected by his curve fitting.

[29] It should be realized that this is a quantitative statement of the results of working in different areas on the work surface. Previous qualitative suggestions (see Figure 11.4) indicated the desirability of the areas given lower difficulty adjustments.

[30] R. M. Barnes, H. Hardaway, and O. Podolsky, "Which Pedal Is Best?" *Factory*, Vol. 100, No. 1, Jan. 1942, p. 98.

TABLE C.1

Difficulty Adjustments for Amount of Body Used

Condition[1]	Per Cent
Fingers used loosely	0 (this is the base difficulty)
Wrist and fingers	1
Elbow, wrist, and fingers (forearm)	2
Arm, elbow, wrist, and fingers (full arm)	5
Trunk, arm, etc.	8
Lift with legs from floor	10

[1] In certain industries special conditions such as walking on slippery floors (18 per cent) or walking knee-deep in loose, granular material (38 per cent) may occur, necessitating the experimental determination of additional values for this difficulty category.

need no adjusting factor and that an increment of 5 per cent for the slowest type of pedal—fulcrum ahead of toe, and heel on rest with contact under ball of foot, as compared with the fulcrum anywhere under the foot–would not be unreasonable. If considerable resistance is offered by the pedal, then category 6 discussed later would also be used to compensate for this.

Hence, the set of adjustments in Table C.2 is suggested for factor 2.

TABLE C.2

Difficulty Adjustment for Foot Pedals

Condition	Per Cent
No pedals or one pedal with fulcrum under foot	0
Pedal with fulcrum ahead of toe, heel on rest, and force applied at ball of foot	5

3. *Bimanualness.* Considerable evidence exists to indicate that the simultaneous use of both hands to perform work on identical parts is highly preferable to the use of one hand. Indeed, this was listed as a basic principle with practically every motion study technique previously discussed as applicable to jobs performed at one work station. However, the use of both hands does not produce a 100 per cent increase in output but somewhat less than that.

It is indicated that the use of both hands slows up the cycle.[31] In these short experiments this increment was found to approximate 30 per cent. However, the two-handed work with untrained operators such as were used in the experiments would be probably subject to considerable change by the training or practice that would occur in an industrial situation. This change could well be greater than that which would be obtained with the one-hand work, which was more normal for the operators used. In addition, the change from one-hand to two-hand work increased, in some of the cases studied, the visual requirements, which are compensated for by the next factor. In actual practice, a figure considerably smaller than the one obtained from the previously referred-to data was used, for some time, with apparent success.

A better estimate of a correct adjustment has been obtained by Ischinger.[32] He studied eight industrial operators on five different jobs that they performed normally with both hands in a simultaneous and symmetrical fashion. He contrasted their maximum performance when doing work with both hands with their maximum performance using one (preferred[33]) hand. The jobs selected had a minimum of eye-hand coordination and the weight of parts handled was negligible. The operators performed the one-hand version of the task 18 per cent faster than the two-hand version. (The two-hand method, of course, gave more production.) While the spread of Ischinger's data indicates that some subfactors may be involved, additional experimentation is needed to more fully ascertain this. Consequently, at the present, the adjustments of Table C.3 are given for this factor. They have been widely used.

TABLE C.3

Difficulty Adjustment for Bimanualness

Condition	Per Cent
Hands help each other, alternate or do different things, with one hand controlling the pace	0
Hands simultaneously doing the same work on duplicate parts	18

4. *Eye-hand coordination.* Eye-hand coordination requirements primarily affect therbligs that are visually aided in performance, such as position and

---

[31] Mundel (with Barnes and MacKenzie), "Studies of One- and Two-Handed Work."

[32] Eric Ischinger, Jr., "An Analysis of Some Differences between One- and Two-Handed Industrial Work," *M.S. thesis*, Purdue University, June 1950.

[33] The right hand for most of the operators; the left hand was used for one-hand work only with left-handed operators.

grasp, although other motions accompanying them, such as preceding transports, are also affected.[34]

Experimentation in this area is greatly hindered by the great effect training
has on the performance of such therbligs. The time required for a not too
difficult *position* may be reduced by 50 per cent after practice with only 3,000
cycles.[35]

Consequently, results obtained in short-run experiments are probably
greatly exaggerated. MacKenzie[36] found that with one-hand work, changing
the positioning requirements with half-inch cubes, from a general location
(3-inch tolerance of placement) to placement in a slot with only $\frac{1}{64}$-inch tolerance in one direction, increased the time for *move to block, pick up, carry,
place and release* by approximately 65 per cent over the 3-inch conditions.
He also found, however, that the change in tolerance from $\frac{1}{8}$-inch, a liberal
tolerance, to $\frac{1}{64}$-inch accounted for only about 18 points of the increase.
The difference between the $\frac{1}{8}$-inch tolerance of placement and the 3-inch was
responsible for approximately 46 points of the increase. This is an unreasonable figure to accept for trained performance (MacKenzie himself places
similar reservations on these data) inasmuch as no visual effort should be
required at either of these last two conditions after practice and they could
well take very similar times.

Another study of a task requiring considerable eye-hand coordination
showed that the pattern of eye usage shifts after practice and that a considerable reduction in cycle time takes place.[37] However, this study did not indicate whether the reduction was greater or less than that with tasks with less
eye-hand coordination. Other experiments[38] showed that radically increasing
the eye-hand coordination increased the time for an extremely simple cycle
by anywhere from 11 per cent[39] to 25 per cent.[40]

In short, these data indicate very little except that eye-hand coordination is
a factor of apparently some magnitude affecting the pace at which work
may be performed. Also, short-run experiments indicate it to be of a magnitude similar to the bimanualness adjustment deduced from short runs of
one-hand versus two-hand work. Consequently, it was scaled down to obtain

[34] Mundel (with Barnes), "Studies of Hand Motions and Rhythm," pp. 30, 38, 40.

[35] M. E. Mundel, "A Study of the Effect of Practice on the Time for Fundamental
Motions," as reported in R. M. Barnes, *Motion and Time Study Applications*. New York,
N.Y.: John Wiley & Sons, 1942, p. 74.

[36] John M. MacKenzie, "Positioning Small Parts," *M.S. thesis*, University of Iowa,
1939, p. 18.

[37] R. M. Barnes, J. S. Perkins, and J. M. Juran, "A Study of the Effect of Practice on
the Elements of a Factory Operation," *University of Iowa Studies in Engineering*, Bul. 22,
1940.

[38] Mundel (with Barnes), *loc. cit.*

[39] *Ibid.*, p. 37. (Percentage is approximate.)

[40] *Ibid.*, p. 26. (Percentage is approximate.)

preliminary figures to produce the adjustments of Table C.4, which have been used now for a long time with apparent success.

TABLE C.4

Difficulty Adjustments for Eye-Hand Coordination[1]

Condition	Per Cent
Rough work, mainly feel	0
Moderate vision	2
Constant but not close	4
Watchful, fairly close	7
Within $\frac{1}{64}$ inch	10

[1] This scale may possibly go much higher in some cases.

5. *Handling requirements.* An experiment was performed with operators moving small cylinders.[41] Some of these were placed on surfaces surrounded by sharp needle points; other open-ended ones were filled (as the subjects were led to believe) with an "ink" that would permanently stain their clothes. The operators were asked to move these cylinders from one electrical contact plate to another as rapidly as possible. The addition of the needle points only increased the time to *get, move, and aside* the cylinders by approximately 2 per cent, and the "ink" by 11 per cent as compared with a plain brass cylinder stored on a plain surface. This second case with the ink, however, would also qualify for approximately a 6 per cent adjustment for eye-hand coordination (Table C.4); consequently, the data indicates an additional adjustment of approximately 5 per cent for such a condition, which may be likened to fragility where the exertion of muscular forces would need careful limitation. The needles surrounding the cylinders suggest a category of "control of location of hand and object but squeezing not ruled out" with a 2 per cent adjustment. In view of the short work spells and lack of training, these figures should be on the generous side. The values of Table C.5 are suggested as adjustments for this factor. They have been used in many time standards and no difficulties have been encountered.

6. *Weight handled or resistance encountered.*[42] Five experiments have been performed concerning this factor. Apparently conflicting data appear

[41] Mundel (with Barnes), "A Study of Hand Motions Used in Small Assembly Work," pp. 20–27.

[42] See M. E. Mundel, "Allowing in Time Standards for Weight Handled," *The Journal of Industrial Engineering*, Vol. VIII, No. 4, July-Aug. 1957, pp. 233–238.

TABLE C.5

Difficulty Adjustments for Handling or Sensory Requirements[1]

Condition	Per Cent
Can be handled roughly	0
Only gross control	1
Must be controlled but parts may be squeezed..........	2
Handle carefully....................................	3
Fragile...	5

[1] This scale may possibly go higher in some cases.

in the literature but, as will be shown, these may be correlated if the correct variables are used. The setup for each experiment is described in the following paragraphs, but results are not discussed until they are summarized in Table C.6 and Figure C.12.

Maass experimented with ten college students.[43] His task consisted of moving, as fast as possible, a weighted box 18 inches across a table followed by an unloaded movement of the hand 18 inches to the point of origin, a free movement back to the box, a movement of the box, and so on, as fast as the operators were able to move. The operators worked roughly half of the experimental period.

A study by Solberg used ten college students (all recently released U.S. Marines) to move, at their maximum pace, a loaded lever up and down for 5-minute work spells with 5-minute rest periods between each work spell.[44] The load on the lever was varied from 0.5 pounds to 50.5 pounds with only one value being used for each 5-minute work spell. Solberg recorded the time-per-cycle for the last minute of each work spell. The subjects worked from low to high weight on one day and from high weight to low weight on another day to minimize the effect of order of presentation.

Sekerci used ten college students to lift a bar to which weights were attached.[45] The weights used varied from 2 pounds to 44 pounds in 7-pound increments. A mechanism returned the bar to the original position (9 inches from the ground) so that lifts to 33 inches, and free movements back, could

[43] W. G. Maass, "The Effect of Weight on Pace," unpublished research, Purdue Motion and Time Study Laboratory, 1947.

[44] R. B. Solberg, "Time Allowances for the Handling of Weights for Use in Stop-Watch Time Studies," *M.S. thesis*, Purdue University, 1946.

[45] O. F. Sekerci, "An Investigation of the Effect of Weight Lifted on Productivity," *M.S. thesis*, Purdue University, August 1953.

be made. Sekerci used 2-minute work spells, with the subjects working at their maximum pace with 2-minute rests between each work-spell, random orders of work for each subject, and two lifting conditions, (1) with arms and trunk, and (2) with legs (by squatting and standing).

In order to relate these data with industrial practice, and in an attempt to determine the reason for the apparent differences, two additional experiments were undertaken. With the cooperation of Patrick Cudahy Co., a Milwaukee concern with an extensive shipping department, a test situation was constructed.[46] The situation required the workers to stand in one spot and lift cartons ($7\frac{1}{2}''$ × $13\frac{1}{4}''$ × $20\frac{1}{4}$ inches) 18 inches up and at the same time move them 2 feet to the left and deposit them on a conveyor which returned them eventually to the operator, but spaced so as to permit free lifting.

The initial position of the carton was 9 inches from the floor and the surface of the conveyor on which they were deposited was 27 inches from the floor. The weight of the cartons varied from 2 pounds to 80 pounds in algebraic steps although all of the cartons being handled during any one run were of equal weight. Figure C.11 shows a worker on the job.

In the first experiment by Lehman, the ten operators, *all of whom normally did work of this type*, moved five boxes from the lower platform to the conveyor, as rapidly as possible, followed by a 2-minute rest.[47] The time to lift the five boxes was recorded.

This procedure was used starting with the lightest box and proceeding up through the heavier boxes. The operators then repeated the work at each weight starting with the heaviest box and proceeding through to the lightest. The weights used in pounds were 1, 2, 2.5, 5, 8, 12, 24, 48, 80. During the experiment, the operators worked a total of approximately 2 minutes out of 38 minutes or 5.3 per cent of the time. The operators were given a strong incentive to work at their maximum pace by paid time-off following the experimental run.

In a subsequent experiment by Kolarec[48] the same apparatus and boxes were used but instead of the five-box sequence, each of five workers lifted the boxes for five minutes followed by a five-minute rest. During the first work period of five minutes, the workers worked with the one-pound boxes, and progressed by work spells to the 80-pound boxes; then repeated the five-minute work, five-minute rest pattern, going from the 80-pound to the one-pound boxes. The workers were induced to work at their maximum pace during the three-hour experimental period by giving them the rest of

---

[46] Special thanks are due to C. J. Allen, Chief Industrial Engineer, who made the experimental facilities and workers available.

[47] J. Lehman, Unpublished experimental report, *The Marquette University Management Center*, 1954.

[48] W. T. Kolarec, Unpublished seminar paper, *Marquette University, School of Business*, 1957.

Fig. C.11 — Worker lifting boxes (Lehman and Kolarec).

the day off with full pay. All of the workers studied were accustomed to handling, loading, and lifting boxes, such as were used, as a normal part of their usual job. The number of boxes handled each minute at each weight was recorded.

Table C.6a gives the data for each of these two, and the experiments previously referred to, in a form similar to their initial reporting. In Table C.6b the data have been converted to pounds lifted or overcome per period of time using a time value in each case that permits charting on one scale.

These data from Table C.6b were plotted using a log-log grid as in Figure C.12.

All of the data exhibit an exceedingly similar slope pattern with a few exceptions. First, Solberg's is slightly flatter than the others but it should be recalled that he recorded only the last minute of a five-minute work spell,

TABLE C.6

C.6a. Data from Weight Experiments

Pounds Pull on Lever or Weight per Lift	Solberg; Time per Cycle in .00001 Minutes	Maass Time per Cycle in Minutes	Sekerci-leg; Relative[1] Time per Lift	Sekerci-arm; Relative[1] Time per Lift	Lehman; Time per Cycle in Minutes	Kolarec; Boxes Lifted per Minute
0.5	20.0					
1.0					.0186	45
2.0			150	136	.0188	47
2.5					.0186	48
3.0	22.0					
4.0		.130				
5.0					.0190	46
5.5	24.0					
8.0	25.0				.0200	44
9.0			157	146		
10.13		.137				
10.5	26.4					
12.0					.0212	42
13.0	27.2					
16.0			165	158		
16.25		.144				
18.0	28.6					
23.0			174	173		
23.13		.156				
24.0					.0226	37
25.5	29.0					
30.0			184	191		
37.0			196	212		
38.0	31.1					
44.0			208	239		
48.0					.0266	25
50.5	33.6					
80.0					.0300	16

[1] In Sekerci's original report these data were in cycles per work spell but access to the original values could not be obtained inasmuch as the thesis was unobtainable.

which may well have tended to maximize the work decrement created by the effort of lifting each weight. Secondly, Lehman's curve does not fall off at the higher weights as do both Sekerci's two curves, Kolarec's curve and Maass'

C.6b. *Data from Table C.6a Converted to Total Pounds Lifted per Unit of Time by Selecting for Each Experiment a Time Value[1] that Permits Plotting on a Similar Scale*

Pounds per Pull on Lever or per Lift	Solberg; (per .02 min)	Maass; (per 20 min)	Sekerci-leg; per 25000 Time Units	Sekerci-arm; per 25000 Time Units	Lehman; per 2.5 Minutes	Kolarec; per 2.5 Minutes
0.5	50					
1.0					134	112.5
2.0			333	368	266	235
2.5					336	300
3.0	272					
4.0		615				
5.0					658	575
5.5	458					
8.0	640				1000	880
9.0			1430	1540		
10.13		1480				
10.5	795					
12.0					1415	1260
13.0	956					
16.0			2420	2530		
16.25		2260				
18.0	1260					
23.0		3300	3320			
23.13		2840				
24.0					2560	2220
25.5	1790					
30.0			4070	3930		
37.0			4720	4360		
38.0	2440					
44.0			5290	4600		
48.0					4500	3000
50.5	3000					
80.0					6660	3200

[1] Various time periods chosen so as to make slope comparisons readily feasible on a log-log presentation.

curve. Thirdly, Sekerci's "leg" curve does not appear to fall off as greatly as the other three. It should be noted that Lehman's experiment did not require the workers to work as great a proportion of the time as the other

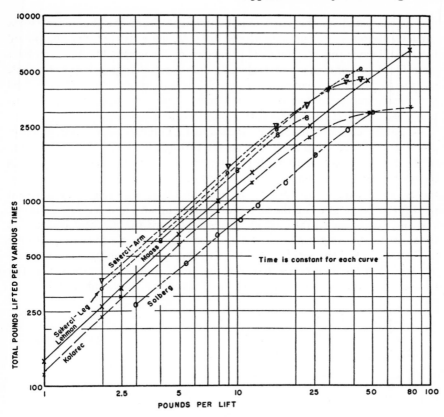

Fig. C.12—Plot of total weight lifted against weight per lift (log-log grid).

experiments. Also, Sekerci's leg experiment involved a different muscle group as compared to the other experiments.

Although a comparison of Lehman's curve with Kolarec's curve, which is plotted using the same time period, would appear to suggest a work decrement all along the scale, the data do not support such a hypothesis inasmuch as Kolarec's workers were slower than Lehman's even during the first minute's work at the lowest weight, suggesting that this difference can be attributed to the difference in the basic abilities of the two working groups used.

The theoretical amounts of work that would be performed, if the heavier weights did not slow down the workers, can be shown by a 45° line passing through the intercept of any of the experimental curves on the *Y* axis (one-pound ordinate). The difference between the intersection of this line with any ordinate erected on an abscissa value and the intersection of the same ordinate with an experimental curve would be the work lost, at that weight lift, as indicated by the particular experiment, from the theoretical work capacity (based on a maintenance of the same pace as with the one-pound lift). In all cases this is obviously a function of the weight lifted. Trend lines were fitted to Lehman's and Kolarec's data after changing Lehman's scale so as to cause it to coincide with Kolarec's curve (taking these two as the most realistically representative of all the data). These last two experiments certainly were closest to actual work conditions and workers.

To put the data obtainable into usable form, Lehman's curve was superimposed on Kolarec's and a 45° line passed through the combined intersection of the Y axis at one pound per lift. Using this 45° line, the theoretical pounds overcome per unit of time was calculated for each lift, by one-pound increments. This value was divided by the actual total weight lifted at each weight per lift (by pounds) using the slopes of both Lehman's and Kolarec's curves, and the excess over 1.00 used as representative of the per cent increase in time due to the weight per lift. This increase in time, in per cent, is plotted in Figure C.13. The slopes of Lehman's curve yielded the per cent increase in time when the load-connected-work was only 5 per cent of the cycle. The two sets of data were identical up to and including 19 pounds per lift.

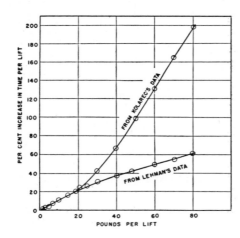

Fig. C.13—*Per cent additional time as a function of pounds per lift* (*based on* Lehman and Kolarec).

Inasmuch as an objective rating applied to a work element converts the time taken to the time that would be taken with the standardized pace (and no difficulty), the time obtained after rating would be similar to the time at one pound (or no load) and expressed on the graph of Figure C.12 as a 45° line. Hence, the time increment from the 45° line to Lehman's or Kolarec's curve would be the difficulty adjustment for weight expressed as a function of the pounds per lift. An assumption was made that the additional increment from 5 per cent of the time to 50 per cent of the time under load was linear, and Table C.7 was computed.

TABLE C.7

Difficulty Adjustment as a Function of Per Cent of Cycle Time under Load or under Load-Connected Work-Tension
(per cent of cycle computed from rated times without adjustments)

Pounds or Force per Lift	Basic Value When Work under Load is 5 Per Cent or Less of Cycle	Increments To Be Added to Basic Value for Load Connected Work in Per Cent in Excess of 5 Per Cent of Cycle														Maximum Possible Total
		1	2	3	4	5	6	7	8	9	10	20	30	40	45	
1	1															1
2	2															2
3	3															3
4	3															3
5	4															4
6	5															5
7	7															7
8	8															8
9	9															9
10	11				Use basic value for all conditions up to 20 lbs. lift or force per application											11
11	12															12
12	13															13
13	14															14
14	15															15
15	16															16
16	17															17
17	18					When adding up to get value, use nearest whole per cent to total sum										18
18	19															19
19	20															20
20	21	.0	.1	.1	.2	.2	.3	.3	.4	.4	.5	1	1.3	1.7	2	23
21	22	.0	.1	.1	.2	.2	.3	.3	.4	.4	.5	1	1.3	1.7	2	24
22	23	.1	.1	.2	.3	.3	.4	.5	.5	.6	.7	1.3	2.0	2.8	3	26
23	24	.1	.2	.3	.4	.4	.5	.6	.7	.8	.9	1.8	2.7	3.6	4	28
24	25	.1	.2	.3	.4	.6	.7	.8	.9	1.0	1.1	2.2	3.3	4.4	5	30
25	26	.1	.3	.4	.5	.7	.8	.9	1.1	1.2	1.3	2.7	4.0	5.3	6	32
26	27	.2	.3	.5	.6	.8	.9	1.1	1.2	1.4	1.6	3.1	4.7	6.2	7	34

TABLE C.7 (Continued)

Pounds or Force per Lift	Basic Value When Work under Load is 5 Per Cent or Less of Cycle	Increments To Be Added to Basic Value for Load Connected Work in Per Cent in Excess of 5 Per Cent of Cycle														Maximum Possible Total
		1	2	3	4	5	6	7	8	9	10	20	30	40	45	
27	28	.2	.4	.5	.7	.9	1.1	1.2	1.4	1.6	1.8	3.6	5.3	7.1	8	36
28	29	.2	.4	.6	.8	1.0	1.2	1.4	1.6	1.8	2.0	4.0	6.0	8.0	9	38
29	30	.2	.4	.7	.9	1.1	1.3	1.6	1.8	2.0	2.2	4.4	6.7	8.9	10	40
30	31	.2	.5	.7	1.0	1.2	1.5	1.7	2.0	2.2	2.4	4.9	7.3	9.7	11	42
31	31	.3	.6	.9	1.2	1.5	1.9	2.2	2.5	2.7	3.1	6.2	9.3	12.4	14	45
32	32	.3	.7	1.0	1.3	1.7	2.0	2.3	2.7	3.0	3.2	6.7	10.0	13.3	15	47
33	33	.4	.7	1.1	1.4	1.8	2.1	2.5	2.8	3.2	3.6	7.1	10.6	14.2	16	49
34	34	.4	.8	1.2	1.6	2.0	2.4	2.8	3.2	3.6	4.0	8.0	12.0	16.0	18	52
35	34	.4	.9	1.3	1.8	2.2	2.7	3.1	3.6	4.0	4.4	8.9	13.3	17.8	20	54
36	35	.5	1.0	1.5	2.0	2.4	2.9	3.4	3.9	4.4	4.9	9.7	14.7	20.0	22	57
37	36	.5	1.1	1.6	2.1	2.7	3.2	3.7	4.3	4.8	5.3	10.7	16.0	21.4	24	60
38	36	.6	1.2	1.7	2.3	2.9	3.5	4.0	4.6	5.2	5.8	11.6	17.3	23.1	26	62
39	37	.6	1.2	1.9	2.5	3.1	3.7	4.4	5.0	5.6	6.2	12.4	18.7	24.9	28	65
40	37	.7	1.4	2.1	2.8	3.4	4.1	4.8	5.5	6.2	6.9	13.8	20.7	27.6	31	68
41	38	.7	1.5	2.2	2.9	3.7	4.4	5.1	5.9	6.6	7.3	14.7	22.0	29.3	33	71
42	38	.8	1.6	2.4	3.2	4.0	4.8	5.6	6.4	7.2	8.0	16.0	24.0	32.0	36	74
43	39	.8	1.7	2.5	3.4	4.2	5.1	5.9	6.8	7.6	8.4	16.9	25.3	33.8	38	77
44	40	.9	1.8	2.7	3.6	4.4	5.3	6.2	7.1	8.0	8.9	17.8	26.6	35.6	40	80
45	40	1.0	1.9	2.9	3.8	4.8	5.7	6.7	7.6	8.6	9.6	19.1	28.7	38.2	43	83
46	41	1.0	2.0	3.0	4.0	5.0	6.0	7.0	8.0	9.0	10.0	20.0	30.0	40.0	45	86
47	42	1.0	2.1	3.1	4.2	5.2	6.3	7.3	8.4	9.4	10.5	20.9	31.3	41.8	47	89
48	42	1.1	2.2	3.3	4.4	5.6	6.7	7.8	8.9	10.0	11.1	22.2	33.3	44.4	50	92
49	43	1.2	2.3	3.5	4.6	5.8	6.9	8.1	9.2	10.4	11.6	23.1	34.7	46.2	52	95
50	43	1.2	2.4	3.7	4.9	6.1	7.3	8.6	9.8	11.0	12.2	24.4	36.7	48.9	55	98
51	44	1.3	2.5	3.8	5.1	6.3	7.6	8.9	10.1	11.4	12.7	25.4	38.0	50.7	57	101
52	44	1.3	2.7	4.0	5.3	6.7	8.0	9.3	10.7	12.0	13.3	26.7	40.0	53.3	60	104
53	45	1.4	2.8	4.1	5.5	6.9	8.3	9.6	11.0	12.4	13.8	27.6	41.3	55.1	62	107
54	46	1.4	2.8	4.3	5.7	7.1	8.5	10.0	11.4	12.8	14.2	28.4	42.6	56.9	64	110
55	46	1.5	3.0	4.5	6.0	7.4	8.9	10.4	11.9	13.4	14.9	29.8	44.6	59.5	67	113

TABLE C.7 (Continued)

Pounds or Force per Lift	Basic Value When Work under Load is 5 Per Cent or Less of Cycle	Increments To Be Added to Basic Value for Load Connected Work in Per Cent in Excess of 5 Per Cent of Cycle														Maximum Possible Total
		1	2	3	4	5	6	7	8	9	10	20	30	40	45	
56	47	1.6	3.1	4.7	6.2	7.8	9.3	10.9	12.4	14.0	15.6	31.3	46.6	62.2	70	117
57	47	1.6	3.2	4.9	6.5	8.1	9.7	11.4	13.0	14.6	16.2	32.4	48.6	64.9	73	120
58	48	1.7	3.4	5.1	6.8	8.4	10.1	11.8	13.5	15.2	16.9	33.8	50.7	67.6	76	124
59	48	1.8	3.5	5.3	7.0	8.8	10.5	12.3	14.1	15.8	17.6	35.1	52.7	70.2	79	127
60	49	1.8	3.6	5.4	7.2	9.0	10.8	12.6	14.4	16.2	18.0	36.0	54.0	72.0	81	130
61	50	1.9	3.7	5.6	7.5	9.3	11.2	13.1	14.9	16.8	18.7	37.4	57.0	74.7	84	134
62	50	1.9	3.9	5.8	7.7	9.7	11.6	13.5	15.5	17.4	19.3	38.7	58.0	77.3	87	137
63	51	2.0	4.0	5.9	7.9	9.9	11.9	13.8	15.8	17.8	19.8	39.6	59.4	79.9	89	140
64	51	2.1	4.1	6.2	8.3	10.3	12.4	14.5	16.5	18.6	20.6	41.3	62.0	82.7	93	144
65	52	2.1	4.2	6.3	8.4	10.6	12.7	14.8	16.9	19.0	21.1	42.2	63.3	84.5	95	147
66	53	2.2	4.3	6.5	8.6	10.8	12.9	15.1	17.3	19.4	21.6	43.1	64.6	86.2	97	150
67	53	2.2	4.5	6.7	9.0	11.2	13.5	15.7	17.9	20.2	22.4	44.8	67.3	89.8	101	154
68	54	2.3	4.6	6.9	9.2	11.4	13.7	16.0	18.3	20.6	22.9	45.7	68.6	91.6	103	157
69	54	2.4	4.7	7.1	9.4	11.8	14.1	16.5	18.8	21.2	23.6	47.1	70.6	94.2	106	160
70	55	2.4	4.8	7.3	9.7	12.1	14.5	17.0	19.4	21.8	24.2	48.4	72.6	96.9	109	164
71	56	2.5	4.9	7.4	9.9	12.3	14.8	17.3	19.7	22.2	24.6	49.3	74.0	98.7	111	167
72	56	2.5	5.1	7.6	10.1	12.7	15.2	17.7	20.3	22.8	25.3	50.6	76.0	101.3	114	170
73	57	2.6	5.2	7.8	10.4	13.0	15.6	18.2	20.8	23.4	26.0	52.0	78.0	104.0	117	174
74	58	2.6	5.3	7.9	10.6	13.2	15.9	18.5	21.2	23.8	26.4	52.8	79.3	105.8	119	177
75	58	2.7	5.4	8.1	10.8	13.6	16.3	19.0	21.7	24.4	27.1	54.2	81.3	108.4	122	180
76	59	2.8	5.6	8.3	11.1	13.9	16.7	19.4	22.2	25.0	27.8	55.5	83.3	111.1	125	184
77	59	2.9	5.7	8.6	11.5	14.3	17.2	20.1	22.9	25.8	28.7	57.3	86.0	114.7	129	188
78	60	2.9	5.8	8.7	11.6	14.5	17.5	20.4	23.3	26.2	29.1	58.2	87.3	116.5	131	191
79	61	3.0	6.0	8.9	11.9	14.9	17.9	20.8	23.8	26.8	29.8	59.5	89.3	119.1	134	195
80	61	3.0	6.1	9.1	12.2	15.2	18.3	21.3	24.4	27.4	30.4	60.8	91.3	121.8	137	198

If a rated element is 50 per cent of the work cycle, it will be more than 50 per cent of the working cycle after the adjustment is added to it. At first glance this suggests a second correction. However, the computed adjustments would appear to have been subjected to a maximizing influence in Kolarec's experiment by "pushing" the workers considerably past the comfortable pace. Indeed, despite the use of some very light boxes, they lifted boxes at the rate of 15,710 pounds per hour for each of the three hours of the experiment. This pace, extended through the work day, would be 120,000 pounds per eight hours. In short, although the data were gathered at a constant level of effort, the level was in excess of what is usually expected, and the heavier boxes may have had a maximum effect. Consequently, Table C.7 is suggested for use with objective rating.[49] Certainly, it should be much more accurate than a subjective evaluation of this complex factor.

Table C.7 would be used, in objective rating, as follows: Let us assume that the task *after rating* has two elements, (1) .15 min., (2) .10 min. Element (2) involves motions connected with moving a 47-pound box or giving a 47-pound pull on a lever. (A spring scale should be part of the normal equipment of the time study man so that he may determine the forces required.) Element (2) is 40 per cent of the rated cycle time;

$$\frac{.10}{.25} = 40\%$$

For 47 pounds, Table C.7 gives a basic value of 42 per cent and an additional increment of 36.5 per cent or, in round figures, 37 per cent for the 35 per cent of the cycle more than the minimum 5 per cent of the cycle affected by the weight. Note that the values given for each weight permit the rapid calculation of the increment for any per cent of cycle under load (or with load-connected-motions) from 5 per cent of the cycle (the minimum value), to a maximum value at 50 per cent of the cycle.

Consequently, the difficulty adjustment for weight for element (2) is 42 + 37 or 79 per cent. This would be used together with the other applicable adjustments to complete the objective rating and adjustment procedure.

The table may be used for leg lifts by using only the basic "5 per cent of cycle" value and the 10 per cent adjustment for "leg lift" of category 1.

It is further suggested that it would not be unreasonable to place an agreed-upon limit on the maximum total lift which will be permitted per day. This limit may be a function of the amount of weight per lift, the manner of lifting, and the height of the lift. Very little data exist for giving values for these variables. However, the difficulty of taking them into account in a consistent

---

[49] It is suggested that one not attempt to use Table C.7 for a "fatigue allowance table" unless the rater is certain that no attention is given to the effect of weight handled or resistance overcome in the formation of the "normal pace" for comparison. This is not a likely situation with subjective rating.

TABLE C.8

Difficulty Adjustments for Time Studies

Category No.	Description	Reference Letter	Condition	Per Cent Adjustment	Example
1	Amount of body used	A	Fingers used loosely	0	
		B	Wrist and fingers	1	
		C	Elbow, wrist, and fingers	2	
		D	Arm, etc.	5	
		E	Trunk, etc.	8	
		E2	Lift with legs from floor	10	
2	Foot pedals	F	No pedals or one pedal with fulcrum under foot	0	
		G	Pedal or pedals with fulcrum outside of foot	5	
3	Bimanualness	H	Hands help each other or alternate	0	
		H2	Hands work simultaneously doing the same work on duplicate parts	18	(Parts are "identical" with respect to work requirements)
4	Eye-hand coordination[1]	I	Rough work, mainly feel	0	Do not need to look other than casually
		J	Moderate vision	2	Occasional need for peripheral vision
		K	Constant but not close	4	Constant peripheral vision
		L	Watchful, fairly close	7	Foveal vision
		M	Within $\frac{1}{64}$ inch	10	Close hand sewing
5	Handling requirements[1]	N	Can be handled roughly	0	No need to consciously control muscular forces
		O	Only gross control	1	Can squeeze or "bang" objects
		P	Must be controlled, but may be squeezed	2	Objects must not be "banged"
		Q	Handle carefully	3	Parts could be damaged by careless handling or too much pressure
		R	Fragile	5	Parts *readily* damaged by normal finger pressures
6	Weight		Identify by the actual weight or resistance	Use Table C.7	

[1] These scales could, in some cases, go higher.

fashion with subjective rating should be obvious. Even the construction of a tentative table for use with objective rating would bring consistency into the adjustment for these factors and allow results to be observed in order to improve the tables. The use of these tentative tables would require that a dummy delay element be inserted in time standards when the use of the basic difficulty adjustment for weight would cause the standard time to call for lifting in excess of these limits.

Also, it is suggested that *carrying an object axially loaded on the body* (or held against the body) be treated as a "leg lift" rather than as an "arm" or "arm and trunk lift." A quick inspection of the muscles involved will indicate the reason for this suggestion.

As can be seen readily, some of the adjustments for weight become sizeable; consequently, it is important that elements containing such activity should be kept short enough to be as homogeneous as the activity from which these adjustments were deduced. If many jobs requiring such adjustments are encountered, then some rather slow step-films should be provided, inasmuch as the pace on such jobs is apt to be rather low.

All of the difficulty adjustments discussed to this point may be combined into a table for use as shown in Table C.8. In actual practice, an additional column giving examples of an embodiment of each category in the actual plant should be added. Specific illustrations would have little meaning for the reader, hence the general ones given in the "example" column of Table C.8.

The adjustments of Table C.8 are to be used separately on each element. For instance, on an element in a foundry operation, consisting of moving a core plate and core totaling 21 pounds, using both hands and a rotation of the body about the trunk, let us assume we obtained an average observed time of 0.16 minute and that this time was reliably representative. Let us further assume that the rating of pace was 60 per cent. Also, the element, after being multiplied by the rating, was 10 per cent of the total cycle time. The difficulty adjustment would be (from Table C.8):

Category	Reference Letter	Per Cent
1. Amount of body	E	8
2. Foot pedals	F	0
3. Bimanualness	H	0
4. Eye-hand coordination	J	2
5. Handling requirements	P	2
6. Weight	21	22.2 or 22
Total secondary adjustment		34%

Therefore, the base time $= 0.16 \times 0.60 \times 1.34 = 0.129$ minute.

This 0.129 minute should be the time called for in our concept of standard time for the single cycle of the actual job being studied, disregarding factors external to the job, and is called the "base time." Additional allowances will have to be added to make it represent "the allowed time," which is the time required to represent standard time on an all-day basis. It is to be noted that the difficulty adjustment is not a measure of the rest time to accompany a job, but a measure of the amount of time to be added to the time for the element at standard pace so that the final time will represent the time for the element at the standard rate of exertion, namely, the required proportion of maximum physical exertion possible on the job with the standard type of operator.

7. *Other special constraints on work speed.* The first six factors which have been discussed, and which have been combined in Table C.8 (together with supporting Table C.7), are all the difficulty adjustments that are commonly used with repetitive work. However, objective rating is used with other work measurement techniques which are used with non-repetitive work; such work situations present additional problems. Some require considerable care and study of the drawings or instructions throughout the task. This creates a slowing down beyond that caused by the physical characteristics of the work. In other cases the worker may be working in cramped quarters, e.g., repairing tubes in a boiler sheet aboard a ship, or welding inside of a box girder. In such cases the cramped or limited room will slow down his motions beyond that of the repetitive worker who is usually working without such constraints. Of course, the cramped quarters may require more allowance or rest time, but the motions will also be slower and special difficulty adjustments must be introduced to allow for this. In still other cases the worker may be working under conditions where the maintenance of his safety requires that he move slowly and carefully; he may be on a partially railed section of a ship's deck far above the ground, on a painting scaffold, and so forth. Taking such a variety of conditions into account in subjective rating seems relatively impossible. In companies where such situations have been encountered, tentative tables of special difficulty adjustment values have been made and used. These introduce consistency into the standards in which such conditions are encountered. The initial values assigned are watched and further adjustments made until the values appear workable and acceptable.

Now that difficulty adjustments have been discussed, we must return our attention to the film of pace used as an anchor for judgment. After management assigns rating values to the bench-mark films, there is a modification to be made to them. Management's ratings are made subjectively when selecting the 100 per cent pace. If this pace was to be used as the 100 per cent value for objective ratings, this pace on this bench-mark operation would then be rated as 100 and then multiplied by 1.0 plus the difficulty corrections resulting in calling it more than 100 per cent. This would be an error. Hence, when the 100 per cent value is selected by management, it is divided by (1 + Adj.), where "Adj." is the sum of the appropriate difficulty adjustments. This correction places the subjective rating in objective form. With this as a starting point, other films of other paces can be assigned comparable values. In short, to place management's subjective ratings onto an objective scale, the *KA* values from the rating session must be divided by (1 + Adj.).

When using objective rating in studies of simple repetitive work, it is desirable to show the details of these secondary adjustments on the time study to facilitate checking. The time study shown in Figure C.14 includes the ratings and the adjustments. These have been used to calculate the base times for the elements.

The presently available data for difficulty adjustments have been applied over an extended period of time to an extensive variety of work. They also have been instrumental in bringing peaceful solutions to situations where standards had been a source of constant arguments. They certainly offer a more consistent basis from which to work than does the conventional procedure in which the time study man subjectively evaluates the difficulty of the job in order to form a mental image of a suitable pace with which to compare the pace he observes. Further experimentation to extend the percentages presented in Table C.8 to unusual conditions is not difficult, provided all parties recognize that the application of additional values may later indicate the need for, and the magnitude of, additional corrections to these new data. If rates are not consistent in ease or difficulty, the elements of sameness in the malfunctioning rates may be compared and the corrections to the table of difficulty adjustments will be indicated.

The problem of the difficulty adjustments, howevei, is still a field for additional motion and time study research but this research much be carefully performed. We must avoid sweeping statements based on short performances of laboratory tasks by students relatively unfamiliar with such work.

Finally, it is also interesting to note that the basic philosophy of the difficulty adjustments makes the time study also a motion study technique. For the most part, changes which will reduce the adjustments will also facilitate the task,[50] and consequently these values may be used as a guide toward better methods.

---

[50] The adjustment for bimanualness is the outstanding exception.

ELEMENTS

No.	TERMINAL POINT	C1 R	C1 T	C2 R	C2 T	C3 R	C3 T	C4 R	C4 T	C5 R	C5 T	C6 R	C6 T	C7 R	C7 T	C8 R	C8 T	C9 R	C9 T	C10 R	C10 T	C11 R	C11 T	C12 R	C12 T	C13 R	C13 T	C14 R	C14 T	C15 R	C15 T
1	RL pen into rack	03	2 57	3	13	3	72	3	34	3	89	3	45	3	02	3	56	3	17	3	77	3	27	3	83	3	34	3	97	3	
2	DA filling cap	21	18 78	19	33	20	99	17	53	19	07	18	64	19	20	18	76	20	34	17	90	19	46	19	03	20	57	18	16	19	
3	RL cap	41	20 96	18	52	19	10	21	72	19	27	20	84	20	39	19	98	22	55	21	10	20	66	20	22	19	79	20	37	21	
4	RL clip top	56	15 10	14	69	17	31	20	86	14	42	15	99	15	53	14	14	14	68	13	24	14	90	14	38	16	94	15	52	15	

RECAPITULATION

ELEMENTS	1	2	3	4	5	6	7	8	9	10	11	12	13	14	15
Amount of body	D-S	D-S	C-2	D-S											
Foot pedals	F-0	F-0	F-0	F-0											
Bimanualness	H-0	H-0	H-0	H-0											
Eye-hand coordination	J-2	J-2	J-2	J-2											
Handling requirements	P-2	P-2	P-2	P-2											
Weight or resistance	0-0	0-0	0-0	0-0											
TOTAL TIME IN *min.*	.45	2.90	2.99	2.07											
NUMBER OF OBS.	15	15	15	14											
PRO-RATE DIVISOR	1	1	1	1											
AVERAGE PER CYCLE	.030	.187	.199	.148											
RATING	115	105	110	95											
RATED TIME	.035	.196	.219	.141											
PER CENT OF CYCLE	—	—	—	—											
1+ ADJUSTMENTS	1.09	1.09	1.07	1.09											
BASE TIME	.038	.214	.234	.154											
1+ ALLOWANCES															
ALLOWED TIME															

SYMBOLS USED

C - Extra unnecessary motion
D - A.D. Dropped part
F - Unnecessary fumble
H - Unnecessary hesitation
P - Includes personal time
R - Made reject by improper work
X - Deviation from std. routine

ALLOWANCES

Personal _____ %

_____

_____

TOTAL _____ %

LOOP VALUES

141	132	120
100	93	82
74	67	53
44	40	36

Fig. C.14 — Time study for filling fountain pens for writing inspection with ratings and difficulty adjustments and with base time computed.

Appendix D: Bibliography

The following selected books will provide additional information on motion and time study and related topics. The references have been numbered to facilitate assignment in academic situations. This is by no means a complete bibliography of the field. This should be a starting list for the serious student.

Books

1. Abruzzi, Adam, *Work, Workers and Work Measurement*. New York: Columbia University Press, 1956.
2. Bailey, N. R., *Motion Study for the Supervisor*. New York: McGraw-Hill Book Co., Inc., 1942.
3. Barnes, R. M., *Motion and Time Study*. New York: John Wiley & Sons, Inc., 5th ed., 1963.
4. Barnes, R. M., *Motion and Time Study Problems and Projects*. New York: John Wiley & Sons, Inc., 1961.
5. Barnes, R. M., *Work Method Manual*. New York: John Wiley & Sons, Inc., 1944.
6. Barnes, R. M., *Work Sampling*. New York: John Wiley & Sons, Inc., 1957.
7. Branston, B., *Time and Motion on the Farm*. London, England: Faber Press, 1953.
8. British Institute of Management, *Outline of Work Study, Part I-Introduction*. London, England: British Institute of Management, 1956.
9. British Institute of Management, *Outline of Work Study, Part II-Method Study*. London, England: British Institute of Management, 1955.
10. British Institute of Management, *Outline of Work Study, Part III-Work Measurement*. London, England: British Institute of Management, 1957.

596

11. Carroll, Phil, Jr., *Better Wage Incentives.* New York: McGraw-Hill Book Co., Inc., 1957.
12. Carroll, Phil, Jr., *Time Study for Cost Control.* New York: McGraw-Hill Book Co., Inc., 3rd ed., 1954.
13. Carroll, Phil, Jr., *Time Study Fundamentals for Foremen.* New York: McGraw-Hill Book Co., Inc., 2nd ed., 1951.
14. Chane, G. W., *Motion and Time Study.* New York: Harper and Bros., Inc., 1942.
15. Churchman, C. W., Ackoff, R. L., Arnoff, E. L., *Introduction to Operations Research.* New York: John Wiley & Sons, Inc., 1957.
16. Eastman Kodak Co., *How to Make Good Movies.* Rochester, N.Y.: Eastman Kodak Co., Inc. (undated, but periodically revised).
17. Factory Management and Maintenance, *Manual of Work Simplification.* New York: McGraw-Hill Book Co., Inc., 1947.
18. Factory Mutual Engineering Division, *Handbook of Industrial Loss Prevention.* New York: McGraw-Hill Book Co., Inc., 1967.
19. Gilbreth, F. B., *Motion Study.* New York: D. Van Nostrand Co., Inc., 1911.
20. Gilbreth, L. E., *et al.*, *Management in the Home.* New York: Dodd, rev. ed., 1959.
21. Gillespie, J. J., *Dynamic Motion and Time Study.* London, England: Paul Elek, 1947.
22. Glassey, W. C., *The Theory and Practice of Time Study.* London, England: Business Publications (Burke), 1966.
23. Gomberg, William, *A Trade Union Analysis of Time Study.* Englewood Cliffs, N.J.: Prentice-Hall, Inc., 2nd ed., 1955.
24. Hadden, Arthur A., and Genger, V. K., *Handbook of Standard Time Data.* New York: The Ronald Press Co., 1954.
25. *Handbook of Human Engineering Data.* Medford, Mass.: Tufts College Institute of Applied Experimental Psychology, 1951.
26. Hedman, R., and Rask, L., *Vad är arbetsstudier?* Stockholm, Sweden: Tilden-Barnangen tryckerier, 1958.
27. Hendry, J. W., *Manual of Time and Motion Study.* London, England: Pitman Publishing Co., 1945.
28. Hendry, J. W., *Work Study in the Laundry and Drycleaning Industries.* London, England: Iliffe Books, 1963.
29. Heiland, Robert E., and Richardson, Wallace J., *Work Sampling.* New York: McGraw-Hill Book Co., Inc., 1957.
30. Hilf, Hubert Hugo, *Arbeitswissenschaft.* Munich, Germany: Carl Hanser Verlag, 1957.
31. Holmes, W. G., *Applied Motion and Time Study.* New York: The Ronald Press Co., 1938.
32. Industrial Management Society, *Proceedings of the Time and Motion Study Clinic.* Chicago, Ill.: Industrial Management Society, 1938–.
33. Lehrer, R. N., *Work Simplification (Creative Thinking About Work Problems).* Englewood Cliffs, N.J.: Prentice Hall, Inc., 1957.
34. Lehrer, R. N., *Management of Improvement.* New York: Reinhold, 1965.

35. Lesperance, J. P., *Economics and Techniques of Motion and Time Study*. Dubuque, Iowa: Wm. C. Brown Co., 1953.
36. Lichtner, W. O., *Time Study and Job Analysis*. New York: The Ronald Press Co., 1921.
37. Lowry, S. M., Maynard, H. B., and Stegemerten, G. J., *Time and Motion Study*. New York: McGraw-Hill Book Co., Inc., 3rd ed., 1940.
38. Maynard, H. B., Stegemerten, G. J., and Schwab, J. L., *Methods-Time-Measurement*. New York: McGraw-Hill Book Co., Inc., 1948.
39. Mogensen, A. H., *Common Sense Applied to Motion and Time Study*. New York: McGraw-Hill Book Co., Inc., 1932.
40. Morrow, R. L., *Motion Economy and Work Measurement*. New York: The Ronald Press Co., 2nd ed., 1957.
41. Morrow, R. L., *Time Study and Motion Economy*. New York: The Ronald Press Co., 1946.
42. Mundel, M. E., *A Conceptual Framework for the Management Sciences*. New York: McGraw-Hill Book Co., 1967.
43. Myers, H. J., *Simplified Time Study*. New York: The Ronald Press Co., 1944.
44. Nadler, G., *Motion and Time Study*. New York: McGraw-Hill Book Co., 1955.
45. Niebel, Benjamin, W., *Motion and Time Study*. Homewood, Ill: Richard D. Irwin, Inc., 4th ed., 1967.
46. Presgrave, R., *Dynamics of Time Study*. New York: McGraw-Hill Book Co., Inc., 1945.
47. Quick, J. H., *et al.*, *Work-Factor Time Standards*. New York: McGraw-Hill Book Co., Inc., 1962.
48. Sampter, H. C., *Motion Study*. New York: Pitman Publishing Corp., 1941.
49. Schutt, W. H., *Time Study Engineering*. New York: McGraw-Hill Book Co., Inc., 1943.
50. Shaw, A. G., *An Introduction to the Theory and Application of Motion Study*. Manchester, England: Columbine Press, 2nd ed., 1960.
51. Shaw, A. G., *The Purpose and Practice of Motion Study*. Manchester, England: Columbine Press, 2nd ed., 1960.
52. Shumard, F. W., *Primer of Time Study*. New York: McGraw-Hill Book Co., Inc., 1940.
53. Spriegel, W. R., and Myers, C. E., eds., *The Writings of the Gilbreths*. Homewood, Ill.: Richard D. Irwin, Inc., 1953.
54. Stegemerten, G. J., and Maynard, H. B., *Operation Analysis*. New York: McGraw-Hill Book Co., Inc., 1939.
55. Vaughan, L. M., and Hardin, L. S., *Farm Work Simplification*. New York: John Wiley & Sons, Inc., 1949.

Bibliographies

56. Barnes, R. M., and Englert, Norma, *Industrial Engineering and Management Literature*. Dubuque, Iowa: Wm. C. Brown Co., 5th ed., 1946.
57. The John Crerar Library, *Bibliography of Time and Motion Study*. Chicago, Ill.: The John Crerar Library, 96 E. Randolph St., 1942.

Periodical Literature

1. There are more than a thousand trade magazines, each devoted to an industry, a group of products, or a group of processes. All of these contain information relevant to the methods aspect of motion and time study problems. The serious student should seek out those pertinent to his work.

2. The annual proceedings, periodic journals, or publications of the following societies or organizations are also of value:

    a. The American Institute of Industrial Engineers, Inc.
    b. The American Management Association.
    c. The American Society for Quality Control, Inc.
    d. The American Society for Value Engineering, Inc.
    e. The British Institute of Management, Management House, 80 Fetter Lane, London, E.C.4, U.K.
    f. The Japan Management Association, 25 Shiba Park, Kyoritsu Building, Minato-ku, Tokyo, Japan.
    g. The Society for Advancement of Management, Inc.
    h. The Ministry of Technology, Industrial Operations Unit, Abell House, John Islip St., London, S. W. 1, U. K.

3. The following reference services provide guides to current periodical literature.

    a. AMS Management Information Guide—
        Administrative Management Society
        Maryland Road
        Willow Grove, Pennsylvania 19090

    b. Applied Science and Technology Index—
        H. W. Wilson Company
        950 University Avenue
        Bronx, New York 10452

    c. Business Periodicals Index—
        H. W. Wilson Company
        950 University Avenue
        Bronx, New York 10452

    d. Cost Reduction Digest—
        Industry Reports, Inc.
        514 10th Street, N.W., 7th Floor
        Washington, D. C. 20004

    e. Dartnell Management Service—
        Dartnell Corporation
        4660 Ravenswood Avenue
        Chicago, Illinois 60640

Appendix E: Problems

Facility with motion and time study techniques is best gained by actual application to real problems. Opportunity for this exists in every organization. Practice in thoroughness in data gathering as well as cognizance of the human problems involved can come best from actual observation and experience. It is usually desirable, however, to check one's knowledge beforehand, in a practice situation; problems are presented here for that purpose.

Chapter 1

1.1. Determine what applications of motion and time study have been made in your own organization.

1.2. Give a short résumé of the lives and work of F.B. and L.M. Gilbreth.

1.3. Describe F. W. Taylor's experiments at the Midvale Steel Company.

1.4. For what accomplishments is the Gilbreth Medal awarded by the Society for Advancement of Management?

1.5. Describe the accomplishments of one recipient of the Gilbreth Medal.

1.6. For what accomplishments is the Frank B. and Lillian Gilbreth Award made by the American Institute of Industrial Engineers?

1.7. Describe the accomplishments of one recipient of the Frank B. and Lillian Gilbreth Award.

1.8. Taking size and color into account, as well as other variables, how many products in:

a. A Sears Roebuck catalog?

b. A Montgomery Ward Catalog?

c. A Spiegel catalog?

d. An A.S.M.E. mechanical catalog?

e. Any catalog (as assigned)?

1.9. What are the quantitative objectives, limitations, and freedoms of:

a. Your employer?

b. Your university?

c. Your immediate organization?

1.10. What means are used to determine the achievement of objectives by the organization cited in answering 1.9 above?

1.11. Suggest and describe, from your own knowledge, a situation where method changes would appear appropriate.

1.12. Suggest and describe, from your own knowledge, a situation where the manpower resources employed appear:

a. Inadequate.

b. Excessive.

1.13. In what professional societies would we find people whose major interest is in motion and time study work?

1.14. Find and summarize an article in the periodical literature (within assigned dates) describing the application of motion study to a situation.

1.15. Through what channels should a proposal for a method change be made in your organization?

1.16. Describe and evaluate the procedure used by the postal employee the last time you:

a. Purchased stamps.

b. Sent a registered letter.

c. Sent an insured parcel.

Chapter 2

2.1 Job Methods Training (JMT) was an important phase of the Training Within Industry program of the War Manpower Commission during World War II. What features of Job Methods Training made it as effective as it was?

2.2. If you knew of a better way to perform some common household task, describe in detail the procedure you would use to persuade your wife or mother to adopt it. (Do not detail the improved method.)

2.3. Try the approach and report on the effects and results.

2.4. Report on the effects after a lapse of one week.

2.5. Interview an industrial production worker and report on his concept of motion and time study. Analyze and evaluate the validity of any conclusions he may have come to.

2.6. Report from your experience on the reactions that accompanied a change of method on a job.

2.7. Interview an industrial engineer and describe his place in the industrial organization.

2.8. Report on a pertinent reading from the literature in sociology or industrial psychology.

2.9. Report on the changes in the past fifty years with respect to:

a. Employment in the manufacturing industries.
b. Employment in the service industries.
c. Employment in the government service:
　　1. Municipal.
　　2. State.
　　3. Federal.
　　4. Total.
d. Employment in the agricultural sector.
e. Horsepower per employee in the manufacturing industries.
f. Purchasing power of money.
g. Value of output per employee-year in the manufacturing industries:
　　1. Gross, unweighted.
　　2. In terms of a constant value dollar.
h. Life span of humans.
i. Population of:
　　1. Your country.
　　2. The world.

2.10. With respect to the use of motion and time study, of what importance are the changes noted in the examination of the assigned item from question 2.9.?

2.11. Examine the news media (of an assigned period) and report on a labor dispute related to method or workload and assigned manpower.

2.12. Suggest the solution you would have proposed for the situation described in 2.11.

2.13. Report on your attitude towards potential changes in your workload. Explain your rationale.

2.14. A group of fifteen executives have been in the habit of dictating letters to their secretaries who record them by shorthand. It is proposed to use tape recording and transcribing equipment (suitably designed). Prepare the speech you would use to make this proposal to:

a. The executives.
b. The secretaries.

2.15. List the possible objections to the proposal of 2.14 by:

a. The executives.
b. The secretaries.

2.16. List your responses to the objections of:

a. 2.15a.
b. 2.15b.

2.17. *The incentive problem.*[1] A junior time and methods man has set a method and rate (standard time for a job) in the finishing department which has created considerable ill feeling. He has asked for 320 pieces per hour per operator. Since the work is on wage incentives (100% Standard Hour Plan) and since none of the operators have come up to standard they are a little disappointed, to say the least. On your way up through the department (you are head of the motion and time study staff) to talk with the foreman of the aforementioned department who has asked for a consultation with you, one of the operators says to you, "This is a — of a rate Mr. Clock set!" (Mr. Clock is the junior.) You tell the operator that the rate will be looked into.

The foreman first practically cries on your shoulder, asking, "How can I get my department up to standard when I get such nutty rates as this?" He further says, "I can't even honestly ask them to do it for me." He turns to the assistant foreman and says, "Moon, do you think it is a fair rate?"

"Heck, no," says the assistant, "and you guys (turning to you) usually do a good job. Now you take that job we are doing for Smith and Co. It is almost like this one and you don't call for anywhere's near as much production. Do you?"

"You make our job tough," says the foreman.

You soothe both of them and tell them that you will restudy the job yourself but ask to reserve discussion and decision until then. You promise to give it your unbiased attention.

The assistant foreman asks, "Does that mean you are just going to look at it and then swear that your department was right the first time." (He says this in a joking manner and not offensively. Once before, a question similar to this came up and you upheld the rate. However, at that time the shortness of the production run precluded the chance of a real test. They think that perhaps the restudy was just a blind.)

You tell the two of them that you will fully consider the job. The assistant foreman is really worried about his crew and in earnestness assures you that instead of being 320 per hour the standard should be 285 per hour. You tell him that you will look into the job but that you cannot commit yourself now at all.

You restudy the job carefully and take a new stop-watch time study. After the inclusion of all normal delays, personal time, and allowing for the tiringness of the task you find that your figures ask for 287 per hour. Mr. Clock missed several highly intermittent but important parts of the operation. Since your policy requires production standards in multiples of five when over 200 per hour this figure of yours would reduce to 285 per hour.

[1] From Mundel, M. E., and Pigage, L. C., *Case Problems in Industrial Organization and Management.* Ann Arbor, Mich.: Edwards Bros., 1945, p. 43.

604   Appendix E: problems

a. How intelligent is the policy of using multiples of five for production standards over 200 per hour? Why?

b. Is there any potential trouble in this situation? Explain.

c. Would you merely issue the rate change and say nothing? Explain.

d. Would you issue the rate change? If so, as of the date or retroactive?

e. Exactly what would you do? (Make a scientific analysis of the problem.)

2.18. *The typewriter.* A friend who works in the same organization as you do has been bringing his reports to you for comments and editing, before making a final copy. He works on them at home at night. Your comments are often extensive but almost always welcomed and accepted. The last report required so many corrections to the equations and suggestions concerning changes in phrasing that, in some places, you could hardly squeeze them in between the double-spaced, typed lines. When you were through discussing the notes with him you suggested that on the next report it would be advantageous if he would type with triple spacing. He replies, "I can't. My typewriter only has a 1, $1\frac{1}{2}$ and 2 throw return lever."

a. Is it possible that he is really as stupid as he sounds?

b. Explain what you think has really happened.

Chapter 3

3.1. List the class of change involved in each of the first six cases described in Chapter 1. Give the reason for your classification in terms of what was actually achieved in each case.

3.2. Find an application of motion study in the periodical literature (within assigned dates); make a brief résumé of the improvement; and indicate the class of change which was involved.

3.3. Use the scientific method in the following problem situations:

a. *Gulliver's travels:* In "Gulliver's Voyage to Laputa," Swift's satire on Oxford and Cambridge, he pokes ridicule at the astronomers by describing how the savants at the University of Laputa claim to have observed a planet, spinning like the earth, but with two moons, one of which rises in the East and sets in the West, while the other moon rises in the West and sets in the East, despite the fact that both moons are moving around the planet in the same direction. The astronomers at one of the universities retorted that two of Jupiter's moons do behave in this fashion. Swift then pointed out that they were really Laputans, his terms for utter nitwits, to propose such a nonsensical situation.

1. Who was "off base"?

2. Defend your position.

b. *The Iwakaze spinning mill.* The product of the mill is fine cotton and blended thread. There are 160 "sets" of spinning machines. Each machine has 60 spinning heads; each head spins a thread (pulls and twists a loose sliver of fiber into a thread) independently, and winds it onto a spool called a bobbin. Hence, each machine has 60 bobbins. The machine stops automatically when any bobbin is full. Each machine in a set of machines is spinning the same thread as the other three machines in the set. However, due to the way production of the various sizes of thread is changed from time to time, all sets spinning a given size of thread are not in the same general area. Some small changes are made to the schedule once each month. The machines are of various types; they are of German, English, American, or Japanese origin. All the machines in any one set are alike. All machines can spin all types of thread.

There are crews of doffers and spinners. Doffers remove all of the bobbins from a set of machines when the machines have stopped automatically, put on empty bobbins, and restart the machines. The spinners patrol the operating machines and repair broken threads and replace the sliver supply cans. When a thread breaks, the head stops spinning. The other 59 heads on the machine continue. The only loss is the loss of production from the idle head until the thread is tied by the spinner, and a "short" bobbin which causes some inconvenience in subsequent processing. If left unattended, from 3 to 10 per cent of the heads would stop each hour. Breakage is a function of thread type and fiber mixture.

There are 18 doffing crews per shift; 10 crews have a manning of four experienced doffers; eight crews consist of one experienced doffer and four trainees. There are 72 spinners per shift. All work an eight-hour shift with $\frac{1}{2}$ hour out for lunch. Spinners are the more experienced group, having been promoted from doffer and given additional training for spinning. During the $\frac{1}{2}$ hour lunch time the machines are shut down. The cycle of work is such that no two days' schedules of doffings are the same despite the fact that all products are made continuously. There are two shifts. (See following table.)

Table of Machine Cycles

Item	Machine Type	Number of Machines	Cycles/Day/Set
SB 20	TN 6"	104	14.08
SB 16	TN 7"	88	12.18
SB 21	TN 7"	80	9.37
SB 30	TN 6"	36	7.50
RB 30	TN 6"	20	8.50
RB 30	OM 6"	24	8.50
RB 60	TN 7"	56	3.75
RB 60	OM 6"	48	4.69
NR 30	TN 7"	24	7.50
NR 38	TN 7"	56	4.69
NR 40	TN 7"	56	4.69
NR 42	NM 7"	48	4.69

The method of operation is for each spinner to patrol a given area of machines on a patrol path. The doffers doff the finished set of bobbins from a set of machines, as a group. A whole set is always doffed at the same time. A crew of doffers is dispatched to doff a set of machines when the bobbins on that machine are full and the machines have stopped. The short bobbins are also doffed at that time. The supervisor who does the dispatching sends any idle crew of doffers that he can find. The spinners on patrol pass the machines which the doffers are working on.

Under this procedure the most conscientious crew of doffers gets the largest workload although all doffers are paid alike. It was decided that a schedule should be developed and crew assignments made to achieve a more equitable distribution of the workload. However, due to the fact that each doffing on a set of machines occurs at a different time each day, the computation of the daily schedule has involved much work.

You have been asked to "Devise a method of reducing the complication of computing the daily schedule for doffers and spinners."

1. What do you do?
2. Explain your rationale.

3.4. List all the similar and all the different aspects of the items in the following list:

a. Mr. Puccini's spaghetti.
b. Mr. Chow Kim's kimchi.
c. Mr. Front-de-beouf's roast beef.
d. Mr. Frost's curry.
e. Mr. Jackson's zither.
f. The Swiss navy.

Chapter 4

4.1. Prepare a preliminary and a detailed possibility guide for the following tasks which were described in Chapter 1:

a. Enveloping plant magazine.
b. Assembling roller wheels.
c. Sorting day-old chicks.
d. Handling materials to sandblast.
e. Manufacturing radar coil.

4.2. a. Make a perliminary and a detailed possibility guide for some job connected with your work or available to you for actual observation. (A household task may be used.)

b. On the basis of the list of economic and psychological factors affecting change, select a suitable tentative objective for the motion study analysis of the job used for part *a*. Justify your selection.

4.3. A chicken-packing plant is shown in Figure E.1. The process is as follows:

The chickens are taken individually from the crates, stuck inside the throat with a thin sticking knife, and then hung by the chicken sticker in a vat of scalding water. The chicken sticker watches these chickens so as to keep a supply ahead of the pickers and to prevent any bird from being kept an undue

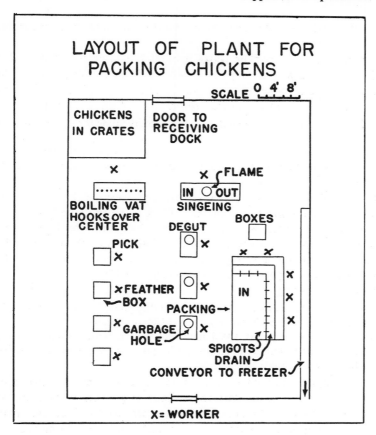

Fig. E.1

length of time in the vat. He tries to keep four or five chickens scalding at once.

When necessary, the pickers walk to the vat, get a bird, take it to their workplace, hang it by one or both legs from a hook, and pick it clean. When it is completely defeathered, they walk with it to the singeing table and place it on the pile on the "in" side. They then walk back to the vat and repeat the process.

The singer singes each chicken and looks at if for pinfeathers. About one chicken out of five has pinfeathers to be pulled. The singer removes the pinfeathers as necessary and piles the singed and depinfeathered chickens on the right side of his table.

The degutters walk to the singeing table as necessary, get a bird at a time, take it to their workplace, and while it lies on their table they draw it (remove the innards), replace the giblets, and then carry the bird and place it on the pile on the packing table. They then walk to the singeing table for another bird.

As necessary, each packer walks around the table to get a bird, takes it to his work area with a box, which he takes from the pile, cuts the chicken into frying sections, boxes these sections, and places the box on the conveyor that carries the box into a quick freezer.

a. Prepare a preliminary and a detailed possibility guide for the degutting operation.

b. For each operation on the chicken, list at least one change, from any one of the five classes of change, that would affect that operation. Indicate the class of change in each case.

4.4. A professional society mails to its members, each month, a notice of the next meeting location and the subject to be presented. The notice is offset-printed on paper, $8\frac{1}{2}'' \times 11''$. It is folded into thirds and together with a business reply card is hand stuffed into a No. 10 envelope and sent by first class mail. The meetings are dinner meetings and meals are planned on the basis of the cards returned. The society has 100 members and about 80 come to each meeting.

a. Prepare a preliminary and detailed possibility guide for "notification of meeting." Select the most feasible possibility. Justify your choice.

b. Assume the society has 1,000 members with a typical attendance of 100. Prepare a preliminary and detailed possibility guide. Select the most feasible possibility. Justify your choice.

4.5. A company manufacturing children's games has a platform in one of its boxes of games. The platform is made of grey chip-board and stayed in the corners, as with a box cover. It is then wrapped with colored paper on a box-cover wrapping machine. The covered platforms are moved by skid to the assembly line where the game, box cover, and bottom are being wrapped on wrapping machines. The platform and other items are hand assembled into the box on a conveyor between the bottom wrap and cover wrap machines. Make a preliminary and detailed possibility guide for the platform manufacture. If any additional information is needed, make reasonable assumptions and record these.

4.6. Examine the method used within your organization to collect and distribute mail. Make a preliminary and detailed possibility guide for:

a. In-plant mail.

b. Regular mail.

Chapter 5

5.1. a. Prepare a process chart-product analysis for the process described in problem 4.3.

b. Prepare a flow diagram for the process.

5.2. a. With the aid of the check list prepare a process chart-product analysis for an improved procedure for the process charted in problem 5.1. Do not exceed a Class 3 change.

b. Prepare a new plant layout and flow diagram.

c. List the information obtained from performing part *a* that you would add to your check list, and indicate the check-list question number and letter under which each item would be filed.

5.3. A factory uses a number of screw machine parts in its finished product. The bar stock for these is kept in the company warehouse in stacks with wood slats between each layer of ten bars. The warehouse employees consult their shipping requisition for type and size only, since the standard order is 50 bars, locate the correct stack, slip crane sling under a layer at a time, and aid the craneman in guiding each slingful into a stake truck. An order usually constitutes a truck-load. The truck carries the bars 1,000 feet to the screw machine department, where a monorail hoist capable of lifting five bars in a sling at a time, carries the bars 50 feet to the proper storeroom rack. The storeroom is adjacent to the screw machine department. When an operator needs another bar of stock, he goes to the stockroom, where it is issued against his job order. The two stockroom employees then lift a bar from the proper rack and carry it to the machine, where the worker helps them load it into his spindle ready-rack. When the stock in the machine is used up, the operator rolls the piece from the ready-rack forward into the spindle and restarts the machine, which then works automatically. As the parts are completed, they are ejected to a chute, which drops them onto the steel-plate floor. When enough parts have accumulated, the machine operator calls for the crane-man to bring a dump pan. When the crane operator complies, the machine operator shovels the dump pan full, while the crane operator waits. The crane then carries the filled pan and sets it down alongside a cleaning tank. When enough work of any one kind has accumulated in pans on the floor next to the tank, the crane comes back, hooks each pan of that kind in turn, without aid, and dumps the contents into the tank. The tank washes the parts in steam-heated and agitated water, and they are automatically lifted out by an open mesh conveyor, dried on a short section of the conveyor, and dumped onto the floor. The tank tender shovels the parts into carts, pushes these carts 60 feet to a storeroom where they are weighed in the cart on a platform scale, moved under a good light, sample inspected for number of threads per inch, size, and so forth. They are then moved to the proper bin, dumped on the floor, shoveled up into the bin, and the net weight entered on the bin control card. All incoming requisitions are charged off this card, so the balance of stores is known at all times.

a. Make a process chart-product analysis of the manufacture of screw machine parts in this plant.

b. Prepare a preliminary and a detailed possibility guide for the manufacture of screw machine parts in this plant.

c. With the aid of the check list prepare a process chart-product analysis for an improved method not exceeding a Class 3 change, assuming one of the following as assigned:

1. A variety of parts are made.
2. Only one type and size of part is made.

d. List the information obtained from part *c* that you would add to your check-list file and indicate the question number and letter under which each would be filed.

5.4. The following is a running description of the preparation of a piece of direct-mail advertising in the Blow, Blat, and Bleat Advertising Agency. The advertisement consists of four $8\frac{1}{2}''\times 11''$ sheets folded and stapled, as shown in Figure E.2. Thousands of sheets come in from the printer, packed

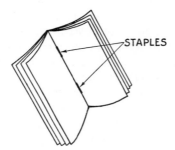

Fig. E.2

in ream (500-sheet) lots and are placed in a stock room. They are withdrawn as called for by order and moved 100 feet to the collating room, where they are placed in a rack with four compartments. The collating operator takes a sheet at a time by hand from each of the four bins, jogs them, lays them in a cross-pile to keep each set of 4 separate, and builds a large stack. From time to time, a cross-pile stack is moved 20 feet to the folding room, where each set is jogged, folded, hand creased, and piled into a stack. From time to time, a stack is moved 20 feet to an angle stapler. An angle stapler has an inverted V rest for the paper, so that the crease, when on the V, is correctly positioned for the stapler. Two staples are driven in. The stapled sheets are restacked. From time to time a pile of stapled sets is taken 200 feet to the mailing room, where the stack is eventually fed, one by one, into an Addressograph, ad-dressed, and placed in a mailbag. All carrying of the stacks is done by hand.

a. Make a process chart-product analysis for the whole process of preparation of the advertisements, as described, from the time they are in ream lots in the stock room to the time they are in the mailbag.

b. Prepare a preliminary and a detailed possibility guide for the process.

c. With the aid of the check list prepare a process chart-product analysis for a better method involving a Class 3 change.

d. List the information gained from part *c* that you would add to your check list and indicate the question number and letter under which each item would be filed.

5.5. The following is the process used in a Chicago hotel to manufacture waiters' table towels. Bolts of material stored in the sixth floor storeroom are issued by the head housekeeper to a handyman with a requisition for a bolt or more. He carries them to an elevator 30 feet away. After waiting for the elevator, he takes them down to the third floor, carries them 100 feet to the sewing room, and places them on a cutting bench. Later, all but one bolt are removed from the cutting table by the cutter, and that bolt is spread out and cut to length, 120 pieces to a bolt. Each bolt is cut separately. The pieces are moved by the cutter, after each bolt is cut, five feet to the sewing bench and stacked. The sewer hems the cut ends and eventually counts and compares the number made to the requested quantity. Any excess is sent back to the sixth floor stock room. The finished towels are then moved 100 feet by the sewer to the elevator, where she and the towels are carried to the fifth floor. She leaves them in the laundry marking room, 60 feet from the elevator. The towels are then machine marked, carried 60 feet to the washing machines, laundered, and wait in wheeled laundry hampers. A washroom assistant wheels these 30 feet to an elevator that carries them to the fourth floor, where an assistant wheels them 50 feet to the mangle room, where they are left. The entire batch waits in the mangle room until one of the mangle crews is ready to take them. Each hamper is then wheeled 25 feet to the designated mangle where it is processed by a crew of four women on a six-roll mangle. Coming off the back end of the mangle, the towels are stacked in piles on a table, then placed in a truck, moved 100 feet to the housekeeping department storage room on the fourth floor, where they are first checked against the requested amount, and then put into storage for future issue.

  a. Prepare a process chart-product analysis for the original method.
  b. Prepare a preliminary and a detailed possibility guide.
  c. With the aid of the check list prepare an improved process chart-product analysis, limiting yourself to the class of change designated by the instructor.
  d. List the information gained from part c that you would add to your check list and indicate the question number and letter under which each item would be filed.

5.6. The following is the routine involved in handling a $3\frac{1}{4}$-lb. jar of hard candy in a large department store. Twenty-four cases (two gross of jars) of hard candy arrive by truck and are unloaded by hand and stored on the receiving platform. Twelve cases are loaded onto a four-wheeled truck, and each twelve, in turn, are transported 85 feet to the freight elevator in building A, wait, are loaded on and taken to the ninth floor of building A and then 50 feet across the floor to the checking area, where the dock helper leaves them and returns to the dock. Each case is eventually checked against the proper invoice and shaken to determine if any of the jars are broken. After the whole

24 cases (two trucks) have been checked and replaced on the trucks, each truck, in turn, is moved back to the freight elevator and left there. The elevator operator, when he stops at that floor, takes them on and down to the ground floor, where he pushes them off the elevator. A ground floor handler eventually moves them 400 feet through a tunnel under the street to the B building elevator and leaves them there. The B building freight elevator operator, when he stops for a load, takes them on, carries them to the fifth floor and pushes them off. A fifth floor storeroom employee eventually takes them 85 feet from the elevator to the candy storeroom. The whole 24 cases are first stacked in the open space in the storeroom and then in turn the cases are carried one at a time 30 feet, and placed on the shelves until needed. When an order comes in for two cases (the usual quantity) from the floor sales department, the cases are removed from the shelves, loaded onto a truck, wheeled back to the elevator, down to the basement, across to building A, and to elevator #9, which is 525 feet away from the B building elevator. After waiting for the elevator, the truck with two cases is loaded on and brought up to the first floor selling department, 80 feet from the elevator, where the two cases are placed on a table. The storeroom employee returns with his truck. The jars are placed in undercounter storage and one is placed on display at a time. When that jar has been sold (send sale), it is moved 12 feet to the sales counter, where a sales check is tied on, and then the jar is placed in a hamper kept there for delivery to elevator #9. Eventually the hamper is moved by a floor handler to the elevator. The elevator operator ultimately takes it on and transports the jar plus other goods to the ninth floor, where he shoves the hamper off. A floor handler eventually wheels the hamper 270 feet to the packing room. In the packing room, the jar is removed from the hamper and checked against the sales check for correctness of merchandise and examined to see if it is in good condition. It is then placed on a shelf two feet away, from which it is taken by the packer when she is ready to pack. After packing, the jar is placed in a hamper alongside the packer with other packages that have been packed by the same packer, and later wheeled 16 feet to elevator #19 or #30 and left. The elevator operator takes this and other hampers on down to the fifth floor, where it has to be transferred to elevator #23, 54 feet away. Elevator #23 then takes its load to the load-level, where the hampers are unloaded and wheeled by handlers 40 feet to the sorting area, where the loads are sorted and marked and placed in a relay truck, which is parked 30 feet away. The relay truck then takes its load 5,000 feet to the shipping-center loading platform, where the goods inside the truck are unloaded and sorted into hampers for wheeling to drivers bins, the average of which is 150 feet away.

    a. Draw a process chart-product analysis for the process described.

    b. Prepare a preliminary and a detailed possibility guide for the process.

c. With the aid of the check list prepare an improved process chart for a send sale, not exceeding a Class 3 change.

d. List the information gained from part *c* that you would add to your check list and indicate the question number and letter under which each item would be filed.

5.7. A gaseous generator separator plate (see *B*, Figure E.3) is manufactured from strip stock, which is kept in large quantities in the plant stores warehouse.

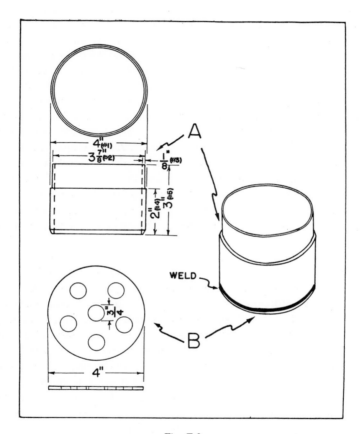

Fig. E.3

Fifty-eight strips are removed from the stack, one at a time, and loaded on a trailer five feet from the pile. A tractor is later hitched to the trailer and the whole load is transported 500 feet to Department 56, where it is unloaded and fed one piece at a time into a machine that pierces and blanks the strip.

As the pieces come out of the machine, they are checked for size and number of holes and dumped into a pan that will hold 500 pieces. The pan is carried, by lift truck, to the next machine, 25 feet away, and again the parts are fed into the machine one at a time for restriking and flattening. At this point, a production checker ascertains whether the quantity (about 3,000) in the tub under the second machine corresponds to the production counter reading on the machine. One tub (3,000 pieces) is picked up by an electric hoist and dumped into an automatic washing machine 12 feet away. As the pieces come out of the washer, they dump into tubs. Each tub is weighed to verify the count, and is then taken by Buda truck to Department 41 (1,265 feet) where the tubs are deposited beside a Wheelabrator. The pieces are loaded into the Wheelabrator one shovelful at a time until the full tub load has been accommodated. The pieces come out of the bottom of the Wheelabrator into a perforated container so that the grits can be extracted. They are shoveled from these containers into tubs and loaded on an electric lift truck that takes them to the inspection area 157 feet away, where the count is again verified, and then by Buda truck back to Department 43 stores, which is located behind the washing area. This move is about 1,125 feet. At the Department 43 stores, the tubs are removed from the Buda truck and the pieces in the tubs put in boxes by the handful until each box contains exactly 3,000 pieces. These boxes are moved by Buda truck to Department 42, where the boxes are emptied into bins by hand. The bins in this case are adjacent to the welding assembly fixture, where the pieces are positioned one at a time to be welded into the generator.

The tubes used for the generator body (see *A*, Figure E.3) are processed as follows. Fifty-five tubes, one crane sling load from a tube cradle, are loaded on a trailer 20 feet from the cradle. A Buda truck moves the trailer 1,500 feet to Department 97 stores, where they are put on a rack with a crane capable of handling ten tubes in a sling. These racks are later emptied one tube at a time by two men into a trailer that takes eleven tubes, and is hand pushed 1,000 feet to Department 91, where the eleven are put one at a time, by hand, onto a wheeled rack that is then moved by hand 100 feet to the chamfering machine. At the chamfering machine, one piece at a time is chamfered, turned, cut-off, the tube chamfered at the cut-off end, and so forth. The cut pieces are placed in a tub, 726 pieces to the tub. The tubs are taken by Buda truck to the inspection area 100 feet away, where the count is verified and a visual quality inspection is made. After the inspection, the pieces are loaded back into the tubs by handfuls, and the tubs eventually lifted by the Buda truck to be taken to Department 41, where they are loaded by the handful into a washer in which they are washed and automatically ejected into a container at the end of the washer. The pieces are loaded from the container, by the handful, into tubs that are taken in turn by an electric lift truck 85 feet to the sandblast room, and deposited beside the sandblast machine. At the sandblast machine, the pieces are taken out individually, sandblasted, dumped back into tubs, removed from the sandblast room and loaded, by the handful, into other tubs (dumping out sand in the operation) for transportation by electric lift truck to the inspection area, which is 157 feet away. At the inspection area the pieces are counted and retubbed, 725 to a tub. Eventually they are lifted by a Buda truck and moved 587 feet to rest beside the fixture where part *A* is to be incorporated into the final assembly.

The welders clamp one separator and one generator body into the fixture and gas weld them into a single unit, as indicated in Figure E.3.

a. Draw a process chart-product analysis for the manufacture of a generator unit from raw component stock to welded unit.

b. Prepare a preliminary and a detailed possibility guide for the process of part *a*.

c. With the aid of the check list prepare a process chart-product analysis for a better process. You may go as high as a Class 5 change but may not buy a completed unit for anything other than reasonable standard stock. Dimensions #1, 2, 3, 4, and 5 on *B* of Figure E.3 may not be appreciably altered.

d. List the information gained from part *c* that you would add to your check list and indicate the question number and letter under which each item would be filed.

5.8. Solve the equations of Case V, Chapter 5 (Supplemental Material), to determine:

a. The most efficient hourly trucking pattern.

b. The amount of trucking time needed per hour.

Chapter 6

6.1. Make a horizontal time bar chart of the pattern of truck-usage required for serving the pattern found in problem 5.8.

6.2. Make a horizontal time bar chart of:

a. A session with the dentist.

b. An efficient pattern for making a large marketing at a super-market.

c. A typical evening's study.

d. Completing registration.

6.3. Propose and chart an improved method for the situation charted for 6.2. What was your criterion of improvement? What class of change is involved?

6.4. Make a horizontal time bar chart of:

a. A national election.

b. The administration of the judicial process with felons (in your area).

c. The processing of a legislative bill by your local government.

d. The processing of a new regulatory bill by:

    1. The House of Representatives of the United States.

2. The Senate of the United States.

3. The Congress of the United States.

6.5. Propose and chart an improved method for the situation charted for 6.4. What was your criterion of success? What class of change was involved?

6.6. Make a horizontal time bar chart for the settlement of a damage claim in an automobile accident when no personal injury is involved.

Chapter 7

7.1. If, in Figure 7.2, the time for the steps is altered to the following:

$$2.1a = 2 \text{ weeks}$$
$$3.1b = 2 \text{ weeks}$$

a. Define the new critical path.

b. Indicate the single activity which has the greatest potential for reducing network time.

7.2. Draw a network diagram of the activities associated with a curriculum change.

7.3. Draw a network diagram of a water-pollution abatement program for your area.

7.4. Draw a network diagram of an air-pollution abatement program for your area.

7.5. Draw a network diagram for a program of economic aid to assist a new nation into the mainstream of the modern world.

7.6. Draw a network diagram for the development of a program to halt the "population explosion."

7.7. Draw a network diagram of a program designed to rid a city of rats.

7.8. Draw a network diagram of a campaign by an individual for an office in a city government.

7.9. Draw a network diagram for the construction of a new five-acre city park with a small lake, theatre, bandstand, ballfield, and picnic area. (Provide a sketch of the completed park.)

Chapter 8

8.1. a. Make a process chart-man analysis and a flow diagram of your activities in the morning from when you awake until you leave the house for school or work.

b. With the aid of the check list prepare a process chart-man analysis and a flow diagram for an improved method for performing the work charted in part *a*.

8.2. Prepare a process chart-man analysis and a flow diagram from direction observation of a woman:

a. Doing the dishes.
b. Baking a cake.
c. Preparing a meal.
d. Cleaning a room.
e. Giving herself a home hair treatment.

8.3. a. With the aid of the check list prepare a process chart-man analysis and flow diagram for a better method for performing the work charted in question 8.2.

b. List the information gained from part *a* that you would add to your check list and for each item indicate the check-list question number and letter under which it would be filed.

8.4. The following was the routine used by a worker loading refrigerators onto a trailer truck which moved them from the plant to the company's warehouse. The layout is shown in Figure E.4.

The loader walked five feet to the trailer at the edge of the dock, pushed the opening bar across the side door of the truck to the right, and then with the assistance of a hand truck located five feet away picked up a steel loading plate right at the edge of the dock and pushed it partly into the truck trailer so that the plate bridged the gap between the dock and the side of the trailer. The loader then pushed the empty hand truck to the conveyor line, ten feet away, picked up a crated refrigerator with the hand truck, and pushed the refrigerator into the trailer. He then returned the 16 feet to the conveyor line and got another load. This procedure was repeated 21 times before the trailer was almost fully loaded. At the end of the next trip, the loader went to the loading plate and with the help of his hand truck picked up the plate and moved it about two feet back on the dock so as to allow more space to stand refrigerators within the truck. He then loaded the twenty-third and twenty-fourth refrigerators. After the twenty-fourth refrigerator was loaded, he pulled back the loading plate with the aid of his hand truck, pushed the empty hand truck to its designated spot five feet away, returned to the trailer, closed the side bar on the trailer, and signaled the driver that his load was ready to move.

a. Prepare a process chart-man analysis and flow diagram for the man completely loading a trailer.

b. With the aid of the check list prepare a process chart and flow diagram for a better method, not exceeding a Class 2 change. The driver of the truck will not handle refrigerators. The warehouse must be used as the plant does not contain enough storage space to hold seasonal accumulation.

c. List the information you would add to your check list and for each item indicate the check-list question number and letter under which you would file it.

d. List all the advantages and disadvantages of the proposal, including all

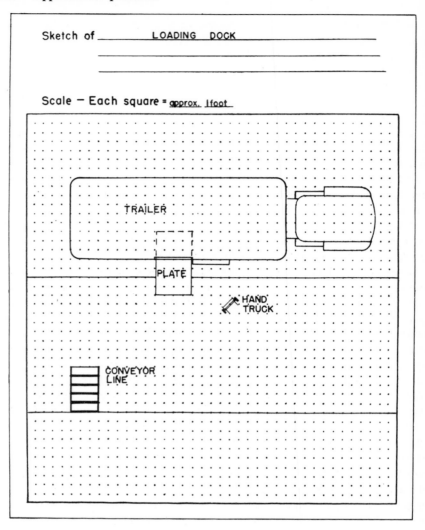

Fig. E.4

estimated savings under advantages and all estimated additional expenditures under disadvantages.

e. What would logically be the job that you would also study at the same time as the one given here?

8.5. a. Visit any industrial plant and observe the activities of any person whose job is such that he moves from place to place during his work. Prepare a process chart-man analysis and a flow diagram of his activities.

b. With the aid of the check list prepare a process chart-man analysis and a flow diagram for a better method.

c. List the information that you would add to your check list and for each item indicate the check-list question number and letter under which you would file it.

8.6. A salesclerk in a department store's sweater department was observed going through the following activities while selling a sweater to a large female customer. (The layout of the department is shown in Figure E.5.)

As the customer approached, the salesclerk, who had been waiting, greeted the customer and inquired as to her wants. The salesclerk then indicated a black cardigan in the showcase, stooped down and brought up a black pullover, which she first held up against herself. She then laid the sweater down on the counter for the customer to examine. The salesclerk then took out and donned the cardigan to display it, put it back on display, looked in her stock for the correct size, and then walked 90 feet to the storeroom. She moved a splintery and unsafe ladder 12 feet, climbed five feet up the ladder, pulled out a box, took out a sweater six sizes larger than the one she showed originally, put the box back, climbed down the ladder, returned 90 feet to the customer, and showed her the sweater from in front of the counter. Subsequently she walked 12 feet around the counter, got the whisk broom, returned, and brushed the sweater. At the customer's request, she gave her the whisk broom. The customer brushed the sweater. The customer gave the whisk broom back, and the salesclerk laid it on the counter. At this point, the customer agreed to buy the sweater. The clerk asked, "Charge or Cash?" "Charge," said the customer; so the salesclerk got her sales book from 12 feet away on the end of the counter, and returned to the customer. Then, remembering another model, she walked 10 feet to the right, and looked; it was not there, and so she returned to the customer. She wrote a sales check and made an entry on her index, handed the pencil to the customer, let her sign the sales slip, then tore out the sales check, and walked 15 feet to the charge-phone. She waited 10 seconds for the operator, called for charge authorization, and received it. She separated the sales checks, placing the original in the charge-phone box, returned to the customer, picked up the sweater, and walked 35 feet with the customer to the wrapping desk for a box. She laid the sweater and sales check on the wrapping desk, thanked the customer, returned to her counter, and waited for the next customer.

a. Prepare a process chart-man analysis and flow diagram for the typical sale that is described.

b. With the aid of the check list prepare a process chart-man analysis and flow diagram for a better method.

c. List the information that you would add to your check list and for each item indicate the check-list question number and letter under which you would file it.

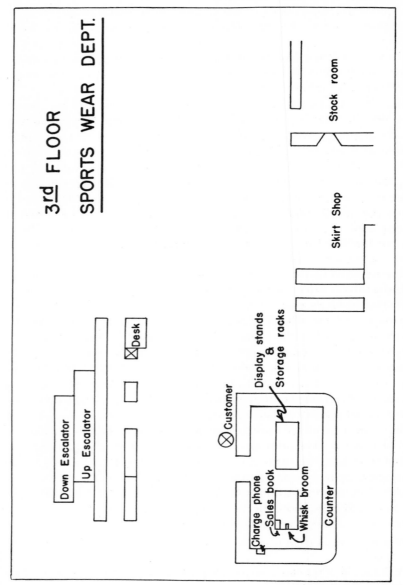

3rd FLOOR

SPORTS WEAR DEPT.

Down Escalator

Up Escalator

Desk

Stock room

Skirt Shop

Display stands & Storage racks

Customer

Charge phone

Sales book

Whisk broom

Counter

Fig. E.5

Chapter 9

9.1. Prepare a work activity analysis:

a. For yourself, at work.
b. For yourself at home, for an evening.
c. For yourself, for a week end.
d. For a gas station attendant.
e. For a store clerk.

9.2. After the necessary preparation, have a work activity analysis prepared by:

a. Your assistant.
b. Your secretary.

9.3. List the recommendations resulting from a study of the work activity analysis prepared in question 9.1 or 9.2.

9.4. a. Treating minutes as strata, assign a random number of seconds to each minute so as to obtain 60 random reading times within the hour. Using these reading values, sample the "number of cars at the pumps in a gas station."

b. Decide what conclusions may be drawn from the above data.

c. Evaluate the reliability of these data and results. (Several samplers may pool results.)

d. Design an adequate study to establish the tentative conclusions in *b*.

9.5. Same as 9.4 for "status of students or personnel in library."

9.6. Same as 9.4 for "status of personnel in lounge."

9.7. Same as 9.4 for "status of personnel at some selected area of cafeteria."

9.8. Same as 9.4 for "some queue."

9.9. Same as 9.4 for "personnel in an office."

9.10. a. Same as 9.4 for "color showing on a selected traffic light."

b. Floor at which elevator is in multi-story building.

c. Status of a flashing sign.

d. Usage of a section of sidewalk, street or stair.

e. Attention given an advertising display.

Chapter 10

10.1. Redesign the wage analysis form shown in Figure E.6 for use on a typewriter. Draw revised form full scale.

10.2. Redesign the intershop movement and identification ticket shown in Figure E.7 for handwritten use. Draw revised form full scale.

10.3. Obtain and redesign any of your company or school forms.

DEPARTMENT LABOR PERFORMANCE ──────────────

Department _3 Buffing_____   Per cent incentive ____90.8____ Week ending 6/24/

Total hours 469.5 ___ Hours on standard 426.5 Hours earned 506.5 Day work 43.0

Department standard performance 118.8 Department actual performance 117.0

No.	Name	Hours Worked T.	Hours on Standard	Hours Earned	%Performance
2	S. Green	31.0	27.0	30.0	111.1
4	S. Doyle	37.0	35.0	34.0	97.1
5	J. Small	35.5	30.5	33.0	108.2
7	H. Suluski	27.5	25.0	30.0	120.0
8	B. Kirk	42.0	40.0	52.0	130.0
9	H. Auxford	45.0	39.0	48.0	123.1
11	J. Justin	44.5	42.0	48.0	114.3
14	R. Allen	39.0	35.0	42.0	120.0
16	K. Kall	40.0	35.0	44.0	125.7
17	M. Nedloeb	42.0	40.0	49.0	122.5
18	S. Kozoff	42.0	38.0	45.5	119.7
20	J. Marks	44.0	40.0	51.0	127.5

SCALE
inches

Fig. E.6

a. Prepare a full scale drawing of the new design.
b. Evaluate the effect of the changes made.

10.4. Obtain a complete set of the forms of your company, school, or of any organization whose forms are available to you.

a. Prepare a functional forms analysis chart.
b. Indicate any unnecessary duplication or any areas for which forms are missing.
c. Comment on the general status of the forms available.
d. Give your recommendations and justify them.

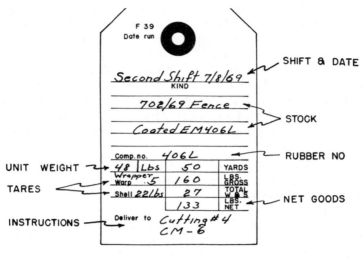

Fig. E.7

10.5. The following is the sequence of events that took place in a certain department store when a woman who expected a broadloom rug delivered on Wednesday failed to receive it. This is typical of several hundred calls per day concerning altered clothes, furniture, knocked-down items assembled by the store, drapes, shades, and other goods worked on before delivery. Some of these calls are caused by rash promises made to close a sale and some by customer anxiousness. A promise for "Tuesday" means Friday in store parlance, "Tuesday sure" means Wednesday, and only "Tuesday positively" means Tuesday. The workrooms overestimate time in self-defense, and the floor staff knows it; consequently they promise more than the workrooms can do, in order to make sales. Mrs. A. who didn't get her rug calls the store and asks for the rug department. The PBX operator rings the rug department telephone; whoever is near it answers, and then gets the section manager, Mr. B., who leaves what he is doing and goes, on the average 50 feet, to the telephone. He picks up the telephone, listens, and makes notes concerning the inquiry, while listening. He tells Mrs. A. that he will call back and hangs up. After a time sufficient for the connection to break, he picks up the telephone, dials the rug workroom, usually gets a busy signal, and hangs up. He places the notes in his pocket and returns to what he was doing. In the usual course of events, Mr. B. makes two more tries, returning to the telephone at intervals, taking out his notes, dialing the rug workroom before he manages to get the line. While he talks to the workroom clerk, the clerk makes notes concerning the inquiry. The workroom clerk tells Mr. B. that she will call back, and they both hang up—Mr. B. putting his notes back into his pocket and the rug workroom clerk, Miss C., going to the file to locate the order. She locates the order, finds the workroom number, hunts, and locates the merchandise in the workroom, determines its status and probable delivery date, adds this to her notes, returns to the telephone and calls Mr. B. He is called to the telephone and takes out his notes and adds Miss C.'s information to them. Miss C. now destroys her notes. Mr. B. finishes what he was doing, returns to the telephone, calls Mrs. A., tells her what he found out, soothes her, hangs up, and destroys his notes. (If Mrs. A. calls Mr. B. or Miss C. later that day or the next, they must rely on memory to reinform her or go through the whole routine again.)

    a. Prepare a process chart-combined analysis for Mr. B., Miss C., Mr. B.'s notes, and Miss C.'s notes for the original procedure.

    b. Suggest steps to take to eliminate most of such calls.

    c. What class of change does each of your suggestions involve?

    d. Plan an improved procedure for handling the remaining calls that will inevitably take place and present it as a process chart-combined analysis. Do not exceed what would be a Class 3 change if the product is the information Mrs. A. receives.

10.6. A group of chain stores use a group of similar procedures in obtaining various types of nonperishable merchandise from the company's district warehouse that supplies these stores.

The following is the procedure used to obtain their supply of all items of a type of nonperishable merchandise we will refer to as Class B.

Once a week, using form #845, prepadded in duplicate, a complete list giving kind and quantity of needed Class B merchandise is made out by the store manager in longhand. Both copies are sent by regular mail to the warehouse to the attention of the Class B merchandise clerk. The manager makes out and seals his own envelope. The mail is received, at the warehouse, in a central mail room, sorted and delivered by house mail to the Class B merchandise clerk. Using the #845 and her balance of stores cards, the Class B merchandise clerk eliminates the out-of-stock items on the list, reduces or increases the quantities according to general weekly instructions from the warehouse manager, adds items as also instructed, reduces her balance of stores by the quantities and kind of merchandise finally listed, and then types form #505, prepadded in triplicate, of the merchandise that will be shipped. She destroys both copies of the #845 and the triplicate of the #505. The first and second copy of the #505 are sent to the warehouse Class B stock room by house mail and there placed in the work basket. When the shipping clerk comes to the #505 we are following, he first uses it to partially fill out the two prepadded copies of the shipping ticket form #86. He enters all full cases only, longhand, on the ticket. The two copies of #86 and the two copies of #505, clipped together, are laid on a picking table, and all the items listed on the #505 are pulled from stock and placed on this wheeled table. All items requiring a full original case lot or several full original cases are pulled first and checked off both sets of forms, which still have inserted carbons. Less than case lots are pulled next, checked off the #505 as pulled and entered on the #86 as they are packed into shipping cases with the contents of each case grouped. Any out-of-stock item, which is a rare occurrence, is crossed off both sets of forms. When the order is finished, the two copies of the #505 are placed in the out-mail basket and the order and its accompanying two copies of #86 are wheeled to the shipping dock by the same clerk who filled the order. He then makes out a bill of lading in duplicate, again using pre-padded forms. The duplicate copy of the bill of lading attached to the duplicate #86 is sent to the warehouse file by house mail. They are filed by stores, chronologically for each store, with all bills of lading and #86 forms for all classes of merchandise. The original shipping ticket and the original bill of lading are sent by mail from the mailing room to the store and the merchandise is shipped by company truck. Whichever arrives first at the store is held until the other arrives. The two copies of the #505 are sent back to the Class B merchandise clerk who, using her unit price file, enters the unit price for all items and places both copies in her desk basket. The computer, who works next to her, takes these as she needs work, extends and adds them twice (to insure correctness), separates the two copies, and puts one in her basket for the mail desk and one in her basket for the bookkeeper. These are moved periodically by the house mail boy. The duplicate #505 is mailed to the store from the mail desk and the original is used by the bookkeeper to post the store ledger and is then sent to the file room, where it is filed indefinitely.

The original shipping ticket is signed by the store manager as soon as feasible (when both it and the merchandise are on hand) and sent back to the warehouse. The store manager files the original bill of lading.

When the warehouse file clerk receives the signed copy of the #86, the file clerk pulls the duplicate #86 and bill of lading, matches them, then destroys the duplicates and files the original signed copy by stores by months.

The merchandise is also held intact at the store until the arrival of the duplicate #505, or vice versa. When both are on hand, them merchandise is unpacked, checked against the #505, and sent to storage or display in the store, as required. The #505 is then used to post to the store's Monthly Buy Sheet, shortages or damages are posted to the store's Monthly Claim Sheet, and the #505 is then filed at the store in a chronological file for one year.

Class C merchandise, also nonperishable, is obtained in the following manner. Form #491, prepadded in quadruplicate and set numbered, is made out once each week, in longhand, by the store manager, giving kind and quantity of needed Class C merchandise. Copies 1 and 2 are sent to the warehouse, attention of the Class C clerk, copy 3 is destroyed, and copy 4 is left in the form book. The manager makes out and seals his own envelope. It is sent to the warehouse by regular mail. The mail is received at the warehouse, in a central mail room, sorted and delivered by house mail to the Class C merchandise clerk.

At the warehouse, the set number from form #491 is first entered on the Control List by the Class C merchandise clerk, then the two copies are sent to the warehouse Class C stock room by house mail and placed in the work basket. When the shipping clerk comes to the #491 we are following, he first uses it to fill out the two prepadded copies of the shipping ticket, form #86. He enters all items calling for full manufacturer's cases longhand on the tickets. The two copies of the #86 and #491 clipped together are laid on a wheeled picking table and all the items called for on the #491 are picked from stock, placed on this table and additional tables as necessary. Items that are out of stock are crossed off the #491 and #86 as necessary, and marked OOS (out-of-stock). As the less than case lots of merchandise are pulled, they are checked off the #491 and entered on the #86 as they are packed into shipping cases with the contents of each case grouped. When the order is finished, the two copies of the #491 are placed in the out-mail basket, and the order and its accompanying two copies of #86 are wheeled to the shipping dock by the same clerk who filled the order, who now makes out a bill of lading in duplicate, again using a prepadded form. The duplicate copy of the bill of lading attached to the duplicate #86 is sent to the warehouse file clerk by house mail. They are filed by stores, chronologically for each store, with all bills of lading and #86 forms for all classes of merchandise.

The original shipping ticket and the original bill of lading are sent by mail from the mailing room to the store, and the merchandise is shipped by company truck. Whichever arrives first at the store is held until the other arrives.

The two copies of the #491 are sent back from the warehouse clerk to the Class C merchandise clerk, who, using her unit price file, enters the unit prices for all items and places both copies in her desk basket. The computer, who works next to her, takes these as she needs work, extends and adds them twice (to insure accuracy), and returns them to the Class C merchandise clerk. The Class C clerk then checks the set number off the Control List, thus making sure she has charge sheets for all Class C merchandise orders sent by her to the stock room; she then places the duplicate #491 in the out-mail basket for the mail desk to mail to the store, and the clerk also sends the original #491 to the bookkeeping file. The original is filed without sorting until the end of the month, at which time all the originals are pulled by the bookkeeping department clerk. The bookkeeping department then posts them to the store ledgers and sends them back to the file room, where they are filed, chronologically by stores for a five-year period.

The original shipping ticket is signed by the store manager as soon as feasible (when both merchandise and shipping ticket are on hand), and sent back to the warehouse. The store manager files the original bill of lading.

When the warehouse file clerk receives the signed copy of #86, she pulls the duplicate #86 and bill of lading, matches them, then destroys the duplicates and files the original signed copy by stores by months.

The merchandise is also held intact in the store until the arrival of the duplicate #491, or vice versa. When both are on hand, the merchandise is unpacked and is checked against the duplicate #491. The quadruplicate #491 and the duplicate #491 are then checked against each other. The quadruplicate copy is then destroyed, and the merchandise is sent to storage or display in the store as required. The #491 is then used to post to the store's Monthly Buy Sheet, shortages or damages are posted to the store's Monthly Claim Sheet, and the #491 is then filed at the store in a chronological file for one year.

a. *Prepare a process chart-combined analysis for procurement of Class B merchandise. (See Figures 10.7, 10.8, or 10.9 for format.)

b. *Using the same general charting pattern so as to make the two charts comparable, prepare a process chart-combined analysis for the procurement of Class C merchandise.

*Note: If the instructor wishes merely to provide some practice in charting, he may assign a limited number of paragraphs from the descriptions of the two ordering procedures.

c. Which is the better procedure? Justify your selection.

d. Under what conditions is it desirable to separate the merchandise into classes for separate ordering as this chain does? Explain your answer.

e. Prepare a proposed improved procedure, for each class, and present it as a process chart-combined analysis.

f. List the information you would add to your check list and for each item indicate the check-list question number and letter under which you would file it.

10.7. a. Follow some form used by your organization and prepare a process chart-combined analysis for the work involved.*

b. Prepare a process chart-combined analysis for a better method of performing the work.

c. Redesign the form or forms involved in the above procedure if they require redesign.

*Note: In school situations the instructor may assign students to examine such as the following:

1. A purchase requisition procedure.
2. The procedure used to pay student help.
3. A library procedure.
4. Charge account procedures in local stores.

10.8. Prepare an improved procedure to replace the one charted in Figures 10.7, 10.8, and 10.9. Indicate why you consider your proposal an improvement. (If you need any additional information, make a reasonable assumption, list your assumption, and proceed.)

Chapter 11

11.1. Films of simple operations[2] suitable for operation charting are easily made. Although operation charts are normally made from direct observation, these films may be used to bring the job before a group. They should be run steadily so as to replace a continuously working operator.

11.2. A flashlight assembly consists of a cylindrical case, a rear cap, a reflector, a lens, and a top ring that screws onto the case to hold the lens and reflector in position. The workplace is shown in Figure E.8.

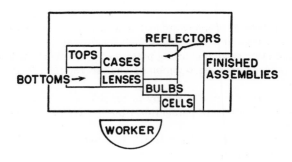

Fig. E.8

The operator picks up the case with the right hand and transfers it to the left hand. Then the right hand picks up the reflector from a pan about 15 inches away and drops it into the top end of the case. The right hand next picks up a bulb from a pan ten inches away and screws it into the reflector. This part of the operation is slow because it is difficult to maintain a firm grasp on the bulb with the finger tips inside and near the bottom of the reflector. With the left hand still holding the case, the right hand places the lens, which was eight inches away, on top of the reflector, where the first finger and thumb of the left hand hold it in position while the right hand reaches to a pan 12 inches away and picks up and assembles the top ring to the case. The right hand then places the cells into the case, getting them one at a time from an area ten inches away, and then assembles the rear cap. The pile of rear caps is also ten inches away. This completes the assembly. The flashlight is then transferred to the right hand, where the thumb operates the switch to make sure the completed assembly is satisfactory. The rear cap is then

---

[2] A film loop of any operation may be used.

removed with the left hand, the cells dumped out, and the rear cap replaced. The flashlight is then placed in a tray about 30 inches to the right of the operator. It is given a final inspection for appearance, by another operator, before packaging.

a. Make a right- and left-hand operation chart of this operation.

b. Prepare a Class 1 or 2 change, and present the new method in the form of a right- and left-hand operation chart and make a sketch of the new workplace layout.

c. List the information you would add to your check list and for each item indicate the check-list question number and letter under which you would file it.

11.3. The workplace used to gage the thickness of piston rings is shown in Figure E.9, and the rings and gage are shown in detail in Figure E.10. The worker with her left hand picks up an ungaged ring from the uptilted box on the left and at the same time disposes of the gaged ring, either to the "passed" box on her right or the reject box in front of her. Using both hands she tries the ring against the slot under the no-go gage three times at points 120 degrees apart on the ring's circumference, each time sliding the ring on the gage-flat. If the ring does not go under the no-go gage, she slides it with her left and up under the go-gage and pulls it through with her right hand. This is the normal sequence. Rejects are disposed of as soon as detected.

a. Make a right- and left-hand operation chart of the original method of gaging piston rings.

b. Develop an improved method, with no greater than a Class 2 change, and present an operation chart of this new method as well as a sketch of the new workplace or gage if required.

c. List the information you would add to your check list and for each item indicate the check-list question number and letter under which you would file it.

11.4. The following is a description of the original method used to finish-pack quart boxes of cultivated blueberries prior to crating. The workplace is shown in Figure E.11. Field-picked boxes of blueberries are placed, by the packer, on the worktable, six at a time, on a flat from a stack of flats and boxes alongside the table. The operator reaches and with both hands gets a field-packed box, *PB*, from the left. (These are standard quart berry boxes.) She sets it down at *S* and adds enough berries from the box at *Ex* to flush-fill the box being packed. The extra berries are poured from the extra box into the box at *S*, and then the extra box is set back. A cellophane sheet is picked up with the right hand, and both hands set it over the box being packed. The left hand then picks up the frame at the left. The frame consists of a wood frame with heavy rubber flaps (marked *A, B, C, D*, in Figure E.11). This is placed over the box at *S* by both hands and allowed to slip over the

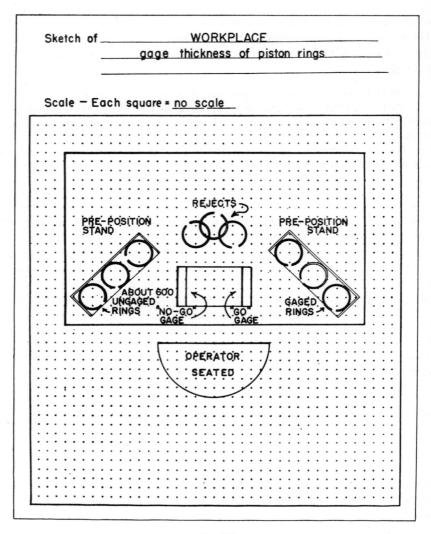

Fig. E.9

box, thus holding the cellophane down on all four sides. The right hand then gets a rubber band from the supply and both hands place it over the box to hold the cellophane down. The two hands then place the finished box in the shipping box at the right rear. When six boxes are in the shipping boxes, the worker sets it on the floor or stack at the right of the table, places the flat over it for a cover, gets a new flat, and finishes the boxes in it. When the box at *Ex* is used up, another box is taken from those on the flat on the table. One box will finish packing about 15 other boxes.

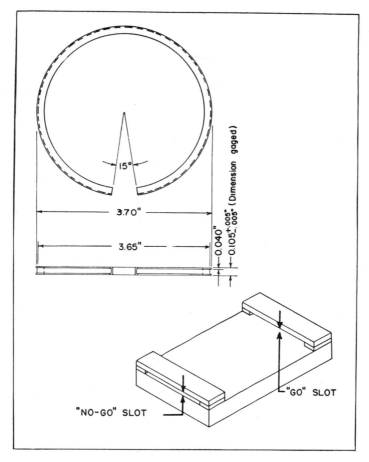

Fig. E.10

a. What is the cyclic nature of the task described?

b. Prepare a right- and left-hand operation chart for the method described.

c. With the aid of the check list prepare an improved method and present a sketch of the revised workplace, if required, and a new operation chart.

d. List the information you would add to your check list and for each item indicate the check-list question number and letter under which you would file it.

Chapter 12

12.1. a. Prepare a man and machine process time chart for centerless grind bearing (see Figure 12.5) for one operator and one machine.

b. Prepare a man and machine process time chart for the same job, for one operator and two machines.

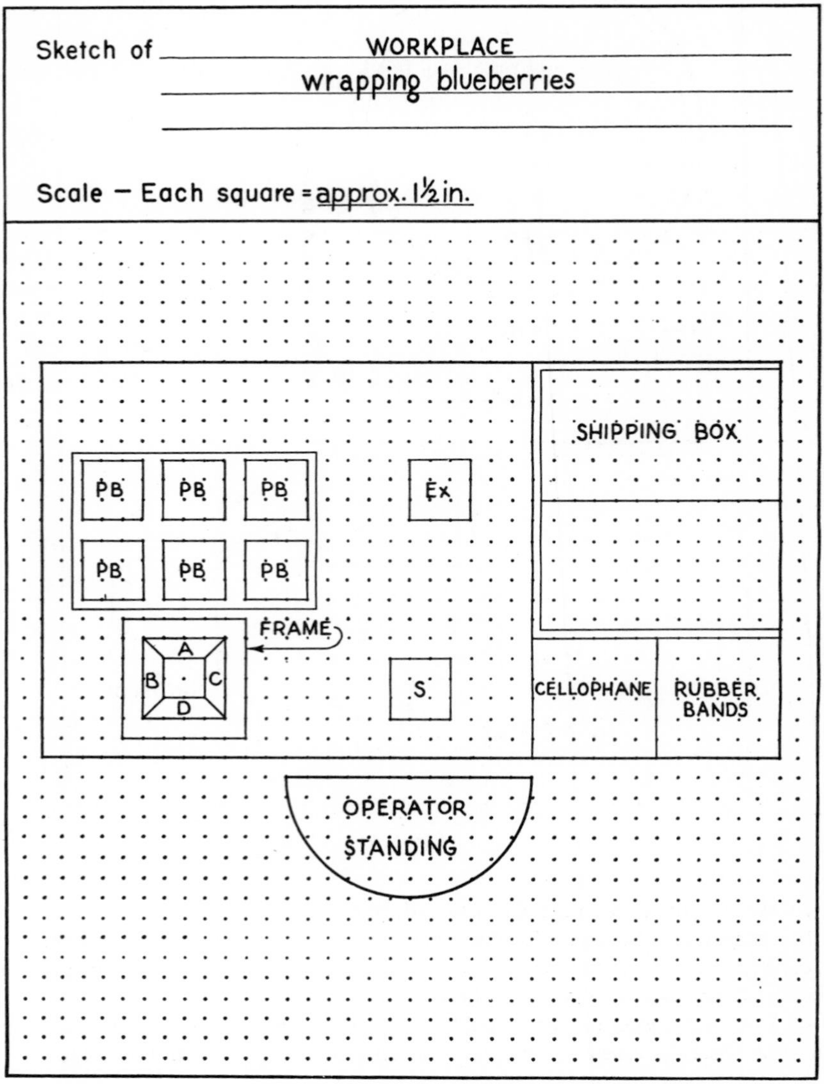

Sketch of WORKPLACE
wrapping blueberries
Scale — Each square = approx. 1½ in.
PB
PB
PB
PB
PB
PB
Ex
FRAME
A
B
C
D
S
SHIPPING BOX
CELLOPHANE
RUBBER BANDS
OPERATOR STANDING

Fig. E.11

c. If the machine-hour rate is $5.00 and the direct labor rate is $3.00 per hour, what is the cost per machine load with the two-machine method as compared with the one-machine method?

d. If the machine-hour rate is $3.00 and the direct labor rate is $5.00 per hour, what is the cost per machine load with the one-machine method as compared with the two-machine method?

e. Prepare a general equation for solving this problem with any dollar values of man and machine time.

12.2. a. Prepare a man and three-machine process time chart for the operation shown in Figure 12.12.

b. If the machine hour rate is $5.00 and the direct labor rate is $3.00 per hour, what is the cost per machine load with this new method as compared with the two-machine method?

c. If the machine hour rate is $3.00 and the direct labor rate is $5.00 per hour, what is the cost per machine load with this new method as compared to the two-machine method?

d. Prepare a general equation for any number "*n*" machines and any values of man and machine time for determining the cost of any combination of hourly values or number of machines.

12.3. What reactions might you expect from the operator in problem 12.1, when his job is changed from a one-machine to a two-machine operation? What would you do if you were his supervisor?

12.4. Under what circumstance would a combination of a number of machines per operator that is not the most economical, be a preferable method?

12.5. a. Observe a task that involves some machine controlled time and prepare a man and machine time chart of a suitable variety.

b. Review the operation with the proper check list and prepare a proposed method in the form of a man and machine time chart.

c. List the information you would add to your check list and for each item indicate the check-list question number and letter under which you would file it.

Chapter 13

13.1. a. Prepare a multiman and machine process time chart for a two-man method of doing the operation shown in Figure 13.4. Do not exceed a Class 1 change. Show the new workplace layout and flow diagram.

b. Compare the man-minutes per stud using this two-man method to the man-minutes per stud using the three-man method.

c. Under what conditions would this two-man method be preferable?

13.2. Prepare a multiman and machine process time chart for a Class 2 change for the job shown in Figure 13.4. Evaluate your proposal.

13.3. a. If, in the job shown in Figure 12.10, 13.6, and 13.7, the direct labor rate was $3.00 and the machine-hour rate was $9.00, which is the most economical setup?

b. If, in the job shown in Figure 12.10, 13.6, and 13.7, the direct labor rate was $5.00 and the machine-hour rate was $3.00, which is the most economical setup?

c. What other factors would have to be taken into consideration when choosing the most desirable setup? Why?

d. Prepare an equation for determining the least cost method given any combination of man and machine hourly costs.

13.4. a. Observe some group work activity and prepare a suitable multi-man time chart.

b. Evaluate the method with the aid of the check list and suggest an improved method in the form of a comparable multiman time chart.

c. List the information you would add to your check list and for each item indicate the check-list question number and letter under which you would file it.

Chapter 14

14.1. Examine the cameras and projectors available in the laboratory:

a. Prepare a check list of desirable camera features for film study and using this as a basis compare the cameras.

b. Prepare a check list of desirable projector features for film analysis and using this as a basis compare the projectors.

14.2. Assuming the use of Eastman Tri-X film, determine with the aid of an exposure calculator the lens speed required to take pictures without special or extra artificial illumination at 16/sec (1/30 sec exposure), 8/sec (1/15 sec exposure), and 1/sec (1/12 sec exposure and 1/8 sec exposure) in the following places:

a. Classroom.
b. Laboratory.
c. Various parts of the shop.

14.3. Prepare a budget for equipping your industrial engineering department for film or video-tape study. Assuming a ten-year life for equipment, compute the annual cost. Find the average direct labor rate of pay and compute the number of hours of direct labor that must be saved per year to pay for the equipment.

14.4. From the literature, report on the use of filming or video-taping to study an actual problem.

Chapter 15

15.1. a. Prepare a film analysis sheet in terms of therbligs, leaving out the clock readings and subtracted time, for the operation of problem 11.2.

b. Prepare an operation chart in terms of these therbligs for this method of performing the operation of problem 11.2.

c. With the use of the check list for therbligs, prepare an operation chart in terms of therbligs for a better method of doing this operation as well as a sketch of the proposed workplace. Do not exceed a Class 2 change.

15.2. Film for film analysis may easily be made as necessary.

a. Make an analysis, in terms of therbligs, of an assigned film.

b. Prepare a simo-chart from the data obtained in part *a*.

c. With the aid of the check list prepare an improved method not exceeding a Class 2 change and:

    1. Synthesize a simo-chart of this new method.

    2. Prepare a sketch of the revised workplace.

    3. Compute the estimated per cent of time saved.

    4. Compute the estimated per cent increase in production.

15.3. On the basis of the distribution of a pharmacist's prescription filling time, as obtained from a memomotion record and given in Chapter 14, what would you suggest, in addition to the suggestions given in Chapter 14, as a means of improving the apparent task?

15.4. With reference to Figure 15.8, suggest:

a. Desirable characteristics for managers of drug stores.

b. Necessary fields of knowledge.

15.5. Devise a set of categories for analyzing films of housework with the eventual aim of making it possible for the work to be performed by:

a. A person with a poor heart.

b. A person without use of legs.

c. A one-armed person.

d. A person of very short stature.

e. A person of extreme height.

15.6. Devise a set of categories for examining the work of:

a. A men's store clerk.

b. A women's store clerk.

c. A gas station attendant.

d. A house carpenter.

e. A plumber.

f. A repairman.

g. A tool setter.

h. A line crew.

 i. A street-repair gang.

j. A surgeon.
k. A nurse.

15.7. Make a memomotion film and:

a. Make a suitable analysis and graphic presentation including a workplace sketch or flow diagram.

b. Apply the proper check list and propose, in the form of a chart similar to that used in part *a*, a better method.

c. Calculate the estimated per cent saving in time.

d. Calculate the estimated per cent increase in productivity.

Chapter 16

16.1. What "general suggestions for improving jobs" were embodied in the improved method of:

a. Figure 1.2.	j. Figure 8.13.
b. Figure 1.5.	k. Figure 8.16.
c. Figure 1.7.	l. Figure 8.18.
d. Figure 1.9.	m. Figure 11.5.
e. Figure 1.11.	n. Figure 11.11.
f. Figure 6.2.	o. Figure 12.3.
g. Figure 6.3.	p. Figure 12.6.
h. Figure 8.3.	q. Figure 12.9.
i. Figure 8.13.	r. Figure 13.4.

16.2. Examine any task. Describe the present manner of performing this task and list "the general suggestions for improving jobs" which would be applicable. Describe your proposed method embodying these suggestions.

Chapter 17

17.1. Describe the extent of use and the uses made of time standards in the plant in which you work or have worked, or in an organization with which you have some familiarity.

17.2. If the range of performance of a random group of operators is roughly two to one, and the average performance is 130 per cent of standard production, what approximate percentage of the operators will probably:

a. Fall below 90 per cent?
b. Fall below 100 per cent?
c. Exceed 100 per cent?
d. Exceed 130 per cent?
e. Exceed 150 per cent?
f. Exceed 160 per cent?

17.3. From the literature summarize an application of time study with special reference to the benefits gained.

17.4. From the literature report on criticism of time study.

17.5. Report on the time study contribution of:

a. F. W. Taylor.
b. Carl Barth.
c. Henry Babbage.
d. Charles Fayol.
e. Charles Bedaux.

17.6. Construct the work-unit hierarchy for:

a. A school cafeteria.
b. A gasoline station.
c. A super-market.
d. A National Park.
e. A city taxing bureau.
f. A police force.
g. A department store.
h. A newspaper.
i. A professional society.
j. A water-pollution abatement project.
k. A central-city improvement project.
l. A U.S. Navy ship repair yard.

17.7. Evaluate the work-unit structure set forth in response to 17.6 in terms of the criteria for a useful hierarchy of work-units.

17.8. Considering the work-unit structure set forth in response to 17.6, at what level of work-unit does it appear that the work-counts will be meaningful with respect to manpower resources required?

17.9. A worker is using an overhead-track cut-off saw for cutting pallet face boards three feet long from random length boards ranging from 10 to 16 feet in length. The elements are:

1. Get one length of random lumber and bring to saw.
2. Cut first end square.
3. Cut off one three-foot length; repeat as possible.
4. If remainder is over two feet but less than three feet long, place in special "save" pile.
4a. If remainder is under two feet, place in scrap bin.
5. Change blade after approximately 5000 pieces.
6. Make out lot ticket for each 1000 pieces.
7. Blow off sawdust after approximately 3000 pieces.
8. Replenish random length boards in 200 board lots.

Let T_1, T_2, etc., equal the time for each element listed above.

Let n_1 = average number of pieces per random length board.

Let n_2 = the number of pieces meeting the criteria for element 4.

Let n_3 = the number of pieces meeting the criteria for element 4a.

a. If the third-order work-unit is described as, *Cut all 16 pieces required for one pallet*, describe the statistical interface between the second-order work-units given and this third-order work-unit.

b. Describe the statistical interface between the third-order work-unit and the fourth-unit, *One pallet completed.*

17.10. The political reporter for the newspaper, the Washington XXX, has the assignment of tracing down all rumors concerning potential political appointments.

a. If the fourth-order work-unit is *An appointment recognized prior to its official announcement*, what is the statistical interface between this fourth-order work-unit and its constituent third-order work-units?

b. What is the nature of the statistical interface between the fourth-order work-unit produced by this reporter and the fifth-order work-unit, *The Washington political scene fully reported*?

17.11. Define *standard time* as it is used in the plant in which you work, have worked, or in an organization with which you have some familiarity.

17.12. Obtain a copy of a union contract. Quote and criticize the clauses dealing with "standard time."

17.13. A plant is going to use a wage incentive plan. Their labor contract stipulates that a typical worker should be able to earn 30 per cent incentive over his base rate.

a. If their incentive plan is:

$$\text{Earnings} = \text{rate per hr.} \times \left(\text{hrs. worked} + \frac{\text{standard hrs. earned} - \text{actual hrs. worked}}{2} \right)$$

what then will be the necessary definition of *standard time*?
Note: The above formula only holds true if the standard hours exceed the actual hours, otherwise the worker is paid (actual hrs. × rate per hr.).

b. If the incentive plan is:

$$\text{Earnings} = \text{rate per hr.} \times \left[\text{actual hrs. worked} + 2 \left(\text{standard hrs. earned} - \text{actual hrs. worked} \right) \right]$$

what then will be the necessary definition of *standard time*? (See note under part *a*).

c. If the incentive plan is:

$$\text{earnings} = \text{rate per hr.} \times \text{standard hrs. earned}$$

what then will be the necessary definition of *standard time*? (See note under part *a*.)

d. What general relationship exists between the contract wage increment, the incentive plan, and the definition of *standard time*?

17.14. A large group of operators average 130 per cent of standard production. The range of performance is 125 to 135 per cent.

a. Give five possible reasons for the existence of such a situation.

b. Indicate what each of these reasons would suggest concerning the correctness of the standard if it was intended to represent the standard time as given in the suggested definition in the Supplemental Material of Chapter 17.

Chapter 18

18.1. Prepare a time study sheet for a time study of the job of inspecting drawn copper wire as shown in:
a. Figures 8.1 and 8.2.
b. Figures 8.3 and 8.4.

18.2. Prepare a time study sheet for a time study for the job of sacking cocktail ice as shown in:
a. Figure 8.15.
b. Figure 8.16.

18.3. Prepare a time study sheet for a time study of the job of assembling hand-hole cover as shown in:
a. Figures 11.2 and 11.3.
b. Figures 11.5 and 11.6.

18.4. Prepare a time study sheet for a time study of the job of drilling holes in hinge channel as shown in:
a. Figures 11.7 and 11.10.
b. Figures 11.11 and 11.12.

18.5. Prepare a time study sheet for a simple job that you may have performed or any job in the shop.

18.6. Assume that the readings for an element were: 0.14, 0.15, 0.14, 0.15, 0.16, 0.13, 0.15, 0.14, 0.15, 0.14, 0.16, and 0.15, all in minutes.
a. What can you state concerning the suitability of these values as a basis for determining an average value representing the performance observed? (Use formula and table and compare results.)
b. What would the next step be?

18.7. Assume that the readings for an element were: 0.03, 0.04, 0.05, 0.06, 0.04, 0.05, 0.04, 0.03, 0.04, 0.06, 0.05, 0.06, and 0.04, all in minutes.
a. What can you state concerning the suitability of these values as a basis for determining an average value representing the performance observed? (Use formula and table and compare results.)
b. What would the next step be?

18.8. Assume that the readings for an element were: 0.07, 0.04, 0.06, 0.08, 0.08, 0.04, 0.07, 0.06, 0.05, 0.06, 0.03, 0.06, 0.05, 0.06, and 0.04, all in minutes.
a. What can you state concerning the suitability of these values as a basis for determining an average value representing the performance observed? (Use formula and table and compare results.)
b. What would the next step be?

18.9. Assume that the readings for an element were: 0.22, 0.21, 0.23, 0.24, 0.20, 0.19, 0.22, 0.22, 0.23, 0.22, 0.24, 0.25, 0.23, 0.22, and 0.21, all in minutes.

a. What can you state concerning the suitability of these values as a basis for determining an average value representing the performance observed? (Use formula and table and compare results.)

b. What would the next step be?

18.10. Set up a job that may be performed in the laboratory, record the method, and observe and record the time values for a series of cycles. Obtain enough readings to yield a reliable average and compute the average for each element.

18.11. Describe the method of rating time studies in use in the plant in which you work or have worked or in a plant with which you are familiar.

18.12. Take one of the references cited in footnotes 24 through 35, of Chapter 18, and describe in detail the method of rating which is proposed by the author of that work.

18.13. The instructor will supply ratings made by (x) men (3 to 15) on ten films. Analyze these data by means of the statistical procedures given in the Supplemental Material of Chapter 18 and prepare a complete critique of this group of men.

18.14. See the rating practice films distributed by the Society for Advancement of Management. Rate with these films and make an analysis of the results following the methods outlined in the Supplemental Material of Chapter 18, or with any method suggested by the instructor.

18.15. Films for rating practice, each 400 feet in length, and each showing ten paces for performing an industrial job, filmed in industrial plants, may be obtained from the author.[3] Current titles include:

Film No.	Title
1.	Roping Salami.
2.	Feeding 28 lb. Tank Heads to Punch Press.
3.	Preassembly of Screws to Insulators.
4.	Set Up Wire Bound Box.
5.	Lift Teletype from Mounting Bolts.
6.	Manual Purge of Requisition File.
7.	Loosen Terminal Block Support.
8.	Plate Radio Crystal and Check Frequency.
9.	Load Piece on Broach.
10.	Wrap $\frac{1}{4}$ cup Aluminum Measuring Cup.
11.	Pick Up Pressure Sensitive Label on Carton Pack.
12.	Make Mold in Foundry, Element 1.
13.	Load 10-lb. Wood Boxes on Skid.

[3] Multi-image loops are also available.

14.	Hand Feed Wrapping Machine.
15.	Interleave Greeting Cards and Envelopes.
16.	Run Natco Multiple-spindle Drill.
17.	Feed Casing-in Machine.
18.	Brush Small Metal Diaphragm.
19.	Cover Doll Boxes.
20.	Trim Meat from Blade Bone.
21.	Measure Hog Casings.
22.	Pull Cable Aboard Ship.
23.	Edge Disc in Tin Shop.
24.	Assemble Deck House to Coaming with Huck Bolts.
25.	Scribe Disc in Tin Shop.
26.	Push Hand Cart.
27.	Spot, Face and Drill Casting.
28.	Assorted Pharmaceutic Operations.
29.	Various Machine Shop Operations.

Rate a selected film. Following the analytical methods given in the Supplemental Material of Chapter 18, or any other suggested method, analyze the results.

18.16. Assuming that 40 per cent of the time is spent in acceleration, 20 per cent traveling at constant velocity, and 40 per cent in deceleration, prove that with a given rate of acceleration the time for the longer movement divided by the time for the smaller movement is equal to the square root of the longer distance divided by the smaller distance.

18.17. Compute the difficulty adjustments for each element in:

Note: If any additional information is required, list a reasonable assumption and proceed.

a. Figure 18.1.
b. Figure 18.3.
c. Figure 18.4.
d. Figure 18.7.

18.18. Compute the difficulty adjustments for the job studied in connection with question 18.10. Assume a rating of 80 for all the hand elements and compute a base time for each element.

18.19. Compute the difficulty adjustments for each element of Figure C.10 and obtain the base time for each element.

18.20. Make a time study of a task, rate objectively, and compute the difficulty adjustments. Compute the base time.

18.21. Compute the allowance for the job described in:

a. Figure 18.1.
b. Figure 18.3.
c. Figure 18.4.
d. Figure 18.7.

Note: If any additional information is required, list a reasonable assumption and proceed.

18.22. What allowance would have to be added to compensate for the machine time effect on a job where the machine controlled 50 per cent of the cycle but the operator worked during the entire cycle? (130 per cent typical production expectancy.) The policy is to equalize potential incentive earnings of machine and manual jobs.

a. What would the allowance be if the operator did not work during the machine controlled time?

b. What would the allowance be if the operator worked for 50 per cent of the machine controlled time?

18.23. Same as problem 18.22 except that the policy is to make the per cent incentive ostensibly proportional to the per cent of cycle worked, with no consideration of the pace increase due to rest.

18.24. Same as 18.23 except that the pace increase due to rest is to be taken into account.

18.25. What allowance would have to be added to compensate for the machine time effect on a job where the machine controlled 75 per cent of the cycle but the operator worked during 45 per cent of the cycle? (130 per cent typical production expectancy.)

a. Where the policy is to equalize the potential incentive on machine and manual activities.

b. Where the policy is to make incentive potential proportional to per cent of time worked with no attention given to the pace increase due to intermittent rest.

c. Same as *b*, but taking the effect of rest into account.

18.26. What allowance would have to be added to a job to compensate for the machine time effect if the machine controls 65 per cent of the cycle, during which time the operator rests, and standards in this shop are set so that the average operator is expected to exceed them by 25 per cent?

a. Where the policy is to equalize the potential incentive on machine and manual activities.

b. Where the policy is to make incentive potential proportional to per cent of time worked with no attention given to the pace increase due to intermittent rest.

c. Same as *b*, but taking the effect of rest into account.

18.27. What allowance would have to be added to a job to compensate for the machine time effect if the machine controls 75 per cent of the cycle, during which time the operator rests, and standards in this shop are set so that the average operator is expected to exceed them by 50 per cent?

a. Where the policy is to equalize the potential incentive on machine and manual activities.

b. Where the policy is to make incentive potential proportional to per cent of time worked with no attention given to the pace increase due to intermittent rest.

c. Same as *b*, but taking the effect of rest into account.

18.28. It is estimated that an activity takes 12 per cent of the total work day. How many observations would we need to take, on a random basis, to measure accurately the percentage of time consumed by this activity, with the probability of 95 chances in 100 of not being in error by more than:

    a. 1 per cent of total.
    b. 1 per cent of 12 per cent.
    c. 5 per cent of 12 per cent.
    d. 10 per cent of 12 per cent.
    e. 2 per cent of total.

Chapter 19

19.1. Using the data of Tables 17, C.8, and 14, compute the standard time for the task shown in:

    a. Figure 11.2.
    b. Figure 11.5.
    c. Figure 11.7.
    d. Figure 11.11.
    e. Figure 11.13.
    f. Figure 12.1.

19.2. Make a time study of a simple task and then compute the time for the same task as given in Tables 17, C.8, and 14. If there is a difference among the three values obtained, attempt to determine the cause.

19.3. Using the data of Tables 17, C.8, and 14, compute the standard time for the best method you can devise for:

    a. Problem 11.5.
    b. Problem 11.11.
    c. Problem 11.13.

Chapter 20

20.1. Make a series of time studies for stripping insulation from wire, varying the size of wire (both diameter and length), its construction (solid or multiconductor), the type of insulation, and the length stripped. Develop standard elemental data for all of the elements in this work.

20.2. Make a series of time studies for half-round (or triangular cross section) sand cores ranging from $\frac{1}{2}$-inch to 4-inch diameter and 4-inch to 14-inch length. Develop a series of standard elemental times for the elements of these operations.

20.3. Develop the standard elemental data for each of the elements in Figure 20.15.

20.4. Using the material from problem 20.3, compute the standard time for assigned operations on any of the parts shown in Figures 20.12. and 20.13.

Chapter 21

21.1. Do all the preparatory work and complete planning for a direct time study-extensive sampling, by tasks, for:

  a. A garage attendant.
  b. A maintenance employee.
  c. A janitor.
  d. A housewife.
  e. A restaurant cook.
  f. A roving inspector.
  g. A gas station attendant.
  h. Any selected, non-repetitive job.
  i. Any designated office group.
  j. A member of any designated athletic team, while in competition.

21.2. For any of the situations in problem 21.1 above, plan direct time study-extensive sampling, by fourth-order work-units.

21.3. Make a direct time study-extensive sampling, by elements, of a repetitive task. (To permit a group to do this in one hour, have similar elements, sampling times stratified by minutes or half minutes and randomized by seconds, and pool the group data.) A film loop may be used and the accuracy of the sampled data verified by comparison with the actual time distribution on the film.

21.4. Three direct time study-extensive sampling data sets have been obtained; these provide the following information:

| | | Work Counts of Fourth-Order Work-Units | | | |
Set	Allowed Time	Work-Unit 1	Work-Unit 2	Work-Unit 3	Work-Unit 4
1	51 minutes	4	3	6	2
2	92	8	1	7	9
3	52	2	3	6	5

Determine the standard time for each work-unit.

21.5. Same as 21.4, but the data are:

| | | Work Counts of Fourth-Order Work-Units | | | |
Set	Allowed Time	Work-Unit 1	Work-Unit 2	Work-Unit 3	Work-Unit 4
1	56 hours	2	2	6	6
2	51	6	6	2	1
3	29	3	1	5	2

Determine the standard time for each work-unit.

21.6. Same as 21.4, but the data are:

Set	Allowed time	Work Counts of Fourth-order Work-Units				
		Work-Unit 1	Work-Unit 2	Work-Unit 3	Work-Unit 4	Work-Unit 5
1	98 hours	6	3	5	4	7
2	74	4	9	6	8	4
3	169	8	1	12	2	11

a. Are all of the work-units appropriate methods of counting the outputs?

b. Determine the standard time for all work-units for which a standard time is appropriate.

21.7. A series of jobs exist, each consisting of the production of a different mix of work-units 1 through 4 of problem 21.4, but each job having a fixed mix. Using the values obtained from problem 21.4 (or values assigned by the instructor) and assuming an 8-hour day:

a. Develop a table showing the relationship between the mix of work-units 1 through 4 to the per cent of the worker's capability required to produce the assigned mix of work-units, from 1 to 100 per cent of a worker's capability.

b. How reliable do you think this table is? Explain your position.

c. If you do not think the table is reliable, describe in detail the steps necessary to obtain a reliable table. Be quantitative.

21.8. A film for practicing rating under conditions simulating direct time study-extensive sampling may be obtained from the author. The film is titled, "Rated Sampling No. 1." There are 50 scenes on this film taking in a wide variety of jobs ranging from stirring paint to shifting heavy containers. Each scene is only ten seconds in length and is preceded by a seven-second title. All the scenes were taken in an industrial environment.

Chapter 22

22.1. Develop an FPE for the following:

a. Preparing a term paper.

b. Completing a shopping at the super-market.

c. Completing registration.

d. Having a parking ticket processed.

e. Preparing a bundle of laundry for the laundry man.

f. Changing from regular tires to snow tires.

g. Washing and polishing a car.

h. Determining the number of different kinds of people that pass a given place at different hours of the day.

i. Determining the details of the flow of traffic at a simple street intersection.

j. Determining the details of the flow of traffic at a complex street intersection.

k. Determining the average number of pairs of shoes examined by the typical woman purchaser in a shoe store.

l. Determining the amount of time spent, per person, at the return-desk at a department store.

22.2. Determine an FPE for any of the intermittent or project-type assignments you are likely to receive in the near future.

22.3. Design a simple reporting form and system for use by a group for reporting their use of time and the status of projects with respect to the FPE's originally set for the projects.

Chapter 24

24.1. The following are the data obtained from the shipping department of a plant, for 15 working days, selected at random from the year's record (numbers rounded):

Man-hours	Items picked, packed, and shipped
340	1600
450	2900
380	2400
560	3800
390	2100
220	1900
200	1200
650	3400
340	2100
400	2400
500	2700
440	2400
510	3100
540	3100
650	3600

a. Compute a gross mathematical standard for this activity.

b. Within what limits would you expect this standard to predict performance? How reliably?

24.2. a. If the policy of the plant is to use the third quartile of the arrayed performance effectiveness as the standard, using the data from 24.1, what is the standard time?

b. How realistic do you feel this value is?

c. Why?

24.3. Develop standard times for the tabular data given in Chapter 24, page 488, and compare these to the standards derived earlier in the chapter by gross techniques.

24.4. Plot the data from the computations of 24.3. Design and compute a table for determining the required monthly manpower, between the units of 1000 to 10,000 man-hours per month, as a function of the work mix of orders to be scheduled that month.

24.5. Design a self-reporting data collection system for:

a. Determining whether the semester-hour values assigned the courses in a university are correct.

b. Determining the realism of an intra-city bus schedule.

c. Determining the effectiveness with which a staff (of any assigned kind) is being employed.

d. Determining the workload in the office of the Dean of Student Affairs.

24.6. The time for a work-unit consists of a set-up time and a performance time. The set-up time is approximately four times the performance time but neither are known. Develop a table for converting the work counts of the work-unit, within the range 1 through 25, to a linear function of time required.

24.7. The time to assemble a large ship section appears to increase with the square root of the tonnage of the section. Prepare a table for converting a work count of tons assembled, between the ranges of 1 to 150 tons, by tons, to a linear function of the time required.

24.8. The data available for the operation of a particular kind of an office of the government are as follows:

		Work Counts, by Work-Units							
Location	Time Used	1	2	3	4	5	6	7	8
1	15,440 man-hours	120	250	180	200	500	150	800	100
2	15,440	140	200	200	300	100	50	1000	50
3	27,020	130	100	280	150	100	500	50	2000
4	21,320	160	100	300	100	800	200	1000	500

Further, the personnel in the office work an actual average of 1930 hours per year.

a. Determine the standard time for each of the work-units by linear programming.

b. Same as a, above, but the smallest standard time is to be one man-hour.

c. Determine the standard time for each of the work-units by multiple regression.

d. Same as c, above, but the smallest standard time is to be one man-hour.

e. Compare the results obtained from a and c.

f. Compare the results obtained from *b* and *d*.

g. Describe the additional information you would need to select the most appropriate values from those available under *a*, *b*, *c*, and *d*.

h. Taking the values obtained from *a*, *b*, *c*, or *d*, develop a table for determining the required manning for workloads ranging from those needing only one person per office to those requiring 20 persons per office. Do not contemplate hiring other than full-time personnel.

Chapter 25

25.1. a. If your plant does not have a definite policy for its routine motion and time study activities, prepare one.

b. If your plant has a definite policy for its routine motion and time study activities, constructively criticize it.

25.2. a. Outline a course of study to acquaint a group of foremen from one plant with motion study procedures.

b. Outline a course of study to acquaint a group of foremen from one plant with time study procedures.

25.3. Lay out, in detail, a procedure designed to improve the rating ability of a group of time study men accustomed to taking time studies with the conventional procedure.

25.4. Lay out, in detail, a procedure designed to continually aid and evaluate a group of time study men accustomed to rating time studies with step-films, or multi-image films, and difficulty adjustments.

25.5. Prepare a methods proposal summary for the two methods shown in Figures 12.5 and 12.6.

25.6. Prepare a methods proposal summary for the two methods shown in Figures 13.2 and 13.4.

25.7. Prepare a procedure proposal summary and supplementary sheet for the two procedures shown in Figures 10.10 and 10.11.

25.8. If the labor rate is $2.95 an hour and the machine hour rate is $3.50 per hour and if the method has been changed from that shown in Figure 12.5 to that shown in Figure 12.6, prepare a work measurement proposal summary such as would accompany the necessary change in the standard.

25.9. Take a job in a plant, do a complete motion and time study analysis, install your proposal and prepare an adequate report on the results.

25.10. Prepare a work-unit structure of the work of your branch.

25.11. Prepare a work-unit structure of the work of your division.

25.12. Prepare a work-unit structure of the work of your service.

Index